ANALYSIS OF BEHAVIORAL CHANGE

In the Harper Psychology Series
Under the Editorship of H. Philip Zeigler

ANALYSIS OF BEHAVIORAL CHANGE

EDITED BY

Lawrence Weiskrantz

PROFESSOR OF PSYCHOLOGY AND
FELLOW OF MAGDALEN COLLEGE
UNIVERSITY OF OXFORD

Harper & Row, Publishers

NEW YORK, EVANSTON, AND LONDON

156

An 1

69512

Contents

Preface

As often must be the case, the Preface is the very last bit to be written. What impresses us—and this must also be a common reflection—is how long it has taken to reach this point. In fact, the main portion of this book was started four years ago. The reader can estimate for himself how punctual or otherwise some (but not all) of the authors have been by seeing how out of date their contributions are. But, as we point out loftily in the Introduction, our references to published material are meant to be more illustrative than exhaustive, more convenient than definitive. Therefore, while some of the references might be improved by amendment or supplantation, we hope this will not detract from the value of the general methodological points being put.

We gratefully acknowledge permission to reproduce illustrations free of charge by McGraw-Hill Book Company, American Institute of Physics Inc., The American Psychological Association, Pergamon Press, Grune & Stratton. In addition, we acknowledge permission by Macmillan (Journals) Limited to reproduce an illustration. We are collectively grateful to the Master and Fellows of Churchill College, Cambridge, for allowing us to use the College to try out our experiment of a working conference (see Introduction) and to CIBA Pharmaceutical Co., Ltd. (Basle) for a grant that helped us to meet some of our expenses. Mrs. C. M. Ellis mastered the seemingly impossible task of deciphering the varied hieroglyphics and vocal cacophonies of all of us and somehow managed to rescue a single manuscript from the welter of the tentative preliminary drafts; it is a pleasure to be able to express our gratitude to her. If the reader feels that anything was best left unrescued, that is our fault, not hers.

L. WEISKRANTZ

Oxford
December, 1967

Contributors

P. P. G. Bateson   Assistant Director of Research,
University of Cambridge,
Sub-Department of Animal Behaviour,
Madingley, Cambridge, England.

A. Cowey   Senior Research Officer, University of Oxford,
Institute of Experimental Psychology,
Oxford, England.

G. Ettlinger   Senior Lecturer,
Department of Experimental Neurology,
Institute of Psychiatry,
London, England.

C. G. Gross   Assistant Professor, Department of Psychology,
Harvard University,
Cambridge, Massachusetts, U.S.A.

M. S. Halliday   Lecturer,
Laboratory of Experimental Psychology,
University of Sussex,
Brighton, England.

Brenda Milner   Head, Psychology Department,
Montreal Neurological Institute,
Montreal, Canada.

M. J. Morgan   Assistant in Research, Department of Psychology,
University of Cambridge,
Cambridge, England.

M. H. Sheldon   Assistant in Research, Department of Psychology,
Hull, England.

J. Steiner   Wellcome Senior Research Fellow in Clinical
Science,
The Institute of Psychiatry,
The Maudsley Hospital,
London, England.

H.-L. Teuber   Professor of Psychology,
Massachusetts Institute of Technology,
Cambridge, Massachusetts, U.S.A.

L. Weiskrantz   Professor of Psychology and Director of the Institute of Experimental Psychology,
University of Oxford,
Oxford, England.

ANALYSIS OF BEHAVIORAL CHANGE

CHAPTER 1

Introduction

L. WEISKRANTZ

SOME YEARS ago, in the early flushes of the Age of Psychopharmacology (or, at least, when the neologism was still neo), we were invited by a publisher to produce a review of that subject. The approach was declined in some haste on the grounds, which are probably still valid today, that the field was changing so rapidly that any review of the literature was bound to be out of date before it was published. But, more important, the difficulties of analyzing the effects of drugs on behavior seemed to be so readily flouted in those headstrong days that it seemed unwise for us to perpetuate some of the previously published conclusions between the solid covers of a book.

Gradually the somewhat more attractive notion emerged that a book addressed to those very problems of analysis might have more durable benefit, especially as the formal situation in psychopharmacology is identical to that in a large number of areas of enquiry in which changes in behavior are being investigated following various treatments. It matters not whether the treatment is a brain lesion; drug administration; shooting an animal into space; keeping it in an impoverished environment; or tickling its hypothalamus—the problems of analyzing the behavioral changes are identical in form and often in content. The imposed variable (treatment) by hypothesis alters the relationship between the organism's behavior (output) and its external or internal environment (input). The problem is to discover an altered relationship, dissect it down to its essentials, characterize it, try to understand why it occurred, and draw inferences about the nature of the mechanism being operated upon by the treatment. No existing single work, so far as we were aware, had addressed itself exclusively to this process. Gradually a larger circle of colleagues and friends came to share the conviction that there was some point in producing such a work, and this book is the result. Large portions of it were written during the summer of 1964 when Churchill College, Cambridge, provided us with attractive but effective monastic isolation to enable several of us to live, eat, discuss, and write with minimal external and internal distraction.

It is a preposterous and pompous endeavor—as we point out in the book itself—to tell anyone how to carry out his research, except for provision of purely technical points about statistical design and analysis, details of existing apparatus and the like. Plenty of books already exist to meet the needs of even the most compulsive researcher, and we have not attempted simply to stomp over such well-trodden ground. Research is to be judged by its fruits, not by its adherence to any particular set of rituals. The book is not a collection of recipes, but an exposure of the reader to various aromas. It is a ventilation of some of the attractions and disadvantages of pursuing certain broad lines of experimental enquiry. Seeing how arduous it was to produce even this incomplete book, and consequently being most reluctant to be forced often to revise it, we hope we have addressed ourselves to the problems in a form that will survive empirical advance and the invention of new techniques (given that it survives at all).

But it is not, nor could it profitably be, empty of empirical content or technical detail. Most of the book is, in fact, a closely reasoned but informative analysis of how treatment-induced changes in various categories of behavior have been or might be attacked. The arguments have both form and content, but we have tried to look at the aspects of form that will be persistent. The empirical content is illustrative rather than exhaustive. While it is no doubt too heavily seasoned with the particular research interests of its authors, at least it has the merit of personal acquaintance with the difficulties of reaching firm conclusions in the analysis of treatment effects.

The book falls into two sections. The first contains a number of chapters dealing with the problems of the analysis of specific aspects of behavior. These include positive and negative reinforcement effects, emotion, activity, exploration, learning, attention, discrimination and memory, the last two topics receiving special elaboration in the context of the neurology of human behavior. They are followed with a few chapters on general pragmatic and logical issues that apply to methods of observing behavior and to research on treatment effects. Some specific traps are exposed, and there is a discussion of the types of inferences that can emerge from such research, particularly in the field of the neurology of human behavior. They are followed by a few advanced research workers in psychology, as well as to others in related disciplines who share a practical and immediate concern with the untangling of the effects on behavior of some imposed variable.

The decision to follow a traditional classification of behavior will no doubt disappoint some of the *avant-garde*, and it was taken not without some heated discussion. Other classifications based on computer technology or on other recent developments, including those that claim to be purely descriptive and, therefore, most likely to be endowed with classificatory merit, might be superior. But the traditional categories at least have the advantage of being generally, if vaguely, understood in advance and will allow the reader, especially if he is not a psychologist, to sample selectively without first undergoing a specialist course. And, of course, the traditional categories have stood the test of time. But, more important, it seemed to us that more or less the same content would require treatment regardless of the classification adopted. We were more concerned with the content than with the labels.

Our categories are terribly broad, as we are at pains to emphasize in the book, but this is a feature not uniquely restricted to this particular classification scheme. Moreover, the point repeatedly is made that the concept of a "pure" behavioral task, reflecting only single category of processes, is not only a fiction but a nonstarter. All tasks must involve consideration of more than one, if not all, of the categories of any classification scheme. The latter is only a convenient device, not a rigid collection of slots, to allow various behavioral aspects to receive momentary emphasis. The task of analyzing treatment effects is one of dissection, of *isolating*, in successive stages, the critical features that alter in particular input-output relationships; the task of classifying those relationships is only subsidiary.

The unevenness of the several chapters will no doubt strike the reader. This reflects not only differences in the scope of categories themselves, but also in the zeal and conciseness of the authors themselves. Although there was considerable interchange among all of us during the writing of the book, it remains the work of several individuals each with his own attitudes and insights. What is shared is an acceptance of the goal, not necessarily the means. If this book is ever rewritten, some chapters will require expansion and others contraction, and there no doubt ought to be some additions. But that would be another book. If this one proves to be of any practical benefit to anyone or stimulates a line of thought that leads to the same end, that will be enough.

CHAPTER 2

Positive Reinforcement

J . STEINER

I F A HUNGRY animal is placed in a compartment such as a Skinner box where a response such as lever pressing can be conveniently recorded, it will usually press the lever a few times in the course of its exploration of the compartment, until after a while the rate of pressing falls to what is known as the operant level. Then, if the lever is connected to a feeder that delivers a pellet of food after each press, the rate of lever pressing will usually show a dramatic increase after two or three pellets have been obtained. This process has been described in various ways by different workers depending on their theoretical orientation, but the empirical data are fortunately not in dispute. Certain events such as the presentation of food, water, sexual contact, or warmth have the common property that they can increase the frequency of the behavior that occurred immediately preceding their presentation, and such events are called reinforcers. A wide range of other stimuli can acquire similar reinforcing properties and are called conditioned or secondary reinforcers (Kelleher and Gollub, 1962; Myers, 1958).

In the previous example, the reinforcement was responsible for the learning of a new response, and it is in this context that most of the theoretical discussion of reinforcement has taken place (Hull, 1943; Hilgard and Marquis, 1962). Here, however, we shall emphasize the importance of reinforcement not only in the acquisition of new behavior but also in the maintenance of established behavior. In the previous example, for instance, the frequency of bar pressing would drop gradually back to its operant level if the reinforcement were withdrawn.

This emphasis means that reinforcement takes on a wider referent than it is given by some theorists who are chiefly concerned with processes of learning and who prefer to use such terms as *incentive*, *goal*, or *motive* for events that maintain behavior (Hull, 1943; Logan, 1960).

Reinforcement Strength

Although we loosely refer to the reinforcing properties of a stimulus, reinforcement is principally a property of the organism. The influence that a stimulus will have on behavior will depend on the physical properties of the stimulus, e.g., type and amount of food, intensity of heat or shock, but also on the type of organism, the history of the organism, and on the state of deprivation of the organism. Thus, food is a potent reinforcer to a hungry animal but not to one which has recently eaten. In this way variables that are usually discussed under the heading *motivation* can be considered to affect behavior by altering the strength of reinforcers.

Although such terms as the *strength, power, value* or *effectiveness* of reinforcers (or incentives) occur frequently in the literature (Hilgard and Marquis, 1962), their meaning is seldom made explicit, and no entirely satisfactory method of quantifying reinforcement strength has yet been developed.

In general, one reinforcer is considered stronger than another if its effect on behavior is greater. However, there are a number of ways to assess this, and it is by no means certain that under the various methods, reinforcers would be ranked in the same order of strength. It is possible that one measure will one day be arbitrarily selected and a quantitative science of reinforcement developed, but in the meantime several possible measures must be discussed.

Measures of Reinforcement Strength

Consummatory Behavior

Of the primary reinforcements, food, water, and sex involve the consummatory responses of eating, drinking, and copulation, respectively, that can be used as measures of reinforcement strength. Although it is an everyday observation that hungry people eat more, it will be seen later that this measure does not always correlate well with other measures of reinforcement strength. When the reinforcement is consumed, the animal becomes satiated, consummatory behavior ceases, and the reinforcing strength is reduced. For this reason most measures of reinforcement strength take care to avoid satiation effects. Consummatory behavior, by its very nature, cannot do this and is probably better considered as a measure of the animal's capacity or of its resistance to satiation. Nevertheless, consummatory behavior is a subject of great intrinsic interest, and it will be further discussed later.

Rate of Response

Rate of response as a measure of reinforcement strength seems a natural development from the defining characteristics of a reinforcer. A reinforcer is defined by its ability to increase and maintain the frequency of a response, and it seems reasonable to suppose that a weak reinforcer maintains a low rate of responding and that a strong reinforcer maintains a higher rate.

Most of the work using rate of response has been done in the free-operant situation introduced by Skinner (1938), but the speed at which rats run up a straight alley is sometimes also used and can be considered as a rate measure.

In the free-operant situation, a response is selected that takes a short time to occur and that leaves the animal in the same place ready to respond again. In the rat or primate, typical responses are lever pressing or chain pulling; in the pigeon, pecking a key; but these responses have been selected principally because of the ease with which their recording can be automated and, within limits, any response can be selected. It is, however, considerably easier to establish and maintain a response that is part of the animal's normal repertoire in its natural state.

It is often useful to measure the rate of response before any reinforcement has been delivered, and this *operant level* can serve as a base line for the assessment of reinforcement effects. Reinforcement can then be arranged to follow a response and changes in the rate of response can then be recorded. If the operant level of responding is very low, it is necessary to encourage the animal to make the response. The various methods of doing this are known as *shaping up*. Skinner introduced this term and developed a technique that reinforces selective approximations to the required response (Skinner, 1953). The procedure usually begins with magazine training, which consists of operating the magazine of the automatic feeder at irregular intervals. The click of the magazine precedes the delivery of food, and the animal quickly learns to approach the food dish at the sound of the click. The next step is to select and reinforce an item of behavior with a reasonably high operant level, which approximates to some extent the desired response. For example, if lever pressing is being shaped up, all movements of the animal into the vicinity of the lever might be reinforced. The responses will increase in frequency, and the next step is to withhold reinforcement until the animal touches the lever. Lever touching then becomes more frequent through reinforcement that can once more be withheld unless the animal this time actually depresses the lever. Originally, the probability of the final response may have been zero, but, through the reinforcement of successive approximations, the spectrum of behavior has been shifted until the desired response occurs with sufficient frequency for reinforcement to be effective. Skinner (1953) claims that this is an effective and rapid procedure but in fact it requires considerable skill, for unwanted responses can be accidentally reinforced and may be very difficult to eliminate. It is often possible to use tricks that increase the frequency of the desired response with much less trouble. For example, key pecking in pigeons can be very rapidly established if, after magazine training, a small piece of grain is attached to the key with celluloid tape. The bird pecks at the grain and operates the feeder. Similarly, a piece of date smeared on the lever will rapidly establish pressing when primates are used.

Rate of response can be recorded in many different ways, but perhaps the most straightforward way is a polygraph or print-out recorder that gives a complete record from which the interresponse times and the rate of response can be computed. However, the amount of work necessary to transcribe the record into a form that is usable often makes this kind of recording unfeasible; these methods also give the experimenter little notion of the state of the experiment until a summary is made by laborious transcription. The most commonly used device is a cumulative recorder in which a pen is stepped across the paper for a small distance for each response. At the same time, the paper feeds at a constant speed so that the slope of the line produced is proportional to the rate of response and changes in rate can be seen in the curvature of the record. Practical advice on the use of these recorders, including selection of the size of step and speed of paper, are provided by Ferster (1953).

In some experiments a record of interresponse times is useful, and for this purpose a bank of counters can be used. Following each response a clock is started that switches the output from the lever to successive counters following a fixed period of time, e.g., 5 seconds. The first counter then records all interresponse times of less than 5 seconds, the second those between 5 and 10 seconds, and so on. In this way a frequency distribution of interresponse times can be read off.

A method that will no doubt be much used in the future is the recording of responses on punched tape for computer analysis, and there is, of course, no reason why several recording methods should not be used concurrently. Even when more elaborate methods are available, a cumulative recorder is useful because it gives the observer an immediate indication of the progress of the experiment. The low grain of most records from these instruments means, however, that the variability of behavior may be obscured. In some cases this is an advantage because important findings are not obscured by random variations, but this fact should be taken into account when the records are interpreted.

It is well known that the rate and pattern of responding varies with the schedule of reinforcement (Ferster and Skinner, 1957), but it should also be noted that the *sensitivity* of the measure to manipulations of the parameters of reinforcement also varies with the schedule.

CRF SCHEDULES. When every response is reinforced (CRF) most of the time is spent eating or drinking, so that the measure approaches that of a simple consummatory response. Rate is then greatly influenced by such variables as the time taken to consume the reinforcement and the distance between the manipulandum and the site of food delivery. Moreover, it is not unusual to find that the rate of response is near the maximum even with a weak reinforcer, so that an increase cannot be measured. This is an example of the *ceiling effects* that may also occur in other schedules and that must be considered in interpreting the results of treatment effects. Another disadvantage of a CRF schedule is that the subject is reinforced so frequently that he is likely to be rapidly satiated, making it impossible for behavior to be observed over any substantial period of time. This schedule is therefore probably most useful for the assessment of weak reinforcers.

INTERVAL SCHEDULES. One method of arranging reinforcements intermittently is to make them available to the subject only after an interval of time has elapsed; at the end of this period the subject's next response will produce a reinforcement, and a time interval will start again. The interval can be kept constant (FI) or made variable (VI).

FI schedules typically produce a pause following each reinforcement, the length of which is related to the duration of the fixed interval. As time elapses the subject begins to respond and reaches a high rate before the next reinforcement. With extensive experience on this schedule it is common for the animal's temporal discrimination to improve with a consequent reduction in overall rate. This improvement may continue for many months, but, provided it is taken into account, the rate of response on the schedule seems to be sensitive to such parameters of reinforcement as the level of deprivation (Ferster and Skinner, 1957, p. 320). It is also sensitive to treatment effects such as the administration of drugs (Dews, 1955) and brain lesions (Pribram, 1958; Ferster and Skinner, 1957, p. 322). On this schedule some treatment effects disrupt the temporal pattern of responding while others principally affect the overall rate.

On VI *schedules* the irregular spacing of reinforcements in time eliminate the cyclic changes in response rate that characterize FI performance. When specifying a VI schedule, it is usual to mention only the mean interval, but a complete description should give the range and distribution of intervals used. The sequence of time intervals can be programed randomly, but a more steady rate of response is obtained if very long intervals are avoided. Various methods of constructing VI schedules are provided by Ferster and Skinner (1957). The linear cumulative record obtained with this schedule makes it easy to read off the rate of response from the record and probably accounts for the popularity of this schedule in assessing reinforcement strength. Performance on this schedule has been shown to be sensitive to the level of deprivation (Ferster and Skinner, 1957; Skinner, 1938; Miller, 1956) as well as amount and quality of reinforcement (Guttman, 1953) and has been recommended by Miller and Barry (1960) for use in studies of motivation. However, some experimenters have found that performance on VI schedules can be resistant to change as the parameters of reinforcement are varied. For example, Jenkins and Clayton (1949) found only small differences in rate of response when they varied the amount of grain with which they reinforced their pigeons. Keesey and Kling (1961) obtained differences in the rate of response as the amount of grain was varied, but found this only at the beginning of each session or immediately after a change in amount. Catania (1963), also using pigeons, found no systematic change as the duration of exposure to the grain hopper was varied from 3 seconds to 6 seconds although the same variations produced marked changes when a concurrent schedule was used (see under heading "Choice Procedures" in this chapter). With extensive experience of a schedule the rate of response sometimes becomes resistant to change as environmental variables are varied, and the animals are said to be "locked in" on the schedule. Ferster and Skinner (1957) noticed this particularly with variable interval schedules. Locking in appears to be less likely on a fixed interval schedule, which for this reason may be more suitable in many circumstances.

RATIO SCHEDULES. On ratio schedules the animal is required to respond a number of time for each reinforcement, and *ratio* refers to the number of responses required per reinforcement. This number can be fixed (FR) or variable (VR). The schedules generate very high rates of response, and it is common to find that the animal responds either at a near maximal rate or not at all. The rate of response is therefore relatively insensitive to the parameters of reinforcement. However, on FR schedules it is common to find pauses following reinforcements, and the duration of these pauses does vary with the parameters of reinforcement. Both Sidman and Stebbins (1954) and Ferster and Skinner (1957, p. 71) observed longer postreinforcement pauses when their subjects were less deprived, although the local rates of responding showed very little sensitivity even to wide ranges in deprivation. On VR schedules postreinforcement pauses are often absent, so that extremely high overall rates are generated. Ratio schedules are often highly resistant to treatment effects such as drugs and brain lesions and are therefore sometimes useful as a control procedure to show that a treatment does not produce a motor impairment.

MULTIPLE SCHEDULES. It is sometimes an advantage to run two or more schedules in each session, and this can conveniently be done by correlating each with a distinctive discriminative stimulus. The effects of a treatment on the components of the mixed schedule can then be compared. Dews (1955) has shown that several drugs affect the rate of response on the FI component of a multiple FI-FR schedule without any change being seen in the FR component.

CHAINED SCHEDULES. The most commonly used chained schedule consists of two components each marked with its own stimulus. In the first component, in the presence of S_1 the animal is reinforced by the presentation of the stimulus marking the second component S_2. Then, in the presence of S_2 responding is reinforced with a primary reinforcer. The schedules of reinforcement in the two components may be the same or different, and the responses may also either be the same (homogeneous chain) or different (heterogeneous chain). Responding in the first component is usually considered to be maintained by the secondary or conditioned reinforcing properties of S_2, and these schedules have been widely used in the study of secondary reinforcement (Kelleher and Gollub, 1962). They may also prove useful in assessing the strength of primary reinforcers. Thus Ferster and Skinner (1957, p. 679) varied the level of deprivation during prolonged sessions on chained schedules and found that the rate of response in the first component of the chain was much more sensitive to the level of deprivation than that in the second component.

These schedules have also been useful in assessing reinforcement strength when electrical stimulation of the brain is used as a reinforcer.

A large number of other schedules have been investigated and are occasionally useful in the study of treatment effects. They are described by Ferster and Skinner (1957), and, because they are not particularly suitable for the measurement of reinforcement strength, they will not be mentioned here.

Speed of Approach

Speed of approach in a straight alley has been used to assess reinforcement strength. Running-time scores have an extremely skewed distribution, giving too much weight to slow performance, and are usually transformed into speed or log-time measures (Miller and Barry, 1960).

Hull (1943), Barry (1958), and Miller and Miles (1936) have all studied running speeds at different levels of food deprivation, and, in general, their animals ran faster the greater the level of deprivation. However, it is difficult to find a systematic study of the relationship between running speed and level of deprivation that is not contaminated by an effect of learning. Terminal asymptotic levels are not often used, probably because they lack sensitivity.

Running speed in an alley is somewhat analogous to FR performance in a free-operant situation because a fixed number of responses is required to reach the goal box and because the faster this is run off the sooner the reinforcement is obtained.

Running speed is sensitive to changes in the amount of food reinforcement (Crespi, 1942; Zeaman, 1949) and has also been used to assess sexual reinforcers (Sheffield, Wulff, and Backer, 1951; Beach and Jordan, 1956).

Miscellaneous Measures of Strength of Approach: Latency and Strength of Pull

Latency measures are occasionally used to assess reinforcement strength. Starting time in a runway often varies systematically with deprivation level and with amount of reinforcement (Logan, 1960). It has also been found useful in a study on the attractiveness of different foods for monkeys by Weiskrantz and Cowey (1963). In their experiment the animal pulled in a trolley on which a piece of food was placed from a distance of 60 centimeters. The force of his pull did not appear to be a useful variable, but the latency of response varied systematically with different foods and with the experience the animal had of each food.

With a different technique, in which rats were restrained by a harness as they ran towards a goal box, strength of pull *has* been a useful measure (Brown, 1948).

Choice Procedures

An alternative method of assessing reinforcement strength is to offer the animal a choice between two reinforcers. If a preference for one over the other can be established, the preferred reinforcer can be considered the stronger. This method has been useful in the study of specific hungers and of preference for various foods in the rat. Thus Young (1936) was able to rank various foods in the following order: fresh milk, sugar, ground wheat, dried-milk powder, white flour, butter fat. The series was found to be transitive in the sense that every food was preferred to every food found below it and there was remarkably little variation in the order between animals. Choice procedures are useful for ranking reinforcers but in general do not provide a good measure of the *extent* of the preference for one reinforcer over another because generally the preferred alternative is chosen on a high proportion of trials.

In a free-operant situation the animal may be allowed to choose between two responses concurrently available, a procedure known as a *concurrent schedule*. For example, Catania (1963) made two keys concurrently available to his pigeons, and responding to either of these was reinforced by grain on a VI schedule. A fairly stable rate of response developed on each key, with the pigeon frequently switching over from one key to the other. Because of the fact that the VI schedules were running simultaneously, a reinforcement could be set up on one key while the bird was working on the other so that the first peck following a switch would be reinforced. Since this might bring behavior on one key under the control of reinforcements on the other, a change-over delay of 2 seconds was introduced so that no response was reinforced within 2 seconds of a response to the other key. When stable behavior had developed, Catania varied the amount of reinforcement given for responding to each key by varying the duration of exposure to the grain hopper. The birds were run until stable rates were maintained under each condition, and the rate of response on each key was found to be a linear function of the duration of hopper exposure. This result should be contrasted with Catania's failure to find any effect when he varied the amount of reinforcement if a rate measure on a simple VI schedule was used.

Choice procedures appear to be more sensitive to the parameters of reinforcement than rate measures and may prove to be more suitable as measures of reinforcement strength. They allow measurements to be made relative to some other reinforcer in the alternative condition that can serve as a standard, and, just as the judgment of sensory magnitude is facilitated by comparison with a standard, this should lead to a greater sensivity and to less variability of results. Another advantage is that they may simplify the isolation and measurement of variables that influence reinforcement strength because the two alternatives can be equated for all variables except the one under study, which may then be held responsible for any preference found. With other techniques, nonrelevant variables are kept constant but may sometimes exert such powerful control that they drown the effect of the variable under study.

Cost Methods

If an animal is required to suffer some cost in order to obtain a reinforcement, the amount of cost required to prevent the reinforced behavior could be taken as an index of the strength of the reinforcement. In other words, the price the animal is prepared to pay for the reinforcement would be taken as a measure of its reinforcement strength.

At one time this principle was quite popular, and the Columbia apparatus (Warden, 1931) in which an animal is forced to cross a charged grid to reach reinforcement is a good example. Various reinforcements were placed on the far side of the grid, and the strength of current required to stop the rat or the number of crossings made at any strength were compared for each. This method probably generates serious emotional effects because of the fear induced by the shock and has not been used in recent years.

A technique similar in principle was developed by Miller (1956), who pitted the aversion produced by quinine against the reinforcing properties of food or water. The animal is offered food that is adulterated by progressively increasing concentrations of quinine, and the concentration of quinine required to stop him eating is used as a measure of reinforcement strength.

In some recent experiments by Hodos (1961; Hodos and Kalman, 1963) the cost took the form of work. Hodos made use of the fact that animals on an FR schedule appear to sustain higher ratios before signs of strain appear when more powerful reinforcers are used. He arranged his ratio schedule to increase in size by a fixed step following each reinforcement. Eventually the ratio became so high that strain developed and the animal paused. If the pause exceeded 5 minutes, the session was terminated. For example, with a ratio step of 20, the first reinforcement required 20 responses, the second 40, the third 60, and so on. The maximum ratio sustained before the terminating pause occurred was taken as a measure of the reinforcement strength. When a sufficient size of step was used to avoid satiation effects, Hodos obtained a linear relationship between the maximum ratio reached and both the amount and concentration of condensed milk used as a reinforcement for rats.

Combined Choice and Cost Measures

Verhave (1963) has recently described a method that uses a cost measure of the extent of a preference in a choice situation. His pigeons were faced with 2 keys, only the left-hand key providing food reinforcement. Pecking this key was reinforced on an FR 300 schedule when the key was red and on an FR 60 schedule when it was green. The purpose of the experiment was to assess the extent of the preference for the shorter ratio schedule. Following each reinforcement, the key was colored red but could be changed to green by a peck on the right-hand key. The pigeon was, therefore, offered the choice of pecking the red key to be reinforced on FR 300 or of pecking the right-hand key to switch to the green and then pecking the left-hand key to be reinforced on FR 60. The pigeons clearly showed a preference for the green condition, and Verhave measured the extent of this preference by introducing a cost in the form of an adjusting ratio schedule on the switching key. On this schedule, the size of the ratio on the switching key increased by a fixed step, in this case by 6, in a similar manner to Hodos' progressive ratio schedule, but had the added condition that, if the ratio was not completed within an arbitrary time criterion (ATC, which in this case was 40 seconds), the size of the ratio was reduced by an equal step. The result was that the ratio reached an equilibrium value (EV) about which it oscillated, and this value was taken as a measure of the preference for the green condition. Verhave obtained an EV at a ratio that oscillated between 66 and 78 for the conditions described above. The method has not yet been applied in any systematic way to the study of reinforcement parameters, but, as Verhave suggests, it could be used as a sort of psychological Wheatstone bridge to determine the value of unknown reinforcers relative to an arbitrary standard. Following each reinforcement the animal can be given a choice between working on the food producing key under given conditions marked by the key being red, which could serve as a standard, or of switching to an alternative condition marked by the key being green. Various reinforcers could be presented in the alternative condition, and the preference for each over the standard could be used as a measure of their reinforcement strength. Steiner (1967) has used a similar method to assess the degree of preference that a monkey has for discriminative stimuli in an observing response situation (cf. Wyckoff, 1952).

Examples of Measurement of Reinforcers

A few examples of the measurement of reinforcers will now be discussed to illustrate the techniques used.

Food

Perhaps the most commonly used reinforcer is food delivered to a hungry animal, and several variables affecting the reinforcement strength of food have been studied.

AMOUNT OF FOOD. In general, the reinforcing strength of food increases with the amount used, but, at least with the range of amounts that have been studied, the effect is relatively small.

Grindley (1929) measured the running speed of chicks along an alley at the end of which they received either 0, 2, 4 or 6 grains of rice, and he found that the larger reward maintained a faster rate of running. Crespi (1942), using rats in a runway, also found an increase in running speed with amount of food and demonstrated, in addition, a contrast effect when the amount of food was suddenly changed. If the amount was increased, the rate of running exceeded the rate normally maintained by the higher amount. If the amount was decreased, the rate fell below that normally maintained by the low value. The strength of a reinforcer may therefore vary not only with amount of reinforcement but also with the conditions that exist before the amount is changed.

Similarly, Guttman (1953), using rate of bar pressing by rats on an FI schedule as his dependent variable, found that the rate increased as the concentration of sucrose, which he used as reinforcement, was increased. On the other hand, rate of response has often proved resistant to change as the amount of reinforcement is varied. Thus Jenkins and Clayton (1949) found little change in the rate of pecking by their pigeons on a VI schedule when the amount of grain used as reinforcement was varied, and Keesey and Kling (1961) found the largest changes in rate occurred immediately after a change in amount. Catania (1963), using a simple VI schedule, found little change in the rate of pecking when his pigeons were given different amounts of grain. However, a choice procedure involving a concurrent schedule was apparently a more sensitive measure because with it Catania (1963) obtained a linear relation between amount of food and rate of response. Hodos (1961), using a cost measure, namely, his progressive ratio schedule, also obtained a linear relationship between the maximum ratio reached and either the amount or concentration of condensed milk used as a reinforcement for rats.

LEVEL OF DEPRIVATION. Most workers are in agreement that the reinforcing strength of food increases with the state of deprivation of the animal. Thus Skinner (1938) found that the rate of response in rats on an FI schedule increased as their period of starvation was increased to about 5 to 7 days and that it thereafter decreased, presumably due to inanition. In another experiment he deprived rats for 24 hours and then prefed them different amounts at the beginning of each session. He found that the rate of response on an FI schedule decreased as the amount prefed increased. Recently it has become common practice to vary the level of deprivation over longer periods and to study the rate of response as a function of the body weight of the animal. Ferster and Skinner (1957) found that in general the rate increased as the animal's weight was reduced but that the relationship was not a simple one.

The importance of the measure of reinforcement strength used was emphasized in an experiment by Miller (1956), who compared the effect of hours of food deprivation on 4 measures of reinforcement strength. The consummatory measure (volume of enriched-milk solution drunk) approached its maximum after 6 hours of deprivation and after 30 hours (probably) declined slightly. However, the other 2 measures (the rate of bar pressing and the amount of quinine required to stop the animal from drinking) continued to increase throughout the test period, which went on as long as 54 hours.

HYPOTHALAMIC OBESITY. Numerous studies have confirmed that bilateral lesions of the ventromedial nuclei of the hypothalamus will cause rats to become obese, and it soon became clear (Brobeck, Tepperman, and Long, 1943) that, at least in the early "dynamic phase" of the syndrome, they overate. These studies have been well reviewed (Teitelbaum, 1961) and will only be discussed here from the point of view of the measures of reinforcement strength that were used. The fact that consummatory behavior was increased in these animals led Miller, Bailey, and Stevenson (1950) to test the animals with other measures. To their surprise they found that operated animals that were eating reliably more than the controls worked at a reliably slower rate on a VI schedule of bar pressing for food. The two measures gave opposite results and led these workers to study further measures. They found that on cost measures the operated animals also performed less well than the controls. Thus with the quinine test they stopped eating at lower concentrations than the controls, and in another test that involved lifting weighted lids from the food dishes they were deterred by a smaller weight. These results were confirmed and extended by Teitelbaum (1957). He found that operated rats made a greater number of bar presses for food than controls when a CRF schedule was in operation but that they made a fewer number of bar presses if the food was delivered on a moderate to high FR schedule.

It appeared, therefore, that although the operated animals ate more than controls, food was less reinforcing to them on all other measures of reinforcement strength that have so far been tested. As we mentioned earlier, the amount of consummatory behavior depends very much on the rate of satiation, and it has been concluded that the medial hypothalamic area is a sort of satiation center that when stimulated inhibits eating, and when ablated leads to delayed satiation.

Electrical Stimulation of the Brain

Since the initial report of Olds and Milner (1954) a great deal of research has shown that electrical stimulation of subcortical structures in the brain can act as reinforcement (see Olds [1962] for a comprehensive review). Some methods that have been used to assess this form of reinforcement illustrate the pros and cons of different measures, and they will therefore be briefly discussed.

APPROACH MEASURES. Olds (1956) described how he first studied the effects of electrical stimulation of subcortical structures with the rat placed in a large box. Stimulation was always applied in a particular corner, and he noticed that the rat kept returning to that corner. When another corner was selected, this in turn became preferred by the animal. Later, other approach measures were used. For example, using a straight runway, Olds (1956) found that hungry rats would run faster for the electrical stimulus reward than they would for food. These measures, however, were not very sensitive to the parameters of stimulation and soon gave way to rate-of-response measures.

RATE MEASURES. By far the most widely used measure has been the rate of response in a Skinner box where each bar press has delivered an electrical stimulus to the brain. With electrodes in some sites, stimulation on this CRF schedule has led to extremely high rates of responding with little or no evidence of satiation. Rates of over 5000 per hour have regularly appeared with electrodes in the lateral hypothalamus, and rates of 300 to 1000 are the rule in certain telencephalic areas. Sometimes this rate of response has been maintained for over 24 hours at a time and at least with diencephalic electrodes tends to go on to the point of physical exhaustion (Olds, 1958).

On other schedules the pattern and rate of responding is in general similar to that seen with food as a reinforcement. Sidman *et al.* (1955), using electrodes in the septal area (rats) or caudate nucleus (cats), maintained *stable* responding on a VI 16 second and an FR 10 schedule but found that responding was not maintained if long interval schedules or high ratio schedules were programed. This led them to suggest that ICS was analogous to small amounts of reinforcement. However, Brodie *et al.* (1960), using electrodes in the median forebrain bundle maintained behavior on ratios as high as FR 100. Olds suggests that the difference is a function of electrode placement (1962).

COST MEASURES. Olds (1958) has revived the principle of the Columbia obstruction box to assess the strength of ICS. He found that a 24-hour hungry rat would cross a grill through which it received a 60 to 180 microamp shock in order to obtain food on the other side. An implanted animal by comparison was prepared to receive 60 microamps on the grill if it received an ICS of 2 times threshold on the other side, and 425 microamps if it received an ICS of 10 times threshold. In addition, he found that animals with diencephalic electrodes would accept a higher grill shock than animals with telencephalic electrodes, which correlated well with the rate of response measures. However, the most intense telencephalic reward placements gave lower response rates but better grid crossings than the least intense hypothalamic placements, indicating that the 2 measures of reinforcement strength do not always vary in the same way.

CHOICE MEASURES. Hodos and Valenstein (1962) offered their animals a choice of 2 levers with which they could stimulate themselves in different brain locations and with different intensities. They showed that the brain stimulus producing the highest rates of response is not always the one preferred in a choice test. Very high intensities of brain stimulation gave lower rates of response than intermediate ones but yet were preferred. Strong shocks to the brain result in motor side effects that may interfere with lever pressing and may account for this discrepancy. Hodos claimed that he devised his progressive ratio schedule to measure the reinforcing strength of ICS on this account, but to date he has not published any results.

However, Hawkins and Pliskoff (1964) confirmed the results of the choice procedure by using a chained schedule. In their experiment, rats were reinforced on a VI schedule for pressing the left-hand lever in their cage by the appearance of a second lever on the right. When this lever appeared, they were allowed to press this 5 times, each press resulting in intracranial stimulation. The rate on the right-hand lever then gave a simple rate measure of the reinforcing strength of the shock while the rate on the left hand lever gave a less direct measure. They found that the simple rate measure increased to a maximum and then decreased as the strength of shock was increased. However, the rate in the first member of the chain continued to increase at all shock levels used.

A great deal of work still remains to be done on this subject, but it seems clear that some of the alternatives to rate-of-response measures have distinct advantages and may turn out to be acceptable measures of the reinforcing strength of ICS.

Conclusion

In this chapter we have considered reinforcement as a quantitative variable and have discussed various possible methods by which it can be measured. This approach makes it possible to consider diverse treatments such as food deprivation, stimulation of the hypothalamus, or administration of a drug, in a unified manner, namely, as treatments that affect the *reinforcing strength* of the stimuli used. It is clear that different treatments affect reinforcement strength in different ways, which need to be investigated and specified in each case, but it may well prove unnecessary to fall back on the often confusing distinctions between reinforcement, drive, incentive and motive. Further work is needed to clarify the advantages and disadvantages of the various measures of reinforcement strength, but one can speculate that reinforcement strength will ultimately be defined in terms of units based on one of these measures. If this proves to be possible, it will make the many advantages of a metric scale available.

REFERENCES

BARRY, H. 1958. Effects of strength of drive on learning and on extinction. *J. exp. Psychol.*, **55**, 473–481.

BEACH, F. A., & JORDAN, L. 1956. Effects of sexual reinforcement upon the performance of male rats in a straight runway. *J. comp. physiol. Psychol.*, **49**, 105–110.

BROBECK, J. R., TEPPERMAN, J., & LONG, C. N. H. 1943. Experimental hypothalamic hyperphagia in the albino rat. *Yale J. Biol. Med.*, **15**, 831–853.

BRODIE, D. A., MORENO, O. M., MALIS, J. L., & BOREN, J. J. 1960. Rewarding properties of intracranial stimulation. *Science*, **131**, 929–930.

BROWN, J. S. 1948. Gradients of approach and avoidance responses and their relation to level of motivation. *J. comp. physiol. Psychol.*, **41**, 450–465.

CATANIA, C. A. 1963. Concurrent performances: A baseline for the study of reinforcement magnitude. *J. exp. anal. Behav.*, **6**, 299–300.

CRESPI, L. P. 1942. Quantitative variation of incentive and performance in the white rat. *Amer. J. Psychol.*, **55**, 467–517.

DEWS, P. B. 1955. Studies on behavior. 1. Differential sensitivity to pentobarbital of pecking performance in pigeons depending on the schedule of reward. *J. Pharmacol. exp. Ther.*, **113**, 393–401.

FERSTER, C. B. 1953. The use of the free operant in the analysis of behavior. *Psychol. Bull.*, **50**, 263–274.

FERSTER, C. B., & SKINNER, B. F. 1957. *Schedules of reinforcement.* New York: Appleton-Century-Crofts.

GRINDLEY, C. G. 1929. Experiments on the influence of the amount of reward on learning in young chickens. *Brit. J. Psychol.*, **20**, 173–180.

GUTTMAN, N. 1953. Operant conditioning, extinction, and periodic reinforcement in relation to concentration of sucrose used as reinforcing agent. *J. exp. Psychol.*, 46, 213–224.

HAWKINS, T. D., & PLISKOFF, S. S. 1964. Brain stimulation intensity, rate of self-stimulation, and reinforcement strength: An analysis through chaining. *J. exp. anal. Behav.*, 7, 285–288.

HILGARD, E. R., & MARQUIS, D. G. 1962. *Conditioning and learning.* (2nd ed.) Revised by Kimble, G. A. New York: Appleton-Century-Crofts.

HODOS, W. 1961. Progressive ratio as a measure of reward strength. *Science*, 134, 943–944.

HODOS, W., & KALMAN, G. 1963. Effects of increment size and reinforcer volume on progressive ratio performance. *J. exp. anal. Behav.*, 6, 387–392.

HODOS, W., & VALENSTEIN, E. S. 1962. An evaluation of response rate as a measure of rewarding intracranial stimulation. *J. comp. physiol. Psychol.*, 55, 80–84.

HULL, C. L. 1943. *Principles of behavior.* New York: Appleton-Century-Crofts.

JENKINS, W. O., & CLAYTON, F. L. 1949. Rate of responding and amount of reinforcement. *J. comp. physiol. Psychol.*, 42, 174–181.

KEESEY, R. E., & KLING, J. W. 1961. Amount of reinforcement and free-operant responding. *J. exp. anal. Behav.*, 4, 125–132.

KELLEHER, R. T., & GOLLUB, L. R. 1962. A review of positive conditioned reinforcement. *J. exp. anal. Behav.*, 5, 543–597.

LOGAN, F. A. 1960. *Incentive.* New Haven: Yale University Press.

MILLER, N. E. 1956. Effects of drugs on motivation: The value of using a variety of measures. *Ann. N.Y. Acad. Sci.*, 65, 318–333.

MILLER, N. E., BAILEY, C. J., & STEVENSON, J. A. F. 1950. Decreased "hunger" but increased food intake resulting from hypothalamic lesions. *Science*, 112, 256–259.

MILLER, N. E., & BARRY, H. 1960. Motivational effects of drugs: Methods which illustrate some general problems in psychopharmacology. *Psychopharmacol.*, 1, 169–199.

MILLER, N. E., & MILES, W. R. 1936. Effect of caffeine on the running speed of hungry, satiated, and frustrated rats. *J. comp. Psychol.*, 21, 179–204.

MYERS, J. L. 1958. Secondary reinforcement: A review of recent experimentation. *Psychol. Bull.*, 55, 284–301.

OLDS, J. 1956. Pleasure centers in the brain. *Scient. Amer.*, 197, 105–116.

OLDS, J. 1958. Self-stimulation of the brain. *Science*, 127, 315–324.

OLDS, J. 1962. Hypothalamic substrates of reward. *Physiol. Rev.*, 42, 554–604.

OLDS, J., & MILNER, P. 1954. Positive reinforcement produced by electrical stimulation of septal area and other regions of rat brain. *J. comp. physiol. Psychol.*, 47, 419–427.

PRIBRAM, K. H. 1958. Neocortical function in behavior. In Harlow, H. F., & Woolsey, C. N. (Eds.) *Biological and biochemical bases of behavior.* Madison, Wisc.: University of Wisconsin Press.

SHEFFIELD, F. D., WULFF, J. J., & BACKER, R. 1951. Reward value of copulation without sex drive reduction. *J. comp. physiol. Psychol.*, 44, 3–8.

SIDMAN, M., BRADY, J. V., BOREN, J. J., & CONRAD, D. G. 1955. Reward schedules and behavior maintained by intracranial self-stimulation. *Science*, 122, 830–831.

SIDMAN, M., & STEBBINS, W. C. 1954. Satiation effects under fixed-ratio schedules of reinforcement. *J. comp. physiol. Psychol.*, 47, 114–116.

SKINNER, B. F. 1938. *Behavior of organisms.* New York: Appleton-Century-Crofts.

SKINNER, B. F. 1953. *Science and human behavior.* New York: Macmillan.

STEINER, J. 1967. Observing responses, and uncertainty reduction. *Quart. J. exp. Psychol.*, 19, 18–29.

TEITELBAUM, P. 1957. Random and food-directed activity in hyperphagic and normal rats. *J. comp. physiol. Psychol.,* 50, 486–490.

TEITELBAUM, P. 1961. Disturbances in feeding and drinking behavior after hypothalamic lesions. In Jones, M. R. (Ed.), *Nebraska symposium on motivation.* Lincoln, Nebraska: University of Nebraska Press.

VERHAVE, T. 1963. Towards an empirical calculus of reinforcement value. *J. exp. anal. Behav.,* 6, 525–536.

WARDEN, C. J. 1931. *Animal motivation: Experimental studies in the albino rat.* New York: Columbia University Press.

WEISKRANTZ, L., & COWEY, A. 1963. The aetiology of food reward in monkeys. *Anim. Behav.,* 11, 225–234.

WYCKOFF, L. B. 1952. The role of observing responses in discriminative learning. *Psychol. Rev.,* 59, 431–442.

YOUNG, P. T. 1936. *Motivation of behavior.* New York: Wiley.

ZEAMAN, D. 1949. Response latency as a function of the amount of reinforcement. *J. exp. Psychol.,* 39, 466–483.

CHAPTER 3

Negative Reinforcement

M. J. MORGAN

N EGATIVE reinforcement presents several clear and interesting problems, but its definition is not one of them. A stimulus is recognized as a positive reinforcer if its presentation after a certain behavior will make that behavior more probable in the future. Negative reinforcers should evidently have the opposite effect, but this could imply either one of two things: a weakening of responses when a stimulus is presented (punishment) or a strengthening of responses when a stimulus is removed or withheld (escape and avoidance). Either of these processes, weakening and strengthening, could properly be called negative reinforcement, but in practice it has been usual to follow Skinner's (1953) choice of an escape definition, which is, in turn, derived from Thorndike's (1913) characterization of an annoying state of affairs as "one which the animal does nothing to preserve, often doing things which put an end to it." A negative reinforcer in this sense is the same as an aversive stimulus, whose "reduction or elimination . . . increases the frequency or probability of the preceding behavioral sequence" (Dinsmoor, 1954).

This choice of definition seems to have arisen partly from theoretical considerations. It is usual to think that punishment and escape and avoidance are closely related and that they are, more or less, behavioral effects of a single class of stimuli. There has been a natural tendency to search for a fundamental kind of behavior that will explain these varied effects of aversive stimuli. Escape has been a highly favored candidate. According to this view, there is no need to mention punishment in the definition of negative reinforcement, for it is simply a special case of escape behavior. Punishment itself is defined not as an effect but as a procedure: the presentation of an aversive stimulus (Skinner, 1953, p. 184). This procedure is called punishment even if it fails to influence behavior and, correspondingly, a weakening of responses will not be called punishment unless it results from the presentation of a known aversive stimulus.

A simplification of this kind has its disadvantages, resting as it does upon theoretical bias. It ignores several points of considerable practical importance. Whatever the fundamental connections might be between escape learning and punishment, it is inconvenient to define punishment solely in terms of a procedure. Indeed, as Church (1963) points out, the consequences of the Escape definition are seldom taken seriously. If an electric shock is capable of suppressing performance, it is called a punishing stimulus, even when it is incapable of producing escape learning. This happens, for example, when the shock is of very short duration (Azrin, 1960). It is also possible to condition an avoidance habit with brief shocks (Sidman, 1953a) and these shocks are not considered the less aversive because the animal is unable to escape from them. Conversely, some stimuli elicit escape much more readily than avoidance, and appeal has been made to different thresholds for the two sorts of behavior in trying to explain why animals can be reluctant to avoid *conditioned* aversive stimuli (Sidman and Boren, 1957). Similarly, it has been suggested by Barry and Miller (1965) that different thresholds for escape and avoidance behavior accounts in part for their different susceptibility to a variety of drugs. To introduce a further difficulty, it may be noted that the type of response being studied provides another source of variation: Bolles and Seelbach (1964) found that a loud noise could not be used to punish a "rearing" response in rats, although exactly the same stimulus was capable of punishing a "window investigating" exploratory response.

These facts are important, but it would be eccentric to pretend that the various properties of aversive stimuli were not in some way connected. A great deal of the literature on negative reinforcement has been devoted to the demonstration of this connection, particularly in the case of escape and avoidance. The theoretical speculations on this point rest upon a fundamental observation: previously neutral stimuli can become aversive if they have been paired with primary negative reinforcers. After this pairing, these stimuli can gain the kind of control over behavior illustrated in the following examples:

1. *Escape.* Miller (1948) demonstrated that rats given an electric shock in a distinctive box would subsequently learn a wheel-turning response to escape from this situation, even when the shock was discontinued. It is not necessary for this kind of learning that the animal should have had previous experience with another escape response at the time when the stimulus was paired with shock. May (1948) showed this in an experiment that is frequently cited to show that avoidance learning is a two-stage process. Rats were trained to escape shock by crossing the midline of a two-compartment box and were then exposed to pairing of a buzzer and a shock while confined in the center of the apparatus. Let loose once more in the box, the rats showed prompt shuttling when the only reinforcement consisted in turning off the buzzer for some time when they entered a new compartment. The stimulus-shock pairing is also found effective in dogs paralyzed with d-tubocurarine, whether the escape from shock is learned before (Solomon and Turner, 1962) or after (Leaf, 1964) the conditioning procedure.

2. *Punishment.* In several experiments (Mowrer and Aiken, 1954; Hake and Azrin, 1965), it has been shown that ongoing food reinforced behavior can be suppressed if it leads also to the presentation of a conditioned aversive stimulus. In Hake and Azrin's experiment, responding in pigeons was maintained by a variable interval schedule of food reinforcement, and an originally neutral stimulus (a clicking tone and a change in the color of the response key) was made aversive by pairings with shock. In the punishment procedure it was arranged that responses produced this stimulus, and a depression in rate was observed. The aversiveness of the stimulus was maintained by presenting it independently of responding on infrequent occasions and by following it with shock.

3. *Incentive effects.* There are several demonstrations that stimuli paired with positive reinforcers can initiate instrumental behavior. Estes (1943), for example, showed that rates of bar pressing during extinction could be raised by presenting to rats a stimulus that had been paired previously with food. In the pairing procedure the bar was withdrawn, and in extinction the stimulus was presented independently of the animals' behavior. Rescorla and Lolordo (1965) report a similar effect with a conditioned negative reinforcer. Dogs were given shuttle-box training without a warning signal (a free-operant procedure described by Black and Morse, 1961) and were then given "fear conditioning." Confined in one compartment of the shuttle box, they were exposed to two tones of different frequency, one of which was followed by unavoidable shock. The shuttle-box habit was then extinguished, and on occasions the tones were presented independently of the shuttling behavior. Rates of responding were increased by presenting the tone previously paired with shock and were decreased by the "safe" stimulus.

These experiments have been described in a number of ways. The simplest is that stimuli, by pairing with a noxious event, come themselves to have aversive properties. Less obvious is the idea that fear or anxiety has become conditioned to the stimuli (Miller, 1951) and that reduction in this fear is reinforcing. On one point, however, there is general agreement: the experiments on avoidance show that this learning can take place in two stages. First, there is a conditioning process that makes stimuli preceding the shock aversive. Second, there is the learning of an escape response from this conditioned aversive stimulation. Avoidance of the shock is incidental.

This formula has become extremely influential, and part of the reason for this has been the reluctance to admit that any other explanation is possible. Mowrer expresses a popular point of view when he claims that the source of reinforcement in avoidance cannot in theory be the withholding of an aversive stimulus because that would be "rank teleology" (Mowrer, 1960, p. 52). Similarly, Skinner (1953, p. 176) states that escape from conditioned aversive stimuli must be assumed if we are to account for avoidance without "violating the fundamental principles of Science." It thus becomes necessary to assume that warning signals are present even when none is apparent, as in free-operant avoidance and punishment. In consequence, as Sidman (1966) complains, "this formula can encompass all the known data on avoidance behavior. There are no exceptions."

This may be putting it a little too strongly. There are, in fact, experiments to embarrass the body of received doctrine and this chapter mentions some of them. In the meantime, however, it can simply be noted that a single theory has dominated the research on avoidance learning and that this research has in consequence proceeded in a rather specialized way. This will become apparent in the following pages, where a necessarily feeble attempt is made to discuss the properties of aversive stimuli under the headings traditionally reserved for positive reinforcement. It turns out that the theoretical interest in conditioned aversive stimuli, which arises for the reasons previously given, has led to a neglect of the properties of primary negative reinforcement and to a lack of basic information on matters of great importance. When solid information on primary reinforcers is available, it has often come from investigations where there was no warning signal to distract the experimenter's attention. The best example is free-operant avoidance, which is discussed at the end of this chapter.

The topics treated are: schedules of reinforcement; extinction; levels of motivation; and delay of reinforcement. The last topic will include the basic evidence for the escape theory of avoidance and will be followed by a discussion of the supposed role of the emotions in avoidance. The remainder of the chapter will be concerned with free operant avoidance and with the theoretical and practical difficulties that sometimes arise in deciding whether a habit is being maintained by positive or by negative reinforcement.

Schedules of Reinforcement

There seems to be a considerable variation in the effectiveness with which intermittent reinforcement will maintain *escape behavior*. At least one experiment (Winograd, 1965) shows that rats will perform under quite a high ratio requirement (FR 20) to escape from shock, although in a study by Hendry and Hendry (1963) performance was found to be unstable when as few as four presses were needed to turn off the aversive stimulation. On FR 8, performance deteriorated further, and the rats "froze" at the opposite end of the chamber from the bar. The explanation of this advanced by Hendry and Hendry assumes that the 60 second time-out period achieved by a reinforced response is insufficient to maintain performance on high ratios. The time-out period is followed by further shocks, which the animal can do nothing to prevent, so that it becomes a conditioned aversive stimulus. In other words, the whole experimental situation is so unpleasant to the rat that the shock itself can only control responding to a limited extent. This is equivalent to saying that aversive stimuli have very broad generalization gradients. More will be said about that later on. Unfortunately for this explanation, it appears that quite short periods of time-out from *conditioned* aversive stimuli can maintain high levels of responding (see following), and it is thus more likely that the important feature of the pure escape situation is that the animal is required to respond in the presence of shock. The "freezing" observed in this situation may have the effect of minimizing the pain from the shock, so that bar pressing in these conditions is more painful than doing nothing at all. This raises a point that is covered more fully in Chapter 4: the operant aspects of an animal's response to strong aversive stimulation. A fairly clear illustration of these operant aspects is provided by Lockard's (1963) observation that rats will choose a compartment where the shock is preceded by a warning signal in preference to a compartment where the shock arrives unannounced. A 720 volt shock was used, so that the rats were presumably burned by the shock's arcing if they were moving when it came on. Movement may thus have been punished, and this is a possible reason for the rats' choice of a compartment where preparatory crouching and freezing responses were possible.

These difficulties do not arise when bar pressing can occur in the absence of shock, that is, in an avoidance situation. A simple case of this is the schedule that Sidman (1966, p. 473) calls "Fixed Interval Avoidance." In this schedule, which is in fact fixed interval with limited hold, shocks occur at regular intervals unless the animal responds. After a successful avoidance response, a "due" shock is postponed for a certain time. During part of the postponement period further responses have no effect, but when this "interval" has elapsed a response will postpone the shock again and restart the cycle. This method generates high levels of responding, and cumulative records show the positively accelerated segments that are typical in interval schedules. More complex cases are described by Dinsmoor (1962) and by Azrin *et al.* (1963). In Dinsmoor's experiment, rats escaped on a variable interval schedule from a series of shocks presented at irregular intervals. A reinforced response produced a safe period during which shocks were not presented; unsafe periods were either unsignalled or (the more usual avoidance situation) were accompanied by a visual or auditory stimulus that was switched off by a reinforced response. Two variables were studied in addition to the presence or absence of the warning signal: (1) the length of safe period and (2) the frequency of shocks in the unsafe period. Rate of responding fell off as the shock frequency was reduced, and this effect was most marked in the case where the avoidance response did not have the additional consequence of turning off a warning signal.

A rather different effect of shock frequency was found by Azrin *et al.* The subjects in this case were squirrel monkeys, escaping from conditioned aversive stimuli on a fixed-ratio schedule. The frequency of shock associated with the stimulus had a rather small effect, and it was necessary to reduce the rate of shock presentation to 0.17 per hour before performance began to break down. The offset of a warning signal is thus able to maintain performance when its degree of association with shock is slight. On another point, however, the results of this experiment agree with those of Dinsmoor: performance begins to break down when the length of the safe period is reduced to below 30 seconds.

Azrin *et al.* suggest several ways in which their results parallel those on positive reinforcement. There is, for example, a pause after reinforcement, when the conditioned aversive stimulus is turned off, and this pause is longer with greater ratios. If the assumption of symmetry between positive and negative reinforcement is carried further, it predicts that intermittent *punishment* will produce effects that are more or less the mirror image of the effects of intermittent reward. There should, for example, be negative acceleration of responding between punishments to parallel the positive acceleration between rewards, and overall rates of responding should be directly rather than inversely related to the size of ratios. Azrin, Holz, and Hake (1963) investigated this by punishing pigeons engaged in responding for food on a variable interval schedule of reinforcement. The ratio of responses to punishments was varied, and one of the expected results appeared: the amount of suppression produced by the punishment decreased as the response/punishment ratio was made greater. On the other hand, there was no evidence for negative acceleration between punishments on any of the ratios employed. Hendry and Van-Toller (1964) believe that this was a result of maintaining the behavior by VI reinforcement, and they were able to show the expected negative acceleration between punishments in rats responding for a water reward on a continuous reinforcement schedule. Rates of responding were high just after each punishment and declined up to the next.

The kinds of intermittent reinforcement considered so far always allow the animal to avoid or escape an aversive stimulus if the requirements of the schedule are met. The intermittent presentation of *un-*

avoidable shock is in a somewhat different category, although, from the animal's point of view, it may not be entirely dissimilar. Sidman, Herrnstein, and Conrad (1957) find that the introduction of a few unavoidable shocks into free-operant avoidance raises the level of responding. If the unavoidable shocks are preceded by a warning signal, the rate of responding during the signal rises. This may be contrasted with the more familiar phenomenon of *conditioned suppression* that is found when conditioned aversive stimuli are presented to an animal engaged in food-reinforced behavior, and it might seem that there is an important difference between approach and avoidance habits in this respect. In fact, however, the matter is more complicated, for approach habits will show the reverse of conditioned suppression if the animal has had experience with avoidance habits on the same manipulandum (Herrnstein and Sidman, 1958). Kelleher, Riddle, and Cook (1963) showed, for instance, that squirrel monkeys increased their rates of responding in the presence of a shock-signaling stimulus when it was presented during the food-reinforced segment of a multiple variable interval-avoidance schedule. The behavior, although it had no programed consequence, was extremely persistent.

There are some doubts about the generality of this effect. Rats, according to Brady and Hunt (1955) show suppression when a stimulus preceding an unavoidable shock is presented during free-operant avoidance of shocks of the same magnitude. On the other hand, a facilitating effect of shock has been described for rats in the work on *punishment extinction* (see Church, 1963, for a review). This procedure involves punishment of an escape or avoidance response as part of an extinction procedure, and it has occasionally been reported to produce greater resistance. The punishment is usually given on every trial, but a facilitating effect of intermittent unavoidable shock has been described by Schoeninger, Simpson, and Brogden (1965). In other experiments, a depressing effect of shock has been found (Seward and Raskin, 1960), and Mowrer (1940) reports that punishing an avoidance response with a delayed shock leads to slower acquisition and faster extinction. The various studies agree with one another to no great extent, but theory is not baffled. If punishment leads to better responding, it has generated a higher level of motivation (Gwinn, 1949); if it has the opposite effect, it is because the punished animals have a smaller opportunity to decrease their anxiety (Mowrer, 1960).

In the unavoidable shock case, the aversive stimulus is occasionally presented whether or not the animal has made an avoidance response. What happens when the stimulus is withheld independently of behavior? Complete removal of shock from an avoidance task is often called an extinction schedule, but it is not evident that it corresponds to the usual method of extinguishing approach habits. In the latter case, reward is removed from the situation so that the habit no longer receives differential reinforcement. How the counterpart of this in avoidance is conceived will depend upon our notions of how it is maintained. If, for example, it is admitted that the withholding of shock has something to do with the reinforcement of behavior, then it is clear that elimination of the shock in an extinction procedure is not quite the same as removal of reward in the approach case. The true counterpart in positive reinforcement would be the continued presentation of reward independently of the animal's behavior. Little is known about the effects of this on established behavior, although it has been shown that "free" reward is capable in certain circumstances of producing so-called superstitious learning. Suppose that a rat is responding in a Skinner box and is obtaining a certain number of rewards per minute. It is quite likely that delivery of pellets at the same frequency would maintain performance for some time, even when the bar was disconnected from the feeder. Performance could only be affected if a reward happened to arrive at a time when the animal was not responding, and this would be an improbable event when response rates were initially high. Similarly, it has often been pointed out that an extinction schedule in avoidance will make little contact with an animal that is already eliminating the shock by successful responding. Even where performance is less than totally efficient, as in free-operant avoidance, the reduction in shock frequency that the experimenter can impose is rather slight compared with the reduction already being achieved by the animal. Sidman and Boren (1957) consider that this explains their failure to effect a significant reduction in the rate of free-operant avoidance by omitting up to seventy percent of the "due" shocks. In discriminated avoidance, where shock is preceded by a warning signal, performance is often so efficient as to eliminate the aversive stimulus altogether, and an "extinction" schedule will have little effect (Solomon, Kamin, and Wynne, 1953). The difficulty of eliminating avoidance habits in this way has led to the use of special techniques that have the object of ensuring that the absence of the aversive stimulus becomes evident to the animal. In the so-called *reality testing* method, matters are somehow arranged so that the animal is confined in the presence of the warning signal without shock. Where this takes the form of physically preventing the avoidance response, there is some evidence that it is rather ineffective. Solomon, Kamin, and Wynne (1953) attempted to extinguish a shuttle-box avoidance response in dogs by confining them in one compartment with the warning signal present and found this to be as ineffective as punishment extinction. Other results are slightly more favorable, and both Weinberger (1965) and Delude and Carlson (1964) find that speed of extinction increases with length of time in the presence of the warning signal. Delude and Carlson's method was to increase during extinction the amount by which rats had to rotate a wheel to turn off the warning signal. This had the effect of detaining the animals in the presence of a warning signal without restraining their responses. The same effect is achieved by presenting the warning signal at a lower intensity than usual and by gradually raising it to the original level; Kimble and Kendall (1953) report that this procedure accelerates extinction of a wheel-turning avoidance response in rats.

Extinction

The practical difficulties that arise in extinguishing avoidance habits have been treated already. In addition, it is sometimes believed that the data on extinction raise theoretical problems (see Hilgard and Marquis, 1961, p. 277), but it is less clear what these are supposed to be. One way of putting the matter is that successful avoidance responding removes the condition that is supposed to be motivating, that is, the occurrence of an aversive stimulus. The habit should thus start to extinguish as soon as it is learned, with the result that avoidance should proceed in a cyclic fashion. This has occasionally been observed (Sheffield, 1948), but is not always evident. For example, Solomon, Kamin, and Wynne (1953) found that dogs in a shuttle box would make several hundred responses without signs of extinction once they had learned to avoid the shock. The possibility of shock could, indeed, be eliminated without affecting performance for some time. Thus, an alternative way of describing the supposed theoretical difficulty is that avoidance habits are surprisingly resistant to extinction.

It has to be asked, unfortunately, how resistant a habit must be before we are obliged to find it surprising. There is no quantitative theory that allows prediction of the exact number of responses emitted during the extinction of any one habit, and in the absence of such a theory it is necessary to take the facts more or less as they come. The principles of "anxiety conservation" and "partial irreversibility" proposed by Solomon and Wynne (1954) merely describe the data and certainly fail to remove any theoretical difficulties that these data might be assumed to raise. The idea that avoidance habits are abnormally resistant to extinction seems to have rather little content. If it means anything it is that avoidance habits are more resistant than comparable habits, but it is not easy to decide what these comparable habits are. The most likely candidate would be escape, but it is far from clear how the extinction of an escape response should be observed. If the aversive stimulus is removed from an escape task, the animal will not respond because there is nothing to escape from. If the aversive stimulus is present, on the other hand, this is not an extinction procedure. And, if the animal does happen to respond in the absence of the stimulus, then one is simply observing the extinction of another avoidance response. Thus the usual procedure for extinguishing escape responses is to place the animal in a situation where it has previously been shocked and to observe how quickly the old escape response disappears. If the animal performs at all in these circumstances, it would appear that it is escaping from stimuli previously associated with a nasty state of affairs, and this (theory would have it) is exactly what animals are doing in an avoidance task. It cannot be pretended, then, that comparison of escape and avoidance in this situation is able to illuminate any underlying difference that there might be between them. The extent to which responding occurs during the extinction of an escape response will presumably depend upon a number of variables, for example, the effectiveness with which the response actually removes the animal from the aversive situation. It should not be thought odd, therefore, that comparisons between escape and avoidance produce different results in the various experiments that have looked at their extinction. Avoidance was found to be more resistant than escape by Sheffield and Temmer (1950) and by Santos (1960), but Seward and Raskin (1960) failed to find any difference.

Comparisons with positively reinforced habits are also difficult, although not perhaps impossible. It has already been pointed out that avoidance and approach habits are usually extinguished by methods that have little in common. In general, the *kind* of motivation in approach and avoidance is only one of the variables that might be expected to produce differences between them. If comparative studies are to be made, at least some of these variables should be controlled. Perhaps the most interesting comparison would be between habits where the level of motivation was believed to be the same, or where the level of motivation was thought to be unimportant. The nearest to this has been the study of discrimination and generalization where, Hoffman (1966) argues, resistance to extinction is reflected by the vigor of responding in the presence of the negative stimulus. The comparison between approach and avoidance described by Hoffman shows that discrimination training produces sharper generalization gradients in the food-reinforced habit, and this is considered to be "consistent with the observations . . . which indicate that avoidance is extremely resistant to extinction."

This comparison does not entirely exclude a possible effect of motivation levels, since a consistent finding with positively reinforced habits has been that increases in motivation broaden the generalization gradient. On the other hand, it is not obvious that the results on generalization are particularly relevant to discrimination learning, and, in fact, Dinsmoor (1952) shows that discriminative control of bar pressing is not apparently influenced by level of food deprivation. Hoffman points out in any case, that the approach gradient *before* discrimination is wider than that for avoidance: in their subsequent sharpening, the gradients cross one another so that approach becomes more sharply discriminated. Simple differences in level of motivation are not able to account for this change with continued training. It is not clear how far these facts agree with the more familiar results of Brown (1948), who used the pull exerted by rats against a harness to measure the strength of approach and avoidance habits at different distances from food and shock. In this case the avoidance gradient was sharper, in the sense that the strength of the avoidance response declined more rapidly than that of approach with distance along the runway. This is the situation described by Hoffman for the gradients before discrimination training, and it could be said that the animals in Brown's experiment had not been given such training. Whether the various results can be compared or not, it is certain that Brown's results cannot depend upon different basal levels of motivation in the approach and avoidance groups. The avoidance gradient, as well as being sharper, had a higher maximum than the approach gradient and actually crossed it at some point along the runway.

These facts may indicate important differences between approach and avoidance habits, but they are a somewhat indirect justification of the idea that avoidance is peculiarly resistant to extinction. Other facts show that avoidance habits can be somewhat unstable, some of them even disappearing spontaneously in the course of training (Coons, Anderson, and Myers, 1960). This decline in performance occurs even though the aversive stimulus is still present, and it has been interpreted as a loss in the effects of an early pseudoconditioning. The effect is particularly evident with certain kinds of warning signals, notably buzzers, and there is a significant effect of different kinds of conditioned stimuli upon avoidance learning (Myers, 1962; 1964). Smith, McFarland, and Taylor (1961) found, for example, that rats were unable to learn a wheel-turning response with a light CS but were able to learn with a buzzer; the learning with the buzzer declined, however, with continued training, and exactly the same was found in a pseudoconditioning control group who had the buzzer and shock presented on different trials. The pseudoconditioning is, as Zerbolio *et al.* (1965) point out, of a special variety, in that it depends upon a reinforcement contingency. It fails to appear in a group whose responses do not turn off the shock, and thus it seems to require instrumental escape training.

There are other interesting problems connected with the retention of avoidance habits. Speed of extinction was found by Reynierse (1966) to be dependent on the time interval between the end of acquisition and the beginning of extinction. A group extinguished immediately upon reaching criterion showed much greater resistance than a number of groups extinguished 24 hours later. A single trial given at some point during the 24 hour period was capable of increasing subsequent resistance and was most effective in this respect when given 40 minutes after the animals had reached criterion. Rats extinguished 1 hour after reaching criterion were also found by Moyer (1958) to be more resistant than those extinguished after 32 days, although there was no significant difference between groups extinguished after intermediate delays. The curious thing is that these results are not to be expected from the known data concerning *relearning* of an avoidance habit. It might have been thought that extinction would proceed most quickly at a time when retention was poor, for this would allow "reality testing." It has been consistently shown, however, that retention of a partially learned avoidance response is worse 1 hour after learning than at any other time (Kamin, 1957d; Brush, Myers, and Palmer, 1963). Brush, Myers, and Palmer find that this "Kamin effect" is peculiar to fear conditioning procedures. If CS-US pairing is given without avoidance learning, and an avoidance response is subsequently learned, then this learning is slowest at 1 hour after conditioning. On the other hand, the effect does not appear in the retention of an escape response. An important influence of postconditioning delay is also mentioned by McAllister and McAllister (1962), who found that rats were incapable of learning a shuttle-box escape from a conditioned aversive stimulus on the same day as the fear conditioning. Learning was only apparent when testing was done after a 24 hour interval. This may be contrasted with Reynierse's (1966) result, which shows greatest resistance to extinction when testing is done as soon as the animals reach criterion.

It is probable that an important variable is the extent to which the behavior has been established. The Kamin effect has been reported with partially learned avoidance habits and with learning of a new response after fear conditioning. One suggestion has been that too high a level of fear disrupts incompletely established habits, and there is some support for this in the results of Tarpy (1966), who measured the conditioned suppression produced by a warning signal at different times after avoidance training. There was a maximum amount of suppression at 1 to 4 hours and a gradual decline with longer and shorter intervals. If high levels of motivation have a facilitating effect upon well-learned habits, the contrast between the extinction and relearning data might be explained. This is obviously an arbitrary explanation, and it should be pointed out that some explanations of the Kamin effect rely upon the assumption that fear is *minimal* at times when performance is bad.

Levels of Motivation and Sensitization Effects

When teaching an animal an escape or an avoidance habit, it is not usually necessary to take much notice of anything that could be called a deprivation schedule. Levels of motivation are studied not by doing something to the animal before it begins performing but by changing the strength of the aversive stimulation. This does not mean, however, that a given level of shock will always maintain the same level of performance regardless of the animal's experience with it. Dinsmoor (1962) has suggested that the "activation sought by drive theorists" may be found in the various *warm-up effects* sometimes encountered in avoidance. These effects seem to arise because a certain amount of exposure to shock is necessary in each session before the animal will respond at maximum strength or, indeed, before it will respond at all. Dinsmoor found that there was a reliable relation between the amount of shock exposure in his avoidance task and the period of time taken by the animal to make its first avoidance response in each session; the more rapidly the shocks were delivered, the sooner responding began. Increases in shock frequency also reduced the time taken for the responding to reach its maximum level once it had started. This means that the initial rate of responding to a given schedule may be an unreliable guide to its effect later on, and for this reason Sidman (1953b) ignored response rates during the first 2 hours of each session.

The warm-up effect does not seem to depend upon practice with the avoidance response. Hoffman, Fleshler and Chorney (1961) found that it could be eliminated if rats were given unavoidable shocks in the apparatus before the session started. The technique was to put the animals in the box with the response lever removed and to deliver a certain number of shocks; when the lever was reintroduced the animals responded on it without warm-up, and it did not make any difference if the unavoidable shocks had been presented without the usual warning signal. The only important variable would thus seem to be experience with shock. Hoffman, Fleshler, and Chorney also note that an extended warm-up period is characteristic of certain rats whose overall performance in the session is so bad that they seem at first sight to have learned nothing. If these nonlearners are given a period of exposure to shock before being allowed to respond, their later performance is as good as that of learners.

The effect of previous exposure is rather different when shock is used to *punish* a response. The usual finding here is that the suppressive effect of shock becomes reduced with time, particularly where the punishment is weak (Azrin, 1960). Moreover, previous experience with mild shocks can somewhat reduce the otherwise catastrophic effects of severe punishment. For example, Miller (1960) punished a running response in rats either with a 335 volt shock or with a series of shocks climbing up to that value, and he found that this high level of shock produced much less suppression when gradually introduced. Experience with shock outside the testing situation had relatively little effect, so it cannot be supposed that simple physiological changes account for the effects of preexposure.

It is difficult to make precise comparisons between the phenomena of warm-up in avoidance and recovery after punishment. On the face of it, the effects of exposure to shock are opposite in the two cases; for it decreases the subsequent effect of the shock in the punishment case and increases it in the avoidance. It must be pointed out, however, that the recovery process is not, as warm-up is, something that begins anew every session. It may thus be necessary to make a careful distinction between the intrasession effects of exposure to shock and the long-term adaptation effects. Even then, there is a difficulty. Preexposure to shock before learning, which reduces its control over behavior in a punishment procedure, leads to *improved* avoidance and escape learning (Baron, Brookshire, and Littman, 1957). Moreover, Azrin (1960) describes an important intrasession effect with punishment that seems genuinely to oppose the warm-up phenomenon. One of the most lasting effects of mild punishment over a number of sessions was found to be a temporary suppression at the beginning of each session; this effect could be observed even when the pigeons had received a large amount of experience with the shock and when the final rates of response in each session had climbed back to their prepunishment level. In this case, therefore, experience with shock inside the session reduced the control that the shock had over behavior: the reverse of a warm-up effect. This fact does not help what Dinsmoor (1954; 1955) has called the *avoidance hypothesis* of punishment, but there is a certain amount of support here for Estes' (1944) suggestion that at least part of the effect of shock is a quite unspecific suppression of activity. In an avoidance task this effect will disrupt all ongoing activity, including the avoidance behavior itself. Baron and Antonitis (1961) suggest that the general suppression habituates with shock exposure, and this would mean that such exposure both facilitates avoidance learning and reduces the suppressive effect of punishment. This is a reasonable solution of the problem, but it has to be remembered that a general suppression can only be part of the effect of a punishment procedure (Church, 1963). For example, Estes (1944, Experiment R) showed that there were two relatively distinct effects of punishing rats for responding on one of two available manipulanda. There was a general suppression revealed by an immediate decline in responding on both bars, and there was a specific effect which showed itself in the slower recovery of the punished response.

The more familiar studies of motivation level in negative reinforcement have concentrated on the effects of different levels of aversive stimulation. The severity of shock has a reliable influence in the case of punishment (see Azrin and Holz, 1966) but its effect upon avoidance behavior is understood less well. An interesting fact reported by Notterman and Mintz (1965) is that the peak force of a bar-pressing response in free-operant avoidance *decreases* as the level of shock is raised from 1 ma. to 3 ma., so long as only those responses occurring at some time away from the shock are considered. Latency of a wheel-turning response, on the other hand, was found by Kimble (1955) to decrease as a negatively accelerated function of shock intensity over a range from 0.2 to 2.0 ma. A similar effect upon rate of responding in free-operant avoidance is described by Boren, Sidman, and Herrnstein (1959) for a range from 0.1 ma. up to the highest tolerable level for each rat (2.6–3.7 ma.). This last study also found the rate of responding during extinction to increase with the shock intensity used during acquisition, but Kimble failed to find a similar effect upon latency in his experiment. This contradiction is not surprising, for experiments on strength of motivation in positive reinforcement have failed to reach agreement on the same point (Hilgard and Marquis, 1961, pp. 411–416). The measure of response strength and the type of apparatus used seem to be as important as anything else.

Brush (1957) failed as Kimble had done to find any effect of shock intensity upon resistance to extinction but found the rate of acquisition equally recalcitrant. The main variable affected by changing the in-

tensity over the range 0.7–5.6 ma. was the percentage of dogs learning the shuttle-box problem. The relation was an inverted U with 4.8
ma. producing the best results. Decline in performance with high levels
of aversive stimulation is also found in rats escaping from bright lights
(Kaplan, 1952) and is in agreement with the Yerkes-Dodson law
(Yerkes and Dodson, 1908). No suggestion of a nonmonotonic relation
appears, however, in the case of rats escaping from cold water, at least
over the range of temperatures studied by Wever (1932), and Boren,
Sidman, and Herrnstein (1959) have suggested that Kaplan's result
depended upon his using an intermittent schedule of reinforcement.

Delay of Reinforcement

Punishment

One of the main reasons for thinking that the effects of punishment
depend in part upon a nonspecific suppression of activity has been that
the punishment effect does not always require precise temporal proximity between the response and the aversive stimulus (Estes, 1944).
Kamin (1959) found, for example, that shock could suppress a response when delivered after a delay as large as 40 minutes. The delayed punishment was not, it is true, as effective as the immediate
delivery of the aversive stimulus, but the considerable effect still found
at long delays argues that the mechanism proposed by Estes has some
importance. Occasionally, however, much sharper gradients are found
and Davitz et al. (1957) found no signs of inhibition with a 10 minute
delay when rats were punished for taking food off the end of a stick.
The gradient was very sharp between 0 and 30 seconds, and Davitz
et al. argue that one of the main reasons for the relatively specific effects of punishment in this case was that the rats had been thoroughly
habituated to the experimental situation before shock was introduced.

Escape and avoidance

The information on delayed reinforcement of escape behavior is almost entirely concerned with conditioned aversive stimuli rather than
with primary negative reinforcers. This is a curious situation, and
the obsession with theories of avoidance behavior is to blame. The interest in delayed offset of conditioned aversive stimuli has arisen because it is vital to the escape account of avoidance. If animals are supposed to be performing an avoidance response because it turns off a
warning signal, any procedure that delays or reduces the CS offset
should interfere with learning. This prediction has been amply verified,
and Mowrer and Lamoreaux (1942) found, for example, that a 5
second delay in CS offset was sufficient to hinder the acquisition of a
shuttle-box response in rats; performance was similarly affected by a
trace conditioning procedure in which the CS was too short to be
escaped. This inferiority of trace conditioning has also turned up in
the various studies of the CS-US interval which have, in general, supported the idea that a classical conditioning process is involved in
avoidance learning (Kamin, 1954; Brush, Brush, and Solomon, 1955;
Church, Brush, and Solomon, 1956).

To be absolutely strict, these facts tell us very little about the aversiveness of warning signals. Before claiming that the harmful effects

of delayed warning signal offset show that it has similar properties to a primary aversive stimulus, it would be necessary to show that there is a delay of reinforcement gradient in primary escape learning. And the literature is not very helpful on that point. There probably is such a gradient, but its existence has been taken more or less for granted. There are certainly no facts that allow a precise comparison between the reinforcing effects of delayed shock offset, on the one hand, and delayed warning signal offset, on the other. In the meanwhile, the precise gradient for warning signal termination has received a certain amount of theoretical and practical attention because of an experiment by Kamin. Kamin (1956) found that learning was possible in rats who were simply avoiding shock without turning off a warning signal (the avoid-US group); this group was better than one whose responses neither avoided shock nor turned off a signal, but it was indistinguishable from a group where responding merely turned off the signal (escape-CS). This result is inconvenient for all existing theories of avoidance, no less than for common sense. Mowrer (1960, pp. 51–53) discusses the problem at some length and concludes that the avoid-US group only learned because the experimental design involved switching off the CS 5 seconds after the response. This gave the rats reinforcement, albeit delayed, so that the results "cannot be taken at face value" (p. 52).

Theoretical speculation on this matter (see, for example, Bixenstine and Barker, 1964) will not be considered here in any detail. It may be noted, however, that Mowrer's account fails to explain why the group receiving immediate reinforcement (escape-CS) is no better than the one with the 5 second delay (avoid-US). In separate experiments Kamin (1957b; 1957c) has shown that the gradient of "secondary reward" is very sharp between 0 and 5 seconds, and this agrees with the findings of Mowrer and Lamoreaux referred to above. In any case, Kamin (1956) had not ignored the problem of delayed reinforcement for the avoid-US group, and had suggested a simple way of dealing with it. Lengthening the CS-US interval from 5 to 10 seconds should delay reinforcement for the avoid-US animals still further and make them definitely inferior to the escape-CS group. The results of this, in the event, are rather ambiguous: the avoidance animals start out by being worse than the Escape but end up somewhat better (Kamin, 1957a). There is little support here for the idea that the critical source of reinforcement for the avoid-US group is the delayed offset of the warning signal. It appears, then, from all these data, that the temporal relation of the avoidance response to warning signal offset is of great importance in learning but that this principle is of limited application.

Role of Fear in Avoidance Behavior

It is widely believed that avoidance habits have an emotional component, and it is important from many points of view to ask what the evidence for this belief might be. One reason for examining this question is that avoidance learning has been used a great deal in the analysis of the effects of drugs and brain lesions. Papers frequently appear in which treatments that have affected avoidance are described as having led to increased or reduced anxiety, and the assumptions behind this conclusion are not always examined with the degree of criticism that they deserve.

When the view is expressed that fear motivates avoidance behavior, it is thought that this fear arises in the first instance from the animal's exposure to a primary aversive stimulus. Various unconditioned effects of the latter are transferred to the warning signal, so that anxiety can then occur in the absence of the noxious stimulus. The source of motivation is thus thought to be a set of conditioned responses arising originally from the primary reinforcer.

It may well be thought surprising that this story has been received favorably although its counterpart in theories of positive reinforcement has been greeted with extreme suspicion. When an animal is rewarded with food, it may be induced to press a bar if a light goes on or to advance on a food cup when the feeder operates. Stimuli of this sort have a function similar to the warning signal in an avoidance task: they elicit behavior. There are limits, however, to our belief that discriminative stimuli affect the animal as if they were food or water. It is not usual to say that they induce a pleasant frame of mind in the animal, still less that they reduce hunger. Drugs that caused discriminative stimuli to lose their control over behavior would not by that fact alone be thought to have changed the animal's motivational state. Even if the stimuli turned out to have a reinforcing function, we should stop short of saying that the animal had mistaken them for a sugar pellet. This at any rate would be the usual point of view.

Certain theories, on the other hand, have placed great emphasis on the conditioning of eating and drinking responses to originally neutral stimuli. When these "fractional anticipatory goal responses" are said to have a motivating function (Spence, 1956), the theory has an evident resemblance to the conditioned-fear account of avoidance. But this kind of theorizing has been criticised because it fails to treat its "responses" as things that should be observed and measured. The theoretical convenience of fictional behavior has not, in general, been thought a sufficient reason for believing in it, and on this point (if on few others) a significant number of learning theorists seem to find themselves following common sense. It is clear, therefore, that the role of conditioned "motivating" responses in avoidance should not be accepted simply because it is theoretically desirable. There should be some evidence that these responses are important.

Such evidence is not altogether lacking. Various responses are commonly accepted as characterizing anxiety, and these can be observed in animals learning to avoid shock. The responses include defecation, freezing, changes in rate of heartbeat, and frantic attempts to leave the apparatus. Paradoxically, however, these responses are often regarded as a mere nuisance. Freezing is a clear example because there is some direct evidence that it hinders the acquisition of avoidance behavior. Thus amygdalectomy in the rat was found by Robinson (1963) both to increase freezing and to result in poorer shuttle box behavior. Robinson also observed that the latency of avoidance was correlated with the amount of freezing in normal animals, and this agrees with the finding of Kriekhaus, Miller, and Zimmerman (1965) that d-Amphetamine reduces freezing in rats and makes them learn a shuttlebox problem more quickly. It has also been suggested that abnormal amounts of freezing account for the curious failure of rats to learn certain avoidance problems, notably bar pressing with a light CS in a

Skinner box. D'Amato and Schiff (1964) confirmed earlier reports of difficulties with this task and suggest that the avoidance habit fails to appear because the warning signal stops all ongoing activity.

To facilitate avoidance behavior in tasks that seem particularly difficult for the rat, it may actually help to *punish* freezing (Feldman and Bremner, 1963). It is plain that we must look elsewhere for evidence that avoidance behavior is motivated by conditioned fear, and it has recently been suggested that use might be made of the *conditioned emotional response.* The technique for producing conditioned suppression (Estes and Skinner, 1941) involves pairing an originally neutral stimulus with an aversive event while the animal is engaged in some activity such as pressing a bar for food reward. Three stages are usually involved: (1) establishment of the positively reinforced base-line response, (2) presentation of a "neutral" stimulus to determine and, if possible, to habituate its unconditioned effects, and (3) pairing of shock with the offset of the stimulus. When the last procedure is repeated a number of times, the rate of responding falls during the periods when the stimulus is presented. The amount of suppression is often expressed as the ratio of the responses during the x minutes of the stimulus to the responses in the $2x$ minute period ending with the stimulus offset (the suppression ratio).

One reason for measuring anxiety by conditioned suppression is that it is a sensitive test for a number of variables. These include intensity of shock (Annau and Kamin, 1961); previous experience with shock (Brimer and Kamin, 1963); intensity of the CS (Kamin and Schaub, 1963); and the kind and frequency of the base-line reinforcer (Geller, 1960; Lyon, 1964). The suppression is, moreover, highly stable once it is learned; and Hoffman, Fleshler, and Jensen (1963) describe excellent retention in pigeons after a 2½ year gap in testing. For these reasons, it appears that conditioned suppression should be a useful monitor of anxiety in avoidance learning, and there have been several attempts to use it in this way. One of these experiments (Tarpy, 1966) has been mentioned already, and it serves to illustrate the difficulties involved in this kind of work. Tarpy found that the point of *minimum* avoidance responding in the Kamin effect corresponded to a *maximum* of conditioned suppression when the warning signal was presented during ongoing positively reinforced behavior. This was considered to support the idea that too high a level of fear disrupts avoidance behavior. In this case, then, there is a negative correlation between level of fear and strength of avoidance; and it cannot be maintained (whatever the plausibility of *post hoc* explanations) that this supports the notion that avoidance habits are motivated by conditioned fear.

In one sense, however, the negative correlation between suppression and avoidance is guaranteed. If the base-line responding were an avoidance habit, then one would look in vain for a positive correlation between conditioned suppression and level of performance. Rats cannot show active avoidance and conditioned suppression at the same time any more than they can press a bar and freeze simultaneously. It is thus necessary to measure the suppression of some other activity—as Tarpy did. Then, however, it is not apparent that anything can be proved about the role of fear (measured by conditioned suppression) in avoidance. Kamin, Brimer, and Black (1963) trained rats in a shuttle-box avoidance task, and concurrently tested the suppressive effects of the warning signal upon food-reinforced behavior in a Skinner box. Suppression was found, but what exactly is this supposed to show? It cannot be said, for the reasons already given, that the conditioned suppression represents the animal's reaction to the signal in the avoidance situation. One is looking, in fact, at the effect of the warning signal when no avoidance response is available; and suppression could then mean a number of things, none of which necessarily implies that the rat is afraid of the signal in the avoidance situation. For example, the signal may elicit a search for an alternative response, or it may be terrifying when no response is available.

In fact, the correlation between conditioned suppression and avoidance level was found by Kamin, Brimer, and Black to break down at certain stages of training. Hoffman and Fleshler (1962) claim a much better correlation, but their experimental method made that result almost inevitable. Rats were in a Skinner box with two manipulanda, one of which delivered food on a variable interval schedule. The other manipulandum could be pressed either to escape or to avoid shock, which was preceded by a tone. Suppression of the food-reinforced behavior was taken as a measure of the animal's emotional state in the periods when the warning signal was on. Unfortunately, this method cannot fail to reveal a certain correlation between avoidance and suppression because, as Hoffman and Fleshler note, the animal is unable to operate the two manipulanda at the same time. It is not surprising, therefore, that the suppression was greater on trials when the avoidance response occurred than on trials when it failed. In a way, the more impressive result was that there was still a considerable amount of suppression on nonavoidance trials. This spoils the correlation but at least shows that a suppressive effect exists in its own right. It could then be claimed (although there is no direct evidence for the assertion) that a stage of anxiety is necessary for the subsequent appearance of active avoidance. To prove this, it would be necessary to analyze the results for different animals in the hope of showing faster avoidance learning in those manifesting the greater initial suppression. Unfortunately, the results on freezing behavior (above) do not encourage the assumption that such an experiment would be successful.

Part of the problem is that emotional "respondents" are not understood well enough to allow their use as monitors of fear or of anything else. In Chapter 4 it is pointed out, for example, that heart rate does not react in any consistent manner to the presentation of aversive stimuli. It may be suspected, then, that its use as a monitor of fear in avoidance would produce inconsistent results, and this indeed is the case. Some of the conflicting data are mentioned by Overmier (1966), who failed himself to find any evidence for differential cardiac conditioning to tones that had (1) different amounts of association with shock and (2) different effects upon instrumental behavior. It seems, then, that there are some difficulties in the way of testing the "conditioned fear" account of avoidance. In the first place, it is not obvious what indices of fear one should look for; and secondly, some of the measures that have been proposed—notably conditioned suppression— have the disadvantage that they cannot be observed while the animal is actually performing the avoidance response.

Alternative tests of the theory have been suggested. An important line of evidence is sometimes considered to be the defects in avoidance that can follow surgical or pharmacological treatments believed to influence the emotions. The situation is confused, however, because it is rather more common to reverse the assumptions underlying this sort of work and to claim that a given treatment has altered the emotions because it has influenced avoidance behavior. A few examples may be given to illustrate the use of the different arguments. The finding by Wynne and Solomon (1955) that sympathectomized dogs are deficient in the acquisition of an avoidance response is sometimes considered to be evidence for the conditioned fear theory (see, for example, Morgan, 1965, p. 478). The argument is that fear is known to be partly determined by sympathetic feedback and should therefore be reduced by sympathectomy. This surgical procedure should consequently impair avoidance learning. But what do we know about the emotions of sympathectomized animals? If removal of the entire sympathetic system in cats leaves them still able to demonstrate hissing, growling, retraction of the ears, and showing of the teeth (Cannon, 1927), the relevance of Wynne and Solomon's data to theories of avoidance is obscure. On the other hand, it is always open to adherents of the James and Lange theory (or any other that considers the emotional behavior to result from something other than emotion) to say that sympathectomized animals are not really afraid after all, despite their respondent behavior. Precisely this argument has arisen around the effects of hypothalamic stimulation, and in this case, avoidance behavior has been used as evidence for a treatment's affecting fear rather than the treatment being used as evidence for a theory of avoidance. Thus Masserman (1941) claimed that stimulation of certain hypothalamic areas produced "sham" emotions, and part of the evidence for this was that the stimulation could not be used to elaborate a conditioned response. Nakao (1958), on the other hand, finds that stimulation can be so used and concludes that "hypothalamic stimulation is meaningful and is experienced by the animal." In settling this question, therefore, the avoidance response has been used as a criterion, while in other experiments it has been the object of study. There has been no clear statement of the reasoning that allows both these policies to be current at the same time.

The use of avoidance habits as a definitive test of the effects of surgery has two points in its favor. In the first place, it effectively defines fear as the motivation for avoidance behavior, and thus solves for learning theorists a problem that they have thought particularly vexatious: the source of drive in avoidance conditioning. Secondly, the use has provided physiologists with a valuable tool in their investigations of the emotions. These advantages might appear insufficient to recommend an approach that involves saying people are terrified when they avoid going out into the rain, but it is traditional not to give much weight to considerations of that sort. Unfortunately, however, there is another matter that cannot be dismissed so lightly. Drugs and brain lesions could evidently impair avoidance behavior in a variety of ways, and we might not wish to say that the emotions were being tampered with in every instance. A complete list of lesion-induced decrements in avoidance would include the observation by Thompson, Lesse, and Rich (1963) that lesions in the pretectal area of cats and rats selectively impair avoidance habits based on a visual conditioned stimulus. It does not seem important to mention all the other instances in which it has been necessary to analyze an avoidance decrement without appealing to changes in the animals' emotions. Another point is perhaps more interesting. Even when there is some reason to think that an alteration in avoidance behavior has arisen from some cause connected with the emotions, it seems desirable to advance beyond the explanation of the results in terms of reduced or increased "anxiety." It is interesting to know something more about the mechanism of the impairment, just as it is when appeal is made to changes in "learning ability." To make this further analysis, it is necessary to look directly at the details of the animal's behavior and at the nature of the testing situation. This has become apparent in studies of impaired shuttle-box learning, for example, and this point may be considered in some detail because of its practical significance.

It is quite common to use a *two-way shuttle box* when testing the effect of some treatment, and this apparatus has an important peculiarity. In the two-way task, the animal avoids shock by leaving whichever of the two compartments he is in when the warning signal is presented; there is thus no safe compartment, and each avoidance response takes the animal into a place where shock has been presented in the past. Worse still, shuttling may actually be punished by shock if the next trial occurs fairly quickly. There are several reasons for thinking that these details are important, the most obvious being that rats find one-way avoidance much the easier task. Also, it can be predicted that the effects of punishment in the two-way box will be greater if the inter-trial interval is short, and some of Brush's (1962) data suggest that this is so. These facts indicate that some avoidance situations involve a concealed-punishment procedure that interferes with learning of the response. The possibility thus arises that lesions affecting avoidance behavior, and in particular those lesions resulting in superior learning, might be doing so because they have influenced the suppressive effects of a punishment procedure.

It is fairly well established that something of the sort can happen. McCleary (1961) found that lesions in the subcallosal area of cats reduced the effectiveness with which shock could punish a response ("passive avoidance"). Active-avoidance learning in a double-grill shuttle box was, if anything, slightly improved. A reduction in shock-induced suppression has been reported to follow a variety of other lesions, mostly in the limbic system. Because these lesions can interfere with the punishment effect, it is not surprising that they are sometimes found to influence avoidance learning: what is really interesting is that the change they produce seems to depend upon the testing apparatus. For example, Vanderwolf (1964) found that septal lesions in the rat caused inferior performance in a simple one-way avoidance task, although King (1958) found an improvement in shuttle-box learning. Vanderwolf (1963) has noted that normal subjects show a tendency to freeze in the two-way apparatus, and he suggests (1964) that septal lesions facilitate learning because they increase activity. Similarly, Isaacson, Douglas, and Moore (1961) find that hippocampal lesions in the rat make for better performance in a two-way box, although Burešová et al. (1962) observe a decrement when testing is done in a simple one-way apparatus. Inferior one-way avoidance after a variety of limbic lesions has also been reported by McNew and Thompson (1966), who conclude that the type of apparatus is an important variable in all these experiments. The conclusion seems to be that a number of lesions have two relatively distinct effects upon avoidance behavior: (1) an impairment, showing up best in easy tasks, and (2) a facilitatory effect that may result from simple changes in the animal's activity.

In other words, avoidance habits are complicated and are influenced by a number of variables of which the level of motivation can only be a single example. The discussion in the last few pages is intended to reveal the limitations of avoidance habits as tests of the effect of treatments upon the emotions, and, as such, it compliments the conclusions reached in Chapter 4 on the relative usefulness of operant and respondent behavior in the analysis of emotional states. If these states are to be recognized primarily in terms of freezing, heart rate, and so on, then there is much to be said for looking at these directly; it is no doubt more difficult to do this than to use an avoidance habit as a criterion, but the results are likely to be less controversial.

Escape or Approach?

The rest of this chapter is concerned with difficulties that all arise, in one way or another, from the similarity that exists between certain escape and approach tasks. It is commonly claimed that escape is easily identifiable and that it provides, for that reason, a definitive test of aversiveness. But how easy is it, in fact, to recognize escape behavior? If a response succeeds both in removing stimuli from a situation and in introducing some, it is not always clear that the behavior is being maintained by the offset of aversive stimuli rather than by the onset of positive reinforcers. This may seem an unduly theoretical problem, but it has been a very real difficulty in investigations of *time-out from positive reinforcement*. Briefly, the problem is that escape from time-out not only removes a possibly aversive event but also leads to an increase in the quantity of food delivered to the animal. This makes it necessary to ask whether the behavior is described more conveniently as approach or escape.

The effects of time-out on behavior are usually reviewed by Leitenberg (1965). In a typical experiment (Ferster, 1958, Expt. IV), chimpanzees could press two levers, food being delivered by right-hand lever presses on a variable interval schedule. Every 45 seconds there was a time-out period during which presses on the right-hand lever were unrewarded, but this period could be postponed by presses on the left-hand lever. The length of this postponement was systematically varied and turned out to determine the rate of responding on the avoidance lever. In free-operant avoidance of shock (see following) it has been found that rates of responding increase when the length of postponement is reduced, and the same effect was apparent in Ferster's experiment. The suggestion thus appears plausible that time-out is an aversive event, capable like shock of motivating avoidance behavior. On the other hand, the results can be explained as easily by supposing that responding on the left-hand lever is maintained by the increase it effects in the amount of food delivered. This source of reinforcement is somewhat indirect but so too is the supposedly aversive reduction in the frequency of reward. It becomes simply a matter of preference whether we choose to describe the behavior as approach or avoidance.

Escape from time-out is even less informative. It occurs every time an animal obtains reward by responding. An increased response rate in these circumstances could be held to mean either that the reward is reinforcing or that its absence is aversive. It is usual to accept the first of these alternatives, but there is nothing in the escape definition of aversiveness to suggest that the other interpretation is silly. The same ambiguity applies to the punishing effects of time-out. Ferster's (1958, Expt. III) demonstration that chimpanzees would stop responding in the presence of a signal when a response led to a time-out period might mean that the withholding of reward is aversive, but it could also mean that not-responding is rewarded by increases in the amount of food subsequently delivered.

It must thus be admitted that certain kinds of behavior, usually thought to demonstrate an effect of aversive stimuli, fail on occasions to do anything of the sort. Leitenberg considers that most of the experiments on time-out are open to this objection, and he concludes that more subtle behavioral criteria are necessary. The most convincing evidence for the aversiveness of time-out from positive reinforcement is considered to come from results that show escape from stimuli *associated* with the withholding of reward, when the escape does not lead simultaneously to positive reinforcers. A well-known experiment of this variety (Adelman and Maatsch, 1956) showed that rats would learn to jump out of a goal box in which they had previously been rewarded; the behavior was very persistent, and resistance to extinction was much higher than in a group of animals rewarded with food for the same jumping behavior. The force of this demonstration is that the escape behavior had no effect upon the delivery of an identifiable positive reinforcer: rather the reverse, because the rats were leaving a box usually thought to be a conditioned positive reinforcer. This may be contrasted with the more familiar observation that rats will learn in a T maze to go to the side on which food is presented. Their learning to do this involves avoiding the negative goal box, but we do not wish to conclude thereby that the latter is aversive. It is required not only that animals should shun unrewarded situations but also that they continue to do so when the avoidance behavior fails to produce a reward or (even better) when the avoidance behavior reduces the probability of a reward.

What happens if a similar strictness is used in the analysis of avoidance learning? The counterpart of the time-out problem in avoidance can be stated quite simply: avoidance can be reinforced as effectively by adding stimuli as by removing them. Bower, Starr, and Lazarovitz (1965) compared three groups of rats avoiding shock in a shuttle box. The responses of one group turned off the warning signal (1000 cps tone); those of the second group did not; and in the third group, avoidance responses left the tone on but produced a light of 15 second duration. The result of this was that groups one and three were very similar, while both were superior to group two. In other words, the important variable is the amount of change produced by the response: it is not necessary to remove the warning signal. A similar effect has been reported by Keehn and Nakkash (1959), and these experiments raise the same questions as those on time-out from positive reinforcement: is the behavior to be called escape or approach?

On the whole, this is not a particularly interesting or sensible question, because it is hard to think of facts that could be entirely inconsistent with either interpretation. If the avoidance response switches on a stimulus rather than removes one, it can still be argued that the essential conditions for escape have been met. The warning signal will have occurred with shock, while the compound of the warning signal and the added stimulus will not; this discriminative training ensures that the stimuli following the avoidance behavior are less aversive than those preceding it, with the result that the behavior is reinforced. It is not necessary to assume that the "safety signal" is rewarding: it may, on the contrary, be aversive. All that is required is that it should be less aversive than the stimuli in existence before the response is made. Escape can also be assumed in cases where no obvious warning signal is presented by the experimenter, as in a punishment procedure or as in free-operant avoidance. It can be conjectured, for example, that warning signals are generated by the animal's own responses (Schoenfeld, 1950) so that the nonavoidance behavior becomes aversive. Alternative candidates for hidden warning signals include the fading trace of a previous response (Mowrer and Keehn, 1958) and the passage of time (Anger, 1963). There do not appear to be many facts that this sort of explanation cannot cover.

Even if there is little hope of testing the "escape" account of avoidance, it can be made to seem forced. The list of aversive stimuli given previously might seem large enough to cover all contingencies, but it is possible that even greater concessions are necessary. Taub and Berman (1963) found that monkeys were able to relearn an arm-flexion avoidance response after deafferentation of the responding limb by intradural section of dorsal roots C3–T3 inclusive. Postoperative acquisition is also possible under the same conditions (Taub, Bacon, and Berman, 1965). The duration of the warning signal, a buzzer, was shorter than the minimum reaction time to sound, and vision of the responding limb was obstructed. It seems unlikely that a response made in these conditions could remove any conditioned aversive stimulus unless there is feedback from some bodily movement of which the limb flexion is merely a component. Gross movements could be reinforced in the respectable manner, but Taub and Berman claim that there was no evidence of them. If that is accepted, the aversive "stimulus" removed by the arm flexion can only be some central state corresponding to the initiation of nonavoidance behavior. There is then little point in referring to it as escape behavior at all; an alternative description does just as well, namely that the animal makes a response and is reinforced if an expected shock fails to arrive. If we are going to rely on inaccessible central states, they may as well be called expectations as anything else.

The only reason for rejecting this alternative is presumably the one advanced by Skinner, who has claimed that the withholding of shock cannot in principle be a reinforcer. To say that behavior is influenced by the nonarrival of an event "violates the fundamental principles of Science." It is a little difficult, however, to discover what these fundamental principles are supposed to be, particularly since they appear to allow the assertion that "failure to receive an accustomed reinforcement is a special case of restraint" (Skinner, 1953, p. 164). Indeed, it would be very difficult to deny that animals show striking behavioral changes when a customary reward is withheld, and there is little reason to assume that the postponement of an aversive stimulus differs greatly in its noneventfulness from the failure of a sugar pellet to arrive at the right time. If it is thought possible that time-out from positive reinforcement is an aversive event, then it must be admitted that the withholding of shock has the chance of being a positive reinforcer.

Free-Operant Avoidance

Sidman (1966) believes that most of the theorizing on avoidance has arisen by historical accident. If it had been known from the beginning that avoidance can be learned when there is no warning signal, it seems quite probable that there would have been less emphasis on the role of conditioned aversive stimuli and more emphasis on the shock itself. In the basic free-operant situation (usually called Sidman avoidance) shocks are not preceded by a warning signal and simply arrive at regular intervals unless the animal presses a bar. A response gains a shock-free period of time known as the response-shock (R-S) interval, and this interval begins afresh with every response. If the R-S interval elapses without a further response, a shock is delivered and the animal returns to the condition in which shocks are presented at regular intervals: the time between successive shocks in the absence of responding is termed the shock-shock (S-S) interval. The procedure is sometimes summarized by saying that a response postpones the next shock, but this is not quite accurate. The point is that shocks are delivered according to a different rule depending on whether a response has occurred or not. Thus a single response will actually bring about the next shock more quickly if it occurs at a time when the remaining S-S interval is longer than the R-S interval. The rate of responding is therefore determined in part by subtle interactions between the two basic parameters of the situation. With either the R-S or S-S interval held constant, response rates tend to rise as the other is made shorter (Sidman, 1953b; Leaf, 1965) but performance breaks down when the R-S interval becomes much shorter than the S-S. This presumably happens when the animal's responding is increasing the number of shocks delivered (Sidman, 1966).

The temporal distribution of responses will affect the number of shocks received. The optimum strategy is to make the interresponse time (IRT) slightly shorter than the R-S interval, and for a given number of responses this strategy avoids the most shocks. In the long run, then, responses occurring just before an R-S interval is over, avoid more shocks than those occurring earlier in the interval. The amount by which a response will contribute to time-out from shock thus increases within limits as a function of time since the last response, just as probability of reinforcement does in a variable interval schedule of food reinforcement. Sidman (1966) suggests this as the explanation of the temporal discriminations found in free-operant avoidance. There was originally some doubt about the existence of these discriminations (Sidman, 1954), but it now appears that appropriate measurements reveal a higher probability of long inter-response times than can be accounted for by chance (Anger, 1963). Free-operant avoidance thus comes partly under discriminative control, and a prediction of this account is that the control will be lost when long IRT's no longer receive selective reinforcement. This happens in adjusting-avoidance schedules, when each response, instead of wiping out the shock-free period gained by the previous response, simply adds to it; in these conditions all responses contribute equally to the time-out from shock, and temporal discriminations are not obvious (Sidman, 1966).

Discriminative control of responding is clearer when a warning signal is introduced into the free-operant procedure. Sidman (1955) observed that the effect of the signal was to increase the probability of long IRT's with the result that the behavior became more effective. The animals received fewer shocks when the signal was added, and they emitted fewer responses. The behavior thus came under the control of a warning signal just as it does in, for example, a shuttle box. The two situations differ in only one respect: in the shuttle box, responses in the absence of the signal (intertrial responses) have no effect upon the delivery of shock, while in the free-operant procedure they are merely less efficient. The effect of adding warning signals to free-operant avoidance may also be compared to that of adding discriminative stimuli to food-reinforced interval schedules (Ferster and Skinner, 1957). The sense in which a warning signal can be termed a discriminative stimulus now becomes fairly clear: responding in its presence is more efficient than in its absence and is therefore differently reinforced. It was noted above that discriminative control is lost in schedules where spaced responding ceases to be more efficient, and the same is found in the warning signal case. Long IRT's decrease in probability if the shock is *unavoidable* once the signal comes on, and most responses are emitted before signal onset (Sidman and Boren, 1957). In this situation, the only reinforced responses are those occurring before the signal. Responding during the signal is unreinforced, and this is sufficient to reverse the pattern of responding found in the case where the signal precedes avoidable shock.

Interpretation of these facts does not seem to require the assumption that warning signals are aversive. On the contrary, it has been suggested that this assumption, far from being required by the data, fails to explain them. Keehn's (1959) conclusion to this effect is based upon the demonstrable failure of the animals to avoid the signals when given a chance to do so. It has just been mentioned that the introduction of a warning signal into free-operant avoidance causes responding early in the R-S interval to decrease, even though the responding would avoid both the shock and the warning signal. Instead of avoiding two nasty events for the price of one, the animals wait until the signal comes on before responding. This, according to Keehn, is a very damaging fact for the account of avoidance that assumes the warning signal to be more aversive than other stimuli in the situation. The suggested alternative is that the signal is a discriminative stimulus, and it has been shown previously that this is an exact use of the term.

This criterion is similar to the one suggested for the aversiveness of time-out from positive reinforcement. There it was required that the escape or avoidance behavior should be maintained even when it had no further advantages as far as the delivery of reward was concerned; in the warning signal case the criterion is that the animal should avoid it when this behavior has no additional influence upon the withholding of shock. Evidently, however, the matter is not that simple. It can be argued that the warning signal, while being aversive enough to maintain escape behavior, is not sufficiently so to motivate avoidance. The introduction of a warning signal into free-operant avoidance ensures, in fact, that other stimuli by themselves are no longer paired with shock, so that they cease to be aversive on that score. There is thus no occasion for the animal to respond in the absence of the signal, unless it be that the nonshocked stimuli are made aversive by second-order conditioning. It can be assumed that this is insufficient, and the fact that avoidance does occur when the signal precedes *unavoidable* shock is consistent with this interpretation; for the inevitable pairing with shock will make the signal highly aversive. This is not as fanciful as it sounds because it can be shown directly that the extent to which the signal is actually paired with shock determines whether the animal will avoid it or not. When the signal precedes avoidable shock the extent of this pairing is slight because the shock is usually avoided. If this is imitated in the unavoidable shock case by presenting the shock only on some of the occasions when the signal arrives, avoidance of the signal breaks down when the frequency of the signal-shock pairings is lowered approximately to that experienced by animals who can avoid the shock by their own responses (Boren and Sidman, 1957).

One final difficulty may be raised for the escape account. Ulrich, Holz, and Azrin (1964) investigated the effect of varying the period for which the avoidance response eliminated the signal (the R-S_1 interval) with S-S and response-shock (R-S_2) intervals held constant. In other words, the warning signal could come on at varying times after the response, but the shock followed after a constant interval. The introduction of a warning signal shortly before the shock had the usual effect of concentrating response in its presence, and this effect continued when the R-S_1 interval was shortened. The consequence of decreasing the R-S_1 interval was thus an increase in response rates. At an interval of 0.3 seconds the responses were scarcely turning off the warning signal at all, but this condition produced the highest rates of responding. If the warning signal is aversive, responses are producing a time-out of less than a second, but are still emitted at a high rate. This does not look much like escape behavior. On the other hand, some analogies for this effect exist in positive-reinforced behavior. Control of fixed-interval performance by discriminative stimuli is described by Ferster and Skinner (1957). Pigeons were presented with a stimulus that varied continuously in size throughout the interval, reaching its maximum size when reinforcement was due. Performance became much more efficient in these conditions, and the effect was similar to that of introducing a warning signal into free-operant avoidance. The next step was to present the stimulus at its maximum strength throughout the whole interval. This produced high, undifferentiated rates of responding in which there were no signs of a temporal discrimination. Even after 12 transitions from the "clock" case to the "maximum size," rates of responding remained much higher than those maintained by interval reinforcement without added stimuli (p. 283). Thus experience with a discriminative stimulus caused it to dominate performance even when it had lost its programed relation to a schedule of reinforcement, and this can be compared more or less directly to the effect of the warning signal in the experiment by Ulrich, Holz, and Azrin.

Whether these apparent analogies between approach and avoidance will turn out to be important is another matter. The difficulty in making comparisons of this sort is that there is not enough information on the approach side; it has already been mentioned that the analysis of extinction is hampered in this way, and the same applies to the problem of discriminative control. For example, the kind of analysis now apparently favored by Sidman relies heavily on the idea that long-term changes in the frequency of shock can affect the animal's behavior; Anger (1963) argues that this is implausible and that it fails in any case to suggest any mechanism whereby the reinforcement could take place. Unfortunately, little enough is known about the effects of long-term reinforcement contingencies in *positive* reinforcement to settle this matter.

REFERENCES

ADELMAN, H. M., & MAATSCH, J. L. 1956. Learning and extinction based upon frustration, food reward, and exploratory tendency. *J. exp. Psychol.*, 52, 311–315.

ANGER, D. 1963. The role of temporal discriminations in the reinforcement of Sidman avoidance behavior. *J. exp. anal. Behav.*, 6, 477–506.

ANNAU, Z., & KAMIN, L. J. 1961. The conditioned emotional response as a function of intensity of the US. *J. comp. physiol. Psychol.*, 54, 428–432.

AZRIN, N. H. 1960. Effects of punishment intensity during variable-interval reinforcement. *J. exp. anal. Behav.*, 3, 123–142.

AZRIN, N. H., & HOLZ, W. C. 1966. Punishment. In Honig, W. K. (Ed.), *Operant behavior: Areas of research and application.* New York: Appleton-Century-Crofts.

AZRIN, N. H., HOLZ, W. C., & HAKE, D. F. 1963. Fixed-ratio punishment. *J. exp. anal. Behav.*, 6, 141–148.

AZRIN, N. H., HOLZ, W. C., HAKE, D. F., & ALLYON, T. 1963. Fixed ratio escape reinforcement. *J. exp. anal. Behav.*, 6, 449–456.

BARON, A., & ANTONITIS, J. J. 1961. Punishment and preshock as determinants of bar-pressing behavior. *J. comp. physiol. Psychol.*, 54, 716–720.

BARON, A., BROOKSHIRE, K. H., & LITTMAN, R. A. 1957. Effects of infantile and adult shock-trauma upon learning in the adult white rat. *J. comp. physiol. Psychol.*, 50, 530–534.

BARRY, H., & MILLER, N. E. 1965. Comparison of drug effects on approach, avoidance and escape motivation. *J. comp. physiol. Psychol.*, 59, 18–24.

BIXENSTINE, V. E., & BARKER, E. 1964. Further analysis of the determinants of avoidance behavior. *J. comp. physiol. Psychol.*, 58, 339–343.

BLACK, A. H., & MORSE, P. 1961. Avoidance learning in dogs without a warning signal. *J. exp. anal. Behav.*, 4, 17–23.

BOLLES, R. C., & SEELBACH, S. E. 1964. Punishing and reinforcing effects of noise onset and termination for different responses. *J. comp. physiol. Psychol.*, 58, 127–131.

BOREN, J. J., & SIDMAN, M. 1957. Maintenance of avoidance behaviour with intermittent shocks. *Canad. J. Psychol.*, 11, 185–192.

BOREN, J. J., SIDMAN, M., & HERRNSTEIN, R. J. 1959. Avoidance, escape and extinction as function of shock intensity. *J. comp. physiol. Psychol.*, 52, 420–425.

BOWER, G., STARR, R., & LAZAROVITZ, L. 1965. Amount of response-produced change in the CS and avoidance learning. *J. comp. physiol. Psychol.*, 59, 13–17.

BRADY, J. V., & HUNT, H. F. 1955. An experimental approach to the analysis of emotional behavior. *J. Psychol.*, 40, 313–324.

BRIMER, C. J., & KAMIN, L. J. 1963. Disinhibition, habituation, sensitization and the conditioned emotional response. *J. comp. physiol. Psychol.*, 56, 508–516.

BROWN, J. S. 1948. Gradients of approach and avoidance responses and their relation to level of motivation. *J. comp. physiol. Psychol.*, 41, 450–465.

BRUSH, F. R. 1957. The effects of shock intensity on the acquisition and extinction of an avoidance response in dogs. *J. comp. physiol. Psychol.*, 50, 547–552.

BRUSH, F. R. 1962. The effects of intertrial interval on avoidance learning in the rat. *J. comp. physiol. Psychol.*, 55, 888–892.

BRUSH, F. R., BRUSH, E. S., & SOLOMON, R. L. 1955. Traumatic avoidance learning: The effects of CS-US interval with a delayed-conditioning procedure. *J. comp. physiol. Psychol.*, 48, 285–293.

BRUSH, F. R., MYERS, J. S., & PALMER, M. E. 1963. Effects of kind of prior training and intersession interval upon subsequent avoidance learning. *J. comp. physiol. Psychol.*, 56, 539–545.

BUREŠOVÁ, O., BUREŠ, J., FIFKOVA, E., VINOGRADOVA, O., & WEISS, T. 1962. Functional significance of corticohippocampal connections. *Exp. Neurol.*, 6, 161–172.

CANNON, W. B. 1927. The James-Lange theory of emotions: A critical examination and an alternative theory. *Amer. J. Psychol.*, 39, 106–124.

CHURCH, R. M. 1963. The varied effects of punishment on behavior. *Psychol. Rev.*, 70, 369–402.

CHURCH, R. M., BRUSH, F. R., & SOLOMON, R. L. 1956. Traumatic avoidance learning: The effects of CS-US interval with a delayed conditioning procedure in a free responding situation. *J. comp. physiol. Psychol.*, 49, 301–308.

COONS, E. E., ANDERSON, N. H., & MYERS, A. K. 1960. Disappearance of avoidance responding during continued training. *J. comp. physiol. Psychol.*, 53, 290–292.

D'AMATO, M. R., & SCHIFF, P. 1964. Long-term discriminated avoidance performance in the rat. *J. comp. physiol. Psychol.*, 57, 123–126.

DAVITZ, J. R., MASON, D. J. MOWRER, O. H., & VIEK, P. 1957. Conditioning of fear: A function of the delay of reinforcement. *Amer. J. Psychol.*, 70, 69–74.

DELUDE, L. A., & CARLSON, N. J. 1964. A test of the conservation of anxiety and partial irreversibility hypotheses. *Canad. J. Psychol.*, 18, 15–22.

DINSMOOR, J. A. 1952. The effect of hunger on discriminated responding. *J. abnorm. soc. Psychol.*, 47, 67–72.

DINSMOOR, J. A. 1954. Punishment: I. The avoidance hypothesis. *Psychol. Rev.*, 61, 34–46.

DINSMOOR, J. A. 1955. Punishment: II. An interpretation of empirical findings. *Psychol. Rev.*, 62, 96–105.

DINSMOOR, J. A. 1962. Variable interval escape from stimuli accompanied by shocks. *J. exp. anal. Behav.*, 5, 41–47.

ESTES, W. K. 1943. Discriminative conditioning. 1. A discriminative property of conditioned anticipation. *J. exp. Psychol.*, 32, 150–155.

ESTES, W. K. 1944. An experimental study of punishment. *Psychol. Monogr.*, 57 (3, Whole No. 263).

ESTES, W. K., & SKINNER, B. F. 1941. Some quantitative properties of anxiety. *J. exp. Psychol.*, 29, 390–400.

FELDMAN, R. S., & BREMNER, F. J. 1963. A method for rapid conditioning of stable avoidance bar-pressing behavior. *J. exp. anal. Behav.*, 6, 393–394.

FERSTER, C. B. 1958. Control of behavior in chimpanzees and pigeons by time-out from positive reinforcement. *Psychol. Monogr.*, 72 (8, Whole No. 461).

FERSTER, C. B., & SKINNER, B. F. 1957. *Schedules of reinforcement.* New York: Appleton-Century-Crofts.

GELLER, I. 1960. The acquisition and extinction of conditioned suppression as a function of the base-line reinforcer. *J. exp. anal. Behav.*, 3, 235–240.

GWINN, G. T. 1949. The effects of punishment on acts motivated by fear. *J. exp. Psychol.*, 39, 260–269.

HAKE, D. F., & AZRIN, N. H. 1965. Conditioned punishment. *J. exp. anal. Behav.*, 8, 279–293.

HENDRY, D. P., & HENDRY, L. S. 1963. Partial negative reinforcement: Fixed ratio escape. *J. exp. anal. Behav.*, 6, 519–523.

HENDRY, D. P., & VAN-TOLLER, C. 1964. Fixed-ratio punishment with continuous reinforcement. *J. exp. anal. Behav.*, 7, 293–300.

HERRNSTEIN, R. J., & SIDMAN, M. 1958. Avoidance conditioning as a factor in the effects of unavoidable shocks on food-reinforced behavior. *J. comp. physiol. Psychol.*, 51, 380–385.

HILGARD, E. R., & MARQUIS, D. G. 1961. *Conditioning and learning.* (Rev. ed.) London: Methuen.

HOFFMAN, H. S. 1966. The analysis of discriminated avoidance. In Honig, W. K. (Ed.), *Operant behavior: areas of research and application.* New York: Appleton-Century-Crofts.

HOFFMAN, H. S., & FLESHLER, M. 1962. The course of emotionally in the development of avoidance. *J. exp. Psychol.*, 64, 288–294.

HOFFMAN, H. S., FLESHLER, M., & CHORNEY, H. 1961. Discriminated bar-press avoidance. *J. exp. anal. Behav.*, 4, 309–316.

HOFFMAN, H. S., FLESHLER, M., & JENSEN, P. 1963. Stimulus aspects of aversive controls: The retention of conditioned suppression. *J. exp. anal. Behav.*, 6, 575–583.

ISAACSON, R. L., DOUGLAS, R. J., & MOORE, R. Y. 1961. The effect of radical hippocampal ablation on acquisition of avoidance response. *J. comp. physiol. Psychol.*, 54, 625–628.

KAMIN, L. J. 1954. Traumatic avoidance learning: The effects of CS-US interval with a trace conditioning procedure. *J. comp. physiol. Psychol.*, 47, 65–72.

KAMIN, L. J. 1956. The effects of termination of the CS and avoidance of the US on avoidance learning. *J. comp. physiol. Psychol.*, 49, 420–424.

KAMIN, L. J. 1957d. The retention of an incompletely learned avoidance response. *J. comp. physiol. Psychol.*, 50, 457–460.

KAMIN, L. J. 1957b. The gradient of delay of secondary reward in avoidance learning. *J. comp. physiol. Psychol.*, 50, 445–449.

KAMIN, L. J. 1957c. The gradient of delay of secondary reward in avoidance learning tested on avoidance trials only. *J. comp. physiol. Psychol.*, 50, 450–456.

KAMIN, L. J. 1957a. The effects of termination of the CS and avoidance of the US on avoidance learning: An extension. *Canad. J. Psychol.*, 11, 48–56.

KAMIN, L. J. 1959. The delay of punishment gradient. *J. comp. physiol. Psychol.*, 52, 434–437.

KAMIN, L. J., BRIMER, C. J., & BLACK, A. H. 1963. Conditioned suppression as a monitor of fear of the CS in the course of avoidance training. *J. comp. physiol. Psychol.*, 56, 497–501.

KAMIN, L. J., & SCHAUB, R. E. 1963. Effects of conditioned stimulus intensity on the conditioned emotional response. *J. comp. physiol. Psychol.*, 56, 502–507.

KAPLAN, M. 1952. The effects of noxious stimulus intensity and duration during intermittent reinforcement of escape behavior. *J. comp. physiol. Psychol.*, 45, 538–549.

KEEHN, J. D. 1959. The effect of a warning signal on unrestricted avoidance behaviour. *Brit. J. Psychol.*, 50, 125–135.

KEEHN, J. D., & NAKKASH, S. 1959. Effect of a signal contingent upon an avoidance response. *Nature*, 184, 566–568.

KELLEHER, R. T., RIDDLE, W. C., & COOK, L. 1963. Persistent behavior maintained by unavoidable shocks. *J. exp. anal. Behav.*, 6, 507–517.

KIMBLE, G. A. 1955. Shock intensity and avoidance learning. *J. comp. physiol. Psychol.*, 48, 281–284.

KIMBLE, G. A., & KENDALL, J. W. 1953. A comparison of two methods of producing experimental extinction. *J. exp. Psychol.*, 45, 87–89.

KING, F. A. 1958. Effects of septal and amygdaloid lesions on emotional behavior and conditioned avoidance responses in the rat. *J. nerv. ment. Dis.*, 126, 57–63.

KRIEKHAUS, E. E., MILLER, N. E., & ZIMMERMAN, P. 1965. Reduction of freezing behavior and improvement of shock avoidance by d-amphetamine. *J. comp. physiol. Psychol.,* 60, 36–40.

LEAF, R. C. 1964. Avoidance response evocation as a function of prior discriminative fear conditioning under curare. *J. comp. physiol. Psychol.,* 58, 446–449.

LEAF, R. C. 1965. Acquisition of Sidman avoidance responding as a function of S-S interval. *J. comp. physiol. Psychol.,* 59, 298–300.

LEITENBERG, H. 1965. Is time-out from positive reinforcement an aversive event? *Psychol. Bull.,* 64, 428–441.

LOCKARD, J. S. 1963. Choice of a warning signal or no warning signal in an unavoidable shock situation. *J. comp. physiol. Psychol.,* 56, 526–530.

LYON, D. O. 1964. Some notes on conditioned suppression and reinforcement schedules. *J. exp. anal. Behav.,* 7, 289–291.

MCALLISTER, W. R., & MCALLISTER, D. E. 1962. Postconditioning delay and intensity of shock as factors in the measurement of acquired fear. *J. exp. Psychol.,* 64, 110–116.

MCCLEARY, R. A. 1961. Response specificity in the behavioral effects of limbic system lesions in the cat. *J. comp. Physiol.,* 54, 605–613.

MCNEW, J. J., & THOMPSON, R. 1966. Role of the limbic system in active and passive avoidance conditioning in the rat. *J. comp. physiol. Psychol.,* 61, 173–180.

MASSERMAN, J. H. 1941. Is the hypothalamus a center of emotion? *Psychosom. Med.,* 3, 3–25.

MAY, M. A. 1948. Experimentally acquired drives. *J. exp. Psychol.,* 38, 66–77.

MILLER, N. E. 1948. Studies of fear as an acquirable drive: 1. Fear as motivation and fear-reduction as reinforcement in the learning of a new response. *J. exp. Psychol.,* 38, 89–101.

MILLER, N. E. 1951. Learnable drives and rewards. In Stevens, S. S. (Ed.), *Handbook of experimental psychology.* New York: Wiley; London: Chapman and Hall.

MILLER, N. E. 1960. Learning resistance to pain and fear: Effects of overlearning, exposure, and rewarded exposure in context. *J. exp. Psychol.,* 60, 137–145.

MORGAN, C. T. 1965. *Physiological psychology.* New York: McGraw-Hill.

MOWRER, O. H. 1940. Anxiety reduction and learning. *J. exp. Psychol.,* 27, 497–516.

MOWRER, O. H. 1960. *Learning theory and behavior.* New York: Wiley.

MOWRER, O. H., & AIKEN, E. G. 1954. Contiguity vs. drive reduction in conditioned fear: Temporal variations in conditioned and unconditioned stimulus. *Amer. J. Psychol.,* 67, 26–38.

MOWRER, O. H., & KEEHN, J. D. 1958. How are intertrial "avoidance" responses reinforced? *Psychol. Rev.,* 65, 209–221.

MOWRER, O. H., & LAMOREAUX, R. R. 1942. Avoidance conditioning and signal duration—A study of secondary motivation and reward. *Psychol. Monogr.,* 54 (5, Whole No. 247).

MOYER, I. K. E. 1958. Effect of delay between training and extinction on the extinction of an avoidance response. *J. comp. physiol. Psychol.,* 51, 116–118.

MYERS, A. K. 1962. Effect of CS intensity and quality in avoidance conditioning. *J. comp. physiol. Psychol.,* 55, 57–61.

MYERS, A. K. 1964. Discriminated operant avoidance learning in Wistar and C-4 rats as a function of type of warning stimulus. *J. comp. physiol. Psychol.,* 58, 453–455.

NAKAO, H. 1958. Emotional behavior produced by hypothalamic stimulation. *Amer. J. Physiol.,* 194, 411–418.

NOTTERMAN, J. M., & MINTZ, D. E. 1965. *Dynamics of response.* New York: Wiley.

OVERMIER, J. B. 1966. Instrumental and cardiac indices of Pavlovian fear conditioning as a function of US duration. *J. comp. physiol. Psychol.*, **62**, 15–20.

RESCORLA, R. A., & LOLORDO, V. M. 1965. Inhibition of avoidance behavior. *J. comp. physiol. Psychol.*, **59**, 406–412.

REYNIERSE, J. H. 1966. Effects of CS only trials on resistance to extinction. *J. comp. physiol. Psychol.*, **61**, 156–158.

ROBINSON, E. 1963. Effects of amygdalectomy on fear-motivated behavior in rats. *J. comp. physiol. Psychol.*, **56**, 814–820.

SANTOS, J. F. 1960. The influence of amount and kind of training on the acquisition and extinction of escape and avoidance habits. *J. comp. physiol. Psychol.*, **53**, 284–289.

SCHOENFELD, W. N. 1950. An experimental approach to anxiety, escape and avoidance behavior. In Hoch, P. H., & Zubin, J. (Eds.), *Anxiety*. New York: Grune and Stratton.

SCHOENINGER, D. W., SIMPSON, W. E., & BROGDEN, W. J. 1965. General and local effects of limited trials of shock US on maintenance of an avoidance CR. *J. comp. physiol. Psychol.*, **59**, 25–30.

SEWARD, J. P., & RASKIN, D. C. 1960. The role of fear in aversive behavior. *J. comp. physiol. Psychol.*, **53**, 328–335.

SHEFFIELD, F. D. 1948. Avoidance training and the contiguity principle. *J. comp. physiol. Psychol.*, **41**, 165–177.

SHEFFIELD, F. D. & TEMMER, H. W. 1950. Relative resistance to extinction of escape training and avoidance training. *J. exp. Psychol.*, **40**, 287–298.

SIDMAN, M. 1953a. Avoidance conditioning with brief shocks and no exteroceptive warning signal. *Science*, **118**, 157–158.

SIDMAN, M. 1953b. Two temporal parameters of the maintenance of avoidance behavior by the white rat. *J. comp. physiol. Psychol.*, **46**, 253–261.

SIDMAN, M. 1954. The temporal distribution of avoidance responses. *J. comp. physiol. Psychol.*, **47**, 399–402.

SIDMAN, M. 1955. Some properties of the warning stimulus in avoidance behavior. *J. comp. physiol. Psychol.*, **48**, 444–450.

SIDMAN, M. 1966. Avoidance behavior. In Honig, W. K. (Ed.), *Operant behavior: Areas of research and application*. New York: Appleton-Century-Crofts.

SIDMAN, M., & BOREN, J. J. 1957. A comparison of two types of warning stimulus in an avoidance situation. *J. comp. physiol. Psychol.*, **50**, 282–287.

SIDMAN, M., HERRNSTEIN, R. J., & CONRAD, D. G. 1957. Maintenance of avoidance behavior by unavoidable shocks. *J. comp. physiol. Psychol.*, **50**, 553–557.

SKINNER, B. F. 1953. *Science and human behavior*. New York: Macmillan.

SMITH, O. A., McFARLAND, W. C., & TAYLOR, E. 1961. Performance in a shock-avoidance conditioning situation interpreted as pseudoconditioning. *J. comp. physiol. Psychol.*, **54**, 154–157.

SOLOMON, R. L., KAMIN, L. J., & WYNNE, L. C. 1953. Traumatic avoidance learning: The outcomes of several procedures with dogs. *J. abnorm. soc. Psychol.*, **48**, 291–302.

SOLOMON, R. L., & TURNER, L. H. 1962. Discriminative classical conditioning in dogs paralyzed by curare can later control discriminative avoidance responses in the normal state. *Psychol. Rev.*, **69**, 202–219.

SOLOMON, R. L., & WYNNE, L. C. 1954. Traumatic avoidance learning: The principle of anxiety conservation and partial irreversibility. *Psychol. Rev.*, **61**, 353–385.

SPENCE, K. W. 1956. *Behavior theory and conditioning*. New Haven, Conn.: Yale University Press.

TARPY, R. M. 1966. Incubation of anxiety as measured by response suppression. *Psychon. Sci.*, **4**, 189–190.

TAUB, E., BACON, R. C., & BERMAN, A. J. 1965. Acquisition of a trace-conditioned avoidance response after deafferentation of the responding limb. *J. comp. physiol. Psychol.*, 59, 275–279.

TAUB, E., & BERMAN, A. J. 1963. Avoidance conditioning in the absence of relevant proprioceptive and exteroceptive feedback. *J. comp. physiol. Psychol.*, 56, 1012–1016.

THOMPSON, R., LESSE, H., & RICH, I. 1963. Dissociation of visual and auditory habits following pretectal lesions in rats and cats. *J. comp. Neurol.*, 121, 161–171.

THORNDIKE, E. L. 1913. *Educational psychology Vol. II. The psychology of learning.* New York: Teachers College, Columbia University.

ULRICH, R. E., HOLZ, W. C., & AZRIN, N. H. 1964. Stimulus control of avoidance behavior. *J. exp. anal. Behav.*, 7, 129–133.

VANDERWOLF, C. H. 1963. Improved shuttle-box performance following electroconvulsive shock. *J. comp. physiol. Psychol.*, 56, 983–986.

VANDERWOLF, C. H. 1964. Effects of combined medial thalamic and septal lesions on active-avoidance behavior. *J. comp. physiol. Psychol.*, 58, 31–37.

WEINBERGER, N. M. 1965. Effect of detainment on extinction of avoidance responses. *J. comp. physiol. Psychol.*, 60, 135–138.

WEVER, E. G. 1932. Water temperature as an incentive to swimming activity in the rat. *J. comp. Psychol.*, 14, 219–224.

WINOGRAD, E. 1965. Escape behavior under different fixed ratios and shock intensities. *J. exp. anal. Behav.*, 8, 117–124.

WYNNE, L. C., & SOLOMON, R. L. 1955. Traumatic avoidance learning: Acquisition and extinction in dogs deprived of normal autonomic function. *Genet. Psychol. Monogr.*, 52, 241–284.

YERKES, R. M., & DODSON, J. D. 1908. The relation of strength of stimulus to rapidity of habit-formation. *J. comp. Neurol. Psychol.*, 18, 459–482.

ZERBOLIO, D. J., REYNIERSE, J. H., WEISMAN, R. G., & DENNY, M. R. 1965. Pseudoconditioning? *J. comp. physiol. Psychol.*, 59, 271–274.

CHAPTER 4

Emotion

L. WEISKRANTZ

CHAPTERS 2 and 3 have been concerned with reinforcers. Our definition of *reinforcers* was based simply on the effects that certain events have upon the likelihood of recurrence of responses that have just preceded those events. In everyday language, a reinforcer is something for which a person will perform some work.

But if reinforcers are response-produced (or terminated) stimuli, it is also the case that reinforcers themselves *produce* responses, and these responses often loom large in the subject matter of accounts of emotion. It may be that "emotion is only a chapter heading" (Bentley quoted in Schlosberg, 1954), and although it is easy to debunk the vagueness of formal accounts of emotion, very few would wish to underestimate the importance of the subject itself. In personal, social, and medical spheres, the subject intrudes all too persistently, and much current research is concerned with attempts to alter emotional states by pharmacological and other treatments, ranging from relatively mild "tranquilizers" to drugs claimed to induce intense metaphysical illuminations. Similarly, a good deal of neuropsychological research is directed towards an understanding of central nervous system mechanisms of emotional control. Lashley once remarked in another context that one has the choice either of being vague or of being wrong. Unfortunately the situation is even worse than that—it is sometimes possible to be vague *and* wrong, which is the judgment that the reader may feel compelled to pass on this chapter. But for both practical and theoretical considerations, the challenge is worth accepting.

We have said that reinforcers are stimuli consequent to responses and that emotion might be dealt with as responses consequent to reinforcers. But if we adopt this approach, we must qualify and amplify certain aspects of both reinforcers and responses, and the relationship which exists between them.

The stimuli which are circularly defined as *reinforcers* are usually called positive or negative, depending upon whether their onset or offset is thought to operate on the probability of preceding responses. The onset of a negative reinforcer or the offset of a positive reinforcer can be defined as a punishment. It will be appreciated that it is virtually impossible experimentally to have reinforcement without the possibility of having punishment, and punishment without the possibility of reinforcement. This is because both positive and negative reinforcers at some point must be terminated. It is, in principle, possible to determine whether critical effects of reinforcers are due to their onset or to their termination, but in practice it is sometimes far from easy. In fact, a good deal of the confusion about the role of punishment stems from this difficulty (see Chapter 3). Some theorists, such as Dinsmoor (1954; 1955), argue in effect that the suppressive effects of punishment can be largely accounted for in terms of the termination of negative reinforcers building up the strength of responses incompatible with punished responses. Others, such as Estes (1944) or Mowrer (1960), implicitly or explicitly assume that it is the onset of a negative reinforcer that is suppressive. It is often difficult to separate the two positions experimentally. The fact that the effects of negative reinforcers such as shock on heart rate or other autonomic responses are so variable in different studies may stem from, among many other reasons, such a simple factor as variations in the duration of the shock, not only for the obvious reason that the aversiveness of a shock may alter with its duration but also because the interaction of onset and offset effects may vary considerably with its duration. At any rate, in this chapter we shall feel obliged to include both the onset and the termination components of both positive and negative reinforcers as fair game.

In reference to *responses*, we would like to argue against being too narrow and too limited. One class of responses we shall be considering is that of the autonomic nervous system, and for many stimuli there is a clear response that ensues, be it a tail-wag, piloerection, or galvanic skin response. But there are many ways in which behavior may be altered without any single specific response being elicited reliably. Hence, when we say that a person is "depressed," this might mean that he will not eat if presented with food, even though deprived; he may fail to carry out sensory discriminations acquired in the past; he may tend to be immobile or hyperactive. In other words, large classes of behavior may be affected, and in some ways these alterations among classes of responses are of greater interest than explicit discrete responses. We will consider not only discrete responses but also general alterations such as "suppressions" and "fixations." Again, although the experimental psychologist is helpless without identifiable responses, the history of experimental psychology is littered with confusions of identity between states of the organism and responses by which these are usually measured. Considerable evidence exists that in mammals autonomic responses are neither necessary nor sufficient for the elicitation of "emotional" skeletal behavior, nor is the elicitation of "emotional" skeletal behavior necessary or sufficient for the elicitation of autonomic responses. But quite aside from the interdependence or lack of it between various types of elicited responses, we wish to admit the possibility that reinforcers induce effects that are not simply equivalent to the composite (let alone a limited sample) of responses by which these effects are recognized. We prefer to talk about emotion being a *state* of the organism in order to stress a change in the probabilities of many classes of responses and in order not to identify emotional effects necessarily with any set of responses. Mammals have central nervous systems, which can alter without any effects necessarily being reflected in the peripheral nervous system despite the fact that we must ultimately rely upon peripherally mediated responses in order to identify and measure the state.

We must also consider the *relationship* between the reinforcers and the subsequent responses. Consider a person who has just been subjected to electric shock. He will no doubt display a gamut of responses. Some responses will probably be directed towards escaping from the shock or towards minimizing its severity, while other responses will be elicited by the shock, such as crying out, having an increase in blood pressure, pupillary dilation, an increase in skin conductance, perhaps defecating. Some of the responses will be operating *upon* the shock, while others will be operated upon *by* the shock. As we have said, it is only the latter that we wish to consider in this chapter. In essence, this is the distinction between "operants" and "respondents" that Skinner (1938) has drawn. No doubt from an evolutionary point of view elicited responses or respondents such as increased blood pressure have adaptive value and might contribute to the efficient execution of an operant response, such as running away from the shock, but they need not themselves directly alter the aversive stimulus. Sometimes it is very difficult, as has already been pointed out, to distinguish experimentally between these two types of responses. An animal who crouches or leaps in response to shock may in fact be making the shock less painful by altering its contact with the electric grid. But in principle the distinction is apparent and useful, and we wish to limit ourselves to respondents in this chapter, operants being the proper subject matter of chapters 2 and 3. In fact, as we shall see, the operant and respondent capabilities of a reinforcer may not always covary. Nor does it affect the issue that responses that are "respondents" in one situation can be "operants" in another, interesting as that fact may be. (For example, it has been shown by Brenner and Hothersall [1965] and Miller and DiCara [1967] that changes in heart rate can be operantly conditioned.) The important issue is not the identity of the response but the nature of the stimulus control of the response. A good deal of the experimental literature on aversive stimulation (i.e., negative reinforcers) is concerned with response-produced aversive stimulation, and here operant effects of shock are likely to be of considerable importance because one way of operating upon the shock is simply not to produce the response (see Church, 1963; Dinsmoor, 1955). From our point of view, the more interesting cases are those where the reinforcer is not contingent on a response by the subject but is entirely under the control of the experimenter.

It may be worth stressing that, although it is customary to assume that respondents are limited to autonomic responses, there is no good empirical or pragmatic basis for making the assumption here. Clearly, the "startle response" or "crying" or a "gasp" is not autonomic and yet qualifies as a respondent. Moreover, given the discussion of the previous paragraph, it is clear that we deliberately do not wish to restrict our discussion to any specific responses but do wish to consider how the distribution of large classes of responses, which may themselves be operants, may be altered. To restrict our indicators of emotional states to autonomic responses would clearly be much too restrictive. In fact, although this will no doubt offend many hard-headed colleagues, we wish to take the position that the "emotional state" itself is a respondent that, in turn, is manifested both by the production of specific and characteristic responses as well as alterations in large classes of responses.

Anyone interested in changes in emotional behavior resulting from a treatment will be tempted to examine the reinforcing properties rather than the respondent properties of reinforcers for these reasons: (1) because of the ease of doing so, (2) because an animal who shows ab-

normal operant conditioning may also be likely to show abnormal respondent responses to the reinforcers, and (3) because of the inherit-
ance of a popular theoretical position that the operant conditioning to
aversive stimuli directly depends upon the respondent properties of the
stimuli for its etiology (Mowrer, 1960). Such an examination is undoubtedly useful empirically. But while an animal who fails to escape
from or to avoid a stimulus that normally produces such behavior may
very likely (but by no means necessarily) turn out to find the stimulus
also emotionally undisturbing, there are also many everyday examples
of effectively maintained operant conditioning to aversive stimuli in the
absence of emotional responses: the sight of a hot stove does not usually produce any response except casual avoidance.

We will now treat the reinforcers themselves, then proceed to a discussion of specific respondents, and finally deal with more general
"dispositional" behavioral consequences.

The Stimuli and Stability

Ask an animal psychologist for a good "emotional stimulus" and he
will probably nominate electric shock, a stimulus that hardly ever is
encountered by animals under natural conditions (although, of course,
they are likely to encounter other painful stimuli). Next on the list
might be air blast or air deprivation. But almost certainly the list will
be one predominantly of aversive (i.e., negative) reinforcers. It is interesting to speculate why this should be so: clearly, sadistic tendencies
in animal experimenters will not wholly account for it.

One obvious reason is that the responses to aversive stimuli are usually much more conspicuous and distinctive, but it is unlikely that this
can be a sufficient explanation. After all, the wagging of a dog's tail, the
purring of a cat, or the smiling of a human are all distinctive events.
Another reason would seem to lie in the fact that many negative reinforcers are relatively independent of the preceding state of the organism and their past history with respect to that reinforcer, whereas
most intense positive reinforcers depend in important ways upon other
conditions being fulfilled. The return of a dog's master is a strong positive event for the dog. But the master must first leave before he can
return, and, more important, only a long history of man-dog interaction
produces a master. Food as a reinforcer depends upon a state of deprivation, and the specificity of food rewards is influenced by the specificity
of past experience with them (Weiskrantz and Cowey, 1963a).

But, although an aversive stimulus such as electric shock generally
produces reasonably stable responses, it would be a mistake to assume
that an animal's history of shock is unimportant in determining its current response. For example, Miller (1960) found that rats exposed to a
gradually increasing series of shocks at the goal performed better in
a runway conflict situation than rats without the prior experience.
Baron and Antonitis (1961) found that punishment had a significant
effect on the rate of unconditioned bar pressing by mice but that there
was gradual recovery over 17 days. Preshocking alleviated subsequent
effects of shock. They interpreted their results as "showing that while
aversive stimulation (preshock) has generalized depressing effect upon
operant behaviour, experience with such stimulation acts to reduce its
later depression. It was concluded that the findings support the hypothesis that exposure to aversive stimulation results in an adaptive process

that reduces the emotionalizing and depressing effects of the stimulation on later occasions" (p. 720). Church, in his excellent review (1963), also endorses the view that "the data consistently support the adaptation hypothesis."

Unfortunately the situation is not quite so simple. Kamin (1961), for example, reported an "apparent" adaptation effect of shock in that prior experience with shock produced decrements in the acquisition of conditioned suppression (see following), the decrement being a direct function of the intensity of the prior shocks. But in an interesting follow-up by Brimer and Kamin (1963), it was found that the apparent decrement in conditioned suppression was a product of a *depressed* base-line level of response plus an increased rate of responding during the conditioned stimulus. The correlation between lowered base-lines and supernormal levels of responding during the CS was 0.83, and this was shown not to be just a simple statistical artifact. When the animal was allowed to recover its baseline rate of operant responding prior to conditioned suppression training, preshock did not influence the development of conditioned suppression. So, in this case we have an adaptation of the base-line suppression but not of the conditioned suppression. In a related study, Hendry and Van-Toller (1965) found that with repetition of a conditioned suppression situation there was initial suppression followed by recovery of responding during the CS and the intervening control periods. With a 1 ma. shock, a pattern gradually emerged in which there was an acceleration of response rate immediately after the CS onset, but with net suppression over the whole CS period. Finally, an experiment by Kurtz and Pearl (1960) showed that animals preshocked showed greater resistance to extinction in a conditioned avoidance situation than control nonshocked animals. Their conclusion is directly opposite to that of Baron and Antonitis: "The pattern of results is consistent with the hypothesis that experiences of intense fear predispose Ss to react with increased fear in subsequent encounters with aversive stimuli" (pp. 205–206). Such a conclusion might also be seen to follow from the study by Sawrey and Sawrey (1964a) that prior experience of shock increases the ulceration rate produced by subsequent aversive experience (restraint for 48 hours). Against this are the wealth of studies showing that early exposure to stress, including shock, increases the resistance to subsequent stress, at least as measured by the adrenal response (Levine, 1962).

The easiest recourse in such a dilemma is to produce the standard phrase of the reviewer, that the results obviously depend upon the precise situation, stimulus parameters, species, response measure, and so forth. But a few speculations are in order. First, just as in the case of the adrenal "adaptation syndrome" (Selye, 1960), whether adaptation occurs to aversive stimulation will depend upon the magnitude and rate of delivery of the stimuli. When the strength is above a certain value and/or the rate too fast, the response becomes progressively stronger with repetition, until exhaustion ensues. Otherwise, adaptation occurs. Secondly, the extent to which the response is operantly or respondently related to the shock is likely to be of critical importance. In general, it seems very likely that operant responses conditioned to shock show much greater stability than respondents, as shock is repeated. An animal will remember what to do about a stimulus long after it continues to disturb him. We have already restricted our discussion in this chapter to respondents, but we have also pointed out that it is often difficult to make the distinction in practice. We will see that conditioned suppression might well have such an operant component. Kurtz and Pearl's extinction measure (1960) was obviously based upon an operant. Finally, this brings us to a related point, that the more predictable the shock the more likely an operant response is to become conditioned, without the experimenter necessarily being aware of it. For this reason, suppression of unconditioned or base-line levels of responding is more likely to be a true measure of respondent effects than conditioned suppression. But aside from this, the actual scheduling of the shock may itself be of considerable importance. Sawrey and Sawrey (1963) found, for example, that animals given completely predictable shocks developed significantly fewer ulcers than animals given 50 percent predictable shock (i.e., only half the signals randomly were paired with shock). Very little systematic work related to these three points can be mustered from the literature, but it seems possible that they might provide a skeleton around which the results might take on some orderliness.

In general, it can be supposed that, if we hold the type of respondent constant, the rate at which the response habituates with repetition is a good measure of the strength of the emotional stimulus and would probably correlate highly negatively with the strength of the actual response measure itself on the first presentation of the stimulus. Here again there is little evidence that bears on such a commonsense view. Virtually any novel stimulus will produce respondent changes in mammals, the changes showing definite habituation with repetition. When the habituation is rapid, as with the heart rate changes to repeated tones (Lang and Hnatiow, 1962) or lights (Geer, 1964), the response is often called the "orienting reflex" (Sokolov, 1960; see Chapter 10). When it is slower it may be called an "emotional response," as in the case of the open-field situation (Hall, 1934; Broadhurst, 1957). For the present position, we need not concern ourselves with the question of labels, except to point out that the reinforcing value of novel stimuli also can probably change from negative to positive as a function of repetition and as a function of the "activation level" of the organism (see Chapter 10). Therefore, while stimuli can be scaled along a single dimension of "rate of habituation," it may be misleading to assume that the stimuli are varying simply in their effects in a unitary fashion. But even taking a scale at face value, the matter would no doubt be complicated by considerations of age, social interaction, past experience, and genetics. Eels (1961), for example, has reported that the type of handling, as well as its "consistency," can affect the subsequent "emotionality" (as judged from a complex set of measures) of rats. Hutchinson, Ulrich, and Azrin (1965) studied aggressive responses between pairs of rats in response to foot shock. They found that they increased with age and that rats reared in social isolation showed less aggressiveness than nonisolated animals. They comment, "aggressive contact may be the critical factor in a history of normal social interaction leading to increased aggressiveness." An interesting related point is made by Riess (1946), that individual rats who are likely to "freeze" and fail to run a maze are often found to be individuals who have been repeatedly defeated in fights with other animals in the living cage. (See also Beach, 1953; Tobach and Schneirla, 1962.) And to fill out the picture, Broadhurst (1959) has strengthened Hall's earlier claim (1934) that "emotionality," as judged by defecation in the open-field situation, has a genetic component.

Bearing in mind, therefore, that effectiveness of a stimulus for producing respondents will not be a function only of its actual physical strength, we can proceed to a brief discussion of some of the practical details concerning their availability and administration. As has already been mentioned, any novel stimulus will elicit respondents that will habituate rapidly unless the stimulus is otherwise an enduring reinforcer or is made a conditioned signal for a reinforcer. The choice of stimulus will obviously depend upon whether one's interest lies in (1) the rate of habituation to relatively mild stimuli, (2) the rate of acquisition of respondents to a "neutral" stimulus (i.e., one to which the respondents have been allowed to habituate) as it is paired with a reinforcer, or (3) with the relatively stable respondents produced by reinforcers themselves. There are, in addition, other experimental questions that arise from the use of combinations of reinforcers, as in "conflict" situations, consideration of which we will defer to another section. For present purposes (2) and (3) can be considered together because both depend on the availability of a stable reinforcer.

There will be no difficulty in finding mild and novel stimuli to which habituation is very rapid, and we need not concern ourselves here with these. One situation that has been used extensively, the open-field test, shows moderately slow but definite habituation. Different experimenters have tended to concentrate either on the rate of habituation of respondents evoked by the situation (Hall, 1934; Evans and Hunt, 1942), particularly defecation and suppression of activity, or on the absolute level of respondents on the first occasion in which an animal is introduced to the situation (Broadhurst, 1957). As used originally by Hall, the open-field situation consisted of an 8 ft. diameter enclosure, enclosed by walls 2 ft. high. The floor was marked off into segments to allow the measurement of ambulation. A high level of illumination evidently makes the situation more effective (Evans and Hunt, 1942). Broadhurst (1957) has carried out the most systematic examination of stimulus dimensions of the open-field and has found that a smaller field (32¾ in. diameter) is just as effective as a 6 ft. diameter field, thereby countering Lebo's (1953) objection to the space-consuming features of the conventional unit. He also found that female rats defecate less and ambulate more than males, that noise (87 db.) is a potent factor in evoking defecation, that preshock reduced defecation, and that food deprivation had no effect. We will return later to a more detailed examination of some results using the open-field situation.

So far as stable reinforcers are concerned, there is in principle no difficulty in finding an adequate supply, although, as has already been mentioned, the choice almost always seems to be of negative reinforcers (one of the few exceptions is an experiment by Wenzel [1961] who studied heart rate changes based on both food and shock). A number of different aversive stimuli have been used: a slap from the lever in a Skinner Box (Skinner, 1938); a bump on the nose and a fall into a net (Lashley, 1930); a toy snake (Masserman and Pechtel, 1956b), a swat with a rolled-up piece of newspaper (Stanley and Elliott, 1962), and sight of the experimenter (Weiskrantz, 1956). Loud noise is sometimes successful, but Campbell and Bloom (1965) report that "the maximum, usable, non-damaging level of noise was found to be far less aversive to rats than shock intensities typically used in psychological research." The present author (unpublished) was unable to suppress food-rewarded bar pressing of monkeys with a noise stimulus of 95 db., although he did succeed in obtaining many verbal complaints from neighbors. In general, as one becomes familiar with a particular species, obvious dislikes of the species become known—such as snakes to monkeys, shrill noises to some dogs, etc. Hebb (1946) has carried out a fascinating analysis of "fear" in chimpanzees induced by a skull, a dummy human head, toy animals, anaesthetized chimpanzees, and a variety of other objects and situations. His conclusions are based upon a theoretical analysis that such situations interrupt "phase sequences." Despite the stimulation of such an analysis (or perhaps because of it—because much is made of the role of learning) our main source of information about the repertoire of aversive stimuli for any specific organism will continue to be largely empirical. On the other hand, electric shock is aversive to animals throughout the whole phylogenetic scale, and its effects are relatively stable. It is therefore likely to reign supreme as the standard aversive stimulus.

Because of convenience and wide popularity of electric shock as an aversive stimulus, some facts concerning its manipulation should be summarized. Its aversiveness will depend to a large extent upon the wave form and mode of application (Muenzinger and Walz, 1932). The most systematic analysis and review has been carried out by Campbell and Teghtsoonian (1958). These authors point out that the resistance of a rat undergoes large changes as a function of the intensity of shock. In general, resistance decreases with increasing shock intensity. On the basis of the electrical properties of four circuits (constant voltage, AC; constant current, AC; constant current, DC; and matched impedance) and on the recorded activity of rats while being shocked, the authors suggest that the matched impedance circuit is the one of choice. Constant-current circuits are not suitable when the current is low because of stray capacitance effects and because, the authors suggest, changes in current density as the animal makes and breaks contacts on a grid can produce changes in the painfulness of the shock.

The administration of electric shock involves certain practical difficulties. Generally the animal is placed upon a grid of metal bars. Careful design is necessary to minimize shorting out by feces, lowering of resistance by urine, and the adeptness of some organisms to discover that standing on bars of the same polarity produces no shock. The last problem can be overcome by a scrambling device that rapidly changes the potential of the bars in an unpredictable order (Skinner and Campbell, 1947; numerous designs have been published since: cf. recent editions of the *Journal of the Experimental Analysis of Behaviour*). Even with scrambling, certain other problems should be anticipated: with organisms that can climb readily, it is often necessary to construct the entire apparatus of conducting bars, and even then a monkey will sometimes learn to hang by a single hand from a single bar. Monkeys have also been known to discover that balancing themselves upon their thickly calloused rumps will effectively reduce shock intensity. For these reasons, contacts fixed directly to the body are sometimes very useful. A simple method of achieving this in the monkey is to set up a shock avoidance situation that has been described by Weiskrantz and Wilson (1955).

An ingenious design has been published by Licklider (1951) for a "gridless, wireless rat shocker," the idea being to place the animal on a metal floor that is connected to one side of a condenser, with the sides of the cage considered as the other side of a condenser, and to treat the animal as part of a capacitive circuit to which a charge can be applied. Beck, Waterhouse, and Runyon (1953) attempted to apply the design to monkeys and found serious practical and theoretical difficulties with it, e.g., no shock could be delivered when the animal remained motionless. Longo, Holland, and Bitterman (1961) have also eliminated the need for a grid and scrambler by using a floor painted with a special compound that allows a gradient of electric potential to be established across the floor. While useful in certain situations, and with small creatures such as insects, the floor is very susceptible to alterations in resistance from urine, and the precise strength of shock will depend upon the splay of the animal's stance. The wide use of grid devices with many species offers ample testimony that, with adequate design, the grid is generally an effective method of delivering shock. Fortunately, many well-designed shock grids are now commercially available, at least for the rat, that have sensible dimensions and that incorporate impedance-matched circuits and scramblers.

Specific Respondents

It would be a simple but space-consuming matter to list several of the respondents that have been said to be indicants of emotional states. We will, in fact, soon consider some of the major examples, but, before we do, it is worth reflecting on their general status. Despite the operational purism of many modern workers in rejecting responses not readily recorded, it is quite certain that these workers would feel some hesitation in speaking of "emotional responses" or "conditioned emotional responses" and other operationally well-defined concepts if they could not also see that their animals were "emotionally" roused. Asked to specify further what he sees, the researcher lists a good many responses, but, feeling a bit uneasy with a mere list, a researcher may then go on to talk, with impressive *savoirfaire*, of the autonomic nervous system or, more recently, of the state of activation of the reticular formation. Basically, however, the methodological operation is that of *pointing*, for such concepts as the emergency function of the sympathetic system and activation of the brain stem (Lindsley, 1951; Woodworth and Schlosberg, 1955) can themselves only be validated in terms of behavior judged to be emotional or "activated," unless autonomic activity and EEG activation are simply *defined* as being indicants of "emotion" because the stimuli that usually produce them are known to be reinforcing or punishing.

But there are, in general, three weaknesses associated with accepting such a definition.

1. Ample evidence exists that intense sympathetic activity or EEG activation is not a sufficient condition for the existence of emotional states, as judged on other criteria. Thus, a sympatheticomimetic agent such as epinephrine is said to produce subjectively "cold emotions" or "as if" states, but not "genuine" states (see Schachter and Singer, 1962, for a review). Similarly, EEG activation can be induced by reserpine even though the animal is made extremely docile and nonreactive by the drug (Rinaldi and Himwich, 1955). And, more recently, we have had the discovery of "paradoxical sleep" in which a sleeping organism shows an activated EEG, thought to be associated with dreaming (Kleitman, 1963). Some would even contend that autonomic or EEG activa-

tion is not a *necessary* condition for the occurrence of genuine emotional states; indeed, this was the basis on which Cannon and others rejected the James-Lange theory, because animals with the sympathetic trunk removed nevertheless respond appropriately to aversive stimuli in terms of gross behavior.

2. Our understanding of the mechanisms of autonomic action are still deficient to a degree that different authorities place different significance upon various components of the response. Arnold (1945), for example, has tried to amend Cannon's theory by arguing that "fear" produces a predominantly sympathetic response and that anger produces a predominantly parasympathetic response. But Ax (1953), who attempted to induce states of anger or fear in human subjects, considers that anger induces a strong reaction of both the sympathetic and parasympathetic systems. The truth appears to be that both branches of the system are interrelated in a delicate and complex fashion, even when engaged in bodily control of a more humdrum sort (such as the control of temperature-regulation mechanisms). Valiant attempts have been made by Gellhorn (1961) and others to produce a synthesis together with a theory of brain mechanisms of emotion but no one can pretend that these speculations are as yet sufficiently solidly based to enable us to make any predictions about emotional state simply from an examination of the state of ongoing autonomic responses. What predictions can be made are based on laborious and strictly empirical correlations of the type produced by Ax (1953). Similarly, with the ascending activating reticular system, a number of problems still require resolution, such as the dissociations produced by drugs and the phenomenon of "paradoxical" or "hindbrain" sleep.

3. The autonomic and EEG changes, even if accepted as being associated with emotional states, cannot be sufficiently differentiated to enable us to discriminate among different emotional states. In the study already mentioned by Ax (1953) both "fear" and "anger" induced complex changes in several of the measures (heart rate, ballistocardiograph, respiration rate, face temperature, skin conductance, and muscle potentials). Anger could be discriminated from fear largely on the basis of which changes were relatively larger in one state or the other. Even if we accept these results, the amount of labor involved in making finer differentiations between degrees of anger and fear or between states other than anger or fear seems formidable and unpromising. There is the well-known study of Wolf and Wolff (1947) in which a chronically implanted gastric fistula enabled changes in the stomach wall to be directly observed. As clear as that study was in demonstrating gastric consequences of emotional situations, Schachter and Singer (1962) aptly comment "that for many months they studied their subject during and following a great variety of moods and emotions and were able to distinguish only two patterns" (p. 379). In the case of activation, no one has proposed anything other than a single intensive scale, and even this is difficult to make quantitative. Schlosberg (1954), who was very sympathetic to the activation theory of emotion, suggested that two additional dimensions are required to differentiate various emotional states: pleasantness-unpleasantness and attention-rejection. His suggestion stemmed from an analysis of ratings of facial photographs, and he admitted some difficulty in instructing his raters to make judgments along these dimensions. The idea of an "emotion solid," like a "color solid," is an intriguing one. Although grave practical difficulties would

seem to arise in establishing their generality, Schlosberg's three dimensions might find counterparts in animal research in the operationally more negotiable terms, positive or negative reinforcer (pleasantness-unpleasantness), onset or offset, or, offset or onset, depending on the sign of the reinforcer (attention-rejection) and some measure of intensity or magnitude (level of activation). At any rate, the relevant point here is that a simple scale by itself is hopelessly inadequate for differentiating different states.

A related point is made for autonomic activity by Schachter and Singer (1962), who argue that emotional states are a joint function of physiological arousal and cognitive states. "Given a state of physiological arousal for which an individual has no immediate explanation, he will label this state and describe his feelings in terms of the cognitions available to him ... precisely the same state of physiological arousal could be labelled 'joy' or 'fury' or 'jealousy' or any of a great diversity of emotional labels, depending on the cognitive aspects of the situation" (p. 398). They report an experiment in which human subjects were given epinephrine or a placebo, under the guise of a study of the effects of vitamins on vision. Conditions were devilishly contrived to make subjects either angry or euphoric. The authors claim that epinephrine enhanced *both* states, as compared to placebo. But the results were of just borderline significance. In another study, Schachter and Wheeler (1962) compared epinephrine, placebo, and chlorpromazine for their effects on subjects' responses to a slapstick film. (Chlorpromazine was selected for its sympathetic blocking effects, the authors arguing that subjects in a psychological experiment might show high levels of secreted epinephrine under placebo conditions.) Subjects were observed through one-way vision screens. Epinephrine subjects were rated as more amused than placebo subjects, who in turn, were more amused than chlorpromazine subjects. It is premature to render more than a tentative judgment on Schachter's hypothesis (which, in any case, we have not presented fully here), but its insistence on the incorporation of both situational and autonomic variables would help resolve some of the paradoxes of experiments on sympatheticomimetic agents, as well as yield some interesting and surprising predictions. Animal studies of the effects of epinephrine give variable results, and many are concerned with avoidance conditioning rather than with respondents as such. But a recent experiment by Singer (1963) deliberately concentrated on respondents (in rats) elicited by an intense flashing light and a bell. Using a composite response scale, it was found that epinephrine animals were more frightened, chlorpromazine less frightened, than a placebo group in response to the stimuli. But, in the absence of the stimuli, there was no difference between the groups. These results can be taken as being in line with Schachter's contention that autonomic arousal yields changes in emotional state only when the situation is appropriate.

In view of the three weaknesses of arousal theories (autonomic and/or EEG) we will not attempt any classification or scaling of respondents based on the theories. Nor will our list be exhaustive; adequate reviews already exist (Lindsley, 1951; Woodworth and Schlosberg, 1955). Whether or not a respondent is somatic or autonomic (or parasympathetic or sympathetic) will be ignored. Instead we will attempt to consider the respondents roughly on a dimension of purely practical concern. Some respondents fall largely under the heading of "physiological responses" (e.g., changes in heart rate, adrenal response) while others are clearly in the province of the "behavioral responses" (e.g., "freezing"). Others, such as defecation, might be thought to be at the interface of these two important domains. It is not easy nor is it particularly helpful to try to distinguish between "physiological" and "behavioral" responses in the present context. In fact, considerable confusion would be introduced by such an attempt. But from a practical point of view it can be said that some respondents are not readily seen by the experimenter's naked eye, and they require some degree of instrumentation, whereas others do not require instrumentation, although instrumentation no doubt is a valuable adjunct. Roughly, this distinction might correspond to one that might be drawn between "physiological" and "behavioral" respondents, but, for present purposes, that is irrelevant.

We will start with respondents requiring some degree of instrumentation and work our way up or out. First, however, we have a piece of unfinished business. We started with an assertion that the definition of emotional state is basically ostensive, and that therefore many of the specific respondents assume the role of "indicants" or "indices." A definition claimed to be ostensive can be judged for its soundness only by studying the correlations among various observers on repeated occasions. Many studies of this type were carried out years ago for certain aspects of human emotional behavior, such as for the identification and rating of facial expression, with only moderate levels of agreement (see Woodworth and Schlosberg, 1955). A number of rating scales have been compiled for animal experimentation, although estimates of their reliability are often lacking. Some investigators have attempted single global estimates of "emotional response." Despite the vagueness of the term, it seems to work quite well where the responses are quite distinctive and intense, as in the establishment of the conditioned emotional response to a neutral signal paired with shock (Weiskrantz and Wilson, 1956). More typically, however, a composite list is prepared requiring both quantitative and qualitative judgments, ranging from number of fecal boli and pupil size, to "tenseness" or "relaxation." Examples of the use of varying components can be found in Masserman and Pechtel (1956b) for monkeys and cats in conflict situations; Norton (1957) for assessing drug effects on cats, hamsters, and monkeys in their home cages; Rosvold, Mirsky, and Pribram (1954) for emotional behavior of brain-operated monkeys in their home cages; Singer (1963) for rats' responses to lights and sounds; Candland, Nagy, and Conklyn (1963) for ratings of the domestic chicken in an enclosure; Eels (1961) for rats in a number of situations; Jacobsen and Sonne (1955) for the emotionality of rats as they are conditioned in a shuttle box; Brady and Hunt (1951) for assessing the establishment of a conditioned emotional response; Ryall (1958) for assessing the effects of drugs on rats in an open-field situation; Solomon and Wynne (1953) for assessing the emotional behavior in the acquisition phase of avoidance in the shuttle box; and Willingham (1956), who factor-analyzed a nineteen-item rating scale of mice in a variety of situations.

Rating techniques suffer from a number of possible weaknesses. Because of their dependence on a varying and far from neutral observer, they may be unreliable, although not necessarily so. Singer (1963) obtained an interobserver correlation of + .92. Certainly they are very time-consuming and tedious, and often only a single animal can be tested at a single time. Regardless of the state of the organism the experimenter is observing, his own state gradually but inexorably approaches that of lethargy. Despite their many drawbacks, important findings have been made using rating techniques to evaluate such treatments as electroconvulsive shock and drugs. Furthermore, the technique is of propaedeutic use if for no other reason than that it forces the investigator to observe the gross behavior of the subject for an extended period of time. Many enigmatic results can sometimes be resolved by simple observation, with a drastic change of interpretation. For example, if one were to examine Jacobsen and Sonne's (1955) data on the effect of benactazine on conditioned avoidance, one might conclude that the drug *increased* "fear" because the number of avoidance responses increased compared with the control base line. Ratings of the animals, however, suggest quite another interpretation. In the control state the animals were rated as being extremely "tense" and "frozen." The effect of the drug was to break up the tense immobility, so that more adaptive behavior could take place. A similar point emerges from the study by Krieckhaus, Miller, and Zimmerman (1965), who found a high negative correlation between avoidance responses by rats given amphetamine in a shuttle box and number of "freezing" responses. The same sort of explanation for the beneficial effects of electroconvulsive shock on avoidance conditioning is offered by Vanderwolf (1963). In addition, rating techniques are sometimes more sensitive than recorded or more objectively defined measures. Solomon and Wynne (1953) found that they could detect the conditioned emotional response by their rating scale about two trials prior to the appearance of the first avoidance response in a shuttle box. The great methodological advances being made currently in the instrumentation of behavior should not make one blind to the need for simple observation any more than simple observation should be judged to be without its own weaknesses. Recording techniques have an extremely limited "channel capacity" and select only a small segment of total behavior. Even such a simple event as a bar-press is sometimes not accurately reflected on the counters or the cumulative recorders (Trotter, 1956; Notterman & Mintz, 1965).

We turn now to a brief discussion of some of the specific respondents, starting with the ones that require special instrumentation or procedures before they can be detected or measured accurately and ending with respondents that are amenable to direct observation. We will not be concerned with the possible empirical relationships that obtain among these measures, with whether they cluster into different patterns in different individuals, or with how they fluctuate "spontaneously" in nonemotional situations. These issues are relevant, but complex and unwieldy, and the use of respondents as "indicants" as such does not depend critically upon them. A number of authors have attempted to deal with such issues, to whom the reader is referred (Ax, 1953; Gellhorn, 1961; Lacey, 1950, 1956; Johnson, 1963; Woodworth and Schlosberg, 1955).

Various measures of the state of the *blood circulatory system* have been extremely popular as respondents (Woodworth and Schlosberg, 1955), and standard medical apparatus is readily adaptable to many experimental applications. Smith and Stebbins (1965) have argued that all measures except *blood flow* are indirect so far as biological utility is concerned. "An increase in heart rate usually indicates an increased cardiac output, but this is not guaranteed if stroke volume is sufficiently decreased by the shortened diastolic filling time and not compensated for by increased ejection. . . . Plethysmographic techniques do not necessarily reveal a greater blood volume because an increased tissue volume may result from pooling of blood on the venous side of the capillary as well as arteriolar dilation." (pp. 434–435). Their technique involved the placing of a molded plastic flow section on the terminal aorta immediately above the iliac bifurcation of a monkey, and connecting wires were brought out the back to a flowmeter. They were able to clearly demonstrate Pavlovian conditioning with light and shock, as well as discrimination of lights of different hue, brightness, and position. They also established that the large cardiac changes occurred with nonexistent changes in respiration and movement, thereby ruling out indirect effects.

Despite the logical cogency of their argument, more conventional measures are much more convenient, and Smith and Stebbins admit that their results compare well with those of Church and Black (1958), who used *heart rate* in a Pavlovian conditioning situation with dogs. Indeed, a large number of investigators have been concerned with conditioned heart rate (e.g., Notterman, Schoenfeld, and Bersh, 1952; Geer, 1964, with human subjects; Bloch-Rojas, Toro, and Pinto-Hamuy, 1964, with rats; Black, Carlson, and Solomon, 1962, with dogs; see Shearn, 1961). There seems to be little doubt that heart-rate conditioning is a genuine phenomenon, especially if we consider the important demonstration by Black, Carlson, and Solomon (1962) that it can be established in the curarized dog, thereby minimizing indirect effects induced by skeletal responses. But there has been considerable conflict about the form and character of the response, some researchers finding an increase in heart rate (with shock US), others a decrease. In the Black paper just referred to, there is a full discussion of various measures, but the one that the authors settled for in their own investigation forced them to eliminate any dog who showed a decrease in heart rate to the CS! In the study by Bloch-Rojas, Toro, and Pinto-Hamuy, it was found that the cardiac response to the conditioned stimulus could be *either* acceleration or deceleration, although the response to the shock was always acceleration. A recent paper by Geer (1964) may offer a resolution because he found that the response in human subjects was biphasic—rapid acceleration followed by deceleration. This pattern he designates as the "cardiac orienting reflex" evoked by a novel CS; the effect of conditioning is to inhibit the habituation of this pattern. He comments that "the difference between a rapidly occurring accelerative phase and a subsequent decelerative phase was the most sensitive measure," and it provided the clearest evidence of lawful habituation of the "orienting reflex" with unreinforced repetition of the CS. A very similar conclusion was earlier reached by Lang and Hnatiow (1962), also with human subjects. Whether these results can be generalized to other mammals remains to be seen.

Heart rate has also been used in a variety of other eliciting situations not strictly involving conditioning. Thus, Black, Fowler, and Kimbrell (1964) found that simply handling rats produced a reliable increase in heart rate that took three hours to dissipate and that showed no habituation in successive sessions. Snowdon, Bell, and Henderson (1964) examined heart rates of rats in the open-field situation and compared them with rates of defecation and ambulation. *Low* heart

rates were consistently associated with indices of heightened emotionality, low activity, and increased defecation. "The finding that high
heart rate correlated with low emotionality is in contradiction to the
expectation of the activation theorists, who maintain that emotion is
directly related to the greater amount of energy release" (p. 425).

Despite the voluminous literature on induced changes in heart rate,
it is surprising how few attempts have been made to employ such
changes for the study of treatment effects. But a few especially instructive studies can be cited. Wenzel (1961) is one of the few who directly
compared the response to positive and negative conditioned stimuli.
The cats were presented with two levers. One tone produced food if
one lever was pressed, the other tone allowed shock to be avoided by a
press of the other lever. Wenzel found an acceleration of heart rate to
the food tone and found a deceleration to the shock tone. The effect of
reserpine was twofold: (1) It had a significant effect only on the heart
rate acceleration associated with the food tone, but the operant response
was not significantly affected. (2) On the other hand, the heart rate
deceleration to the shock avoidance tone was not significantly affected,
although the operant response was suppressed. Unfortunately, inspection of the graphs suggests that reserpine had the effect of somewhat
decreasing the degree of heart-rate change to both stimuli as well as of
decreasing the latency of both operant responses, and the dissociation
might not hold up with larger numbers of animals, with more stable
responses, or with slightly different parameters. As far as it goes,
however, the study shows a clear difference of effect on heart rate of
positive and negative stimuli and suggests a dissociation between respondent and operant effects of those stimuli. The situation itself seems
sensibly designed to uncover treatment effects.

Another study of Bloch-Rojas, Toro, and Pinto-Hamuy (1964) also
shows that treatment effects, this time of 65 percent neodecortication
in rats, can also dissociate heart-rate changes from somatomotor responses to a conditioned stimulus paired with unavoidable shock. In
normal animals, cardiac responses to the conditioned stimulus and
motor responses (any overt reaction) were acquired in a parallel
fashion. On the other hand, in neodecorticate rats, cardiac changes to
the CS were more frequent than in normals. "If overt behavioral signs
had been taken as the only index of learning, the conclusion would
have been that the neodecorticate rats are unable to associate CS-US."
The authors also suggest parenthetically that the neodecorticates
showed more defecation and piloerection to the CS. These results attest
not only to the difference in possible neural levels between the two types
of response (McCleary, 1960, also found interocular transfer in the
goldfish of a cardiac conditioned response but not of an avoidance
response; and Ross [1964] has found that cortical spreading depression
in the rat interferes with simple operant conditioning but not with
conditioning of a respiratory respondent) but also to the high degree
of sensitivity that autonomic respondents may possess in uncovering
relationships not easily detected by amplification and recording of skeletal muscular responses.

The measurement of heart rate presents no particular difficulty with
conventional EKG machines, but with infrahuman unrestrained subjects the placing of electrodes may be troublesome. A simple electrode
arrangement has now been worked out for the rat, which has almost
become standard. It involves the suturing of a pair of silver or stainless

steel wires subdermally on the back in the midthoracic region, although the placement is not critical (cf. Bélanger and Feldman, 1962). Telemetric methods will no doubt become more popular, particularly for agile creatures who can detach electrodes or who cannot, for various experimental reasons, be closely restrained. Pressure-sensitive "radio pills" suitable for implantation are described by Jacobsen (1963) (see also Essler and Folk, 1962). Many such devices suffer from limited battery life, but one can look forward to future developments.

Two other measures of circulatory state are available. *Blood pressure* is easily measured in the resting state, but there are technical difficulties in making rapid and continuous measurements. (See Ax, 1953; Dykman and Gantt, 1960; Woodworth and Schlosberg, 1955; Forsyth and Rosenblum, 1964.) *Vasomotor constriction or dilation* has been used occasionally in classical conditioning experiments, and also as one of the more distinctive components of the "orienting reflex" of the Russian workers (Bykov, 1957; Sokolov, 1960). In Sokolov's work, for example, the vasomotor response to novel stimuli is vasodilation in the temple region of the head and is a vasoconstriction in the hand. Details of the recording technique used by Russian workers are not easily available, but their inferences about vasomotor responses seem to be based upon pneumatic volume plethysmographs. The traditional volume plethysmograph response suffers from possible artifacts derived from external and body temperature levels and from muscle responses (see Woodworth and Schlosberg, 1955). Thermopiles and thermisters fixed to the finger also have been used to infer vasomotor changes, but these suffer from the necessity of keeping the tissues being monitored in a cool chamber. Under certain conditions it is possible to use a photocrystal plethysmograph that has marked advantages: it has minimal inertia, is not very sensitive to small movements, is small and light, and is satisfactory at room temperatures. One such device has been described by Shmavonian (1959), who also reviews some of the disadvantages of traditional techniques; the device consists essentially of a small photocell that measures the amount of light passing through the finger. Changes in blood volume produce changes in the amount of light absorbed by the tissue. Such a device cannot be used where it is impossible to pass light through the tissue, as in the temple response of Sokolov (1960). It has been used successfully to demonstrate classical conditioning (sound-shock) in the human finger (Shmavonian, 1959) and in the rabbit's ear (Fromer, 1963). Shmavonian also provides evidence that the vasomotor changes were not grossly related to changes in heart rate or in respiration.

Another popular respondent is the *galvanic skin response*, an electrical conductance change in the skin that just precedes a sweat-gland response (McCleary, 1950). There is voluminous literature that attests both to its great sensitivity of response to aversive stimuli as well as to its readiness to become classically conditioned. Fortunately, an excellent treatment of technique and results is available (Woodworth and Schlosberg, 1955), and it would only be superfluous for us to attempt a review here. A similar recourse is available for the various measures of *EEG* changes, which in recent years have become a useful index of "arousal," and for demonstrating cerebral electrical changes during conditioning (Lindsley, 1951; Gerard, Fessard, and Konorski, 1961).

All of the responses discussed so far are not discernible without special instrumentation or procedures. The same can be said for various biochemical and histological changes that occur in response to aversive stimulation, but the time scale along which these changes occur are generally very slow. A considerable amount of work has demonstrated that aversive stimulation produces a complex chain of responses involving the hypothalamus, the anterior pituitary gland, and the adrenal cortex. Changes in the activity or size of the *adrenal cortex* have been used to assess the effects of "stress" of various sorts, either by measuring the size of the gland itself (which is an irreversible procedure!) or by assessing various biochemical by-products of adrenal steroid secretion (Selye, 1960). Thus, Levine (1962) has shown that the size of the adrenal gland, the level of circulating corticosteroids, and the leukocyte count (which provides an indirect assay of adrenal activity) of rats in response to aversive stimulation are influenced by the early experience of the animals. The results are significant but complex: animals stimulated in infancy "are more reactive to distinctly noxious and threatening situations, but the nonstimulated (in infancy) animal appears to react to a greater variety of environmental change" (p. 250). While some adrenal effects can be assessed with reasonable speed, changes in adrenal size and indirect effects on eosinophile and circulating lymphocyte levels are slower and, as such, will probably tend to be restricted to research specifically concentrated on the physiological and developmental basis of adrenal mechanisms.

Another effect on internal histology lies in the definite demonstration of an increase in incidence of *gastric ulcers* in animals under various conditions of aversive stimulation. Extensive work has been carried out by Sawrey and his colleagues (Sawrey and Weisz, 1956; Sawrey, Conger, and Turrell, 1956; Sawrey and Sawrey, 1963, 1964a, 1964b). In their early work they demonstrated that a conflict situation, in which approach responses based on hunger and thirst were shocked, yielded a high incidence of ulcers (in six out of nine animals) whereas nonshocked control animals developed none. In a later analytical study it was shown that conflict as such is an important factor but that interaction of hunger and shock is also important. In another study (Sawrey and Sawrey, 1963), it was shown that shock that follows a signal with 100 percent predictability is less effective in augmenting ulceration rate than one that follows with only 50 percent predictability. More recently (Sawrey and Sawrey, 1964a and 1964b), the incidence of gastric ulcers has been used as a dependent variable to assess various regimes of shock delivery as well as to assess the effect of reserpine. Thus, it has been shown that the periodic presentation to restrained rats of a CS previously paired with shock will enhance ulcer formation, the rate depending directly upon the number of conditioning trials prior to restraint. Finally, it was shown that reserpine *increased* the ulceration rate in rats put into the "food and water vs. shock" conflict situation, a result which agrees with the earlier finding of Hartry (1962). This untoward treatment effect of a "tranquilizer" is probably due to the fact that reserpine itself increases gastric motility. Like the study of adrenal function, gastric ulceration rate obviously is not a convenient, "rough and ready" respondent, particularly as ulcers take time to develop and animals cannot be used as their own controls. But the results of such studies are likely to be of interest for the study of treatment effects and could be of considerable medical value.

We can now turn to three respondents that sometimes can be detected by the naked eye, but only with poor reliability and sensitivity: (1) change in *respiration,* (2) change in *muscular tension,* and (3) change in *pupil size.* Respiration is conveniently monitored by strain gauges, and respiratory changes have been used in Pavlovian conditioning experiments (Ross, 1964; Freedman, 1951) as well as in many polygraphic approaches to "lie detection" and "reactivity." Various analyses of respiratory changes are conveniently summarized by Woodworth and Schlosberg (1955), particularly alterations in the ratio of inspiratory to expiratory phase, which appears to increase markedly under "excitement" or "sudden fright." *Muscle potentials* are not difficult to record with modern electronic amplification devices, but, as in the case of the EEG, their value rests on empirical experience rather than on rational understanding. It is not uncommon to process the output of the amplifier through an integrator, to yield an "integrated muscle potention" (Ax, 1953; Woodworth and Schlosberg, 1955). Although such a method is no doubt very gross, some useful results have been obtained with it (e.g., Ax, 1953). On the other hand, there is such a multitude of choices in the placing of electrodes and there are so many variables that are difficult to control that it is difficult to recommend the choice of muscle-tension records for general use in monitoring emotional states.

Changes in *pupil size,* on the other hand, suffer from no such ambiguities. It has been known for a long time that the pupil is under autonomic control, and it can be seen to dilate dramatically in animals exposed to aversive stimuli. But recently it has been shown that pupil size can be a particularly sensitive index of the evocative properties of more commonplace, everyday objects and pictures (Hess and Polt, 1960; Hess, 1965). Hess finds that, with human subjects, interesting and pleasing pictures produce pupillary dilation, whereas distasteful pictures produce constriction. Not surprisingly, the sex of the viewer and the content of the picture are joint determinants of pupil size in certain instances: a male subject's pupils dilate more than a female's when exposed to a picture of a partially nude female, and just the opposite when to a partially nude male. Hess has argued convincingly that the many varied aspects of the "attitude" of the observer and the "interest value" of stimuli can be sensitively gauged.

In the case of sexual material and (where these are different!) advertising or packaging displays, it is easy to assess the validity of such claims, but it is too early to pass judgment on the general validity of the pupillary measure; nor has Hess provided details of the degree of variability between and within subjects. Also (Hess, 1965) the dynamics of the response to certain stimuli are not simple: constriction and dilation can follow each other in rapid succession. But these are problems for future research; meanwhile the pupillary response seems to be a particularly promising respondent with which to assess emotional states.

But the recording of this response does involve certain practical difficulties. Hess and Polt (1960) used conventional light photography, having matched their control stimuli with the experimental stimuli for mean brightness level. In many situations, however, the levels of illumination required for photography can themselves set a limit on the pupillary response, and, in any case, there are occasions when one wishes to study the response in darkness. Perhaps the simplest solution is to employ infrared light in conjunction with an infrared image converter that transforms the infrared energy back into visible light for conventional photography (Alpern and Campbell, 1962). Television cameras can be obtained that are sensitive to infrared light, which provide a more expensive but only marginally more convenient technique. Photocells sensitive to infrared light have also been used, an inference being made about pupil size from a measure of the light absorbed by the cell. Although it would appear to be much simpler than the photographic methods just described, it suffers from a number of inadequacies, such as from variations in the pigmentation of different eyes, from unequal reflection of infrared light from different parts of the same eye, and, most important, from errors introduced by head and eye movements. Perhaps the most convenient and satisfactory device is that designed by Lowenstein and Loewenfeld (1958), consisting of an infrared television scanning device that, in effect, cancels out eye and head movements and that produces a direct read-out of pupil size on a pen recorder. The device is commercially available but is very expensive, and most experimenters will no doubt settle for a photographic technique.

We can now dispense with instrumentation and turn to those respondents detectable by the naked eye. It would be rash to make an estimate of the numbers of rats' *feces* counted by experimenters over the past few decades, but they must surely be in the millions: it might be unfortunate if the popular image of experimental psychology were to reflect such a statistic. Anyone working with rats knows that they (and many other organisms, including man—Stouffer *et al.*, 1950) defecate in response to aversive stimulation (until the feces are exhausted), and moreover the feces are conveniently hard, pill-like and reasonably standard in size. Being, as it is, a kind of externalized material trace of an internal process, it might be possible to develop some sort of philosophical justification for the supremacy of the fecal bolus. At any rate, it has been the object both of warm loyalty and hard skepticism. Thus, Broadhurst (1957) states confidently that "defaecation is *the emotionality index of choice*, measured preferably by amount rather than frequency" (p. 10, italics added), while Bindra and Thompson (1953) are skeptical as to whether it has any utility whatsoever.

The answer appears to lie in the situations employed and the strength of claims made for it. The most popular situation is that introduced by Hall (1934) over 30 years ago—the "open-field situation" (see above), consisting of a simple illuminated enclosure. The situation seems to be aversive to the rat primarily because of its strangeness but also because of the common incorporation of bright lights and loud noises. There seems to be almost universal agreement that rats are likely to defecate and urinate when first placed in such an apparatus, the responses habituating over the course of a few days (with a 2 to 10 minute trial per day).

The question arises for the first time in our discussion as to how one sets about validating a response as an index of "emotionality." The problem has not arisen before now mainly because the evocative stimuli were already known on other grounds to be potent reinforcers (see the introductory discussion). This is not known directly for the open-field situation, and, therefore, recourse has to be made to the correlations between defecation and other responses in the open-field test or between defecation and other responses in situations already known to involve potent reinforcers. Both approaches are revealing, but for different reasons. Consider the latter question first: a study by Hunt and Otis (1953) examined changes in defecation during the course of classical conditioning to a neutral stimulus paired with shock and compared the changes with other behavioral signs (mainly crouching) of conditioning. They found a clear rise in defecation rate to the CS during conditioning and found a decline during extinction. But they also found that the increase in crouching appeared earlier than defecation in conditioning and disappeared later in extinction, and accordingly they argue that defecation is a response with a relatively high threshold. They repeated Bindra and Thompson's (1953) comparison between defecation in the open-field test and latency of response in a "timidity test" (in which the animal's cage was placed at the end of a runway, with food at the other end) and confirmed the absence of significant correlations between the two measures. Hunt and Otis conclude that defecation is a reliable response to aversive stimuli that are strongly evocative and conclude that the open-field and timidity situations are probably too mild to produce cross-correlations. An equally tenable hypothesis is that the timidity test is simply measuring something different from the open-field test. At any rate, very little is known about the timidity test, and it seems a bit pointless to attempt to validate the open-field test by correlating it with another about which even less is known.

Consider now the constellation of responses within the open-field situation itself: in addition to incidence of defecation and urination, two other measures are commonly taken. First, the amount of *ambulation* is easily assessed simply by noting the number of sectors of the field the animal enters. A common respondent noted in this situation, as well as in many others employing aversive stimulation, is the strong tendency of the rat to "freeze," or to engage in "preening" and "rearing" on its hind legs. We have already noted the observations of Jacobsen and Sonne (1955) and of Krieckhaus, Miller, and Zimmerman (1965) on the ability of certain drugs to decrease freezing responses and concurrently to increase the number of adaptive avoidance responses to shock. But there is some suggestion that ambulation is less suitable than defecation in the open-field and similar situations, particularly for studying treatments thought to alter emotional states. Broadhurst (1957), for example, found an absence of any marked trend towards increased ambulation scores with repeated testing in the open-field situation, whereas, as we have already noted, defecation clearly habituates. This does not enable us to say that one measure is better than the other, but at least it demonstrates that they do not consistently covary. However, we will soon argue that habituation of yet another pattern of behavior is an important feature of the open-field test, which in turn does covary with defecation. Another argument against the utility of ambulation lies in the fact that it is presumably sensitive to a large number of factors that are not particularly relevant for the study of emotion, such as species variation (in the domestic chicken defecation and ambulation in the open-field are postively correlated, in the rat negatively correlated—Candland, Nagy, and Conklyn, 1963) and such as physical dimensions of the field (Broadhurst, 1957). Treatments such as lesions and drugs can easily affect gross activity levels, and this is the likely explanation of the results of Krieckhaus, Miller, and Zimmerman (1965) on the effects of amphetamine on freezing responses. A related effect on activity is produced by frontal lesions; for example, Maher and McIntire (1960) measured immobility and defecation by rats in a Pavlovian CS shock situation. Postoperatively there was a loss of immobility but no loss in the defecation component. "The results are interpreted as evidence that ablation produced hypermotility but does not reduce anxiety." A similar interpretation of the effects of frontal lesions in the monkey is given by Pribram and Weiskrantz (1957). Conversely, a treatment such as thioridazine, which affects defecation to aversive stimulation more than it affects ambulation (or "normal" home-cage defecation; Taeschler and Cerletti, 1959), seems most promising. In other words, it is the dissociation between ambulation and defecation in response to treatments rather than their covariation that is illuminating.

Ambulation is a very gross measure that may reflect the influence of a large number of variables. Mobility or immobility certainly can come under operant control, and the open-field situation probably involves such a factor insofar as it is an "exploratory situation." On the other hand, it is probably very difficult to condition operantly the characteristic posture of "freezing" elicited by aversive stimuli, just as it is probably difficult (but possible) to condition operantly the other responses we have been talking about heretofore. But a second measure commonly taken in the open-field situation deliberately uses an operant response as a base line upon which to reflect the effect of an emotional state: *approach to consumption of food*. The measure was introduced by Hall (1934) with an explicit and interesting justification:

> The problem of finding another measure of individual differences in emotionality was not easy, and was finally solved by the following reasoning. It is commonplace that an upset condition hinders the adjustment of the animal. Emotionality may act as a barrier to the satisfaction of needs. Hence it was reasoned that if a rat which would eat under normal living cage conditions immediately upon the presentation of food was placed in a strange enclosure, where food was readily obtainable, its failure to eat could be said to be due to the emotionality of the animal (pp. 389–390).

A few years earlier, much the same kind of idea was exploited by Bousfield and Sherif (1932), who measured the depressing effect of loud shots upon eating rate in chickens and guinea pigs. In the open-field situation, Hall reported a high negative correlation between willingness to eat and defecation and urination scores. This result was essentially confirmed by Evans and Hunt (1942), although they stress that their correlations are less impressive than Hall's. (Interestingly, in view of what we have just said about activity, they also found that willingness to eat in the open field could not form the basis of a prediction about activity levels in various other situations.)

So the open-field situation induces changes of two types: (1) the production of a specific respondent, such as defecation (no doubt many if not all of the other specific respondents we have considered before could also be detected; cf. Snowdon, Bell, and Henderson, 1964, for a study of heart-rate) and (2) an interference with behavior (eating) that one would expect to have a high probability of occurring in a familiar environment. Both effects habituate with repeated exposure of the situation, and the two effects are correlated in populations of rats. The second type of effect takes us out of the specific respondent category into a consideration of changes in the flow of larger classes of behavior.

Modulation of Behavior

When, in everyday speech, we talk of someone being "emotionally upset" we generally mean more than the exhibition of certain facial expressions or than the appearance of signs of an active sympathetic nervous system. Frequently, in fact, we infer that someone is upset because characteristic patterns of behavior are altered: "Do not try to talk to X" or "X is not eating" or "You must forgive X" because "X is upset." Similarly, when X is "pleased" many characteristics of his behavior alter, other than mere simple smiling or chest-thumping. It is not so much that he does anything unusual; rather, he does the usual things differently—more quickly, with more verve. The whole flow of behavior can be modulated by strong evocative stimuli without necessarily changing the fundamental processes being modulated.

This sort of interpretation of emotion as an alteration in large classes of probabilities rather than as the triggering off of specific responses follows from the notion of emotion as a *state*. It would appear that it was on this notion that Hall based his prediction of a correlation between defecation and eating behavior in the open-field test. The state concept of emotion was put forward forcefully, if only briefly, by Skinner (1938) in *Behavior of Organisms*. Although his own experimental analysis of emotional behavior was, in that work, confined principally to the irregularities in the extinction curve and to the effects of aversive stimulation superimposed on a bar-pressing (for food) task, much of the current work on the experimental analysis of "anxiety" finds its direct historical roots in the ideas set forth there.

But it was not until the 1940s that the approach was really directly exploited in the form of some well-known experiments of Estes (1944). Among other things, he showed that the effect of punishment (shock) in a bar-pressing (food-reward) situation was a temporary depression in the rate of response, followed frequently by a compensatory increase in the rate afterwards. Shocks delivered during lever pressing produced no greater depression of rate than did shocks delivered so as not to coincide directly with lever pressing. The effects of punishment could be dispelled by placing the animal in an "adaptation box" following punishment. It would be a mistake to exaggerate these findings to the point of asserting that punishment that is not contingent on a response is equally effective as contingent punishment (Estes showed quite clearly, for example, that responses could be selectively suppressed by punishment—Experiment L.). But Estes' experiments strongly suggested a view of punishment formulated in terms of a temporary state of "suppression," a state that could be induced by punishment per se and dissipated by the mere passage of time. It was a simple but extremely important extension of Estes' work to put the "suppressing" effect of punishment under stimulus control. Estes and Skinner (1941) showed that, after a few pairings of a three-minute buzzer with inescapable brief shock, the buzzer acquires the capacity to suppress bar pressing for food reinforcement. Following the shock, the rate returns to its normal level.

The conditioned suppression paradigm is also discussed in Chapter 3. It has been used in a large number of treatment studies, particularly in psychopharmacological research. It has two attractive properties:

(1) The measure of depression can readily be made quantitative simply by relating the output during the CS to the output during a prior period in which the CS was not present. (2) It offers the opportunity to measure the effect of a particular treatment upon the base-line rate of bar pressing itself. For example, in seeking a drug with a "tranquilizing" effect, one clearly would prefer one that diminishes the conditioned suppression but leaves the base-line rate of response for food during the non-CS period unchanged. Some reports do suggest that suppression during the CS can be more markedly influenced by reserpine, for example, than the base-line rate of response (Brady, 1956).

Such a study, like any other attempting to show dissociation, serves to introduce some thorny problems. The analysis of treatment effects that claim to show differential effects on the base-line rate and the CS rate depends for its interpretation on the manner in which the two measures covary *without* treatment. First of all, it should be borne in mind that the base-line rate itself is affected by the introduction of shock into the conditioned suppression situation (Hendry and Van-Toller, 1965; Brimer and Kamin, 1963). Hendry and Van-Toller's study is instructive, for it shows that there at first is a general suppression of performance, which is, however, more severe during the CS. Gradually, as the training continues, both the base-line and CS rates increase, and the ratio of CS to base-line responding also increases.

> These quantitative results are all predictable from the observation that suppression (becomes) more and more confined to the time just before shock. The suppression ratios showed that suppression during the CS was more pronounced in early sessions, but in fact performance in later sessions showed more highly discriminated or localized suppression. These observations indicate the need for caution in interpreting suppression ratios in terms of "strength" of suppression (p. 459).

Brimer and Kamin's (1963) study introduces a further complication because, as we have already noted, they found that under certain circumstances a *negative* correlation between base-line and CS rates obtains in the early stages of training.

Secondly, very little is known about the dependence, if any, of the CS rate on the absolute level of base-line rate when the latter is set either by schedule or deprivation variables. Suppose, for the sake of argument, that slight variations in the base line (as manipulated by changes in deprivation level) produce relatively large changes in suppression during the CS (obviously, as the base-line approaches zero, suppression during the CS becomes meaningless). To then argue that a drug primarily affects the emotional response rather than the level of hunger because of a large change in suppression during CS but only a slight change in the base line clearly would be fallacious. Actually, it seems doubtful that a high degree of interdependence does obtain. The author (1953) found in a preliminary study with monkeys that the suppression ratio (rate during CS divided by base-line rate) was largely independent of large variations in the base-line rate induced by different periods of food deprivation. But the issue needs further investigation.

The moral of these points is clear for the interpretation of treatment effects on conditioned suppression: Both the base-line rate and the CS rate must be analyzed separately; due attention must be paid, in cross comparisons, to the amount of conditioned suppression experience the

animal has had; and use of the animal as his own control in repeated treatment studies (as with drugs) is hazardous. Moreover, the
fact that both the base-line and the CS rate are affected by shock (and
perhaps other independent variables) makes the interpretation of treatment effects complex. For example, in the previously mentioned study
by Brady (1956), reserpine was found to lower the base-line rate but
to eliminate the decrease in rate during the CS. From Hendry and Van-
Toller's (1965) and from Brimer and Kamin's (1963) studies we might
expect that a treatment that specifically acts on elimination of "suppression" ought to yield, if anything, an increase in the base-line rate;
on the basis of Brimer and Kamin's study it even would be possible to
conclude that giving reserpine was equivalent to giving the animals
preshock! And, in any case, it is known that reserpine decreases the
rate of bar pressing for food even when no shock is introduced into the
study (Weiskrantz and Wilson, 1955).

These problems are merely specific examples of the type that are
bound to arise in the dissociation of any treatment effects (a general
analysis is presented in Chapter 15, together with suggested logical
paradigms such as "double dissociation" for their disentanglement).
So no particular discredit is being cast on the "conditioned suppression"
paradigm in this connexion. On the contrary, we have paused here to
discuss some of the questions that are specific to the technique, because
it is likely to continue to be a popular and important one.

If for the moment we consider conditioned suppression to be a conditioned respondent such as heart rate or defecation, it can be used as
a "probe" or "monitor" of an emotional state that develops in the course
of other situations. A study by Kamin, Brimer, and Black (1963) is
particularly instructive in such a connection. Rats were given either
classical conditioning (tone-shock) in a shuttle box, in which no avoidance or escape from the shock was possible, *or* conventional operant
avoidance conditioning in the same box, where a transfer to another
compartment was sufficient to terminate the CS or the US. Prior to such
experience, the animals had been trained to bar press in a Skinner
box, and, after various regimes of classical or operant shuttle-box experience, were returned to the Skinner box. The same CS was then
introduced in the bar-pressing situation (but the US was omitted) and
its suppressant effect measured. It was discovered, first, that suppressant effect was a monotonic function of the number of CS-US
pairings the animals had received in classical conditioning. For the
operant avoidance group, however, the function relating suppression
to the number of overtraining trials (consecutive successful avoidance
trials) was U shaped. An additional important finding was that, when
the avoidance response had been allowed to extinguish, the suppressant
effect of the CS was still very strong. Thus, on the assumption that suppression is a respondent, there is clear evidence that the operant and
respondent components of a conditioned aversive stimulus do not
covary. The authors comment that their results are consistent with
the report of Sheffield and Temmer (1950) in that, as training progressed, the avoidance response decreased in vigor while increasing
in probability of occurrence. "The data on the whole reveal a considerable lack of parallelism between fear and instrumental behavior, and
thus encourage speculation that variables other than fear of the CS are
largely responsible for the maintenance of avoidance behavior" (p.
501). Thus, operant aversive conditioning, while very popularly used

to study the effects of treatments on "emotional response," may give a picture that is significantly different and, from the present point of view, much less direct than respondent conditioning.

But, before we accept the suppression of operantly controlled behavior as a legitimate respondent, we must examine it somewhat more closely. In what sense can it be asserted that bar pressing is *suppressed,* other than by definition? Obviously, bar-press rate is decreased, but this might be because of the production during the CS of other responses that are themselves incompatible with or that interfere with bar pressing. Such responses could, in turn, be either operants or respondents. An incompatible operant response might be generated in the following manner: although it is true that the shock in the conditioned suppression situation cannot be avoided entirely, it is possible that certain body postures minimize the painfulness of shock. Crouching, a commonly observed response of rats during the CS, may have such an effect, and it is difficult for an animal to both crouch and bar-press concurrently. It is difficult to eliminate such a possibility from the analysis of published studies. A few obvious suggestions for future research come to mind. One would be to use a shock stimulus that is not likely to change in strength as a function of the animal's own behavior—such as one delivered through attached electrodes (Hake and Azrin, 1965). Other aversive stimuli might be used, such as loud sounds, where there is not much that can be done behaviorally by many species to attenuate the sound. It is of some interest, in this connection, that Leitenberg (1966), using loud noises, failed to find conditioned suppression in pigeons, although the familiar suppression effect was obtained with electric shock. As mentioned earlier, the author had a similar experience with monkeys. On the other hand, Brody (1966) found a clear but incomplete suppression effect in monkeys using one second bursts of 115 db. noise.

The fact (Hendry and Van-Toller, 1965) that rats after continued exposure to the conditioned suppression situation tend to show an acceleration of response rate just following CS onset followed by suppression prior to the shock (at least, this is so when the shock intensity is 1 mamp.) strongly suggests that an operant adjustment is being made by the animal during at least part of the CS interval—either that, or the emotional state induced by the CS is complex and biphasic. In either case, the global designation "conditioned suppression" is somewhat misleading. A similar, and probably related, operant adjustment is suggested by results of using a period of "time-out" (during which no reward is delivered) as the aversive stimulus rather than shock. A warning stimulus preceding "time-out" is apt to produce an increase in response rate (Ferster, 1958; Leitenberg, 1966), as though the animal ensures that it obtains maximum reward prior to a period of temporary denial. Clearly, the possibility of operantly maintained behavioral adjustments during conditioned suppression demands careful experimental examination.

Even if all operant components were eliminated or excluded from the "conditioned suppression" situation, the phrase might still be misleading, although in a less important sense. With further fine-grained analysis, it could turn out that a few characteristic respondents such as crouching or cowering are elicited by the CS that happen to be incompatible with bar-pressing only in a strictly topographical and geographical sense.

It does not follow that other responses based on positive reinforcement would be "suppressed" by the CS if they were responses that could be emitted relatively independently of the posture or locus of the animal. Response such as head turning or paw lifting might be suitable. In addition, reward would have to be delivered to the animal independently of its location in the cage, and the technique described by DeBold, Miller, and Jensen (1965) might be so adapted. Other reward alternatives might be a change in illumination (Lockard, 1963) or intercranial stimulation in a "pleasure center" (Olds, 1962). (It is interesting, in the present connection, that conditioned suppression has been found more difficult to establish using intracranial reinforcement than using conventional food or liquid reinforcement [Brady and Conrad, 1960]. In a recent paper, McIntire [1966] concludes that "the absence of interrupting behaviors associated with food-rewarded behavior, such as travel to a food cup and consummatory behaviors, leads to the demonstrated resistance to conditioned suppression" when intracranial reward is used.) Of course the question is just hypothetical at this stage, but if it were found that "suppression" is limited only to operant responses physically incompatible with responses elicited by the CS, then the value of using the term "suppression" or any other term that suggests a general emotional state involving large classes of behavior would be diminished, and the parsimony urged by Dinsmoor (1955) would find strong support. But, before the issue can be decided, further analysis on two fronts is necessary: a much more careful description and measurement of the behavior directly elicited by the CS and the extension of the "conditioned suppression" paradigm to a much larger range of operants that are independent of locus and posture, along the lines just suggested.

Just as punishment, even when uncorrelated with the response, can decrease the rate of response, so it appears likely that reward might enhance performance under similar noncontingent conditions (Herrnstein and Morse, 1957). It would be difficult in these circumstances to argue that the enhancement caused by "free rewards" is indirectly produced by the operant conditioning of ongoing responses, because that should, if anything, have the opposite effect on the base-line rate of responding. Rather, it appears to be, in Pavlovian terminology, a type of disinhibition phenomenon. We would consider it to be a respondent state analogous but opposite to that of "suppression." Enhancement has been studied only slightly, but it represents one of the few opportunities available for quantitative analysis of the emotional effects of pleasant stimuli. Treatments that are being sought for the clinical control of depression, for example, might well be more sensitively detected in an enhancement experiment rather than in the commonly used aversive stimulation situation.

Fixated Behavior

The "suppression" of behavior, if it turns out to be legitimate to use the term, is but one example of how behavior may be modulated by aversive situations. Other types of changes have been described as regression and fixation (Dinsmoor, 1960). Fixation is the more interesting case, both theoretically and practically, as a potential tool for the analysis of treatment effects; and our discussion will be limited to it. The type of issue we have just raised, whether the "suppressed" behavior is really suppressed or simply made incompatible with other elicited responses, does not really enter into the analysis of fixated behavior. Here we are talking about the seemingly maladaptive persistence of behavior rather than its supplantation. But we will see that there are other unresolved issues.

The most extensive experimental analysis of fixated behavior is due to Maier and his colleagues (Maier, 1949). Maier found that rats presented with insoluble problems in a Lashley jumping stand—that is, problems where neither stimulus of the pair nor position was consistently rewarded or punished—tend to develop stereotyped responses. Two stereotypes were found: *position stereotypes,* in which the animal always jumps to the same position; and *stimulus stereotypes,* in which the animals always jump to the same card. When the animals are subsequently presented with a soluble problem, the previous stereotyped response patterns are likely to remain strongly persistent. Roughly 75 percent of animals with position stereotypes are unable to change their response pattern when the problem is made soluble, whereas only about 25 percent of animals previously *taught* a position habit (i.e., by consistently rewarding one position) are unable to change from position responding to stimulus responding. But one of the more tantalizing facts that emerged from Maier's studies was that despite the "fixated" response pattern, the animals nevertheless provide clear evidence of learning something about the soluble problem because their response latencies to the positive stimulus are much shorter than their latencies to the negative stimuli. Often, in fact, their responses to the negative stimuli are "abortive." The fact that the animal has learned something about the stimuli but appears unable to practice the adaptive response, together with other facts, led Maier to conclude that the fixated behavior is a form of "compulsion." Fixated behavior he considers to be one of a number of maladaptive behavior patterns that are induced by frustrating situations and that cannot be satisfactorily explained on the grounds of ordinary learning theory. An excellent review of both the empirical background and the theoretical controversies involved in the analysis of "fixations" can be found in Yates (1962).

The mere fact that conventional learning theory might have difficulty in explaining the facts of fixation—and this has been heatedly disputed —does not in itself make them unique or even interesting. From our present point of view the interest stems from the claim that distinctive modifications of behavior occur in aversive situations and that these might have properties akin to other respondents, that is, they may be patterns indicating an emotional state rather than patterns (operants) that emerge because their consequences alter the situation. But we must admit, at once, that to attempt to draw such a parallel, forces one to recognize that both the stimulus situation and the response patterns involved in fixation studies are of a high order of complexity. For one thing, the definition of *frustrating* is far from simple because it seems to require, in Maier's formulation, that the animal be faced with an "insoluble" problem from which there is no escape. An "insoluble" problem is one with a random pattern of rewards and punishments and, as such, is one of a class of schedules in which not every response is consistently rewarded or punished, i.e., "partial reinforcement" or "partial punishment" schedules. Schedule parameters for both the "insoluble" and "soluble" tasks are undoubtedly important but complex (cf. Yates, 1962). It is difficult to vary the "solubility" of a problem without also varying the overall rate at which reward or punishment is administered in the Lashley jumping stand. It seems likely that the overall rate of punishment is more important than whether or not the punishment is administered according to a rule. Wilcoxin (1952), for example, compared rats on a Maier-type random schedule of reward and punishment (both responses rewarded and punished equally often) with one in which the incorrect response was consistently punished and the correct response rewarded and punished equally often. The latter group was more persistent in maintaining fixations than the former when switched to a soluble problem. But it would be rash to suggest that only a single factor, rate of punishment, is predominant. Examples can be found where rats able to abandon stereotypes had received significantly more shocks than rats unable to abandon them (cf. Yates, 1962, p. 60). In his later formulations, Maier incorporated both "insolubility" and punishment rate as factors in "frustration."

But another question is whether the administration of punishment is a *necessary* albeit complex condition for the development of fixations. The present author and K. Nott (unpublished) gave a group of monkeys a series of 64 insoluble discrimination problems (10 trials per problem), based entirely on food reward in a Wisconsin testing apparatus. "Fixations" were not noteworthy and subsequently, when given soluble problems, this group was just as efficient as animals without previous experience. The Lashley jumping stand involves severe punishment for incorrect responses (the animal bumps against the locked door and falls into a net), and in addition, in the bulk of studies by Maier and his collaborators the animal was forced to jump by air-blast or electric shock. It has even been claimed by Wolpe that all of Maier's results are due directly to the air-blast. Although this seems too extreme a position (see Yates, 1962, p. 60), it is difficult to find examples of rigid fixations without severe punishment intruding into the procedure at some point.

The experimental situation in which fixations develop can be described, then, as one involving a complex sequence of inconsistently administered punishments. In such a situation we would certainly expect to find the appearance of some of the respondents we have already considered. The question is whether it is fair to consider the fixation pattern itself to be a type of respondent. But this dependent variable side of the equation is also complex, if for no other reason than that it too is based on a characteristic pattern within a sequence of responses. In addition, the pattern is one of fixation only if the scores are calculated on the basis of *which* of the two responses is made, but not if they are calculated on the basis of latency. Indeed, this is the basis, as we have seen, for Maier's contention that "the animal has made the required differentiation but is unable to practise the required response. This property of the fixation makes it appear as a form of compulsion" (1949, p. 43). However, Wilcoxin (1952) has shown that differences in latency between correct and incorrect responses appear long before correct choices, even in animals who are not fixated. We have the option of concluding either that all animals tend to pass through a "fixation" stage or that the animal is able to display his willingness to respond more readily than his choice of a specific response.

Given the complexity of the situation and the effects, then, we must weigh judgment on the theoretical status of "fixated" behavior. But the phenomenon is a tantalizing one, and Maier's treatment of the notion of frustration-induced fixation is not only provocative but also would find application in the interpretation of a large range of abnormal behavior. Not only would treatment effects be of interest in their own right, but also the discovery of treatments that act specifically on the development or persistence of fixations would lend support to the view that they are an entity in their own right, dissociable from the conventional operant features of discrimination learning. Unfortunately, the literature, such as it is, does not lend encouragement to this position. Drug-induced convulsions do not reverse fixations (Maier and Klee, 1941). In a series of studies (Neet and Feldman, 1954; Feldman and Neet, 1954, 1957) it was shown that fixations could not be reversed by a series of 10 or 25 electroconvulsive shocks, that a guidance procedure (for helping break fixations) was not improved by ECS supplementation, and that there was no relation between the duration of the insolvable-problem phase and the effects of ECS. In a later paper Feldman and Neet (1960) showed that an ECS administered daily after each set of trials on an insoluble problem reduced the number of fixations when the animals subsequently were presented with a soluble problem. But they quite properly comment that "there seems to be no way to assess the relative importance of the anxiety-reducing and the amnesic effects of ECS" (p. 534). Neither chlorpromazine (Feldman *et al.*, 1959) nor reserpine (Feldman and Liberson, 1960) affected the prevention or reversal of fixations. On the other hand, the range of treatments attempted so far is still relatively restricted, and it is possible that future research may prove more fortunate.

Responses to Conflict

In the experiments described previously on fixation, the animal had the option of jumping to one of the two doors in the Lashley apparatus and of thereby risking punishment (by bumping its nose and falling into a net) or of not jumping and thereby eventually sustaining punishment (by air-blast or electric shock) until it did jump. It is a moot point just to what extent the animal's abnormal behavior develops not as a result of the application of punishment per se but by virtue of being presented with a choice between unpleasant alternatives, i.e., a conflict. Conflict has been the subject of study from a number of points of view, some of them of interest to our present discussion. In general, two types of conflict will be considered here: (1) punishment-punishment—where only two courses of action are open, either of which leads to punishment, as in the case just considered; and (2) reward-punishment—where an animal is under strong drive but can obtain reward only by sustaining punishment. (Of course, it is possible to define many situations broadly as being "conflictful," either by claiming that single stimuli may have both rewarding and punishing effects or by assuming that responses themselves may be self-punishing. Thus, as an example of the former, it could be argued that some of the respondents of open-field testing stem not only from the strangeness of the novel situation but because the animal is both frightened and fascinated by the same situation. As an example of the latter case, we might consider that any situation involving sustained and demanding rates of response might induce fatigue. For example, Porter *et al.* [1958] have reported that a monkey that was required to respond every 20 seconds for a period of 6 hours in order to avoid shock with complete success was more likely to develop a gastric ulcer than a yoked control animal who received a shock whenever the experimental monkey did but could do nothing about it. This might be taken as evidence that the conflict between punishment for responding [fatigue] and punishment for not responding [shock] produces greater effects than shock alone. [It should be mentioned that this study was based on small numbers of animals and that it was in any case not confirmed when the session was lengthened to 18 hours (Brady *et al.*, 1958)]. The inclusion of these examples under the heading "conflict" could be defended, but only with difficulty and at the cost of considerable further experimental analysis, and we will limit our discussion here to those situations where the definitions of reward and punishment are relatively unambiguous.)

There is evidence that the delivery of punishment in a conflict context is more disturbing than an equivalent amount of punishment not contingent upon responses (i.e., nonconflictful). Thus, Sawrey, Conger, and Turrell (1956) showed that experimental rats developed more gastric ulcers in a conflict situation in which their approach responses based on hunger and thirst were electrically shocked than did "yoked control" rats who were shocked whenever the experimental group was shocked, so that no contingency existed between approach responses and shock. The same conclusion is also strengthened by many anecdotal accounts that behavioral disturbances in a reward-punishment situation are maximal when the punishment is made directly contingent upon and made to occur simultaneously with the approach response to the reward. So, although there is abundant evidence that nonconflictful punishment is sufficient for the production of respondents (see above), evidently punishment in a conflictful situation may enhance the intensity and persistence of the respondents.

No doubt, not only ulcer formation but also any of the specific respondents treated above could be shown to be readily produced in conflict situations. But many experimenters have been interested in more broadly based and more clinically oriented syndromes, such as "neurosis," that is said to be produced by conflict. Whether or not *neurosis* is an apt phrase need not concern us immediately, but, whatever the designation, quite complex effects have been described, which transcend any categories we have discussed so far. "Such deterrent experiences [resulting from the punishment of rewarded responses] set up reactions of hesitation and ambivalence, internal 'tensions' accompanied by all the physiological components of anxiety, and failures of adaptation more or less affecting all associated experiences. There may then appear a wide variety of 'neurotic' patterns including what in humans we would call compulsions, or psychosomatic disorders, such as asthma, or gastrointestinal dysfunctions in which, if the monkey eats a banana, it will come out the other end within an hour undigested. Alternatively, the animal may have pseudomanic disturbances, or epileptiform seizures, or functional paraplegias, or continuous homo or autoerotic preoccupations, or cataleptic trances. And, if I may borrow the terms, also 'hallucinations and delusions.' " (Masserman and Pechtel, 1956a, p. 97).

"Experimental neurosis" has been claimed to have been produced in animals by situations other than those involving the punishment of rewarded responses (cf. reviews by Russell, 1950; Wolpe, 1952). Historically, reports from Pavlov's laboratory made a great impact, particularly the account of an experiment by Shenger-Krestovnikova (Pavlov, 1927) in which "neurotic" behavioral patterns were seen in a dog faced with a discrimination that became progressively more difficult. While not falling under our definition of conflict, such manifestations were discussed by Pavlov as a conflict between processes of excitation and inhibition. But we will not dwell on either the experimental material or Pavlov's theoretical interpretations because the original experimental results are themselves based on a small number of animals and because recently Soviet workers have attempted without success to create experimental neuroses in monkeys by the use of difficult discriminations (personal communications from Cherkovitch to Steiner, 1964). Many studies on monkeys, in fact, have been carried out on discriminations gradually made very difficult for the purposes of measuring sensory thresholds, without significant disturbances in behavior having been seen (e.g., Weiskrantz and Cowey, 1963b). At any rate, treatment studies on Pavlovian "neurosis" are virtually nonexistent, with the possible exception of the famous case of the frontal lobe removal in a chimpanzee said to have been made "neurotic" when a delayed response task was made more difficult (Jacobsen, Wolfe, and Jackson, 1935). It was claimed that the brain operation completely abolished the disturbed behavior, but the generality of the claim has often been questioned. In this case, and in many other accounts of abnormal behavior induced by difficult discriminations, it seems possible that one is dealing with the occasional animal already made unstable (before the onset of the experiment) by past experience or constitutional factors.

Aside from the situations of "ambivalent stimulation," all other "neurosis-inducing" experimental situations seem to use punishment, either in a conflictful context or not. It is worth bearing in mind that nonconflictful punishment can itself sometimes produce behavior as severely "neurotic" in character as conflictful punishment (Wolpe, 1952). So, although we have labeled this section "Responses to Conflict," we are as much concerned with analysis of behavior broadly termed *abnormal* or *maladaptive* as we are with the situations said to provoke such behavior.

These broadly based descriptions really bring us back full circle to our introductory discussion on ostensive definitions and rating scales; for there are no practical alternatives when one is interested in a broad profile of behavioral manifestations.

"Neurotic" profiles have been of considerable interest to psychiatrists, and, not unnaturally, their susceptibility to treatments such as brain lesions and drugs has been examined in a number of studies. The bulk of these have used reward-punishment conflict situations, with rating scales of varying elaborateness. In one study (Masserman and Pechtel, 1956a) 64 rating scales were used (30 for monkeys and 34 for cats). In the circumstances it is not easy for us (or sometimes for the original investigators) to summarize the results. Briefly, it has been claimed that orbitofrontal, amygdaloid, and mediodorsalthalamic lesions cause an amelioration of neurotic patterns (Masserman and Pechtel, 1956b; Pechtel *et al.*, 1955) but at the expense of untoward effects on learning and retention. Although barbiturates seem to be more "neurosis-relieving" than reserpine or alcohol, their effects do not persist (Masserman and Pechtel, 1956a).

The clinically oriented experimenter is on the horns of a dilemma

—the more permissive his behavior profile the more complex and un-manageable his task of analysis. Masserman and his colleagues take great care to stress the difficulties of their task, but they sometimes seem to be preaching a counsel of despair that they would apply to treatment studies generally; e.g., "it is impossible to state the effects of any drug on any organism without considering the latter's genetic characteristics, past experiences, biologic status, and perceptions, mo-tivations toward and evaluations of its current physical and social milieu" (Masserman and Pechtel, 1956a, p. 110). If this were strictly true, no pharmacology textbook could ever have been written, nor any anaesthetic given with confidence. No doubt the "neurotic" profile itself is influenced by such diverse variables, but they may have achieved undeserved prominence because of the relative lack of success in dis-covering treatments powerful enough to outweigh the variance intro-duced by these factors. Or it may be that the profile itself is too broad and that advances in the evolution of treatments having desirable and reliable effects on the alleviation of emotional responses will come from the analysis of much simpler and more easily measured respondents such as those dealt with earlier in this chapter. While that is my per-sonal belief, the issue is fundamentally pragmatic, and there is no point in trying to convert or divert.

But it does behoove us to delve a bit more deeply into the question what is meant by "neurotic" behavior. There are two questions of relevance to our general approach: (1) Is "experimental neurosis" any more than a constellation of specific responses of the type we have already encountered, or does it possess a more global or emergent quality? (2) Is "neurosis" operantly or respondently generated? The answer to the first question is, of course, partly semantic: it is difficult to think of critical tests of emergent properties. But descriptions of "neurotic" behavior depart from our previous descriptions in two ways: (1) Some of the specific responses we have not actually en-countered previously, such as epileptiform seizures, functional para-plegias, erotic preoccupations, and hallucinations. (2) Almost all descriptions imply or actually make explicit that the responses are "aberrant" or "maladaptive." To a certain extent the variety and type of specific responses noted in conflict situations may be a result simply of clinical zeal and predilection. Wolpe, for example (1952), unlike Masserman and Pechtel (1956a), lists very few response patterns we have not already encountered in earlier sections of this chapter when describing the effects of a reward-punishment situation. Perhaps all that need be concluded is that some conflict situations produce quan-titatively more severe effects than we have already discussed but pro-duce qualitatively the same type as produced by punishment alone. But it is still convenient to refer to the constellation of effects under some such rubric as "emotional state" or "anxiety" and to attach some functional significance to the state and to use specific responses as in-dicants—as we have already suggested—without isolating "neurosis" as a special kind of state.

When the behavior in conflict situations is described as "maladap-tive," it bears directly on the question of whether the behavior is re-spondently or operantly controlled. According to Wolpe (1952) "an animal is said to have an experimental neurosis if it displays unadap-tive responses that are characterized by anxiety, that are persistent, and that have been produced experimentally by behavioural means."

An adaptive response is one "that has the *effect* of leading directly or indirectly to the reduction of the organism's needs or to the prevention of pain or fatigue. An *unadaptive* response, on the other hand, does not lead to either" (p. 243, italics in original). We can paraphrase this by saying that the maladaptive responses have no direct consequences on the stimulus situation but have been elicited by the present or past situation; that is, they are respondents. Whether or not they really are "maladaptive" depends on how broad a view of utility one takes in evolutionary terms; in Cannon's emergency theory of sympathetic activity, respondents have obvious survival value. It would seem wise to avoid the designation "maladaptive" as a critical part of one's definition. But before concluding that all features of "experimental neurosis" are respondents (Wolpe, 1952, it should be pointed out, would not accept such an interpretation because he considers that neurotic responses themselves are established by "drive reduction" at the cessation of punishment), one would have to tease apart all of the components carefully and provide specific analyses for each. A response such as "clawing at the wire-netting" (Wolpe, 1952) might well be an escape or avoidance response previously established operantly. It is possible that some of the "hysterical" symptoms, such as ritualistic posturing, might be established fortuitously by their contiguity with shock termination. And so on. Because many, if not most, of the components of "experimental neurosis"—defecation, urination, heart-rate changes, increased muscle tension, crouching, respiratory changes, refusal to eat, etc.—have already been discussed and because the problem of operant-respondent classification, when in dispute, has been ventilated, there is no need to go over that ground again. Suffice to say that the behavioral pattern is no doubt complex, but certainly contains many respondents that are (we would like to argue) indicants of an emotional state that is itself a respondent.

Because of this complexity, a direct analysis of the *operant* aspects of conflict situations offers certain attractions, because the problem of measurement is very much simpler. We have already seen that we cannot make a simple translation from operant strength to respondent strength—for example, the time course of the two can be different—but neither are the two behavioral patterns entirely independent. One might speculate that, although a change in respondent strength is quite likely to occur when the operant strength remains steady, a changing operant level generally is accompanied by a change in respondent strength, although not necessarily in the same direction (e.g., Kamin, Brimer, and Black, 1963). So, a change in operant level might give one a clue about alterations in an emotional state and might do so with greater reliability than could be done by studying the constellation of respondents evoked by conflict situations. The most systematic use of approach and avoidance tendencies in a reward-punishment conflict situation is that carried out by Miller and his associates by using a straight alley runway with food and/or shock at one end and by measuring the speed of approach (Miller, 1961, 1964; Miller and Barry, 1960; cf. review by Yates, 1962). Various theoretical conclusions have been drawn from these studies, such as the claim that the gradient of approach to reward is less steep than the gradient of avoidance of shock. Here we need only mention a few results with drugs to illustrate the utility of this type of situation for studying treatment effects.

One of the more notable studies is that by Barry and Miller (1962), who developed a "telescope alley" that was shown to overcome successfully the most common drawbacks of the conventional reward-punishment conflict runway situation for treatment studies, namely, that it is difficult to repeat the conflict experience more than once with the same animal and that it is necessary to train the approach response to reward prior to introducing the punishment. A drug that disrupts the more recently learned response cannot be distinguished from one that genuinely alters the emotional state. In the Barry and Miller study, progressive changes in the length of the "telescope alley" were associated with progressive changes in the intensity of shock delivered at the reward point. "The animals [rats] readily learned to approach the goal unhesitatingly when it was set at the no-shock distance and to run progressively more slowly and become more likely to be deterred when the goal was set at distances associated with progressively stronger shock" (p. 209). It was reported that alcohol and amobarbital sodium decreased the speed of approach on "safe" trials but produced faster approach responses to reward plus shock than when under placebo conditions, and it is therefore argued that these drugs decrease the strength of avoidance more than of approach. In contrast, chlorpromazine and morphine reduced approach speed on the safe trials as well as on the reward-punishment trials, although the decrements on the latter were smaller and less consistent. It is argued that these drugs are general depressants. A formally similar study was carried out by Grossman (1961) using a Skinner box rather than a runway situation. Rats were trained to press for food reward, but the bar was shocked when an auditory warning signal was present. The strength of the shock varied directly with the intensity of the warning signal. It was found that chlorpromazine and perphenazine depressed performance under nonavoidance conditions, but the drug rates during conflict were higher than the corresponding placebo rates. The chlorpromazine results, thus, are not in complete agreement with those of Barry and Miller (1962) with the runway situation, and, indeed, Grossman also mentions a discrepancy between the two situations in the case of alcohol.

Even leaving the discrepancies aside, it would be premature to conclude from these results alone that any of these drugs had specific effects on the emotional response to punishment (or to threat of punishment). For one thing, there is the hazard of translating directly from operant to respondent strength. But in a later paper Miller (1964) indicates that conditioned suppression (see previous) is also significantly alleviated by amobarbital sodium, which may provide a bridge between the two types of behavior patterns. Second, it is possible that the drugs were acting to depress rate generally and nondifferentially across all stimulus conditions; i.e., the animals may have been somewhat "dazed" by the drugs. This alternative interpretation illustrates the fact that all treatment studies are inevitably capable of multiple interpretations that can only be eliminated by a step by step sequence of analytical studies. Miller has, in fact, appreciated the nature of and the need for this sequential analysis: he effectively proceeded to provide evidence against the hypothesis that animals are "dazed" or made undiscriminating by amobarbital by showing that changes in stimulation associated with nondelivery of food (rather than with punishment) are detected normally in the drugged state (Miller, 1964). Although not all the results on discrimination are unequivocal, an impressive body of material allows one to "zero in" on the demonstration that amobarbital, at least, affects the punishment component more than the approach component in a conflict situation. For an example of how effective step by step analysis of treatment effects should proceed, it will be difficult for the reader to find a better model.

Concluding Comments

Having plucked the bird clean, it might be as well to brush some of the feathers aside and see the essential profile of the victim. We started with the assertion that emotion is best considered to be a state induced by certain potent stimuli, including rewards and punishments. The verb *induced*, we made it clear, was meant to imply that emotional behavior is in the general class of "respondent" behavior, that is, behavior that is elicited by stimuli rather than behavior that emerges because of its consequences. After some consideration of the types of stimuli generally available for the evocation of emotional states, we proceeded to deal with a large number of specific respondents, mainly autonomic, dwelling on a number of technical points about their measurement and about the situations in which they are most readily or conveniently detected. We then broadened our definition of respondents to include general changes in behavior patterns, even in instrumental behavior itself. This involved us in an analysis of conditioned suppression and fixated behavior. A number of questions arose as to the extent to which the designations were legitimate and as to whether the patterns were entirely respondent. While judgment must be weighed, it is consistent with our general position that emotional states are manifested in changes in the profiles of large classes of behavior. Even more caution must be exercised when dealing with our final category of effects, those seen in conflict situations. The position was advanced that "experimental neurosis" contains qualitatively similar patterns as are elicited in somewhat simpler situations, but perhaps of greater quantitative intensity and range.

Whether or not the constellation of responses elicited by certain potent situations are lumped together into an "emotional state" is partly a matter of semantics and preference, but there is at least a heuristic advantage in so doing. Provided full weight is given to the situational context, "emotional states" can be described that could not be adequately encompassed or differentiated simply by a listing of various component responses. Above all, the respondent character of such states means that they follow quite different time courses than those reflected in operant conditioning evolved in the same situations. Although the latter can give a hint as to the status of respondent strength, it can never be taken as equivalent. The important advance made in recent years in the instrumentation and analysis of operant conditioning has tended to eclipse the study of respondents, even when the principal aim has been the study of emotional behavior. Although the study of respondents may be more complex and less convenient, our understanding of emotional behavior and the analysis of changes effected by treatments will not be adequate until the balance is redressed.

REFERENCES

ALPERN, M., & CAMPBELL, F. W. 1962. The behavior of the pupil during dark-adaptation. *J. Physiol.*, 165, 5–7P.
ARNOLD, M. B. 1945. Physiological differentiation of emotional states. *Psychol. Rev.*, 52, 35–48.

Ax, A. F. 1953. The physiological differentiation between fear and anger. *Psychosom. Med.*, 15, 433–442.

Baron, A., & Antonitis, J. J. 1961. Punishment and preshock as determinants of bar-pressing behavior. *J. comp. physiol. Psychol.*, 54, 716–720.

Barry, H., & Miller, N. E. 1962. Effects of drugs on approach-avoidance conflict tested repeatedly by means of a "telescope alley." *J. comp. physiol. Psychol.*, 55, 201–210.

Beach, F. A. 1953. Animal research and psychiatric theory. *Psychosom. Med.*, 15, 374–389.

Beck, L. H., Waterhouse, I. K., & Runyon, R. P. 1953. Practical and theoretical solutions to difficulties in using Licklider's rat shocker. *J. comp. physiol. Psychol.*, 46, 407–410.

Bélanger, D., & Feldman, S. M. 1962. Effects of water deprivation upon heart rate and instrumental activity in the rat. *J. comp. physiol. Psychol.*, 55, 220–225.

Bindra, D., & Thompson, W. R. 1953. An evaluation of defecation and urination as measures of fearfulness. *J. comp. physiol. Psychol.*, 46, 43–45.

Black, A. H., Carlson, N. J., & Solomon, R. L. 1962. Exploratory studies of the conditioning of autonomic responses in curarized dogs. *Psychol. Monogr.*, 76, No. 548, 31 pp.

Black, R. W., Fowler, R. L., & Kimbrell, G. 1964. Adaptation and habituation of heart rate to handling in the rat. *J. comp. physiol. Psychol.*, 57, 422–425.

Bloch-Rojas, S., Toro, A., & Pinto-Hamuy, T. 1964. Cardiac versus somatomotor conditioned responses in neodecorticate rats. *J. comp. physiol. Psychol.*, 58, 233–236.

Bousfield, W. A., & Sherif, M. 1932. Hunger as a factor in learning. *Amer. J. Psychol.*, 44, 552–554.

Brady, J. V. 1956. Assessment of drug effects on emotional behavior. *Science*, 123, 1033–1034.

Brady, J. V., & Conrad, D. G. 1960. Some effects of limbic system self-stimulation upon conditioned emotional behavior. *J. comp. physiol. Psychol.*, 53, 128–137.

Brady, J. V., & Hunt, H. F. 1951. A further demonstration of the effects of electroconvulsive shock on a conditioned emotional response. *J. comp. physiol. Psychol.*, 44, 204–209.

Brady, J. V., Porter, R. W., Conrad, D. G., & Mason, J. W. 1958. Avoidance behavior and the development of gastroduodenal ulcers. *J. exp. anal. Behav.*, 1, 69–73.

Brenner, J., & Hothersall, D. 1965. Control of heart rate. Paper presented at Experimental Psychology Society Meeting, Oxford.

Brimer, C. J., & Kamin, L. J. 1963. Disinhibition, habituation, sensitization, and the conditioned emotional response. *J. comp. physiol. Psychol.*, 56, 508–516.

Broadhurst, P. L. 1957. Determinants of emotionality in the rat. I. Situational factors. *Brit. J. Psychol.*, 48, 1–12.

Broadhurst, P. L. 1959. Application of biometrical genetics to behavior in rats. *Nature*, 184, 1517–1518.

Brody, J. F. 1966. Conditioned suppression maintained by loud noise instead of shock. *Psychon. Sci.*, 6, 27–28.

Bykov, K. M. 1957. *The cerebral cortex and the internal organs.* New York: Chemical Publications; 1957.

Campbell, B. A., & Bloom, J. M. 1965. Relative aversiveness of noise and shock. *J. comp. physiol. Psychol.*, 60, 440–442.

Campbell, B. A., & Teghtsoonian, R. 1958. Electrical and behavioral effects of different types of shock stimuli on the rat. *J. comp. physiol. Psychol.*, 51, 185–192.

Candland, D. K., Nagy, Z. M., & Conklyn, D. H. 1963. Emotional behavior in the domestic chicken (White Leghorn) as a function of age and developmental environment. *J. comp. physiol. Psychol.*, 56, 1069–1073.

CHURCH, R. M. 1963. The varied effects of punishment on behavior. *Psychol. Rev.*, 70, 369–402.

CHURCH, R. M., & BLACK, A. H. 1958. Latency of the conditioned heart rate as a function of the CS-US interval. *J. comp. physiol. Psychol.*, 51, 478–482.

DEBOLD, R. C., MILLER, N. E., & JENSEN, D. D. 1965. Effect of strength of drive determined by a new technique for appetetive classical conditioning of rats. *J. comp. physiol. Psychol.*, 59, 102–108.

DINSMOOR, J. A. 1954. Punishment: I. The avoidance hypothesis. *Psychol. Rev.*, 61, 34–46.

DINSMOOR, J. A. 1955. Punishment: II. An interpretation of empirical findings. *Psychol. Rev.*, 62, 96–105.

DINSMOOR, J. A. 1960. Studies of abnormal behavior in animals. In Waters, R. H., Rethlingshafer, D. A., and Caldwell, W. E. (Eds.), *Principles of comparative psychology.* New York: McGraw-Hill. Pp. 289–324.

DYKMAN, R. A., & GANTT, W. H. 1960. Experimental psychogenic hypertension: Blood pressure changes conditioned to painful stimuli (schizokinesis). *Bull. Johns Hopkins Hosp.*, 107, 72–89.

EELS, J. F. 1961. Inconsistency of early handling and its effect upon emotionality in the rat. *J .comp. physiol. Psychol.*, 54, 690–693.

ESSLER, W. O., & FOLK, G. E. 1962. A method of determining true resting rates of unrestrained mammals by radio telemetry. *Anim. Behav.*, 10, 168–170.

ESTES, W. K. 1944. An experimental study of punishment. *Psychol. Monogr.*, 263, 1–40.

ESTES, W. K., & SKINNER, B. F. 1941. Some quantitative properties of anxiety. *J. exp. Psychol.*, 29, 390–400.

EVANS, J. T., & HUNT, J. McV. 1942. The emotionality of rats. *Amer. J. Psychol.*, 55, 528–545.

FELDMAN, R. S., ELLEN, P., LIBERSON, W. T., & ROBINS, J. 1959. The effect of chlorpromazine on the brightness discrimination of rats with habits and fixations. *J. comp. physiol. Psychol.*, 52, 322–326.

FELDMAN, R. S., & LIBERSON, W. T. 1960. The effect of reserpine on behavior fixations in rats. *J. comp. physiol. Psychol.*, 53, 483–487.

FELDMAN, R. S., & NEET, C. C. 1954. The effect of electroconvulsive shock on fixated behavior in the rat. II. The effect of ECS supplemented by guidance. *J. comp. physiol. Psychol.*, 47, 210–212.

FELDMAN, R. S., & NEET, C. C. 1957. The effect of electroconvulsive shock on fixated behavior of the rat: III. The effect of ECS as a function of the duration of the conflict. *J. comp. physiol. Psychol.*, 50, 97–99.

FELDMAN, R. S., & NEET, C. C. 1960. The effect of electroconvulsive shock on fixated behavior in the rat. IV. The prevention of fixations with ECS. *J. comp. physiol. Psychol.*, 53, 532–534.

FERSTER, C. B. 1958. Control of behavior in chimpanzees and pigeons by time-out from positive reinforcement. *Psychol. Monogr.*, 72 (Whole No. 461).

FORSYTH, R. P., & ROSENBLUM, M. A. 1964. A restraining device and procedure for continuous blood pressure recordings in monkeys. *J. exp. anal. Behav.*, 7, 367–368.

FREEDMAN, B. 1951. Conditioning of respiration and its psychosomatic implication. *J. nerv. ment. Dis.*, 113, 1–19.

FROMER, R. 1963. Conditioned vasomotor responses in the rabbit. *J. comp. physiol. Psychol.*, 56, 1050–1055.

GEER, J. H. 1964. Measurement of the conditioned cardiac response. *J. comp. physiol. Psychol.*, 57, 426–433.

GELLHORN, E. 1961. Prolegomena to a theory of emotions. In *Perspectives in biology and medicine,* Vol. 4, No. 4., 403–436. Chicago: Univ. of Chicago Press.

GERARD, R. W., FESSARD, A., & KONORSKI, J. 1961. *Brain mechanisms and learning*. Springfield, Ill.: Charles C Thomas.

GROSSMAN, S. P. 1961. Effects of chlorpromazine and perphenazine on bar-pressing performance in an approach-avoidance conflict. *J. comp. physiol. Psychol.*, 54, 517–521.

HAKE, D. F., & AZRIN, N. H. 1965. Conditioned punishment. *J. exp. anal. Behav.*, 8, 279–293.

HALL, C. S. 1934. Emotional behavior in the rat. I. Defecation and urination as measures of individual differences in emotionality. *J. comp. Psychol.*, 18, 385–403.

HARTRY, A. L. 1962. The effects of reserpine on the psychogenic production of gastric ulcers in rats. *J. comp. physiol. Psychol.*, 55, 719–721.

HEBB, D. O. 1946. On the nature of fear. *Psychol. Rev.*, 53, 259–276.

HENDRY, D. P., & VAN-TOLLER, C. 1965. Alleviation of conditioned suppression. *J. comp. physiol. Psychol.*, 59, 458–460.

HERRNSTEIN, R. J., & MORSE, W. H. 1957. Some effects of response-independent positive reinforcement on maintained operant behavior. *J. comp. physiol. Psychol.*, 50, 461–468.

HESS, E. H. 1965. Attitude and pupil size. *Scient. Amer.* (April 1965), 46–54.

HESS, E. H., & POLT, J. M. 1960. Pupil size as related to interest value of visual stimuli. *Science*, 132, 349–350.

HUNT, H. F., & OTIS, L. S. 1953. Conditioned and unconditioned emotional defecation in the rat. *J. comp. physiol. Psychol.*, 46, 378–382.

HUTCHINSON, R. R., ULRICH, R. E., & AZRIN, N. H. 1965. Effects of age and related factors on the pain-aggression reaction. *J. comp. physiol. Psychol.*, 59, 365–369.

JACOBSEN, B. 1963. Endoradiosonde techniques—A survey. *Med. Electron. Biol. Engng.*, 1, 165–180.

JACOBSEN, C. F., WOLFE, J. B., & JACKSON, T. A. 1935. An experimental analysis of the functions of the frontal association areas in primates. *J. nerv. ment. Dis.*, 82, 1–14.

JACOBSEN, E., & SONNE, E. 1955. The effect of benziliz acid diethylamino-ethylester, HCl (benactyzine) on stress-induced behavior in the rat. *Acta pharmacol. et toxicol.*, 11, 135–147.

JOHNSON, L. C. 1963. Some attributes of spontaneous autonomic activity. *J. comp. physiol. Psychol.*, 56, 415–422.

KAMIN, L. J. 1961. Apparent adaptation effects in the acquisition of a conditioned emotional response. *Canad. J. Psychol.*, 15, 176–188.

KAMIN, L. J., BRIMER, C. J., & BLACK, A. H. 1963. Conditioned suppression as a monitor of fear of the CS in the course of avoidance training. *J. comp. physiol. Psychol.*, 56, 497–501.

KLEITMAN, N. 1963. *Sleep and wakefulness*. Chicago: University of Chicago Press.

KRIECKHAUS, E. E., MILLER, N. E., & ZIMMERMAN, P. 1965. Reduction of freezing behavior and improvements of shock avoidance by d-amphetamine. *J. comp. physiol. Psychol.*, 60, 36–40.

KURTZ, K. H., & PEARL, J. 1960. The effects of prior fear experiences on acquired-drive learning. *J. comp. physiol. Psychol.*, 53, 201–206.

LACEY, J. I. 1950. Individual differences in somatic response patterns. *J. comp. physiol. Psychol.*, 43, 338–350.

LACEY, J. I. 1956. The evaluation of autonomic responses towards a general solution. *Ann. N.Y. Acad. Sci.*, 67, 123–164.

LANG, P. J., & HNATIOW, M. 1962. Stimulus repetition and the heart rate response. *J. comp. physiol. Psychol.*, 55, 781–785.

LASHLEY, K. S. 1930. The mechanism of vision: I. A method for rapid analysis of pattern vision in the rat. *J. genet. Psychol.*, 37, 453–460.

LEBO, D. 1953. A simplified method for measuring emotional defecation in the rat. *Science*, 118, 352–353.

LEITENBERG, H. 1966. Conditioned acceleration and conditioned suppression in pigeons. *J. exp. anal. Behav.*, 9, 205–212.

LEVINE, S. 1962. Psychophysiological effects of infantile stimulation. In Bliss, E. L. (Ed.), *Roots of behavior*. New York: Harper & Row. Pp. 246–253.

LICKLIDER, J. C. R. 1951. A gridless, wireless rat shocker. *J. comp. physiol. Psychol.*, 41, 334–337.

LINDSLEY, D. B. 1951. Emotion. In Stevens, S. S. (Ed.), *Handbook of experimental psychology*. New York: Wiley.

LOCKARD, R. B. 1963. Some effects of light upon the behavior of rodents. *Psychol. Bull.*, 60, 509–529.

LONGO, N., HOLLAND, L. R., & BITTERMAN, M. E. 1961. The resistive sheet: A gridless and wireless shocking technique. *Amer. J. Psychol.*, 74, 612–618.

LOWENSTEIN, O., & LOEWENFELD, I. E. 1958. Electronic pupillography. A new instrument and some clinical applications. *Arch. Ophthal.*, 59, 352–363.

MCCLEARY, R. A. 1950. The nature of the galvanic skin response. *Psychol. Bull.*, 47, 97–113.

MCCLEARY, R. A. 1960. Type of response as a factor in interocular transfer in the fish. *J. comp. physiol. Psychol.*, 53, 311–321.

MCINTIRE, R. W. 1966. Conditioned suppression and self-stimulation. *Psychon. Sci.*, 5, 273–274.

MAHER, B. A., & MCINTIRE, R. W. 1960. The extinction of the CER following frontal ablation. *J. comp. physiol. Psychol.*, 53, 549–552.

MAIER, N. R. F. 1949. *Frustration: A study of behavior without a goal*. New York: McGraw-Hill.

MAIER, N. R. F., & KLEE, J. B. 1941. Studies of abnormal behavior in the rat. VII. The permanent nature of abnormal fixations and their relation to convulsive tendencies. *J. exp. Psychol.*, 29, 380–389.

MASSERMAN, J.H., & PECHTEL, C. 1956a. An experimental investigation of factors influencing drug action. *Psychiat. Res. Reports* (April 1956), 95–113.

MASSERMAN, J.H., & PECHTEL, C. 1956b. How brain lesions affect normal and neurotic behavior. *Amer. J. Psychiat.*, 112, 865–872.

MILLER, N. E. 1960. Learning resistance to pain and fear: Effects of overlearning, exposure, and rewarded exposure in context. *J. exp. Psychol.*, 60, 137–145.

MILLER, N. E. 1961. Some recent studies of conflict behavior and drugs. *Amer. Psychologist*, 16, 12–24.

MILLER, N. E. 1964. The analysis of motivational effects illustrated by experiments on amylobarbitone sodium. In Steinberg, H. (Ed.), *Animal behaviour and drug action*. London: Churchill.

MILLER, N. E., and BARRY, H., III. 1960. Motivational effects of drugs: Methods which illustrate some general problems in psychopharmacology. *Psychopharmacologia*, 1, 169–199.

MILLER, N. E., & DI CARA, L. 1967. Instrumental learning of heart rate changes in curarized rats. *J. comp. physiol. Psychol.*, 63, 12–19.

MOWRER, O. H. 1960. *Learning theory and behavior*. New York: Wiley.

MUENZINGER, K. F., & WALZ, F. C. 1932. An analysis of the electrical stimulus producing a shock. *J. comp. Psychol.*, 13, 157–171.

NEET, C. C., & FELDMAN, R. S. 1954. The effect of electroconvulsive shock on fixated behavior of the rat: I. The effect of a ten- and twenty-five-day series of ECS on the stability of the fixated response. *J. comp. physiol. Psychol.*, 47, 124–129.

NORTON, S. 1957. Behavioral patterns as a technique for studying psychotropic drugs. In Garattini, S., and Ghetti, V. (Eds.), *Psychotropic Drugs*. Amsterdam: Elsevier.

NOTTERMAN, J. M., & MINTZ, D. E. 1965. *Dynamics of response*. New York: Wiley.

NOTTERMAN, J. M., SCHOENFELD, W. N., & BERSH, P. J. 1952. Conditioned heart rate response in human beings during experimental anxiety. *J. comp. physiol. Psychol.*, 45, 1–8.

OLDS, J. 1962. Hypothalamic substrates of reward. *Physiol. Rev.*, 42, 554–604.

PAVLOV, I. P. 1927. *Conditioned reflexes.* (Translated and edited by G. V. Anrep.) Oxford: Oxford University Press.

PECHTEL, C., MASSERMAN, J. H., SCHREINER, L., & LEVITT, M. 1955. Differential effects of lesions of the medio-dorsal nuclei of the thalamus on normal and neurotic behavior in the cat. *J. nerv. ment. Dis.*, 121, 26–33.

PORTER, R. W., BRADY, J. V., CONRAD, D. G., MASON, J. W., GALAMBOS, R., & RIOCH, D. 1958. Some experimental observations on gastro-intestinal lesions in behaviorally conditioned monkeys. *Psychosom. Med.*, 20, 379–394.

PRIBRAM, K. H., & WEISKRANTZ, L. 1957. A comparison of the effects of medial and lateral cerebral resections on conditioned avoidance behavior by monkeys. *J. comp. physiol. Psychol.*, 50, 74–80.

RIESS, B. F. 1946. "Freezing" behavior in rats and its social causation. *J. Soc. Psychol.*, 24, 249–251.

RINALDI, F., & HIMWICH, H. E. 1955. A comparison of the effects of reserpine and some barbiturates on the electrical activity of cortical and subcortical structures of the brain of rabbits. *Ann. N.Y. Acad. Sci.*, 61, 27–35.

ROSS, R. B., 1964. *Spreading cortical depression and behaviour.* Unpublished doctoral dissertation, University College, London.

ROSVOLD, H. E., MIRSKY, A. F., & PRIBRAM, K. H. 1954. Influence of amygdalectomy on social behavior in monkeys. *J. comp. physiol. Psychol.*, 47, 173–178.

RUSSELL, R. W. 1950. The comparative study of "conflict" and "experimental neurosis." *Brit. J. Psychol.*, 41, 95–108.

RYALL, R. W. 1958. Effect of drugs on emotional behavior in rats. *Nature*, 182, 1606–1607.

SAWREY, J. M., & SAWREY, W. L. 1964b. Ulcer production with reserpine and conflict. *J. comp. physiol. Psychol.*, 57, 307–309.

SAWREY, W. L., CONGER, J. J., & TURRELL, E. S. 1956. An experimental investigation of the role of psychological factors in the production of gastric ulcers in rats. *J. comp. physiol. Psychol.*, 49, 457–461.

SAWREY, W. L., & SAWREY, J. M. 1963. Fear conditioning and resistance to ulceration. *J. comp. physiol. Psychol.*, 56, 821–823.

SAWREY, W. L., & SAWREY, J. M. 1964a. Conditioned fear and restraint in ulceration. *J. comp. physiol. Psychol.*, 57, 150–151.

SAWREY, W. L., & WEISZ, J. D. 1956. An experimental method of producing gastric ulcers. *J. comp. physiol. Psychol.*, 49, 269–270.

SCHACHTER, S., & SINGER, J. E. 1962. Cognitive, social and physiological determinants of emotional state. *Psychol. Rev.*, 69, 379–399.

SCHACHTER, S., & WHEELER, L. S. 1962. Epinephrine, chlorpromazine and amusement. *J. abnorm. soc. Psychol.*, 65, 121–128.

SCHLOSBERG, H. 1954. Three dimensions of emotion. *Psychol. Rev.*, 61, 81–88.

SELYE, H. 1960. *The physiology and pathology of exposure to stress.* Montreal: Acta, 1960.

SHEARN, D. W. 1961. Does the heart learn? *Psychol. Bull.*, 58, 452–458.

SHEFFIELD, F. D., & TEMMER, H. W. 1950. Relative resistance to extinction of escape training and avoidance training. *J. exp. Psychol.*, 40, 287–298.

SHMAVONIAN, B. M. 1959. Methodological study of vasomotor conditioning in human subjects. *J. comp. physiol. Psychol.*, 52, 315–321.

SINGER, J. E. 1963. Sympathetic activation, drugs and fear. *J. comp. physiol. Psychol.*, 56, 612–615.

SKINNER, B. F. 1938. *Behavior of organisms.* New York: Appleton-Century-Crofts.

SKINNER, B. F., & CAMPBELL, S. L. 1947. An automatic shocking-grid apparatus for continuous use. *J. comp. physiol. Psychol.*, 40, 305–307.

SMITH, O. A., & STEBBINS, W. C. 1965. Conditioned blood flow and heart rate in monkeys. *J. comp. physiol. Psychol.*, 59, 432–436.

SNOWDON, C. T., BELL, D. D., & HENDERSON, N. D. 1964. Relationships between heart rate and open-field behavior. *J. comp. physiol. Psychol.*, 58, 423–426.

SOKOLOV, E. N. 1960. Neuronal models and the orienting reflex. In Brazier, M. (Ed.), *The central nervous system and behavior*. New York: Josiah Macy, Jr. Foundation.

SOLOMON, R. L., & WYNNE, L. C. 1953. Traumatic avoidance learning: Acquisition in normal dogs. *Psychol. Monogr.*, 67, No. 4, 1–19.

STANLEY, W. C., & ELLIOTT, O. 1962. Differential human handling as reinforcing events and as treatments influencing later social behavior in Basenji puppies. *Psychol. Rep.*, 10, 775–788.

STEINER, J. 1964. *The reinforcing properties of discriminative stimuli.* Unpublished doctoral dissertation, University of Cambridge.

STOUFFER, S. A., GUTTMAN, L., SUCHMAN, E. A., LAZARSFELD, P. F., STAR, S. A., AND CLAUSEN, T. A. 1950 *Studies in social psychology in World War II*. Vol. 4. Princeton, N.J.: Princeton University Press.

TAESCHLER, M., & CERLETTI, A. 1959. Differential analysis of the effects of phenothiazine-tranquillizers on emotional and motor behavior in experimental animals. *Nature*, 184, No. 1, 823–824.

TOBACH, E., & SCHNEIRLA, T. C. 1962. Eliminative responses in mice and rats and the problem of "emotionality." In Bliss, E. L. (Ed.), *Roots of behavior*. New York: Harper & Row. Pp. 211–231.

TROTTER, J. R. 1956. The physical properties of bar-pressing behavior and the problem of reactive inhibition. *Quart. J. exp. Psychol.*, 8, 97–106.

VANDERWOLF, C. H. 1963. Improved shuttle-box performance following electroconvulsive shock. *J. comp. physiol. Psychol.*, 56, 983–986.

WEISKRANTZ, L. 1953. Behavioral changes associated with ablation of the amygdaloid complex. Unpublished doctoral dissertation, Harvard University.

WEISKRANTZ, L. 1956. Behavioral changes associated with ablation of the amygdaloid complex in monkeys. *J. comp. physiol. Psychol.*, 49, 381–391.

WEISKRANTZ, L., & COWEY, A. 1963a. The aetiology of food reward in monkeys. *Anim. Behav.*, 11, 225–234.

WEISKRANTZ, L., & COWEY, A. 1963b. Striate cortex lesions and visual acuity of the rhesus monkey. *J. comp. physiol. Psychol.*, 56, 225–231.

WEISKRANTZ, L., & WILSON, W. A., Jr. 1955. The effects of reserpine (Serpasil) on emotional behavior of normal and brain-operated monkeys. *Ann. N.Y. Acad. Sci.*, 61, 36–55.

WEISKRANTZ, L., & WILSON, W. A., JR. 1956. Effect of reserpine on learning and performance. *Science*, 123, 1116–1119.

WENZEL, B. M. 1961. Changes in heart rate associated with responses based on positive and negative reinforcement. *J. comp. physiol. Psychol.*, 54, 638–644.

WILCOXIN, H. C. 1952. "Abnormal fixation" and learning. *J. exp. Psychol.*, 44, 324–333.

WILLINGHAM, W. W. 1956. The organization of emotional behavior in mice. *J. comp. physiol. Psychol.*, 49, 345–348.

WOLF, S., & WOLFF, H. G. 1947. *Human gastric function*. New York: Oxford University Press.

WOLPE, J. 1952. Experimental neurosis as learned behaviour. *Brit. J. Psychol.*, 43, 243–268.

WOODWORTH, R. S., & SCHLOSBERG, H. 1955. *Experimental psychology*. New York: Holt, Rinehart and Winston.

YATES, A. J. 1962. *Frustration and conflict*. London: Methuen.

CHAPTER 5

General Activity

C. G. GROSS

L IVING organisms display a great variety of behavior that to the casual observer appears independent of changes in external stimuli or of internal need. Most of a laboratory rat's day is spent sniffing, grooming, scratching, biting, running, walking, and just resting. A caged monkey climbs down from its perch, examines particles on the floor, grooms itself, paces around the cage, and sits down. By various simple methods, such as placing the cage on microswitches (stabilimeter), suspending it from a transducing spring (jiggle cage), or giving the animal access to a running wheel, it is possible to obtain measures of this "spontaneous" or "general activity."

This chapter will consider first, uses of activity measures; second, techniques for measuring activity, and, finally, it will argue for a distinction between measuring basal activity level and measuring *reactivity* to the environment.

Uses of Activity Measures

Devices for measuring locomotor activity have been ubiquitous in animal behavior laboratories for over forty years. They have been used in the study of animal motivation, in the analysis of effects of brain lesions and drugs, and in the investigation of biological rhythms.

Motivation

Experimental analysis of motivation began in the 1920s with C. P. Richter. Influenced by Cannon's theory of homeostasis (Cannon, 1932), Richter viewed motivated behavior as a homeostatic process. Behavior, he thought, was "driven" by various biological needs, and such "physiological drives" manifested themselves in the amount of general activity (Richter, 1922; 1927). A large number of studies were carried out that demonstrated relationships between general activity and endocrine, pharmacological, developmental, experimental, and neural variables (cf. Shirley, 1929; Reed, 1947; Munn, 1950).

In subsequent decades psychologists have turned away from studying "homeostatic drives" as manifested by running in a running wheel. Emphasis has changed to such problems as the specific physiological mechanisms involved in specific types of motivated behavior (e.g., eating behavior), "non-homeostatic" motivation (e.g., curiosity and exploration) and the effect of motivation on learning. Yet, study of many of the phenomena first discovered by Richter has yielded considerable insight into behavior. One of the most striking of these phenomena was the marked increase in activity of the laboratory rat with food deprivation (Richter, 1922; 1927). Subsequent experiments on this relationship will be outlined in order to illustrate uses of activity measures in the study of motivation and some of the difficulties therein.

Although the positive relationship between activity and hunger had been demonstrated mainly in the running wheel, it also seemed to remain true when activity was measured in a Dashiell maze (Dashiell, 1925), in an open-field (Fehrer, 1956), in a treadmill (Baba, 1959), in stabilimeter devices (Richter, 1922), and by means of photocells (Siegel and Steinberg, 1949). This relation between general activity and hunger was invariably interpreted as reflecting an increased drive state arising from an increased need.

In 1953, Campbell and Sheffield challenged this interpretation and suggested that deprivation does not increase activity but, rather, increases reactivity to external stimuli and that this increased reactivity is manifested as more locomotor activity. Drives, they said, decrease the stimulus threshold. They supported this view by demonstrating that, under rigorously controlled environmental conditions, brief presentation of a stimulus increased activity much more markedly in deprived rats. Furthermore, they pointed out that previous studies relating activity to hunger had not made a specific attempt to maintain a constant environment. Subsequently, Teghtsoonian and Campbell (1960) supported this criticism by demonstrating that deprived rats increased their activity in a stabilimeter by up to 400 percent in a "well-trafficked" laboratory environment but by only up to 70 percent in a constant environment.

Hall, however, repeatedly failed to find any effect of stimulus conditions on the level of activity in either deprived or satiated rats (Hall et al., 1953; Hall and Hanford, 1954). Hall's studies differed from Campbell and Sheffield's both in the use of activity wheels rather than stabilimeters and in the use of a 23 hour deprivation schedule rather than denial of food for a 3 day period. Both these procedural differences turned out to be of crucial importance. First, it is clear that deprivation increases activity in running wheels much more than in stationary cages when the two devices are directly compared (Treichler and Hall, 1962; Weasner, Finger, and Reid, 1960). This is probably due to the fact that locomotion in a running wheel produces greater visual, auditory, and kinesthetic stimulation than locomotion in a stationary cage. Second, under the 23 hour deprivation schedule, animals are disturbed once a day at feeding time (Hall et al., 1953; Hall and Hanford, 1954). As animal caretakers know and as Sheffield and Campbell (1954) and Amsel and Work (1961) showed, deprived rats are particularly active in the presence of stimuli that normally precede feeding. This controversy was largely resolved when Hall (1956) studied activity (still in a running wheel) as a function of continual deprivation under both normal and increased environmental stimulation. His results are summarized in Fig. 5-1. Under ad lib feeding conditions, rats exposed to increased environmental stimuli were more active than control rats. When food was removed, the activity of both groups increased by about the same amount.

The results of this series of experiments, extending over more than thirty years and deriving directly from Richter, may be summarized as follows. Under constant environmental conditions, food deprivation increases the activity of rats only slightly; this effect may be markedly enhanced by increasing environmental stimuli and by using running wheels rather than stationary cage devices (for a detailed review of this subject see Baumeister, Hawkins, and Cromwell, 1964). These experiments emphasize the importance for activity studies of the type of apparatus used, the exact environmental conditions, the deprivation schedule, the distinction between activity and reactivity, and the role of possible learning artifacts.

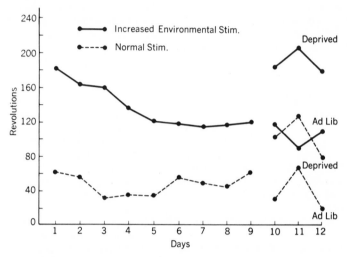

FIG. 5-1.

In recent years the physiological mechanisms underlying the increased reactivity with increased food deprivation have been clarified. As the normal blood glucose level falls, glucose is liberated from the liver, where it is stored as glycogen, and there is an increase in secretion of adrenaline into the blood stream. As Cannon, McIver, and Bliss (1924) first showed, this circulating adrenaline facilitates the conversion of glycogen to glucose. In addition, adrenaline is a powerful stimulant of the reticular activating system and thus produces cortical arousal and facilitation of motor activity (Dell, 1958). These physiological effects of reticular-formation activation manifest themselves as increased reactivity to sensory stimuli.

The study of non-homeostatic motives has also attracted locomotor activity measures, particularly the study of exploratory behavior. Typically in such studies, rats are placed in an open-field or maze for several minutes, and the amount of locomotor activity is recorded. This is then taken as a measure of exploratory behavior. Such measures may be particularly hazardous in the study of exploration because basal activity level and fear are likely to confound them (see Chapters 4 and 6). The latter point is exemplified by the following experiment. When a small, darkened compartment was attached to one side of an open-field maze and rats were placed in the open-field, they entered the small compartment as soon as they found it and tended to remain there (Welker,

1959). Thus, fear seems to have been a more important determinant of behavior than any exploratory tendency. The inadequacies of level of locomotor activity in an open-field or maze as a measure of exploratory behavior become even greater in studies of the effects of brain lesions or drugs because these variables may affect basal activity level and avoidance behavior as well as exploratory behavior.

An animal's opportunity for locomotion will affect the level of its subsequent activity. Confinement may increase activity in running wheels (Shirley, 1928; Skinner, 1933; Hill, 1956) and in stationary cage devices (Siegel, 1946; Hill, 1958). It also increases the operant level of bar pressing (Baron, Antonitis, and Beale, 1961). These types of phenomena led some to postulate the existence of an autonomous "activity drive." As in the case of instinct theory in the 1920s, postulation of more and more drives to "explain" behavior soon revealed the dubious value of drives as explanations.

Behavioral Effects of Drugs and Brain Lesions

General activity measures have proved to be powerful screening tests for psychotropic drugs. In general, drugs clinically described as sedatives depress activity and drugs clinically described as excitants increase activity. As typical in pharmacological studies, the effect of a drug on activity depends both on the dosage and on the species tested. In rats, small doses of azacyclonel decrease activity, and large doses increase it (Brown, Braun, and Feldman, 1956). Benactyzine increases activity in rats and reduces it in monkeys (Berger, Hendley, and Lynes, 1956).

One of the more intriguing uses of activity measures as empirical screening tests in psychopharmacology is the study of drug suppression of increased activity induced by another drug. Among the drugs used to increase activity are (1) stimulants such as amphetamine, pipradrol, and methyl phenidate; (2) drugs such as iminodipropionitrile, which induce circling activity in mice, similar to the genetic "waltzing" syndrome; and (3) hallucinogens such as lysergic acid diethylamide and mescaline. This technique seems to be helpful in the discovery of clinically useful tranquilizers and in differentiating the various classes of psychotropic drugs. An introduction to this growing literature may be found in Riley and Spinks (1958). Similarly, drug antagonism of decreased activity produced by a second drug is also proving a useful psychopharmacological technique (Smith and Dews, 1962). These uses of activity measures are often more empirical than analytical.

A more analytical use of activity measurements is for the study of behavioral mechanisms of drug and brain-lesion effects. A particular treatment may affect performance in a shuttle box or maze, not by impairing discrimination or learning, but, rather, by increasing the level of locomotor activity. On the other hand, both changed activity and impaired performance may be independent effects of a single treatment. Because alterations in activity level may confound measurement of learning, discrimination and avoidance, in order to study the effect of a drug or lesion on these types of behavior it often becomes essential to obtain an independent measure of activity level.

Examples of the role of activity measures in the analysis of behavioral change will be drawn from studies of the effect of brain lesions. Frontal cortex lesions in monkeys produced faster extinction of preoperatively acquired avoidance habit in a shuttle box (Pribram and Weiskrantz, 1957). However, these animals also showed more loco-motor activity in this situation. Thus, it was not clear whether increased activity was secondary to the faster extinction as had been found in a previous study (Stewart and Ades, 1951) or whether the faster extinc-tion was due to an increase in activity. When the monkeys could avoid shock by bar pressing (Sidman avoidance), it became feasible that the postoperative changes found in the shuttle box were, in fact, a result of the increased activity (Weiskrantz and Wilson, 1958).

However, there is another situation where this change in activity after frontal lesions is not responsible for a performance deficit. In addition to increased locomotion, frontal lesions in monkeys produce a severe deficit on delayed response tasks. Increased locomotor activity might impair delayed response by either shortening or eliminating the monkey's perception of the cue or by increasing the intratrial delay period. Thus, one might be tempted to ascribe the delayed response deficit to the enhanced locomotion. However, a series of experiments have shown that increased activity is neither necessary nor sufficient to impair delayed response performance. Specifically, delayed response impairment may be produced independently of hyperactivity, e.g., by frontal lesions in squirrel monkeys (Miles and Blomquist, 1960) and in dogs (Lawicka and Konorski, 1959) and by electrical stimulation of frontal cortex (Weiskrantz, Mihailović, and Gross, 1962). Pharmaco-logical treatment may drastically reduce the activity of frontal monkeys without simultaneously improving delayed response performance (Prib-ram, 1950; Blum, Chow, and Blum, 1951). On the other hand, food deprivation improves delayed-response performance (Gross, 1963a) but does not affect basal activity level (DeVito and Smith, 1959). Further-more, in a study involving various frontal lesions, degree of delayed-response impairment and increase in activity were not correlated (Gross, 1963b). In summary, in this case, the increased locomotion and the behavioral deficit are independent results of frontal lesions.

Another case in point may be drawn from the study of the behav-ioral effects of hippocampal lesions in rats. This lesion not only impairs passive avoidance but also actually improves active avoidance learning (Isaacson, Douglas, and Moore, 1961; Kimble, 1963; Kimura, 1958; Teitelbaum and Milner, 1963). Another effect of this lesion is to in-crease activity in a novel situation, i.e., to increase reactivity (Roberts, Dember, and Brodwick, 1962; Teitelbaum and Milner, 1963; Douglas and Isaacson, 1964). Increased reactivity might be expected to impair passive avoidance and to facilitate learning of active avoidance. Thus, it is possible that the change in locomotor behavior after hippocampal lesions underlies their effects on avoidance behavior.

Biological Rhythms

Perhaps the most exciting recent gift of natural history to experi-mental biology has been the recognition of temporal organization in living systems; organisms can measure time and use these measure-ments to regulate physiological processes and behavior (cf. Pittendrigh, 1961; Harker, 1964; Bünning, 1964; Cold Spring Harbor Sympos., 1960; Hague, 1964). One of the most pervasive indicators of physio-logical clocks is general activity rhythms.

The knowledge that animals engage in certain activities at particular times of the day undoubtedly antedates experimental science. However, it was not until the turn of the century that it was realized that some rhythms of behavior would persist under constant environmental conditions; that is, that they were *endogenous*. Perhaps the first described endogenous rhythm in animals was the persistence in rate of a 24 hour cycle in a running wheel under constant illumination (Slonaker, 1907; Richter, 1922). Soon afterwards, endogenous rhythms of a variety of other processes were discovered, such as pigment migration in arthropods, body temperature in vertebrates, and glycogen rhythms in the liver (Bünning, 1964). Although the existence of a time sense in bees has been known for over thirty years, it was only recently that it was realized that a common clock system underlies both time sense and diurnal rhythms (Bünning, 1964).

The manifestations of biological clocks may be grouped into three classes (after Pittendrigh and Bruce, 1957):

1. *Sun-compass clocks.* Many animals are able to use a sun-compass by correcting for the change of the azimuth of the sun during the day.

2. *Internal clocks.* Internal clocks control discrete events such as spore discharge, emergence of the adult form in insects, and onset of activity.

3. *Rhythmic clocks.* In rhythmic clocks, the amplitude of a process varies cyclically with time, e.g., body temperature, pigment dispersion, and locomotor activity.

The most common biological periodicity is the circadian or "about 24-hour" rhythm. Although clock systems are characteristic of probably all organisms as well as of single cells within an organism, very little is known about their physiological mechanisms. However, a great deal has been discovered in recent years about their behavioral properties. The salient characteristics of circadian rhythms and their underlying clock mechanism may be summarized as follows (after Harker, 1964).

1. *In a natural environment*, the phase timing of rhythms of most animals is affected by the light conditions of the environment. These include (1) increase in light intensity at dawn or decrease at dusk, or both, (2) light intensity during a day or night, or both, and (3) the photo fraction, i.e., the ratio of light to dark (or high intensity to low intensity) in any 24 hour cycle. Variations on the basic pattern imposed by the light cycle (and the organism's genetic constitution) may be produced by humidity, temperature, feeding conditions, age, sex, number and sex of other animals present, and occasionally other aspects of the biological and physical environment.

2. *In a constant environment*, both the phase and period of circadian rhythms remain amazingly constant. For example, the period of running activity of the flying squirrel in continuous darkness may be as accurate as ± 2 minutes (DeCoursey, 1960). Period and phase of a circadian rhythm may even persist throughout the drastic reorganization that occurs in metamorphosis or throughout generations continuously kept under constant conditions. The phase of a free-running rhythm can be easily shifted by changing the environmental conditions, but the range of periodicity of a free-running rhythm can virtually never be extended beyond 24 ± 2 hours. Within these limits the period of free-running rhythms is not only a function of genetic factors, physiological state, and prior experience but also of characteristics of the constant environment. Here again, light is the most important variable. For example,

continuous light tends to cause a decrease in the period of the rhythm of diurnal animals and an increase in the period of nocturnal animals, a relationship known as "Aschoff's rule." The intensity of the constant light conditions may also affect the periodicity of the rhythm. Temperature, however, has little or no effect on the period of free-running rhythms.

Circadian rhythms are found in unicellular organisms. They also are characteristic of individual cells, tissues, and organs of higher organisms. The fact that the rhythms within an organism are normally either synchronous or in locked-phase relations with one another suggests that, in the course of evolution, specialized mechanisms have evolved for control, coordination, and perhaps origin of circadian rhythms in the body. Since such a mechanism would have both to receive sensory information and be able to influence numerous bodily functions, it seems reasonable to search for a neuroendocrine clock or clock synchronizer and controller.

In spite of the apparent affinity of psychologists for measuring general activity in vertebrates and the growing interest of zoologists in circadian rhythms, there has been very little systematic attempt to search for such central-clock mechanisms. In a brilliant series of experiments, Harker (1960) seems to have discovered just such a mechanism in the cockroach. It "not only participates in the production of the behavioral rhythm, that of running activity, but can act itself as an autonomous clock system." She removed neurosecretory cells from the subesophageal ganglion of one cockroach and implanted them in another cockroach that had previously been decapitated. The headless cockroach's activity cycle then showed the phasing set by the donor's previous experience.

In vertebrates, the hypothalamus is a likely candidate for the site of the central-clock regulation. This is supported by the effects of discrete hypothalamic lesions and by known hypothalamic involvement in virtually every bodily function that shows circadian rhythms. Transection of the anterior portion of the hypothalamus produces loss of the sleep-waking cycle and permanent sleeplessness resulting in eventual death (Nauta, 1946). Transection or destruction of its posterior region results in loss of the sleep-waking cycle and permanent somnolence (Ranson, 1939; Nauta, 1946).

The anterior mechanism seems to work by inhibiting the posterior one since destruction of both results in somnolence (Nauta, 1946). The posterior hypothalamus probably exerts its effect on behavior through the ascending reticular activating system with which it is intimately associated (Lindsley, 1960). An animal's place on the sleep-waking cycle is determined by the level of reticular formation activity that in turn is a function of cortical influences, sensory input via collaterals from the classical sensory pathways, and, as here conceived, posterior hypothalamic influences.

The effect of hypothalamic lesions on the sleep-waking cycle has been interpreted in terms of hypothalamic sleep and waking centers. Perhaps these mechanisms have a more basic function. They might be a specialized central mechanism for the control and coordination of circadian rhythms. Aside from their effect on the sleep-waking cycle through the reticular system, they may affect other rhythms through autonomic and endocrine mechanisms. The sleep center has been associated with the hypothalamic parasympathetic center, and the waking center has been associated with the hypothalamic sympathetic center

(Nauta, 1946). Furthermore, the hypothalamous directly controls the anterior pituitary by neurohumors carried by the hypophysial portal system (Harris, 1955). The anterior pituitary hormones in turn control directly, or by their influence on other glands, many functions showing circadian rhythms (Hague, 1964; Cold Spring Harbor Sympos., 1960).

Whereas the hypothalamus may be the site of the mechanisms for endogenous rhythms and for the coordination of environmentally phased rhythms, it is unlikely itself to contain any environmental phasing mechanism. There is some evidence that the superior colliculus may serve a role in the phasing for circadian rhythms by light. Destruction of this structure in rats seems to produce abnormal activity rhythms and to free the estrous rhythms from light phasing (Richter, 1964).

With so much now known about the behavioral mechanisms of circadian rhythms, the time seems ripe for systematic investigations of their physiological mechanisms in vertebrates, perhaps along the lines of the present speculations about the hypothalamus and superior colliculus.

Procedures for Measuring Activity

Apparatus for measuring the level of general activity may be roughly divided into two classes: running wheels and devices in which the cage remains relatively stationary.

The running wheel or revolving drum has been the most common method of measuring general activity in small mammals. It consists of a drum mounted on a horizontal axle. The animal is free to run on the inner surface of the drum, causing it to rotate; the number of rotations is the usual measure of activity used.

In long-term activity studies, a very small cage (to minimize the activity occurring in it) containing food and water is usually connected to the wheel. In order to minimize measurement of activity other than running in the wheel (e.g., jumping into the wheel, running, and then coasting) a friction brake may be incorporated. The principal sources of variance between running wheels are the moment of inertia and the torque produced by friction. The moment of inertia will not vary significantly if the cages are built of the same materials and dimensions. A slight difference in the torque produced by friction, however, can yield running measure differing by 100 percent for a given rat. A simple method for calibrating the torque of running wheels is given by Lacey (1944). Skinner (1933) has suggested that a moment of inertia equal to about twice the rat's weight be utilized. He has also advocated that the radius of the wheel be at least twice the length of a running rat in order to approximate running on a level surface.

The most common "stationary" cage apparatus for measuring activity are stabilimeters, jiggle cages, and photocell devices. A stabilimeter consists of a cage placed on some sensing device that detects slight movement of the cage produced by the animal's activity. Tambours were once a common sensing device, but measures derived from microswitches or pressure transducers are more reliable and quantitative. Jiggle cages are similar devices in which a cage is suspended from a spring whose displacement is the basic measure of activity. In the third common type of apparatus, cages are transected by infrared light beams falling on photocells. Interceptions of the light beams provide the activity data.

Details of the construction of stabilimeters have been given by Campbell (1954); Eayrs (1954); Bousfield and Mote (1943); Strong (1957); Issac and Ruch (1956); and many others (see reviews by Munn, 1950; Reed, 1947; Riley and Spinks, 1958). Jiggle cages have been described by Kopf and Nielsen (1959); Chappel *et al.* (1957); and others (see reviews just cited). Since Siegel's (1946) first use of a photocell device to measure activity, this method has been frequently employed for both rats and monkeys. There are a variety of electronic activity devices that are sensitive to very small movements, such as respiratory or oral motions, as well as to grosser movements (e.g., Wood and Stern, 1958; Peacock and Williams, 1962; Mitchell, 1959).

Activity measures derived from running wheels differ from measures derived from stationary cage devices in a number of ways. First, running wheels are sensitive almost exclusively to locomotor activity. By contrast, stabilimeters, jiggle cages and photocell devices may be made sensitive to a variety of nonlocomotor behaviors such as grooming, climbing, and scratching.

Second, an important difference between these two types of measures is that running wheels provide much more visual, auditory, vestibular, tactile, and kinesthetic feedback.

Third, rats in a running wheel may take up to five weeks to attain a stable rate (Anderson, 1938; Finger, Reid, and Weasner, 1957), whereas habituation to a stabilimeter is usually a matter of a few hours or, at most, a few days. The slower rate of habituation in the running wheel might be a function of the greater sensory feedback provided, but there is no direct evidence on this question. Because of this rather slow and variable attainment of a stable base line in a running wheel, failure to extend the pretreatment period until each S has reached a stable base line may lead to a confounding of activity and rate of habituation to the wheel. Thus, running wheels may not be a good way of studying the effect of brain lesion on basal locomotor activity rate. For example, following a brain lesion it might be difficult to distinguish a transient increase in activity, as after caudate nucleus lesions in the rat (Whittier and Orr, 1962) from an increased rate of habituation to a novel situation as after hippocampal lesions in the rat (Teitelbaum and Milner, 1963).

A fourth difference between running wheels and stationary cage devices is that running in a wheel will reinforce other responses such as bar pressing. Rats will bar-press to obtain access to a wheel (Kagan and Berkun, 1954). This phenomenon offers another possible explanation of the much slower habituation to running wheels: running is probably "self-reinforcing."

A difficulty with measurement of wheel running while animals are fed on a restricted feeding schedule has been emphasized by a number of experimenters in recent years. Feeding animals once a day either when they have continuous access to a wheel or immediately upon removal from the wheel differentially reinforces their activity in the immediately preceding period (Finger, Reid, and Weasner, 1957, 1960; Sheffield and Campbell, 1954). A dramatic illustration of this is an experiment in which Finger, Reid, and Weasner (1960) measured activity in a wheel for one hour daily after three hours of food deprivation. One group was then immediately fed in its home cage, whereas the other group's return was delayed for 60 minutes. Only the former group showed a steady and marked increase in activity during the experimental hour. When both groups were deprived for 75 hours, the former (no delay) group was much more active than the latter (delay) group. Thus, the effect of the reinforcement contingencies provided by the previous feeding schedule persisted.

Not surprisingly, in view of these apparatus differences, various treatments have been shown to affect differentially level of activity in running wheels and in stationary cage devices. As mentioned earlier, food deprivation has a much greater effect on wheel running than on activity in a stationary cage (Finger, 1958; Weasner, Finger, and Reid, 1960; Treichler and Hall, 1962). This is at least partially due to the greater sensory stimulation provided in running wheels. Estrus cycle (Eayrs, 1954; Finger, 1961), castration (Hoskins, 1925; Hunt and Schlosberg, 1939), caffeine, metrazol, and picrotoxin (Tainter, 1943), also differentially affect activity in a running wheel and activity in a stabilimeter.

In a recent, very helpful paper Douglas and Isaacson (1964) demonstrated an interesting interaction between type of activity device and method of lesion production. After hippocampal lesions, rats were placed in a photocell activity cage for an hour and a week later in a wheel for an hour. Electrolytic lesions but not aspiration lesions (which also damaged the overlying cortex) produced rats more active than controls in the running wheel. In the photocell device both groups of hippocampal rats were more active than controls, but the aspiration group showed a slower decline of activity within the test session.

The difference between various activity measures may be qualitative as well as quantitative. For example, in female rats, estrous activity cycles as measured in a running wheel not only have amplitude twice as large (relative to males) as those measured in a photocell device but also actually have slightly different periods (Finger, 1961).

The output of activity measuring devices can be most easily recorded on counters or cumulative recorders. Counters, brought into operation for a set period of time by a stepping switch operated by a clock mechanism, can record such parameters as total amount of activity, total time spent in activity, distribution of activity in time, and proportion of time in which activity occurred. These parameters plus qualitative aspects of activity, rate of change of activity, and the pattern of activity within any period of time may be read directly off a single cumulative recorder. The distribution of periods of activity, cycles, or other patterns will also be easily discernible. Furthermore, it may be possible to correlate the specific responses of the animal with the pattern produced on the cumulative record. Issac and Ruch (1956), for example, show how pacing, leaping, and changes in sitting position are differentiable from a cumulative record whose input is from an electric-eye device.

In the study of activity rhythms, it is often necessary to use statistical techniques for detecting periodicities that may be obscured by random fluctuations or by other simultaneous rhythms. Recent developments in statistical communication theory have provided tools for detecting periodic phenomena (Mercer, 1960). It should be noted, furthermore, that at least one older technique, that of running or sliding means, has the property of actually introducing cycles into a random series (Mercer, 1960; Cole, 1957).

General activity is a potpourri of behaviors (Bindra, 1961). Thus, the different components of activity may be differentially affected by experimental treatments. For example, under food deprivation, rats seem to sleep less but walk around and "posture" more (Bolles, 1963). Even in a running wheel, food deprivation changes the pattern of activity rather than merely increases the amount of it. Premack and Schaeffer (1962) measured the frequency distribution of (1) response duration (defined as a single wheel revolution), (2) burst duration (defined as "collections of one or more responses separated by an interval of at least 25 seconds"), and (3) interburst interval. They found that the increased activity under food deprivation could be attributed to an increase of burst duration. By contrast, the increased activity following activity deprivation could be attributed primarily to a shortening of the interburst interval.

Basal Activity and Reactivity to Stimulus Change

There are a number of apparent contradictions among different activity studies that do not simply depend on the type of apparatus used. Rather, they seem to result from differences in the degree of immediately prior exposure to the testing situation. Thus, it is important to distinguish between activity measures obtained under constant and familiar environmental conditions and those obtained soon after or during some environmental change. The former measure may be termed one of *basal locomotor activity* and the latter one of *locomotor reactivity.* It is clear that the animal must be habituated to the activity apparatus before one can be sure of measuring basal activity as opposed to reactivity. By contrast, measures of reactivity are measures of movement after a stimulus change, or during a period (minutes to hours) after introduction into the activity apparatus.

Failure to recognize this distinction has resulted in some discrepancies in the literature. For example, as discussed previously, the effect of food deprivation on basal locomotor activity (measured in a constant environment) is small or nonexistent as compared with its effect on reactivity. Some additional examples may be taken from studies of the effect of brain lesions. Whereas anterior cortical lesions in rats increased activity in a situation to which the animals were habituated (Zubeck and DeLorenzo, 1952), they did not change the amount of activity recorded in a novel environment (Glickman, Sroges, and Hunt, 1964). The opposite relation seems to hold for hippocampal lesions in rats. In a long-term, constant environment study using a stabilimeter, hippocampal lesions did not change activity (Kim, 1960). By contrast, animals with hippocampal lesions were more active during short periods in a photocell device (Teitelbaum and Milner, 1963; Douglas and Isaacson, 1964), a maze (Teitelbaum and Milner, 1963), an open-field (Roberts, Dember, and Brodwick, 1962), and a running wheel (Douglas and Isaacson, 1964).

It is possible, nevertheless, that the procedural differences just emphasized may not have been the sole or even principal basis of these apparent discrepancies. All these experiments were conducted by different investigators and conceivably involved differences in site, size, or method of production of the brain lesions. Yet, it seems worth testing the suggestion that these discrepancies are in fact explicable by the basal activity-reactivity distinction.

In the next two experiments, both base-line activity and reactivity were studied with the same subjects in the same apparatus. In an ingenious experiment, Meyer (1965) habituated kittens with either septal or amygdaloid lesions to an open-field. He then made a small change in the floor of the apparatus. Although septal lesions produced a decrease in basal activity, amygdaloid lesions produced an increase. On the other hand, septal lesions but not amygdaloid lesions increased reactivity to the novel stimulus.

Similarly, the activity changes after frontal lesions in monkeys were studied in order to determine whether they were ones of basal activity, reactivity, or both (Gross, 1963b). When placed in the dark, frontal monkeys were initially more active than controls, but this difference disappeared by the end of an hour. Only then were visual, auditory, or tactile stimuli presented. Light and familiar sounds increased the activity of the frontals much more than that of controls, whereas novel sounds and tactile stimulation depressed their activity much more than that of controls. Thus, frontal lesions affect locomotor reactivity and not basal activity level.

Two aspects of reactivity are of some interest: the absolute amount of locomotion in a novel situation and its rate of habituation. Some treatments may affect both parameters. Monkeys with frontal lesions, when placed in a novel environment, show both initially increased activity and a slower decline of activity (French and Harlow, 1955). Other treatments may affect only one of these parameters. For example, ventral brain-stem lesions in rats produced increased activity in an open field but left unaffected the rate of habituation in this situation (Glickman, Sroges, and Hunt, 1964). Hippocampal lesions, on the other hand, have been reported to have the opposite effect (Roberts, Dember, and Brodwick, 1962). These experiments suggested that brain-stem mechanisms are involved in the initiation of arousal, whereas limbic structures are concerned with its maintenance.

There is another intriguing way in which previous experience can affect activity measures. Rats made hyperactive with amphetamine and placed in an activity apparatus showed greater activity than controls when they were returned to the apparatus a week later, no longer drugged. That is, centrally induced arousal resulted in conditioned arousal when the animals were returned to the original situation (Ross and Schnitzer, 1963; see also Herrnstein, 1962). Similar conditioning to the environment in which a drug exerts its effects presumably underlies the placebo effect in man.

Conclusion

Although general activity is a heterogeneous collection of responses, the specific causes of which are unknown, the measurement of general activity is likely to remain useful for the student of animal behavior. Once a central tool in the study of motivation, activity measures are today playing an increasing role in the analysis of drugs and brain lesions and an increasing role as indicators of biological clocks. The simplicity of activity measures is only apparent. Type of measuring device, previous and concurrent experience, and environmental stimuli are all crucial and easily neglected sources of variance in activity studies. These variables also determine to what extent the amount of activity reflects the basal locomotor activity level or the degree of locomotor reactivity to a novel or changing environment.

REFERENCES

AMSEL, A., & WORK, M. S. 1961. The role of learned factors in "spontaneous" activity. *J. comp. physiol. Psychol.*, 54, 527–532.

ANDERSON, E. E. 1938. The interrelationship of drives in the male albino rat. II. Intercorrelations between 47 measures of drives and of learning. *Comp. Psychol. Monogr.*, 14, No. 6.

BABA, M. 1959. An experimental study of the effect of starvation on the activity in the white rat. *Psychol. Abstr.*, 33, 744.

BARON, A., ANTONITIS, J. J., & BEALE, R. H. 1961. Effects of activity deprivation on bar pressing. *J. comp. physiol. Psychol.*, 54, 291–293.

BAUMEISTER, A., HAWKINS, W. F., & CROMWELL, R. T. 1964. Need states and activity level. *Psychol. Bull.*, 61, 438–453.

BERGER, F. M., HENDLEY, C. D., & LYNES, T. E. 1956. Pharmacology of the psychotherapeutic drug benactyzine (β-diethylaminoethyl benzilate hydrochloride). *Proc. Soc. exp. biol. Med.*, 92, 563–566.

BINDRA, D. 1961. Components of general activity and the analysis of behavior. *Psychol. Rev.*, 68, 205–215.

BLUM, J. S., CHOW, K. L., & BLUM, R. A. 1951. Delayed response performance of monkeys with frontal removals after excitant and sedative drugs. *J. Neurophysiol.*, 14, 197–202.

BOLLES, R. C. 1963. Effect of food deprivation upon the rat's behavior in its home cage. *J. comp. physiol. Psychol.*, 56, No. 2, 456–460.

BOUSFIELD, W. A., & MOTE, F. A., Jr. 1943. The construction of a tilting activity cage. *J. exp. Psychol.*, 32, 450–451.

BROWN, B. B., BRAUN, D. L., & FELDMAN, R. G. 1956. The pharmacologic activity—a—(4 piperidyl)—benzhydrol hydrochloride (azacyclonol hydrochloride) an ataractive agent. *J. Pharmacol. exp. Ther.*, 118, 153–161.

BÜNNING, E. 1964. *The physiological clock*. Berlin: Springer-Verlag.

CAMPBELL, B. A. 1954. Design and reliability of a new activity recording device. *J. comp. physiol. Psychol.*, 47, 90–92.

CAMPBELL, B. A., & SHEFFIELD, F. D. 1953. Relation of random activity to food deprivation. *J. comp. physiol. Psychol.*, 46, 320–322.

CANNON, W. B. 1932. *The wisdom of the body*. New York: Norton.

CANNON, W. B., McIVER, M. A., & BLISS, S. W. 1924. A sympathetic and adrenal mechanism for mobilizing sugar in hypoglycemia. *Amer. J. Physiol.*, 69, 46–66.

CHAPPEL, C. I., GRANT, G. A., ARCHIBALD, S., & PAQUETTE, R. 1957. An apparatus for testing the effect of drugs on the spontaneous activity of the rat. *J. Amer. Pharm. Assoc.*, 46, 497–500.

COLD SPRING HARBOR Symposia on Quantitative Biology. 1960. Vol. XXV: *Biological clocks*.

COLE, L. C. 1957. Biological clock in the unicorn. *Science*, 125, 874–876.

DASHIELL, J. F. 1925. A quantitative demonstration of animal drive. *J. comp. Psychol.*, 5, 205–208.

DeCOURSEY, P. 1960. Phase control of activity in a rodent. *Cold Spring Harbor Sympos. Quant. Biol.*, 25, 49–54.

DELL, P. 1958. Some basic mechanisms of the translation of bodily needs into behaviour. *Neurological basis of behaviour*. Boston: Little, Brown.

DeVITO, J. L., & SMITH, O. A. 1959. Effects of temperature and food deprivation on the random activity of *Macaca mulatta*. *J. comp. physiol. Psychol.*, 52, 29–32.

DOUGLAS, R. J., & ISAACSON, R. L. 1964. Hippocampal lesions and activity. *Psychon. Sci.*, 1, 187–188.

EAYRS, J. T. 1954. Spontaneous activity in the rat. *Brit. J. Anim. Behav.*, 2, 25–30.

FEHRER, E. 1956. The effects of hunger and familiarity of locale on exploration. *J. comp. physiol. Psychol.*, 49, 549–552.

FINGER, F. W. 1958. Seventy-two hours of food deprivation in wheels vs. photo-cage. Unpublished manuscript cited in Baumeister, A., *et al.* 1964.

FINGER, F. W. 1961. Estrous activity as a function of measuring device. *J. comp. physiol. Psychol.*, 54, 524–526.

FINGER, F. W., REID, L. S., & WEASNER, M. H. 1957. The effect of reinforcement upon activity during cyclic food deprivation. *J. comp. physiol. Psychol.*, 50, 495–498.

FINGER, F. W., REID, L. S., & WEASNER, M. H. 1960. Activity changes as a function of reinforcement under low drive. *J. comp. physiol. Psychol.*, 53, 385–387.

FRENCH, G. M., & HARLOW, H. F. 1955. Locomotor reaction decrement in normal and brain-damaged monkeys. *J. comp. physiol. Psychol.*, 48, 496–501.

GLICKMAN, S. E., SROGES, R. W., & HUNT, J. 1964. Brain lesions and locomotor exploration in the albino rat. *J. comp. physiol. Psychol.*, 58, 93–100.

GROSS, C. G. 1963a. Effect of deprivation on delayed response and delayed alteration performance by normal and brain operated monkeys. *J. comp. physiol. Psychol.*, 56, 48–51.

GROSS, C. G. 1963b. Locomotor activity under various stimulus conditions following partial lateral frontal cortical lesions in monkeys. *J. comp. physiol. Psychol.*, 56, 52–55.

HAGUE, E. B. (Ed.). 1964. Photo neuro-endocrine effects in circadian systems with particular reference to the eye. *Ann. N.Y. Acad. Sci.*, 117, No. 1, 1–645.

HALL, J. F. 1956. The relationship between external stimulation, food deprivation, and activity. *J. comp. physiol. Psychol.*, 49, 339–341.

HALL, J. F., & HANFORD, P. V. 1954. Activity as a function of a restricted feeding schedule. *J. comp. physiol. Psychol.*, 47, 362–363.

HALL, J. F., SMITH, K., SCHNITZER, S. B., & HANFORD, P. V. 1953. Elevation of activity level in the rat following transition from ad libitum to restricted feeding. *J. comp. physiol. Psychol.*, 46, 429–433.

HARKER, J. E. 1960. Endocrine and nervous factors in insect circadian rhythms. *Cold Spring Harbor Sympos. Quant. Biol.*, 25, 279–287.

HARKER, J. E. 1964. *The physiology of diurnal rhythms.* Cambridge: Cambridge University Press.

HARRIS, G. W. 1955. *Neural control of the pituitary gland.* London: Edward Arnold.

HERRNSTEIN, R. J. 1962. Placebo effect in the rat. *Science*, 138, 677–678.

HILL, W. F. 1956. Activity as an autonomous drive. *J. comp. physiol. Psychol.*, 49, 15–19.

HILL, W. F. 1958. The effect of varying periods of confinement on activity in tilt cages. *J. comp. physiol. Psychol.*, 51, 570–574.

HOSKINS, R. G. 1925. Studies on vigor. II. The effect of castration on voluntary activity. *Amer. J. Physiol.*, 72, 324–330.

HUNT, J. McV., & SCHLOSBERG, H. 1939. The influence of illumination upon general activity in normal, blinded and castrated male white rats. *J. comp. Psychol.*, 28, 285–298.

ISAACSON, R. L., DOUGLAS, R. J., & MOORE, R. Y. 1961. The effect of radical hippocampal ablation on acquisition of avoidance responses. *J. comp. physiol. Psychol.*, 54, 625–628.

ISSAC, W., & RUCH, T. C. 1956. Evaluation of four activity techniques for monkeys. *Science*, 123, 1170–1171.

KAGAN, J., & BERKUN, M. 1954. The reward value of running activity. *J. comp. physiol. Psychol.*, 47, 108.

KIM, C. 1960. Nest building, general activity and salt preference of rats following hippocampal ablation. *J. comp. physiol. Psychol.*, 53, 11–16.

KIMBLE, D. P. 1963. The effects of bilateral hippocampal lesions in rats. *J. comp. physiol. Psychol.*, 56, 273–283.

KIMURA, D. 1958. Effects of selective hippocampal damage on avoidance behavior of the rat. *Canad. J. Psychol.*, 12, 213–217.

KOPF, R., & NIELSEN, I. M. 1959. Pharmakologische Eigenschaften einiger Phenylindolderivate. *Arch. Int. Pharmacodyn.*, 119, 119–132.

LACEY, O. L. 1944. A revised procedure for calibration of the activity wheel. *Amer. J. Psychol.*, 57, 412–420.

LAWICKA, L., & KONORSKI, J. 1959. Physiological mechanisms of delayed reaction: III. The effects of prefrontal ablations on delayed reaction in dogs. *Acta. Biol. exper.*, 19, 221–232.

LINDSLEY, D. B. 1960. Attention, consciousness, sleep and wakefulness. *Handbook of physiology*, Sec. 1, Vol. 3. Washington, D.C.: American Physiological Society.

MERCER, D. M. A. 1960. Analytical methods for the study of periodic phenomena obscured by random fluctuations. *Cold Spring Harbor Sympos. Quant. Biol.*, 25, 73–85.

MEYER, D. R. 1965. Personal communication.

MILES, R. C., & BLOMQUIST, A. J. 1960. Frontal lesions and behavioral deficits in monkey. *J. Neurophysiol.*, 23, 471–484.

MITCHELL, W. G. 1959. Differentiation of activity of three mouse strains with magnetic pick-up apparatus. *Science*, 130, 455.

MUNN, N. L. 1950. *Handbook of psychological research on the rat*. Boston: Houghton Mifflin.

NAUTA, W. J. H. 1946. Hypothalamic regulation of sleep in rats; an experimental study. *J. Neurophysiol.*, 9, 285–316.

PEACOCK, L. J., & WILLIAMS, M. 1962. An ultrasonic device for recording activity. *Amer. J. Psychol.*, 75, 648–652.

PITTENDRIGH, C. S. 1961. On temporal organization in living systems. *Harv. Lec.*, 56, 93–126.

PITTENDRIGH, C. S., & BRUCE, V. G. 1957. An oscillator model for biological clocks. In Rudnick, D. (Ed.), *Rhythmic and synthetic processes in growth*. Princeton: Princeton University Press.

PREMACK, D., & SCHAEFFER, R. W. 1962. Distributional properties of operant-level locomotion in the rat. *J. exp. anal. Behav.*, 5, 89–95.

PRIBRAM, K. H. 1950. Some physical and pharmacological factors affecting delayed response performance of baboons following frontal lobotomy. *J. Neurophysiol.*, 13, 373–382.

PRIBRAM, K. H., & WEISKRANTZ, L. 1957. A comparison of the effects of medial and lateral cerebral resections on conditioned avoidance behavior of monkeys. *J. comp. physiol. Psychol.*, 50, 74–80.

RANSON, S. W. 1939. Somnolence caused by hypothalamic lesions in the monkey. *Arch. Neurol. Psychiat.* (Chicago), 41, 1–23.

REED, J. D. 1947. Spontaneous activity of animals. *Psychol. Bull.*, 44, 393–412.

RICHTER, C. P. 1922. A behavioristic study of the activity of the rat. *Comp. Psychol. Monogr.*, 1, 1–55.

RICHTER, C. P. 1927. Animal behavior and internal drives. *Quart. Rev. Biol.*, 2, 307–343.

RICHTER, C. P. 1964. Behavioral and physiological changes produced by removal of the superior colliculi of the brain. *Science*, 146, 429–430.

RILEY, H., & SPINKS, A. 1958. Biological assessment of tranquillizers. Part I. *J. Pharmacol.*, 10, 657–671.

ROBERTS, W. W., DEMBER, W. N., & BRODWICK, M. 1962. Alternation and exploration in rats with hippocampal lesions. *J. comp. physiol. Psychol.*, 55, 695–700.

ROSS, S., & SCHNITZER, S. B. 1963. Further support for a placebo effect in the rat. *Psychol. Rep.*, 13, 461–462.

SHEFFIELD, F. D., & CAMPBELL, B. A. 1954. The role of experience in the "spontaneous" activity of hungry rats. *J. comp. physiol. Psychol.*, 47, 97–100.

SHIRLEY, M. 1928. Studies in activity II. Activity rhythms; age and activity after rest. *J. comp. Psychol.*, **8**, 159–186.

SHIRLEY, M. 1929. Spontaneous activity. *Psychol. Bull.*, **26**, 341–365.

SIEGEL, P. S. 1946. Activity level as a function of physically enforced inaction. *J. Psychol.*, **21**, 285–291.

SIEGEL, P. S., & STEINBERG, M. 1949. Activity level as a function of hunger. *J. comp. physiol. Psychol.*, **42**, 413–416.

SKINNER, B. F. 1933. The measurement of general activity. *J. gen. Psychol.*, **9**, 3–23.

SLONAKER, J. R. 1907. The normal activity of the white rat at different ages. *J. comp. Neurol. Psychol.*, **17**, 342–359.

SMITH, C. B., & DEWS, P. B. 1962. Antagonism of locomotor suppressant effects of reserpine in mice. *Psychopharmacol.*, **3**, 55–59.

STEWART, J. W., & ADES, H. W. 1951. The time factor in reintegration of a learned habit lost after temporal lobe lesions in the monkey Macaca mulatta. *J. comp. physiol. Psychol.*, **44**, 479–480.

STRONG, P. N., Jr. 1957. Activity in the white rat as a function of apparatus and hunger. *J. comp. physiol. Psychol.*, **50**, 596–600.

TAINTER, M. L. 1943. Effects of certain analeptic drugs on spontaneous running activity of the white rat. *J. comp. Psychol.*, **36**, 143–155.

TEGHTSOONIAN, R., & CAMPBELL, B. A. 1960. Random activity of the rat during food deprivation as a function of environmental conditions. *J. comp. physiol. Psychol.*, **53**, 242–244.

TEITELBAUM, H., & MILNER, P. 1963. Activity changes following partial hippo-campal lesions in rats. *J. comp. physiol. Psychol.*, **56**, 284–289.

TREICHLER, F. R., & HALL, J. F. 1962. The relationship between deprivation weight loss and several measures of activity. *J. comp, physiol. Psychol.*, **55**, 346–349.

WEASNER, M. H., FINGER, F. W., & REID, L. S. 1960. Activity changes under food deprivation as a function of recording device. *J. comp. physiol. Psychol.*, **53**, 470–474.

WEISKRANTZ, L., MIHAILOVIĆ, L., & GROSS, C. G. 1962. Effects of stimulation of frontal cortex and hippocampus on behavior in the monkey. *Brain*, **85**, 489–504.

WEISKRANTZ, L., & WILSON, W. A. 1958. The effect of ventral rhinencephalic lesions on avoidance thresholds in monkeys. *J. comp. physiol. Psychol.*, **51**, 167–171.

WELKER, W. I. 1959. Escape, exploratory and food seeking responses of rats in a novel situation. *J. comp. physiol. Psychol.*, **52**, 106–111.

WHITTIER, J. R., & ORR, A. 1962. Hyperkinesia and other physiological effects of caudate deficit in the adult albino rat. *Neurology*, **12**, 529–539.

WOOD, T., & STERN, J. A. 1958. A simple stabilimeter. *J. exp. anal. Behav.*, **1**, 201–205.

ZUBECK, J. P., & DE LORENZO, A. J. 1952. The cerebral cortex and locomotor activity in rats. *Canad. J. Psychol.*, **6**, 55–70.

CHAPTER 6

Exploratory Behavior

M. S. HALLIDAY

D ESPITE the great importance of the types of reinforcer discussed in the preceding chapters, there is still a large and interesting range of behavior that does not seem to be easily explicable in terms of these reinforcers. This area includes built-in and "imprinted" behavior, spontaneous activity (see Chapter 5), and a miscellaneous category often called exploratory behavior. The main criterion for putting behavior in this latter category is that it appears primarily to give the animal information about its environment; in some cases this information is directly related to obtaining a conventional reinforcer, and the behavior is then usually called an "observing response" (Wyckoff, 1952); in other cases the information does not seem to be related to such a reinforcer, and behavior of this sort is usually put in the exploratory category. Of course it can never be shown that exploratory behavior is not an observing response for some unspecified reinforcer, but in many cases it looks as though another mechanism is at work. During the ascendency of drive-centered theories of behavior, exploration was either completely ignored or else was treated as a tiresome irrelevance; but, in the past fifteen years a great deal of work has been done in this area, and there is a general realization of the empirical and theoretical importance of this field. The greater part of the work has been done with rats and monkeys, and I shall therefore concentrate on these two species in the following discussion.

Exploratory behavior may be usefully, if somewhat arbitrarily, divided into inquisitive and inspective behavior. Berlyne, who first used these terms, defines *inquisitive exploration* as behavior that "brings the animal into contact with objects that are not already represented in the stimulus field"; *inspective exploration* "yields further stimulation from objects already acting on receptors" (1960, p. 80). Essentially, inspective exploration is concerned with objects that the animal can already see, and inquisitive exploration with those that it cannot. The distinction has a certain analogy with the ethological distinction between appetitive and consummatory behavior.

In considering the evidence from experiments on rats, it is appropriate to begin with the subject of spontaneous alternation (for a full review see Dember and Fowler, 1958). In a typical experiment a rat is placed in the stem of a T maze, and, in moving around the maze, the rat enters one of the arms (the choice of arm may be forced on this trial by blocking off one arm in order to compensate for position preferences); it is usually retained in the arm it has chosen for a brief period.

It is then removed, and shortly afterwards it is placed at the start again; on this trial the rats show a strong tendency to choose the arm that was not visited on the last occasion (about 70 to 75 percent).[1] The animals are frequently run hungry or thirsty and find food or water at the end of either arm, but the results are basically similar whether the rat is satiated or not and whether or not it finds food or water. It was originally assumed that this alternation was due to a response tendency, Hull's reactive inhibition being the favorite candidate; a number of experiments have shown, however, that this cannot be the case. Montgomery (1952b) and Glanzer (1953a) have both shown that, when response alternation is set against stimulus alternation, the animal varies the stimuli it visits although it repeats the responses. Both researchers used cross mazes (see Fig. 6-1); on the first trial the animal

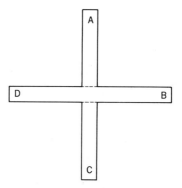

Fig. 6-1. Plan of the maze used to compare response and stimulus alternation.

would be started from arm A. Arm C being blocked, the animal would then choose either arm B or arm D. On the next trial arm A would be blocked, and arm C would be open, and the animal would be started in arm C. If on this second trial the rat made a different response (left or right turn) from the one it made on the first trial (response alternation), it would have to reenter the arm it visited on the first trial; if, on the other hand, it went to the arm it did not visit on the first trial (stimulus alternation), it would have to repeat its response. In both experiments the major source of alternation was stimulus alternation rather than response alternation. Equally strong evidence against the importance of response alternation is provided by Estes and Schoeffler (1955). It has also been shown that preexposure to the stimuli in one of the arms of a T maze, without the rat's having chosen the arm, will lead the animal to choose the other arm on a subsequent trial (Glanzer, 1953a; Sutherland, 1957). An experiment by Walker et al. (1955) that appears to be in conflict with this result probably failed to give the animal an adequate opportunity to know on which side of the maze the different goal boxes were.

These basic findings on spontaneous alternation could be explained without appealing to reinforcement at all. It can reasonably be supposed that some stimuli have properties that elicit approach and in-

1 This tendency does not appear in all species (see e.g., Hayes and Warren, 1963).

spection when the stimuli are presented to an animal; exactly what these properties are I shall consider later, but for the moment I shall, for convenience, talk about the "novelty" of stimuli. When first presented, a stimulus elicits approach and investigation because of its novelty; as the animal inspects it, the novelty decreases, and so the animal inspects less and is more likely to be attracted to other stimuli that have not yet lost their novelty. Exploration of a particular stimulus should therefore decline within any exposure period; this I shall call an *intrasession* decline. If an animal investigates a stimulus and is then taken away from it, the novelty of the stimulus increases again, presumably due to the animal's forgetting it, so that on a second exposure the animal will investigate the stimulus more actively than it did at the end of the first exposure. For this reason an animal, when choosing between two stimuli, both of which it has seen before, may be expected to investigate the stimulus that it has seen least recently. In some cases this recovery of investigatory behavior with time is complete (i.e., the animal investigates a stimulus as much on a second exposure, after an interval away from it, as it did on the first), in other cases there is an *intersession* decline in exploratory activity.[2] Whether or not this intersession decline occurs is a function of the length and nature of the intersession interval, the nature of the stimulus and the methods of measuring exploration that are used. An approach of this sort (which is essentially that of Glanzer, 1953b) says nothing about reinforcement but can deal with the spontaneous alternation results cited above; it can also be successfully applied to the results on exploration of a simple maze. For example, Montgomery (1951) found that animals moved around a novel maze in an orderly manner but that the amount of locomotor activity decreased with time in the maze; he also showed that with time away from the maze there was a recovery in the amount of exploratory activity. These results can easily be accommodated by supposing that, as an animal moves around a maze, all the stimuli in the environment will lose their novelty, and so the rat will explore less and less, although, with time away from the maze, the stimuli recover some of their novelty. Most of the results on the exploration of simple environments can be dealt with in much the same way; the material up to 1960 is fully reviewed by Berlyne (1960). We can also account for the strong tendency of rats, during exploration of a Y maze, to enter that arm of the maze least recently visited when they reach the choice point (Montgomery, 1952a). With time away from a stimulus, the satiation decreases, so that faced with two stimuli, one of which was inspected recently and the other less recently, the animal will be likely to inspect the latter stimulus; this is usually also called alternation.

The tendency for rats to alternate while freely exploring a Y maze is clearly analagous to the spontaneous alternation results and is of some importance. The fact that they do so shows that they are not merely being active, because in this case a random sequence of turns would be predicted. As in the case of spontaneous alternation, it might be suggested that this is a response-controlled effect. This has been shown not to be so (Montgomery, 1952a) because there is no regularity in the pattern of physical turns made by the animal, either in the maze as a whole or at the choice point; autocorrelations for each animal,

---

2 For a discussion of these effects see Berlyne (1955).

carried up to nine displacements, showed no significant difference from chance.

Sutherland (1957) has demonstrated a case of spontaneous alternation that cannot be explained along the lines outlined above. He found that when the two arms of a T maze led to different goal boxes, invisible from the choice point, there was 65 percent alternation on the second of two trials, whereas, if both arms were extended to lead to a common goal box, there was only 49 percent alternation. The animals were run hungry and fed in either box, but this should make no difference according to the stimulus satiation hypothesis; the result shows that stimuli that only become visible after the choice, are of great importance in producing alternation (i.e., it is an inquisitive situation). Presumably the animals were alternating the places they approached rather than alternating the stimuli at the choice point, and this may possibly be true in other alternation situations.

Although the results cited above can mostly be explained without making reference to reinforcement, there are other findings with rats that cannot be so explained. The most convincing evidence comes from experiments in which it has been shown that rats will learn in order to have the chance to explore. Montgomery and his associates (Montgomery, 1954; Montgomery and Segall, 1955) have shown that an animal will learn a T maze or a discrimination problem in order to get two minutes' exploration in a Dashiell maze. Various controls made it very unlikely that the result could be attributed to a position habit or to a reduction of some "activity drive" by running around in the Dashiell maze. Nor can it be supposed that the animals were avoiding retention in the incorrect arm, because in the Montgomery and Segall experiment animals were removed almost at once after an incorrect choice. Berlyne has claimed, however, that "novelty" as such is not reinforcing. He performed an experiment in which animals showed no tendency to run to the side of a T maze in which a novel stimulus card was presented rather than to that on which the card was familiar; the animals clearly distinguished between these cards because they spent significantly more time sniffing at the novel rather than at the familiar cards when they reached the end of the maze (Berlyne and Slater, 1957); in view of the poor visual capacities of the rat, such purely visual stimuli would hardly be expected to be very attractive. There are a number of reasons for doubting the validity of Berlyne and Slater's result. They themselves found that if the novel arm was made "complex" by having three stimulus cards attached to the walls and an electric plug on the floor,[3] the animals preferred this side of the maze. It is hard to see that the conditions differed qualitatively in the two cases; in the "novelty" condition there was simply less of interest to explore in the goal box, and presumably the choice measure was not sensitive enough to detect a preference, although Berlyne and Slater report that in the latency scores there was a significant interaction between "novelty or familiarity x subjects"; the "complexity" case seems merely to offer more novel objects, which would presumably act as a more powerful reinforcer, and under this condition the choice measure was sensitive enough to detect a preference. This conclusion, that Berlyne and Slater failed to get a result because of test insensitivity, is supported by a result of Ryder and Watson's (personal communication).

[3] It is not clear from the paper whether these were changed from trial to trial, although, from certain comments in the discussion it appears that they were.

They repeated the experiment and confirmed the main finding; however, further analysis of the results revealed regularities in behavior that could only be accounted for by supposing that the relative novelty of the cards in the arms of the maze was influencing the animals' choice. In particular, they divided the animals into 2 groups on the basis of their behavior during the experiment: Group 1 (alternators) being those animals that, over the whole course of the experiment, alternated their choices more than 50 percent of the time; Group 2 (nonalternators) being those that alternated less than 50 percent of the time. In general, one would be inclined to say that the nonalternators (which showed a position preference rather than random behavior) were the less exploratory group. Ryder and Watson found that the nonalternators showed a significant tendency to alternate more on trials when they had just visited the novel side of the maze than on those when they had just visited the familiar side. The other group (the alternators) showed the reverse tendency, alternating more on trials when they had just visited the familiar side. A second finding was concerned with an animal's behavior on the first trial on the day after it had been once to the unchanging side of the maze and twice to the changing side; this was the first occasion on which the animal could be expected to show a preference for the changing side, and on this trial there was a significant tendency to choose the changing (novel) side of the maze. These results merely emphasize that Berlyne and Slater's choice measure was insufficiently sensitive. Chapman and Levy (1957) ran animals in an alley leading to a box that was invisible from the alley itself; after 10 daily runs the walls of the box were changed from plain peg board to stripes; on the day after the animals had first seen the change there was a considerable reduction in latency in running up the alley. Schneider and Gross (1964) have shown that in hamsters novelty is reinforcing; they allowed their animals to run up an alley to a box that either contained nothing (spaciousness), contained 4 stimulus objects that were rearranged from trial to trial (complex), or contained 4 stimulus objects, one of which was changed on each trial (novel). The animals were given 4 blocks of massed trials at varying intervals, and it was found that on the first block of trials both the complex and the novel group ran faster than the spacious group; on the second and subsequent blocks of trials the spacious and complex groups did not differ in running speed but were both significantly slower than the novel group, which kept up essentially the same speed throughout the four blocks of trials. It appears that the complex stimuli were reinforcing in the first session because they offered a large variety of novel stimulation but that as the animal became familiar with them they lost their reinforcing effect, while the constantly changing novel stimuli retained theirs. In a similar experiment, Stretch (1960) gave 2 groups of rats 2 trials a day in an alley leading to a box in which there was a stimulus card; for one group of animals this card was changed from day to day, for a second group it remained the same. The group with the novel card showed a striking reduction in latency of running over 10 daily periods, whereas the other group showed an overall increase in latency. Further evidence for this is supplied by an experiment by Myers and Miller (1954) who found that satiated rats will learn to press a bar to go from a white to a black box or vice versa; they attribute the result to the operation of an exploratory motivation. The evidence is thus very strong that the exploration of a stimulus or environment is positively reinforcing in the sense used in the first section of this chapter. It is well known that rats will learn to press a bar in a Skinner box to switch on a light, and it seems that this behavior is partly exploratory in nature (for a discussion see below); if so, it is a further example of reinforcement. Additional evidence is supplied by Nissen's (1930) early finding that rats will cross the electrified grill of a Columbia obstruction box to reach a Dashiell maze.

In the case of primates, there is relatively little direct evidence on the subject of inspective exploration, although it is obvious enough that monkeys are exploring much of the time. There is, however, excellent evidence for the reinforcing value of visual exploration in situations where an animal has to learn a problem for a visual reward (e.g., Butler, 1953). Similarly it has been shown that animals will learn in order to have the opportunity to manipulate latch puzzles (Harlow, Harlow, and Meyer, 1950).

The general conclusion may be drawn that theories that do not involve the idea of reinforcement (e.g., Glanzer's stimulus satiation theory) will deal with many of the results on exploration, particularly those dealing with inspective exploration, but that in order to explain another large range of results it is necessary to say that the exploration of novel stimuli is itself a positive reinforcer, in the sense used in Chapter 2. It is clearly not the locomotor activity itself that is the reinforcer (although under other circumstances activity can be a reinforcer, Premack, 1962); it is, rather, the stimuli or certain properties of the stimuli[4] that are reinforcers; the act of exploring merely serves to bring the animal in contact with these stimuli. This view also leads to difficulties because, although it deals with the cases of inquisitive exploration discussed previously, it does not explain spontaneous alternation, where the animal chooses the opposite arm to the one in which it was previously reinforced. Much time has been spent on the theoretical discussion of this problem, and it would be inappropriate to go into the matter in more detail here. As an approximation, however, I suggest that in an exploratory situation an animal uses all the information it has about the environment, immediate sensory information (the inspective case) and information stored as a result of previous experiences of the environment (the inquisitive case), to behave in such a way that it will come into contact with stimuli that are "novel" in a very general sense.

So far in this discussion I have not considered just what properties of stimuli elicit exploratory behavior. There has been considerable discussion on this point, and, I believe, some confusion. An animal does not in general examine a stimulus to which it has been exposed for a long time. It does examine one which is new to it. However, it should be noted that novelty can only be defined with reference to the animal's previous experience. This experience may be a relatively brief recent one or a long-term one. As an example of the latter case, Montgomery and Zimbardo (1957) found that animals that had been reared in an environment containing marbles, toys, and colored blocks explored a Y maze less than animals reared in normal cages or reared with sensory or behavioral deprivation. Possibly the Y maze was less novel to the animals with the wider range of experience. In most experiments the

4 What these properties are will be discussed later.

experience to which the novelty or otherwise of the situation is being compared is a relatively recent one. In this context experiments in which changes in the situation are introduced between two experiences are of special interest. For example, Williams and Kuchta (1957) ran two groups of rats in a Y maze for 10 minutes a day; the experimental group explored a maze with 3 black arms for 4 days and then, for a further 3 days, a maze with 2 black arms and 1 white arm. On the day after the change they explored the white arm significantly more than a control group, who explored only the second maze, did on their first exposure to it. In this case presumably more exploration was elicited in the experimental group by the white arm because they were matching their previous and present experiences of the maze and finding that they did not correspond. In an experiment by Dember (1956), rats were allowed to explore the stem of a T maze. They could not enter the arms but could see into them through glass doors. During this exposure period one arm was painted white and the other black. The rats were put into the maze again shortly afterwards (about 2 minutes later) with the glass doors removed; both arms were now either white or black. It was found that the animals chose to enter first the arm that had changed color. Once again the animal appears to be matching past and present experiences. Another interesting example of this is supplied by an experiment by Isaacson, Karoly, and Caldwell (1957), who allowed rats to explore a cross maze with one of the arms blocked by a door (i.e., it was effectively a T maze) for 10 minutes. One group of animals was then confined for 10 minutes in the blocked-off arm of the maze and another in a delay box; both groups were then given the opportunity to explore the maze again without the block, and both groups showed a marked and equal preference for the previously blocked-off arm. In this case the preference for the previously blocked-off arm, even among the animals that had been confined in it, suggests that they were concerned to match their previous and present experiences.

If it is necessary to suppose that matching takes place in order to explain the results discussed above, then it is natural to suggest that an animal explores a stimulus situation if it cannot match it on the basis of its past experience. Such an approach would be in accordance with present views on attention (see Chapter 10; also Berlyne, 1960). An animal would therefore explore a situation with which it was unfamiliar until its "internal representation" of the situation matched the external environment; intratrial declines in exploration would be due to increasing accuracy of matching. Intertrial declines in exploration would occur when there was no striking mismatch between the situation on the second exposure and what the animal remembered from the first exposure. The principal difference between a "complex" and a "novel" stimulus is therefore that the complex stimulus requires more exploration before an adequate match can be made; once this has happened the complex stimulus should offer no special attraction. This is, indeed, what appears to have happened in the experiment by Schneider and Gross reported previously. Berlyne has tried to separate out complexity and novelty, but it seems that the distinction is an arbitrary one, and he himself admits (1960, p. 111) that "the most complex environments will generally offer the greatest wealth of novel sights and smells." I have already suggested how "surprisingness" and "novelty" can be considered similar in that they both represent failure of matching: in the former case, present input does not match with the "internal representation"; in the latter case, there is as yet no basis for a match.[5] "Spaciousness" is also sometimes suggested as a separate dimension eliciting exploration. It may be that some species will actively seek out open spaces simply because they are open; and, if so, "spaciousness" would indeed be a reinforcer, although whether the behavior involved should be called exploratory is doubtful. In general, however, situations are usually called "spacious" when, as in a Dashiell maze, they offer a large amount of novel stimulation some of which may not be immediately present to the animal when it enters the environment; "spaciousness" seems to be "complexity" spread thin. It should not be assumed that, by categorizing situations in ways that seem useful or natural to us, we are exposing any underlying differences in behavioral mechanisms. It is extremely hard to specify just what it is about a stimulus that makes it capable of eliciting exploration, and certainly it would be impracticable to try to delimit exploratory behavior by listing goal objects; under appropriate conditions almost any object or any change in relationship between objects can elicit exploration.

Many conventional reinforcers can be influenced by deprivation procedures, and one might expect that deprivation of stimulation preceding an exploratory exposure would have this effect. Butler (1957) found that if his monkeys were confined in a small box with solid walls for varying periods of time before being given the opportunity to show visual exploration, the subsequent number of responses to open the door in the box increased as a function of time up to four hours, after which there was little further increase. This suggests a deprivation effect arising, perhaps, because the animal requires a certain rate of information input, and, if, over a period of time, the rate of input falls below this, the animal subsequently compensates by exploring more. In rats there have been a number of experiments on the long-term effects on exploratory behavior of rearing in various types of environments (e.g., Zimbardo and Montgomery, 1957; Woods, Ruckelshaus, and Bowling, 1960) but little evidence for short-term "deprivation" effects of the sort Butler has demonstrated in monkeys. Charlesworth and Thompson (1957) found no significant difference in exploration between rats that had been kept in normal living cages and animals that had been confined for three, six, or nine days in an empty box with opaque walls. Stretch (1960), on the other hand, confined two groups of rats for one hour before an exploration period in small cages that allowed normal visual stimulation but little movement, or large dark cages that allowed movement but no visual stimulation, and found that both groups explored an enclosed H maze more than controls that had had no preceding deprivation. The difference between this result and Charlesworth and Thompson's is hard to interpret, but there were a number of differences between the two situations. Woods (1962) found differences in the frequency of occurrence of sniffing and grooming behavior in a 30-inch-square field between groups of rats that had had 24 hours' previous experience of large and varied cages, normal laboratory cages, or restricted cages with opaque walls; once again the more restricted the previous environ-

[5] Except in terms of the animal's total previous experience. Presumably matching would be faster (exploration less) for animals that have experienced a wide variety of stimuli than for animals with more restricted experience.

ment the greater the amount of exploratory behavior, particularly during the latter part of the session. It appears, therefore, that "deprivation" effects can be found in rats but that they are relatively slight; certainly much more work is needed in this area before very firm conclusions can be reached. But, although food and water do show deprivation effects, other reinforcers, notably electric shock, usually do not; so exploration is not alone in this respect.

Methods of Studying Exploration

Because the greater part of the work on exploration has been concerned with rodents and primates, I shall deal mainly with these two orders in my discussion of methods. Many different techniques have been used here, but only a few have been used often and supply the sort of data suitable for discussion; I have therefore concentrated on these techniques.

Rodents

MAZES. Most of the work on rodents has in fact been concerned with the laboratory rat, and inevitably the favorite method of study has been in mazes. It would be futile to try to summarize all the different types of mazes that have been used. If ever standardization of technique was required, it is in this area; however, certain general principles apply to most of this work, and some generalizations can be made about different types of mazes.

In any work on exploration it is particularly important that the extra-maze environment should be reasonably constant. To obtain a constant visual environment, the maze is usually placed in an enclosure that is either made of white muslin, allowing the experimenter to see the animal as a result of differential illumination inside and outside the enclosure, or of blackout material with a hole in the curtains, or of a one-way screen. A white noise of low intensity should also be used to mask extraneous noises that may be disturbing to the animal, although higher intensities are to be avoided because they may have a direct effect on the amount of exploratory behavior (Broadhurst, 1957).

Serious difficulties arise over the recording of responses. Typically two measures are used: amount of locomotor activity and amount of alternation of parts of the maze visited. Locomotor activity is usually measured by dividing the maze into a number of arbitrary sections and by counting the number of section entries made. Sometimes the sections are just the arms of the maze, but this is unsatisfactory because it is often important to know whether a rat has merely gone a short way into a maze arm and retreated or whether it has gone right to the end of the arm and back. It is a minimum requirement that each arm of the maze should be divided into two sections. Furthermore, Foster (1958) has shown that if an "entry" is scored whenever an animal puts its head and shoulders over the border line between two sections significant differences can be detected that are not found if only whole-body entrances are counted. In general, it is better to record both measures.

Independently of any difficulties in measurement, there are a number of objections to locomotion in a maze as a measure of exploration:

1. In moving around a maze a rat might just be exercising itself rather than exploring; however, there is experimental evidence that contradicts this view. Montgomery (1953b) showed in H mazes of different albedos that there is a decline in locomotor activity when the rats are returned to the same maze but that there is a decreasing decline as the albedo of the second maze differs from that of the first. Similarly (Halliday, 1966) it has been shown that, although after 3 minutes' exploration of an elevated Y maze, rats returned to the same maze 1 minute later will be only about 25 percent as active as on a first exposure, they will explore an enclosed T maze as actively, after the same interval, as rats with no recent exploratory experience. Further evidence comes from another experiment by Montgomery (1951), who showed that the more complex the maze the greater the amount of activity. None of these results are compatible with the view that the rats are just exercising themselves. This is not to say, however, that the rats' level of activity as measured in other ways does not correlate with the amount that it explores; indeed, in an experiment in which Montgomery showed that activity deprivation did not affect exploratory activity (1953c), he also showed that there was a correlation between the amount of activity animals showed in activity wheels and in a maze. Thus any treatment that changes an animal's activity level will probably affect the amount of locomotion in a maze.

2. A second objection is that, even if a rat is not just exercising itself when it moves around a maze, it may not be true that the animal that moves around most is exploring most; just as the person who moves around a museum most may not be the one who is seeing most of the exhibits. In an environment in which, apart from the choice point, no part is noticeably more interesting than another, this argument loses part of its force; furthermore, if one part of the maze is deliberately made more interesting than another (e.g., Williams and Kuchta, 1957), the rats are significantly more active in this area. However, we could only get satisfactory information on this point by correlating the same animal's investigatory responses in a situation where no locomotion was called for with their activity in a maze; this has not, I believe, yet been done.

3. A third objection to the use of locomotion measures is that, if an animal is merely observed to move from A to B, we cannot be sure whether it was doing so in order to avoid B or to approach A, and this may be an important question. For example, after being exposed to one stimulus, A, does an animal approach another one, B, because it is bored with A or because it is interested in B? Within the context of maze exploration it is usually very difficult to answer questions of this sort.

Despite these drawbacks, maze activity results have given a good deal of information about exploratory activity, and, if used with caution, the measure seems to be adequate although probably not very sensitive.

The other measure commonly used has been the amount of alternation of maze arms during free exploration (see the previous discussion).[6] To get a satisfactory measure of alternation it is necessary that at the choice point of the maze the alternatives open to the animal

---

[6] *Alternation* in a Y maze means the tendency to choose the arm that has been least recently visited. Thus the sequence of arm entries A-B-C constitutes an alternation, although the sequence A-A-B does not.

should be equally "easy" for it; a Y maze fulfills this requirement better than other designs. In Y mazes the rate of alternation is found to be rather constant (around 65 to 70 percent) if the rats alternate at all; alternation can therefore be used as an indicator of exploratory behavior, but its all-or-none characteristics mean that it is not a very helpful measure. No correlations have been found between the amount of alternation and the amount of activity in a Y maze although it has been found (Halliday, 1967) that alternation drops to chance at about the same time as activity reaches an asymptotic minimum. On the other hand, Roberts, Dember, and Brodwick (1962) have found that hippocampal lesions in rats increase the amount of activity in a Y maze, especially during the later stages of an exploratory period but that the lesions abolish alternation during separate trials in a T maze; unfortunately, the researchers do not report what the effect was on alternation in the Y maze, and the lack of alternation in the T maze may well have been due to a marked preference for the darker arm of the maze.

Bindra and Spinner (1958) have pointed out that far too little attention has been paid to other forms of activity in exploratory situations of any type. (The criticism applies equally to the other techniques to be described later.) They suggest that a time-sample method should be used in which the animal's behavior is observed every x seconds during the exploratory period and in which on a prepared sheet an entry is made of what the rat was doing at that time. The categories they suggest are: freezing, sniffing, locomotion, grooming, lying down, and miscellaneous (the last category being introduced to make the categories jointly exhaustive). Reliability and interjudge concordance in this categorization seem to be satisfactory (Bindra and Blond, 1958). Much of the detailed grain of behavior can be studied by this method; however, with so much to measure and with so much variability between animals there is a danger that the results may become mere botonizing that cannot be integrated into any larger framework. Nevertheless, as a form of amplification of the more conventional measures, the method is obviously extremely valuable; it is important to know, for example, when locomotor activity declines, whether the animal is sniffing at a particular stimulus, grooming, or freezing. A further advantage is that this technique is likely to draw attention to individual differences between animals; any worker on exploration in rats is familiar with the fact that some animals are "freezers," a fact that is usually hidden in group data, and a detailed analysis of the differences in behavior of these animals would be useful (see Bindra and Spinner, 1958).

It should also be noted that differences in behavior appear in elevated and enclosed mazes of a similar pattern. The amount of activity in an enclosed maze is greater on the first exposure but in general it appears that with daily exposure to the same maze there is a decline in activity from day to day in enclosed mazes (Montgomery, 1953b; Carr and Williams, 1957) although in elevated mazes constant activity from day to day or increases in activity have been reported (Montgomery, 1952a; Rushton and Steinberg, 1964). It is usually accepted that the elevated maze is a more frightening situation (Montgomery, 1955), and the difference is attributed to the gradual habituation of fear responses incompatible with locomotor exploration with repeated exposures to the elevated maze. However, although Miller (1964) has shown that amylobarbitone sodium is effective in reducing fear responses in a number of situations, Rushton and Steinberg (1964) found very little difference in locomotor activity on the first exposure to an elevated Y maze between animals injected with similar doses and saline controls. A full analysis of the differences in exploratory behavior in simple elevated and enclosed mazes is clearly needed, and, until this is available, comparison between the two should be made with some caution.

It is also helpful to distinguish between two rather different types of situations involving what McReynolds (1962) calls "novelty adjustive" and "novelty seeking" behavior. In the first case an animal is put in a novel environment from which there is no escape to somewhere familiar; here it has to adjust to the novelty of the situation, and it appears to do so by moving around in the way described above until the situation becomes familiar. In other cases the animal may be in a familiar environment and is suddenly faced with the opportunity to explore a novel environment. For example, a runway, maze, or open field may be attached to the home cage; here, as would be predicted from the results demonstrating the reinforcing properties of exploration, the animal does venture out to explore but does not explore as vigorously as in a novelty adjusting situation, and the animal frequently returns to its home cage. Despite the apparent differences between these two types of exploration, a correlation has been found between locomotor activity in the two cases (Hayes, 1960). Treatment effects, however, may have a very different result on behavior in the two types of situations. A good deal of attention has been devoted to the relationship between hunger and exploration, and despite somewhat contradictory findings it has been shown that both in simple (Montgomery, 1953a) and in complex (Zimbardo and Montgomery, 1957) mazes hungry animals will explore less than satiated ones. Fehrer (1956), however, showed that hungry animals leave a familiar environment to explore a novel one faster than satiated animals. It seems that in a novelty adjusting situation hungry animals explore less, presumably because they soon discover that no food is available, but that, when it is a question of venturing out from a familiar to a novel environment, the hungry animal is more "exploratory."

OTHER LOCOMOTOR SITUATIONS. The open field developed by Hall (1934) has often been used to measure exploration. In this case the only measure that can be obtained, apart from the type of observation recommended by Bindra, is the amount of locomotor activity. Alternation cannot be measured in this situation, and measures of variability of behavior would involve a prohibitive amount of mathematical analysis and have not been attempted. The open-field technique, therefore, suffers from all the disadvantages of the maze without compensating advantages. The open field is most commonly used to measure "emotionality" (see Chapter 4), and, if the aim was to study the relationship between exploration and emotionality, then this would appear to be a suitable measure. However, it appears that to make the open field a satisfactory test of emotionality it is necessary to make it fairly aversive for the rat (Broadhurst, 1957); and this might well reduce the value of activity as a measure of exploration. It would seem better to test for exploration in other types of apparatus and to reserve the open field for emotionality.

Berlyne (1955) has used a situation that appears to have many advantages but that has not, apparently, been widely used. This consists of a rectangular box with opaque walls, a frosted glass lid, and an alcove at one end; patterns can be introduced at the back of the alcove, or objects can be placed in the alcove. The number and duration of entries to the alcove is automatically recorded by the breaking of a narrow beam of infrared light operating a photocell. The advantages of this situation over a maze follow from what has been said about mazes: there is much less confusion between amount of locomotion and amount of exploration; we can be fairly sure that our measure is one of approach to the stimulus we are interested in rather than of avoidance of some other stimulus; and the measure we are taking (how long the animal is spending with its head in the alcove) is directly related to the investigation of the stimulus. Berlyne reports a number of results on short- and long-term decrements in exploration of various stimuli in this apparatus, but the work has never been followed up. Nor is there any direct information on the relationship between the amount of exploratory behavior in this situation and in a maze; however, Stretch (1960) found that, while in an H maze rats injected with sodium amytal explored less (were less active) than controls, they showed more interest in a novel stimulus in a box like that used by Berlyne. It would seem that comparison of results in a maze with results in a Berlyne box might offer a powerful means for detailed analysis of the effects of various treatments on exploratory activity.

LIGHT CONTINGENT BAR PRESS. It has frequently been shown that rats will press a bar in a darkened box in order to switch on a light of moderate intensity. A great deal of work has been done in this area recently, and it would be inappropriate to attempt to review it here. A review by Lockard (1963) is in any case available (although see the comments by Kiernan, 1964). This may be an inquisitive exploratory response, and, if so, it might be a good measure of exploration. The response could be exploratory in one of two ways:

(1) *Change hypothesis:* It might be that mere change in the stimulus conditions is reinforcing regardless of what the change is. This might well be because the situation does not otherwise offer sufficient stimulation to keep the animal interested (cf. Butler's, 1957, results with monkeys and sensory deprivation studies in human beings).

(2) *Viewing hypothesis:* It might be that the rats want to see around the box and that the only response that enables them to do so is pressing the bar; in this case the situation would be directly analogous to locomotor exploration. These two possibilities are not mutually exclusive. Let us first note what evidence is available on either of these two hypotheses.

It should be emphasized that light is a relatively feeble reinforcer, and for this reason all sorts of independent variables, which can normally safely be ignored in the case of the stronger reinforcers discussed in the last section, have to be taken into consideration. For detailed consideration of these effects the reader is referred to the reviews cited previously. I shall merely try to extract some facts relevant to the present discussion.

The possibility that the light contingent bar press rate (LCBP) is a secondary reinforcing effect due to association of light with food has been fairly adequately disposed of, at least as a main source of the effect (e.g., Roberts, 1954; Roberts, Marx, and Collier, 1958). It has also been suggested that the switching on and off of the light has a facilitating effect on activity and that it is this rise in activity that increases the LCBP, not the contingency of light following bar press. Kling, Horowitz, and Delhagen (1956) ran a yoked control experiment in which the illumination for the control group was provided by the bar presses of the experimental group, thus separating out the effects of facilitation and bar press/light contingency; the control group showed no increase in their previous low rate after the light was connected, although the experimental group showed the typical sudden increase in LCBP. Forgays and Levin (1959) used two levers, only one of which turned on the light; the researchers were able to demonstrate both discrimination between the levers and reversal when the light was made contingent on the previously nonreinforced lever; neither result could be explained on the facilitation hypothesis. As Kiernan (1964) points out, there is other evidence that makes it hard to be sure that there is *no* facilitation effect, but, as a main contender, the facilitation hypothesis is untenable.

Given these conclusions there is a good case for supposing that the change or the viewing hypothesis is correct. The change hypothesis would predict that a bar press that produced light offset in a lighted box should be as reinforcing as one that produces light onset in a dark box. In general, this does not appear to be so (Barnes and Kish, 1958; Hurwitz, 1956; Robinson, 1957) although there is evidence that light offset is more likely to be reinforcing if the animal has first been given trials in which the bar press produces no changes in illumination (Leaton, Symmes, and Barry, 1963). Nevertheless, it is generally agreed that light onset in the dark is a more effective reinforcer than light offset in the light; there is, therefore, over and above any effect of change, some special property of light onset that increases its reinforcing effect.

This suggests that perhaps the viewing hypothesis is indeed correct and that the value of light to the animal is that it permits visual exploration. A number of investigators (e.g., Hurwitz, 1956) have reported that, when the light is on in the box, the animal looks around the box making rapid scanning movements of the head. Robinson (1961) predicted, from the viewing hypothesis, that light increase in an already lighted box should be *less* reinforcing than light onset in a dark box because no extra viewing is involved, while light decrease in a lighted box should be *more* reinforcing than light offset because viewing is not prevented; his results were in accordance with this prediction and suggest that both the change and the viewing hypotheses are partially correct. Barnes and Baron (1961) showed, with mice, that, if the LCBP produced a pattern rather than diffuse illumination, the rate of pressing corresponded to the complexity of the pattern; this result could be taken to support either the change or the viewing hypothesis.

If the LCBP is indeed an exploratory response, we should expect to find the familiar intrasession decline in rate of exploration. Some experimenters have found this decline (Kling, Horowitz, and Delhagen, 1956; Thomson, 1955; Kish and Baron, 1962), but others have not (Hurwitz, 1956; Levin and Forgays, 1959). The reasons for these discrepancies are not obvious, but the fact that a decline has been found in several cases fits in with an exploratory explanation. Changes in rate between sessions are even more confusing; both increases and decreases from day to day have been reported. (For a full discussion of this see the two review articles previously cited.)

There is sufficient evidence to support the claim, on one of the two hypotheses put forward, that the LCBP reflects an exploratory response. However, the effect is very much affected by other variables; some of these are listed below:

1. *Light intensity.* It is generally assumed that very bright light is aversive to the rat, and clearly a subthreshold light cannot be reinforcing; we might therefore expect an inverted U shaped function relating light intensity to LCBP. In fact, Henderson (1953; 1957) found a maximum LCBP at about 16 millilamberts, and a minimum at 50 and 0 millilamberts, but the values between 0 and 16 millilamberts were not arranged in order of brightness. Levin and Forgays (1959), using three intensities of light, found a maximum LCBP at 1.76 millilamberts for 70-day-old rats and at 33.04 millilamberts for 110-day-old rats; it seems, therefore, that if there is an optimally reinforcing strength of stimulation it may vary with age.

2. *Deprivation of light.* Premack and Collier (1962) have shown that the LCBP increases with the intersession interval regardless of whether the animals were kept in darkness or in light. Kish and Baron (1962) gave animals a 30 minute pretest period in a box during which one group was in light, one in darkness, one presented with a regular blinking light and one with an irregular blink; they were then immediately given a 30 minute test period in the same box. It was found that the dark group showed by far the greatest LCBP, that the light group showed a lesser increase, and that both the blinking-light groups showed little or no increase as compared to a control group in which the light was not produced by bar pressing. This result shows a clear "deprivation" effect and is consistent with the view outlined previously because the dark group (greatest LCBP) was deprived of both viewing and change, the light group of change only, and the other two groups of neither viewing nor change.

3. *Schedules of reinforcement.* Stewart and Hurwitz (1958) report that although rats would show a higher rate on a fixed ratio of 3 than on continuous reinforcement there was a decrease when they shifted from 3:1 to 6:1. Stewart (1960) extended the result to show that with differing intensities of light there was no difference in LCBP on continuous reinforcement, but when the schedule was progressively shifted up to 6 (in successive daily trials) the animals with the brighter intensities increased their LCBP while the ones with dimmer intensities did not. It seems that rats are unprepared to work very hard for a dim light but that they will for a brighter one. Furthermore, we have the interesting result that differences that do not appear on CRF can be brought out with ratio schedules. It would be interesting to see what the effects of other types of schedule might be.

Primates

Despite a number of experiments on chimpanzees (see Welker, 1961), the greater part of the work on exploration in subhuman primates has been done with monkeys, and it is only in this field that a fairly standard technique has been developed.

This work derives from experiments on visual exploration from the Wisconsin laboratory. The apparatus in all these studies consists essentially of a small enclosed box (normally with a light inside it) with a door in it that the monkey can open, either directly or by means of a manipulandum, in order to see the outside world. Butler (1953) first of all showed that an animal would learn a simple visual discrimination in order to get the reward of looking out of the box; this appeared to establish that visual exploration was a reinforcer (cf. Montgomery and Segall, 1955, and Levin and Forgays, 1959, in rats). The most striking feature of Butler's results is the complete absence of inter-session or intrasession declines in rate of response (although, as mentioned previously, he does report deprivation effects). Butler and Harlow (1954), for example, tested animals continuously on a discrimination problem until they failed to produce a response within 5 minutes of presentation of the problem; they found no systematic change in latency during the trial, and the animals took from 9 to 19 hours to fail to respond. In another experiment (Butler and Alexander, 1955) animals were tested for 10 hours a day on 6 consecutive days (in this case, there was a single spring-loaded door, no discrimination being required); no consistent decrease in response rate was found either between or within trials. Despite this, Butler (1954) found different rates of responding for different visual stimuli; monkeys responded most rapidly to see another monkey, less rapidly for an electric train, and least rapidly for an empty chamber. In a further experiment Butler and Woolpy (1963) have compared monkeys' preferences for various types of visual display and have found that they spend more time looking at moving or colored pictures than at still or monochromatic ones and that they prefer pictures that are in focus, fairly bright and right side up; in general, the more lifelike the picture, the more it is preferred. Butler and Alexander (1955) found different rates of response at different times of day during a 10 hour period when the visual stimulus was a view of the primate keeping room; these rates could be attributed to differing amounts of activity, and attractiveness in the primate room. In most of Butler's situations in which long periods of responding occurred, the visual reinforcers were particularly interesting, e.g., a view of the primate room or of some part of the laboratory in which various different activities took place. Thus, although his results show that the animal's requirements for visual stimulation remain fairly constant over long periods, they do not show that intrasession declines do not occur for one particular stimulus, because in these cases the stimuli were constantly changing. To draw an analogy from the rat work, a rat may stop exploring one maze after a few minutes because the stimuli in the maze no longer "interest" it, but it is still prepared to explore another maze just as vigorously as a control group with no previous exploratory experience (Halliday, 1966). In fact, intrasession declines in visual exploration have been reported in monkeys when the visual reinforcers were relatively simple and unchanging. Butler (1960) shows a graph demonstrating almost complete satiation of visual exploration in 30 minutes when the reinforcer was a homogeneous white screen. Schwartzbaum (1964) also reports considerable intrasession reductions in responding when the reinforcer was the illumination of a panel outside the box by a plain white light or by multicolored flashing lights. It appears therefore that, although a monkey will continue to respond for changing and complex visual reinforcers, it will not necessarily continue responding at a high rate for any one reinforcer. Butler's results can thus be brought in line with the other results on exploration.

A number of different testing procedures may be used in Butler-type situations. The monkeys may be given separate trials as in the Wisconsin General Testing Apparatus, a screen being lowered between re-

sponses and latency of response being the measure; this may be necessary in cases where a discrimination is involved (although here the
procedure could be automated), but it would seem preferable to use a
rate measure if possible. This can be done simply by allowing the
animal to press open the door itself (Butler and Alexander, 1955) or
to expose the visual reinforcer by a separate manipulandum (Schwartzbaum, 1964). But in this case, if rate is being measured, intrasession
declines may be a confusing factor when the visual reinforcer is a
simple one. To avoid this, Lindsley, Weiskrantz, and Mingay (1964)
used a bar press as the response that opened the door on a variable
interval schedule; this would appear to be one satisfactory solution to
the problem.

Another difficulty arises when the door is opened for a fixed period
after a response (e.g., Butler, 1953) because in this case it is not possible to know for how much of the period the animal is in fact looking
out. Two solutions to this have been tried: (1) A photocell is so arranged that its beam is broken only when the animal puts its head in
a position to look out of the window; in this case a separate window
opening response can be dispensed with, and the photocell can be used
to count both number and duration of responses (e.g., Symmes, 1963;
Butler and Woolpy, 1963). The difficulty with this method is that the
animal may break the beam in some other way, with its hand or arm,
although Butler and Woolpy claim to have gotten around this. (2) The
animal may have to hold the manipulandum or window open itself
(e.g., Butler and Alexander, 1955; Lindsley, Weiskrantz, and Mingay,
1964), the assumption being that, so long as the animal is holding the
window open, it is also looking out. Probably a combination of the two
procedures is the best.

In any case it is important to measure both the frequency and the
duration of responses, particularly when looking for treatment effects,
because the two may vary independently. Butler and Woolpy (1963)
found that the mean duration of response was the most sensitive measure for distinguishing the reinforcing properties of various two-dimensional displays. Lindsley, Weiskrantz, and Mingay (1964) found that,
although both temporal and frontal monkeys showed a decreased total
viewing time as compared with normal animals, the decrease in the
frontals was mainly due to decreased average duration of viewing. The
temporals showed both decreased average duration of viewing and decreased rate.

REFERENCES

BARNES, G. W., & BARON, A. 1961. Stimulus complexity and sensory reinforce-
    ment. *J. comp. physiol. Psychol.*, 54, 466–469.
BARNES, G. W., & KISH, G. B. 1958. On some properties of visual reinforce-
    ment. *Amer. Psychol.*, 13, 417.
BERLYNE, D. E. 1955. The arousal and satiation of perceptual curiosity in
    the rat. *J. comp. physiol. Psychol.*, 48, 238–246.
BERLYNE, D. E. 1960. *Conflict arousal and curiosity.* New York: McGraw-Hill.
BERLYNE, D. E., & SLATER, J. 1957. Perceptual curiosity, exploratory be-
    havior and maze learning. *J. comp. physiol. Psychol.*, 50, 228–232.
BINDRA, D., & BLOND, J. 1958. A time-sample method for measuring general
    activity and its components. *Canad. J. Psychol.*, 12, 74–76.
BINDRA, D., & SPINNER, N. 1958. Response to different degrees of novelty:
    The incidence of various activities. *J. exp. anal. Behav.*, 1, 341–350.

BROADHURST, P. L. 1957. Determinants of emotionality in the rat. I. Situational factors. *Brit. J. Psychol.*, 48, 1–12.

BUTLER, R. A. 1953. Discrimination learning by rhesus monkeys to visual-exploration motivation. *J. comp. physiol. Psychol.*, 46, 95–98.

BUTLER, R. A. 1954. Incentive conditions which influence visual exploration. *J. exp. Psychol.*, 48, 19–23.

BUTLER, R. A. 1957. The effect of deprivation of visual incentives on visual exploration motivation in monkeys. *J. comp. physiol. Psychol.*, 50, 177–179.

BUTLER, R. A. 1960. Acquired drives and the curiosity-investigative motives. In Waters, R. H., Rethlingshafer, D. A., & Caldwell, W. E. (Eds.), *Principles of comparative psychology.* New York: McGraw-Hill.

BUTLER, R. A., & ALEXANDER, H. M. 1955. Daily patterns of visual exploratory behavior in monkeys. *J. comp. physiol. Psychol.*, 48, 247–249.

BUTLER, R. A., & HARLOW, H. F. 1954. Persistence of visual exploration in monkeys. *J. comp. physiol. Psychol.*, 47, 258–263.

BUTLER, R. A., & WOOLPY, J. H. 1963. Visual attention in the rhesus monkey. *J. comp. physiol. Psychol.*, 56, 324–328.

CARR, R. M., & WILLIAMS, C. D. 1957. Exploratory behavior of three strains of rats. *J. comp. physiol. Psychol.*, 50, 621–623.

CHAPMAN, R. M., & LEVY, N. 1957. Hunger drive and reinforcing effect of novel stimuli. *J. comp. physiol. Psychol.*, 50, 233–238.

CHARLESWORTH, W. R., & THOMPSON, W. R. 1957. Effect of lack of visual stimulus variation on exploratory behavior in the adult white rat. *Psychol. Rep.*, 3, 509–512.

DEMBER, W. N. 1956. Response by the rat to environmental change. *J. comp. physiol. Psychol.*, 49, 93–95.

DEMBER, W. N., & FOWLER, H. 1958. Spontaneous alternation behavior. *Psychol. Bull.*, 55, 412–428.

ESTES, W. K., & SCHOEFFLER, M. S. 1955. Analysis of variables influencing alternation after forced trials. *J. comp. physiol. Psychol.*, 48, 357–362.

FEHRER, E. 1956. The effects of hunger and familiarity of locale on exploration. *J. comp. physiol. Psychol.*, 49, 549–552.

FORGAYS, D. G., & LEVIN, H. 1959. Discrimination and reversal learning as a function of change of sensory stimulation. *J. comp. physiol. Psychol.*, 52, 191–194.

FOSTER, S. G. 1958. The effect of maze, age and sex on the relationship between hunger and exploratory behavior. Unpublished doctoral dissertation, Northwestern University.

GLANZER, M. 1953a. The role of stimulus satiation in spontaneous alternation. *J. exp. Psychol.*, 45, 387–393.

GLANZER, M. 1953b. Stimulus satiation: An explanation of spontaneous alternation and related phenomena. *Psychol. Rev.*, 60, 257–268.

HALL, C. S. 1934. Emotional behavior in the rat. I. Defecation and urination as measures of individual differences in emotionality. *J. comp. Psychol.*, 18, 385–403.

HALLIDAY, M. S. 1966. The effect of previous exploratory activity on the exploration of a simple maze. *Nature*, 209, 432–433.

HALLIDAY, M. S. 1967. Exploratory behavior in elevated and enclosed mazes. *Quart. J. exp. Psychol.*, 19, 254–263.

HARLOW, H. F., HARLOW, M. K., & MEYER, D. R. 1950. Learning motivated by a manipulation drive. *J. exp. Psychol.*, 40, 228–234.

HAYES, K. J. 1960. Exploration and fear. *Psychol. Rep.*, 6, 91–93.

HAYES, W. N., & WARREN, J. M. 1963. Failure to find spontaneous alternation in chicks. *J. comp. physiol. Psychol.*, 56, 575–577.

HENDERSON, R. L. 1953. Stimulus intensity dynamism and secondary reinforcement. Unpublished doctoral dissertation, University of Missouri.

HENDERSON, R. L. 1957. Stimulus intensity dynamism and secondary reinforcement. *J. comp. physiol. Psychol.*, 50, 339–344.

HURWITZ, H. M. B. 1956. Conditioned responses in rats reinforced by light. *Brit. J. Anim. Behav.*, 4, 31–33.

ISAACSON, R. I., KAROLY, A. J., & CALDWELL, J. S. 1957. Alternation phenomena in a cross maze exploration by rats. *Pap. Mich. Acad. Sci. Arts Lett.*, 42, 271–279.

KIERNAN, C. C. 1964. Positive reinforcement by light: Comments on Lockard's article. *Psychol. Bull.*, 62, 351–357.

KISH, G. B., & BARON, A. 1962. Satiation of sensory reinforcement. *J. comp. physiol. Psychol.*, 55, 1007–1010.

KLING, J. W., HOROWITZ, L., & DELHAGEN, J. E. 1956. Light as a positive reinforcer for rat responding. *Psychol. Rep.*, 2, 337–340.

LEATON, R. N., SYMMES, D., & BARRY, H. 1963. Familiarization with the test apparatus as a factor in the reinforcing effect of change in illumination. *J. Psychol.*, 55, 145–151.

LEVIN, H., & FORGAYS, D. G. 1959. Learning as a function of sensory stimulation of various intensities. *J. comp. physiol. Psychol.* 52, 195–201.

LINDSLEY, D. F., WEISKRANTZ, L., & MINGAY, R. 1964. Differentiation of frontal, inferotemporal and normal monkeys in a visual exploratory situation. *Anim. Behav.*, 12, 525–530.

LOCKARD, R. B. 1963. Some effects of light upon the behavior of rodents. *Psychol. Bull.*, 60, 509–529.

McREYNOLDS, P. 1962. Exploratory behavior: A theoretical interpretation. *Psychol. Rep.*, 11, 311–318.

MILLER, N. E. 1964. The analysis of motivational effects illustrated by experiments on amylobarbitone. In Steinberg, H., (Ed.) *Animal behaviour and drug action.* London: Churchill.

MONTGOMERY, K. C. 1951. The relation between exploratory behavior and spontaneous alternation in the white rat. *J. comp. physiol. Psychol.*, 44, 582–589.

MONTGOMERY, K. C. 1952a. Exploratory behavior and its relationship to spontaneous alternation in a series of maze exposures. *J. comp. physiol. Psychol.*, 45, 50–57.

MONTGOMERY, K. C. 1952b. A test of two explanations of spontaneous alternation. *J. comp. physiol. Psychol.*, 45, 287–293.

MONTGOMERY, K. C. 1953a. The effect of activity deprivation on exploratory behavior. *J. comp. physiol. Psychol.*, 46, 438–441.

MONTGOMERY, K. C. 1953b. The effect of the hunger and thirst drives upon exploratory behavior. *J. comp. physiol. Psychol.*, 46, 315–319.

MONTGOMERY, K. C. 1953c. Exploratory behavior as a function of "similarity" of stimulus situations. *J. comp. physiol. Psychol.*, 46, 129–133.

MONTGOMERY, K. C. 1954. The role of the exploratory drive in learning. *J. comp. physiol. Psychol.*, 47, 60–64.

MONTGOMERY, K. C. 1955. The relation between fear induced by novel stimulation and exploratory behavior. *J. comp physiol. Psychol.*, 48, 254–260.

MONTGOMERY, K. C., & SEGALL, M. 1955. Discrimination learning based upon the exploratory drive. *J. comp. physiol. Psychol.*, 48, 225–228.

MONTGOMERY, K. C., & ZIMBARDO, P. G. 1957. The effect of sensory and behavioral deprivation upon exploratory behavior in the rat. *Perc. Mot. Skills*, 7, 223–229.

MYERS, A. K., & MILLER, N. E. 1954. Failure to find a learned drive based on hunger: Evidence for learning motivated by "exploration." *J. comp. physiol. Psychol.*, 47, 428–436.

NISSEN, H. W. 1930. A study of exploratory behavior in the white rat by the obstruction method. *J. genet. Psychol.*, 37, 361–376.

PREMACK, D. 1962. Reversibility of the reinforcement relation. *Science*, 136, 255–257.

PREMACK, D., & COLLIER, G. 1962. Analysis of non-reinforcement variables affecting response probability. *Psychol. Monog.*, 76 (5, Whole No. 524).

ROBERTS, C. L. 1954. A comparison of the postive and negative reinforcing effects of light on the albino rat. Unpublished Master's thesis, University of Missouri.

ROBERTS, C. L., MARX, M. H., & COLLIER, G. 1958. Light-onset and light-offset as reinforcers for the albino rat. *J. comp. physiol. Psychol.*, 51, 575–579.

ROBERTS, W. W., DEMBER, W. N., & BRODWICK, M. 1962. Alternation and exploration in rats with hippocampal lesions. *J. comp. physiol. Psychol.*, 55, 695–700.

ROBINSON, J. S. 1957. Light as a reinforcer for bar pressing in rats as a function of adaptation, illumination level and direction of light change. *Amer. Psychologist*, 12, 411.

ROBINSON, J. S. 1961. The reinforcing effects of response-contingent light increment and decrement in hooded rats. *J. comp. physiol. Psychol.*, 549, 470–473.

RUSHTON, R., & STEINBERG, H. 1964. Modification of behavioural effects of drugs by past experience. In Steinberg, H. (Ed.), *Animal behaviour and drug action*. London: Churchill.

SCHNEIDER, G. E., & GROSS, C. G. 1964. Curiosity in the hamster. *J. comp. physiol. Psychol.*, 59, 150–152.

SCHWARTZBAUM, J. S. 1964. Visually reinforced behavior following the ablation of the amygdaloid complex in monkeys. *J. comp. physiol. Psychol.*, 57, 340–347.

STEWART, J. 1960. Reinforcing effects of light as a function of intensity and reinforcement schedule. *J. comp. physiol. Psychol.*, 53, 187–193.

STEWART, J., & HURWITZ, H. M. B. 1958. Studies in light-reinforced behavior: III. The effect of continuous zero, and fixed-rate reinforcement. *Quart. J. exp. Psychol.*, 10, 56–61.

STRETCH, R. G. A. 1960. An experimental analysis of perceptual curiosity and exploratory behaviour in the rat. Unpublished doctoral dissertation, University of Sheffield.

SUTHERLAND, N. S. 1957. Spontaneous alternation and stimulus avoidance. *J. comp. physiol. Psychol.*, 50, 358–362.

SYMMES, D. 1963. Effect of cortical ablations on visual exploration by monkeys. *J. comp. physiol. Psychol.*, 56, 757–763.

THOMSON, R. 1955. The reward-value of changes in illumination for the rat. Unpublished Master's thesis, University of Aberdeen.

WALKER, E. L., DEMBER, W. N., EARL, R. W., FLIEGE, S. E., & KAROLY, A. J. 1955. Choice alternation: II. Exposure to stimulus or stimulus and place without choice. *J. comp. physiol. Psychol.*, 48, 24–28.

WELKER, W. I. 1961. An analysis of exploratory and play behaviour in animals. In Fiske, D. W. and Maddi, S. R. (Eds.) *Functions of varied experience*. Homewood, Ill.: Dorsey.

WILLIAMS, C. D., & KUCHTA, J. C. 1957. Exploratory behaviour in two mazes with dissimilar alternatives. *J. comp. physiol. Psychol.*, 50, 509–513.

WOODS, P. J. 1962. Behavior in a novel situation as influenced by the immediately preceding environment. *J. exp. anal. Behav.*, 5, 185–190.

WOODS, P. J., RUCKELSHAUS, S., & BOWLING, D. M. 1960. Some effects of free and "restricted" environmental rearing conditions upon adult behavior in the rat. *Psychol. Rep.*, 6, 191–200.

WYCKOFF, L. B. 1952. The role of observing responses in discrimination learning. Part I. *Psychol. Rev.*, 59, 431–442.

ZIMBARDO, P. G., & MONTGOMERY, K. C. 1957. The relative strengths of consummatory responses in hunger, thirst and exploratory drive. *J. comp. physiol. Psychol.*, 50, 504–508.

CHAPTER 7

Learning

M. H. SHELDON

THE READER whose taste runs to definitions of *learning* may indulge it with Bugelski (1956) or Hilgard and Marquis (1961). For
the purpose of this chapter a statement about usage will do better than
a definition. By *learning* we shall mean any systematic change in a
response brought about by the contingencies of reinforcement associated with it. That is, we shall be concerned, quite arbitrarily, with the
phenomena of instrumental conditioning and not with classical conditioning, latent learning, or nonspecific perceptual learning.

We need to ask two kinds of question about treatments and learning. (1) How sensible is it to look for the effects of a treatment in the
area of behavior we have marked off as *learning*? Part of the business
of this chapter will be to suggest that very often it is not at all sensible.
(2) If we do decide that a treatment has its effect in the area we call
learning, how can we best use the information we get?

The treatment in search of an effect is best served by standardized
techniques and well-attested behavioral regularities. Despite, or, as
Skinner (1950) would have it, because of, the energetic activity of
several generations of learning theorists, there are surprising lacunae
in our elementary knowledge. If we wish to know, for example, how
intertrial interval interacts with deprivation or with effortfulness of
response, we shall not find the literature helpful. On the whole there
has been little interest in establishing a body of knowledge of this kind.
Many experiments have been designed solely to gather evidence for or
against particular theoretical positions, and their usefulness rarely
outlives interest in the theories they refer to. Similarly, apparatus for
learning experiments shows little sign of systematic standardization.
Frequently the apparatus design is determined by highly specialized
theoretical considerations. Even among such relatively standard pieces
of equipment as the T maze, the Skinner box, or the Wisconsin General
Testing Apparatus (WGTA) the exact details of design and construction depend on the materials available in the particular laboratory and
on the mechanical aptitude of the experimenter.[1] There is every reason

[1] A cursory analysis of the pieces of apparatus used to study learning in rats
in experiments reported in four recent issues of *Journal of Comparative and Physiological Psychology* reaveals an impressive variety:

1. *Mazes*: Straight alleys of 3, 4, 5 and 6 feet; a U maze; an L shaped runway; a variety of T mazes, e.g. 10″ start box, 54″ stem, and 15″ goal boxes;
8″ start box, 47″ stem, 12″ goal boxes; 28″ stem, 36″ arms; alley widths vary
from 2.5″ to 5″.

2. *Discrimination apparatus.* Discrimination apparatus where to avoid shock

to think that details of this kind are of great importance and that differences in, say, the pressure required to work the lever in operant conditioning, or the placement of cues in a discrimination experiment, are sufficient to make comparison between different experiments dangerous. Because of this variability I shall make no attempt to review the apparatus available for studying learning. Insofar as review is possible, details will be found in Munn (1950) for the rat and in Harlow (1951) for primates.

Probably the most important practical distinction among the pieces of apparatus in which we can study learning is between those in which the animal is free to respond at any time and those like the maze, alley, or problem box in which training proceeds in a series of discrete trials timed by the experimenter. In the first kind of situation the principal dependent variable is rate of response; in the second it is speed, or proportion of trials correct. Free responding situations lend themselves to automatic control, and this may well have an importance beyond its obvious economy and convenience for the experimenter. Rosenthal and Fode (1963) for example, have shown that in a maze situation the performance of rats is liable to be influenced unintentionally by the experimenter's enthusiasms.

If there are uncertainties over the design of apparatus and the details of experimental procedure, there are even greater difficulties over interpreting the results of learning experiments. If we were ever to be in a position to draw a block diagram that said anything useful about behavior, it is doubtful whether one of its boxes would be labeled *learning*, although boxes, or sets of boxes, might quite profitably be called *memory, attention,* or *discrimination*. In our thinking about the system responsible for behavior we are likely to appeal to processes concerned with the receipt and classification of inputs (attention, discrimination, categorization, and so on), with the storage and extraction of information (memory), and with processes that determine the level of performance (motivation, reinforcement, and so on). It is hard to find a place among these for a category including most of the things we mean by *learning*.

Learning represents the accumulation of the effects of reinforcement, and it is likely to be sensitive to almost anything that has a measurable effect on the organism. Sensory loss, failures in attention or discrimination, changes in the characteristics of memory, and variations in motivation or the strength of reinforcement could all be shown to affect the way an animal learns. To say, then, that a treatment affects learning may be to say very little more than that it affects behavior. In some cases this is so obvious as to be trivial: the rate at which monkeys with total lesions of the striate cortex learn even the simplest visual problem is greatly reduced, but no one would want to call the effect of striate lesions a loss in visual learning. We can, however, show that

---

the animal has to push through the correct door; γ maze with the color of the floors of the arms as discriminanda; an apparatus involving a dry-spaghetti feeder, for studying learning set; a "modified" jumping-stand, and a rat WGTA.

3. *Skinner boxes.* Various internal dimensions; some homemade, various commercial varieties; various materials from metal to unpainted pine.

4. *Avoidance apparatus.* Several kinds of shuttle box with a variety of interconnecting doors; a box (no dimensions given) where the escape/avoidance response was jumping up to grasp a 0.5″ gap between the top of the wall and the lid; a γ maze; a "trapezoidal" box with two escape compartments.

the point is by no means always so trivial. Inferotemporal lesions in the monkey have long been known to produce a loss in visual discrimination. This has been widely described as an effect on learning: the animals appeared not to have any sensory loss, and it seemed that their difficulty was not in telling the difference between objects but in learning to respond appropriately to them. Recently, however, Iversen and Weiskrantz (1964) have shown that their animals were deficient in what they call long-term retention.

If we are to use the term *learning* in the way we have agreed, there is nothing logically improper about describing the effects of striate or temporal lesions as effects on learning: they affect the rate at which a response changes with reinforcement. In the case of the striate lesion it is immediately obvious that this is not a helpful way of describing the loss; with temporal lesions this has become clear only after careful analysis. It will be a large part of the purpose of this chapter to suggest that one should almost never be content to describe a treatment as producing a change in learning. The analysis should always be taken further.

However, to place severe restrictions on the kinds of conclusions to be drawn from learning experiments does not alter the fact that in assessing the effects of a treatment we shall often, and very properly, make use of the animal's performance on a learning task. If animals could not learn, we should be able to discover very little about their behavior. The rest of this chapter will be concerned with some of the ways we can use learning situations to tell us about the effects of a treatment.

Acquisition

The things we know about learning in animals are of two main kinds. (1) We know, for each species, something about what kinds of task can be learned; for instance, we know that rats can learn discriminated avoidance and that monkeys can solve oddity problems. (2) We also know a good deal—although, as we have pointed out, far less systematically than we should like to—about some of the factors, given that a problem can be learned at all, governing the course of acquisition and extinction. For the moment it is this second kind of knowledge that concerns us.

What can we usefully infer from the fact that treated and untreated animals show different acquisition curves in the same learning situation? In the first place, we need to be careful about our measure of acquisition. If we are training a rat in a maze or runway, a variety of measures is available. In the runway (where we are not offering the animal a choice of responses), our measures will be time-based. But what intervals shall we measure? We might take starting latency (time taken to leave the start box) or total running time (from leaving the start to arriving at the goal), or we might divide the alley into several sections and measure running speed separately over each of them. In a choice situation (the T maze for instance), in addition to one or more of a variety of time measures, we can record the proportion of correct choices. There is some evidence (Tolman and Nyswander, 1927) that time and error measures are negatively correlated. Error scores fail to give us any information about changes in performance beyond the stage at which the animal ceases to make mistakes. Which of these measures is used in a particular experiment is often decided by practical convenience as much as by theoretical conviction. We know very little about the relationships among these measures, but the occasional pieces of information we do have suggest that they are complicated. Thus, Hillman, Hunter, and Kimble (1953) report that changes in drive affect running speed but not errors. Teel (1952) found that rate of learning a position habit in a T maze (counting errors) was independent of deprivation. These results may mean that different measures reflect different kinds of process or may mean merely that one measure is more sensitive than another. It should be clear, however, that there is no single measure of the rate of acquisition.

Similar difficulties apply to measuring the rate of extinction. When reinforcement is withdrawn, behavior changes in many ways, and which features of this complex change we attend to is largely a matter of choice. Again we can use time measures or changes in the distribution of choices. In the Skinner box, rate of response has not always been found to be a very useful measure of extinction, but we are not restricted simply to counting responses, and Millenson and Hurwitz (1961) have shown lawful increases in the duration of individual bar presses under extinction.

Whichever measure we use, we are likely to find that the course of acquisition and extinction is susceptible to influences from many sources. Among them are: degree of deprivation; amount of reinforcement (Zeaman, 1949) and its quality (Guttman, 1953); delay of reinforcement, which may be imposed simply by the size of the apparatus (Montpellier, 1933) or may consist of a waiting period (Grice, 1948; Perin, 1943); ease of response; interval between trials (Mayer and Stone, 1931); and frequency of reinforcement. This list is not intended to be complete, and more information may be had in Munn (1950) or Hilgard and Marquis (1961). There are few adequate studies of the effect of any one of these variables in a single situation, and when it comes to their effect in combination, we know almost nothing.

This would seem to suggest that, although a treatment that affects, for instance, motivation, will indeed produce a change in the curve for acquisition, this would not be a sensible place for studying the effect. Almost any treatment that has a detectable effect on behavior is likely to influence the course of acquisition; different treatments will have their effect for different reasons, but the acquisition curve will not tell us anything about what the reasons are.

One of the disadvantages of using acquisition for detecting the effects of a treatment is that it is, by definition, an irreversible process. (An acquired habit can be extinguished, but the fact that rate of learning with successive reacquisitions of the same habit increases suggests that we can never restore the animal to its primal innocence.) One of the reasons why the Skinner box is rarely used for measuring the acquisition of a simple habit is that there are great advantages in relating the effects of variables to stable performance (see, for example, Sidman, 1960). Once a steady rate of bar pressing has been achieved, we can use it as a base line for observing changes in behavior, and (with reversible treatments at least) we can return to this base line as often as we wish. This has the advantage of allowing us to obtain reliable data from a small number of animals. It has the further advantage that the period over which we can make observations of changes in behavior is not limited (as it is if we use acquisition).

Screening

So far we have been concerned to point out that when we are interested in saying anything precise about the effects of a treatment, there is good reason to think that learning measures will not be helpful. That is not to say, however, that for other purposes they may not be very useful. The clinical thermometer is an unsophisticated diagnostic instrument in that it tells us very little about what is wrong with a patient. It is, however, very valuable for telling us whether *anything* is wrong with him and for giving us some idea about how serious it is. Learning situations can do the same kind of job in assessing the effects of treatments.

There may be occasions—during the preliminary analysis of a new kind of treatment or with treatments whose effect is likely to be non-specific—when we shall be satisfied to say simply that a treatment has some effect on the animal or that its effect is greater than that of a second treatment. In these circumstances, learning measures promise a convenient and sufficiently reliable answer. At many points in this book the importance of developing sensitive techniques is stressed— techniques capable of detecting small effects or of distinguishing accurately between two different treatments. What is needed here is a different kind of sensitivity—almost a hypersensitivity—that will allow us to detect the presence of almost any effect and that will give us some measure of its size. What we need ideally is a set of learning tasks ranked in order of difficulty, all employing as many of the animal's faculties as possible.

For this purpose maze problems seem to offer the most likely solution. Once early comparative psychologists had succeeded in teaching rats to run mazes, the second generation seems to have spent a large part of its time in trying to find out how the rats had managed it. Watson (1907) trained normal rats in a complicated multichoice Hampton Court maze and, in a classic series of experiments, found that rats trained in the light performed well in the dark and that blinded rats did as well as normals. Separate groups of rats were deprived of taste, smell, sight, and hearing; their vibrissae were removed or the soles of their feet were anaesthetized. None of these treatments alone had any serious effect on maze performance, and Watson was led to the improbable conclusion that rats fumble their way about in some kind of kinesthetic twilight. It remained for Honzik (1936), using a multiple elevated maze, to show that rats are not altogether solipsistic and that sensory information is important in maze learning. The efficiency of an animal's performance is, roughly speaking, a function of the total range of sensory input available to it. Thus, Honzik's blind rats were worse than normals, blind and deaf rats were worse still, and blind, deaf, anosmic rats learned nothing at all.

These and a number of other studies are fully described by Munn (1950). The point that they make very clearly is the complexity of maze learning. Whereas for many purposes this complexity is a serious disadvantage, for our present purposes it is an advantage. Maze learning appears to engage the animal's faculties fully and to depend on the integration of sensory information in several modalities from inside and outside the maze.

The classical demonstration of how the maze can be used to assess treatment effects is to be found in Lashley's (1929) work on cortical lesions in the rat. He used a battery of mazes: mazes with 1, 3, or 8 blind alleys, and an elevated maze with 8 blinds. The extent of brain damage correlated highly with the learning impairment on each of these mazes, and the degree of impairment for a lesion of given extent increased with the apparent complexity of the mazes. This is not to say that the effect of Lashley's ablations was in any important sense on the learning process. One of Lashley's chapters is headed "The Influence of Cerebral Lesions upon the Capacity to Learn," but the title of his book is *Brain Mechanisms and Intelligence*. It is clear from his findings that maze learning provides a very general test of the animal's surviving capacities, and, if we are not concerned to use the word too precisely, this comes close to saying a test of intelligence. When we are dealing at this unspecific level of analysis an effect on learning means little more than an effect on behavior; it is simply that maze situations, like the clinical thermometer, allow us to detect the presence of effects and to rank them approximately in order of severity.

Munn (1950) summarizes a number of early studies that looked for the effects on learning of such treatments as temperature variations, diet, hormones, sleep deprivation, and selective breeding. Most of these studies used complex maze-learning tasks, and many of them found effects. They serve to emphasize the point that performance in maze situations provides a reasonable indication of an animal's general efficiency. Such studies completely fail, of course, to give us any information about the precise nature of the learning deficit. This may lie in something far less mysterious than the capacity to "learn." Thus, for instance, Wechkin, Elder, and Furchtgott (1961), studying the effects of prenatal irradiation on rats, find that their animals are impaired in climbing inclined planes. They describe this as a deficit in "motor performance," but, if they had tested their animals in certain kinds of learning situation, it would almost certainly have appeared as a deficit in learning.

The maze-learning tasks that Lashley found sensitive to the effects of lesions were fairly difficult single tasks. It has been suggested, however, that although such tasks have been used as measures of something like "intelligence" in the rat, it might be possible to construct batteries of tests analogous to those used in measuring human intelligence. Lansdell (1953) makes this point:

> The type of test situation usually used in studying rat intelligence is a difficult learning task which has none of the diversity of the various sub-tests used in the human situation. Hebb and Williams have suggested that rat intelligence could be assessed better with a "closed-field" test in which rats are presented with a variety of standard problems: in each test item the rat is required to solve quickly a simple problem and remember the solution for a few trials. A priori this test is more similar to the Binet type of test than a maze in which the rat may take some hundred trials to reach a criterion.

A battery of "closed-field" tests of this kind was developed by Hebb and Williams (1946) and modified and refined by Rabinovich and Rosvold (1951). Hebb and Williams call their original paper "A Method of

Rating Animal Intelligence," and this clearly invites us to compare their test battery with human intelligence tests. Two basic requirements for such a test are reliability and validity. Rabinovich and Rosvold show that their battery is reliable by testing the same animals at different times and obtaining high test-retest correlations. But neither they nor Hebb and Williams produce any evidence for the validity of their tests; that is, they give us no information about how performance on their tests correlates with any other aspect of behavior.

Acceptance of the usefulness of these tests requires the assumption that they measure some general undifferentiated quality of insightfulness or intelligence. Early evidence suggested that this might be so. Rabinovich and Rosvold found that rats reared in a free environment performed better than cage-reared animals and that these were better than animals with miscellaneous small cortical lesions. Similarly, Forgays and Forgays (1952) and Hymovitch (1952) found that performance on the Hebb-Williams battery was sensitive to the effect of rearing.

Recent evidence, however, suggests that the sensitivity of tests of the Hebb-Williams type may be less general than was originally thought. Lansdell (1953) found, using rats reared in a free environment, that anterior cortical lesions had little effect on performance, whereas posterior lesions had. Smith (1959) found that this was true only for rats raised in a free environment: for cage-reared rats, loss was related more closely to the extent of a lesion than to its locus. The small posterior cortical lesions made by Smith had no effect on the cage-reared rats. Gross, Chorover, and Cohen (1965) extend Lansdell's findings to cage-reared rats and find a very clear dissociation between the effects of anterior and posterior lesions. They test their rats on two problems: alternation in bar pressing, and the Hebb-Williams test battery. Anterior lesions affect only alternation, and posterior lesions affect only the Hebb-Williams task. It seems then that the capacity tested by the Hebb-Williams maze is specialized and that animals can perform well on this test and yet be seriously impaired on the alternation test.

This experiment also revives an early explanation of Lashley's results that denies that the whole of the cortex is equipotential in maze learning. Gross, Chorover, and Cohen suggest that the maze problems used by Lashley contain both an alternation component (represented in their experiment by the bar-pressing task) and an element of visually guided behavior (measured by the Hebb-Williams maze). If we assume that anterior cortex is specialized for the former and that posterior cortex is specialized for the latter, it becomes possible to account for Lashley's results not in terms of equipotentiality but in terms of progressive invasion of separate critical areas. But whatever the interpretation it seems that the conventional maze is a more general test of the animal's capacity than the Hebb-Williams maze is.

Several other general tests have been suggested, and among them one might mention those of Krechevsky (1937) and Polidora (1963). Krechevsky studied the behavior of rats on successive journeys through a Dashiell maze—a maze in which a large number of paths, all of equal length, is available to the animal. He recorded how many different paths each animal made use of and found that this number correlated negatively with the extent of cortical damage without regard to its locus. Polidora has developed a multilever operant conditioning apparatus where reinforcement is made contingent on the performance of certain sequences of bar presses. He reports that brain-damaged animals are capable of performing less complex sequences than normals. He points out that this is a testing situation that is potentially adaptable for work with different species.

Some Comparative Psychology

If we are to make any use of learning situations in gathering precise information about the effects of treatments, we shall have to break down the area covered by "learning" into units that are differentially sensitive to treatments. If we can say that treatment A affects task X but not task Y and that treatment B affects Y but not X, we have done two things: we have shown that the two treatments have distinguishable effects and also that the mechanisms serving the two tasks are, to some degree at least, different. There is, in fact a two-way traffic between treatments and learning. We can use learning situations to tell us something about treatments, but we can also, in principle at least, use treatments to help us break down into distinct categories the class of situations that we describe as measuring learning.

The problem is that it is not clear along which lines we should expect learning to break down. We shall not, to begin with, expect that the categories that finally emerge will be congruent with any of our present classifications—avoidance learning, discrimination learning, classical and instrumental conditioning, and the like. And yet it is not uncommon to find papers with titles like "Effects of Atropine on Discrimination Learning in the Rat" or "Effects of Amygdalectomy on Fear-Motivated Behavior in Rats," which, whatever their authors intend, seem to suggest that they refer to meaningful categories of learning rather than merely to different experimental arrangements.

It is even less likely that learning will divide neatly along the lines prepared for it by the major systematic theories, but certain theoretical distinctions of a relatively informal kind seem likely to be helpful. Thus, for instance, Mowrer's recent presentation of his theory (1960) places great emphasis on the way in which neutral stimuli, environmental or proprioceptive, have conditioned to them responses of the autonomic nervous system characteristic of what Mowrer calls the emotions of hope, fear, and so on. But in addition to this kind of learning, in the course of which neutral stimuli become "baited," as Mowrer puts it, we need to think of some kind of system responsible for response learning. It would not be surprising if these two kinds of learning were to respond differently to treatments.

A second example of a promising theoretical distinction between different kinds of learning is that developed to deal with some of the phenomena of visual discrimination learning in rats. Following suggestions by Lawrence (1949), Reid (1953), and others, Sutherland (1959) has suggested that, in a discrimination task, animals perform two different kinds of learning: They learn what features of the environment to attend to, and, given that they are attending appropriately, what responses to make. A series of papers by Mackintosh (1962; 1963a; 1963b; 1964) suggests that if we add to this the assumption—made earlier by Reid—that the two kinds of learning are acquired and extinguished at different rates, we can account for many of the phenomena effects of irrelevant cues, and (Sutherland and Mackintosh, 1964) additivity of cues. In addition, it appears from the evidence presented by Mackintosh (1965) and by Mackintosh *et al.* (1966) that some of the differences between species can be explained by assuming different relationships between these kinds of learning.

There are, of course, dangers in any attempt to conclude from the effects of treatments that two problems test different kinds of learning. We cannot conclude from the fact that treatment X affects learning in situation A but not (or not as much) in situation B, that problems A and B involve different systems. There is, as we showed in a previous section, an important interaction between magnitude of effect and problem difficulty. If two problems of different degrees of difficulty use the same system, a treatment that affects that system will affect the harder problem more than the easier one (see Chapter 15).

This interaction is sometimes forgotten. Thompson and Malin (1961) report that frontal lesions hamper rats in learning a successive but not a simultaneous visual discrimination, and they argue from this that the two kinds of problem involve different mechanisms. But this does not follow. Most of the evidence suggests that normal rats find successive discriminations harder than simultaneous problems using the same stimuli; so Thompson and Malin's results could be explained simply as showing an interaction between treatment and difficulty. This interpretation is favored by the fact that Kimble (1963) reports the same difference between successive and simultaneous discrimination with lesions in a very different area of the brain—the hippocampus. If it could be shown that frontal lesions did not affect performance over simultaneous problems of a wide range of difficulty but that they did for the simplest successive problem, then the case would be made convincingly.

It is possible that an important analysis of learning has already been performed for us. There is a sense in which the process of evolution can be regarded as a treatment and the differences between species as its effects. If we are looking for functionally significant categories of learned behavior, it is possible that we may find them by attending to the differences in capacity between species, and it might be possible to find other treatments that mimic the evolutionary process.

The formal problems involved in analyzing the differences between treated and untreated members of the same species are the same as those involved in investigating the differences between different species. Indeed one could argue that interspecies comparisons are easier from certain practical standpoints. The treatment has been performed for us by the evolutionary process: we have a convenient supply of subjects, and we can be more confident about the homogeneity of each of our groups than we can with, say, brain-operated monkeys. It is possible that the problems that arise in studying differences between species, and the techniques that have been used for solving them, will turn out to be relevant to analyzing the effects of treatments. That is the reason for considering them here.

But how do we approach the problem of interspecies comparison? We might try to show that the ability to perform a certain type of problem—delayed response or successive discrimination—is possessed by all animals above a certain point in the phylogenetic scale, but by none below it, and we might try to relate this discontinuity in capacity to some anatomical discontinuity. But it is inherently improbable that animals have evolved in steps that coincide neatly with the differences between our laboratory tasks; although it is possible that certain tasks require a single unique activity, the structures for which appear only at a particular stage in evolution, it is more likely that difficult tasks merely require some new combination of activities of which simpler organisms are capable. A further difficulty with this kind of approach is that it requires us to be able to say that a certain task is impossible for an animal. Apart from the logical impossibility of ever doing this, there is evidence to suggest that an animal's abilities may be stretched surprisingly far by ingenious training techniques. Lloyd Morgan might have been surprised to hear that pigeons can play table tennis.

Another approach to measuring phylogenetic differences is to find a single task that will not only differentiate among species but also will arrange them in an order correlating highly with phylogenetic status. All attempts in this area have failed, and it is not difficult to see why. How does one set about comparing the ability of, say, birds and mammals in performing delayed responses or in learning a simple position habit? The only species for which a large amount of formal data is available are the rat, the monkey, and the pigeon, and for these species we know that apparently trivial features of apparatus design or experimental procedure can produce major differences in performance. It has been suggested by Gardner and Nissen (1948) that if we were to find the set of experimental conditions under which the members of each species performed best on the problem, then comparison of performance would be justified. Clearly, however, we could never state with confidence that we had found the optimum.

Such attempts as have been made at interspecies comparison using a single task have not repaid the labor involved. Razran (1933) reviews the literature on classical conditioning (which had been suggested as a relatively pure test) and concludes that phylogenetic status is not correlated with the rate of conditioning.[2] Gardner and Nissen presented a single discrimination problem to sheep, cows, horses, goats, chimpanzees, and human aments and failed to find systematic differences. Harlow, Uehling, and Maslow (1932) had slightly more success in using the delayed-response task on a wide variety of primates, all of whom—orangutan, white-handed gibbon, rhesus monkey, Java monkey, Barbary ape, sooty mangaby, guenon, baboon, mandrill, and capuchin—could be tested in the same apparatus.

It is important to ask, however, whether a single test, distinguishing reliably among species, would be of any value. The position is not analogous with that in human intelligence testing. Human tests that distinguish between the dull and the bright—insofar as they can be validated against socially accepted standards—have a practical value that does not depend on our theoretical understanding of what they measure. It is convenient to be able to distinguish between dull and bright men, and, on the whole, despite the persistent popularity of the interview, one cannot tell by looking at them. We do not, however, need performance on the delayed-response task to help us tell the difference between a Barbary ape and a Norwegian rat.

Interspecies tests would be useful, then, only if performance on them

---

[2] This is confirmed by Grindley's (1965) recollection of an occasion when Lashley presented 20 individual records of the course of salivary conditioning to a distinguished audience; he told them that the 20 records came from two different kinds of subject. The audience was unable to find any systematic differences. Lashley told them that 10 records were provided by dogs, 10 by Harvard Professors.

told us not simply that the species were different, but something about the reasons for the difference. They can do this only when we can say with confidence exactly what it is about the task that produces the difference. Tasks may distinguish correctly between species for reasons that, as far as the animal's intellectual capacity is concerned, are trivial, and the simple fact that by some chance one task did turn out to rank species correctly might be of very little importance.

Bitterman (1960) rejects early attempts to rank species by their performance on a single problem, for the kind of reason we have mentioned. He suggests that we should look instead for differences in what appear to be the basic regularities of learning. We are unlikely to find an interspecies difference—or a treatment—that seriously challenges the Law of Effect if only because of the circularity built into our definition of reinforcement. But beyond this it might be profitable to look. It is difficult, of course, in advance to say where we ought to look for this kind of difference. Bitterman and his associates have concentrated on habit reversal, probabilistic behavior, and the effects of partial reinforcement on extinction, although they never explain what led them to this choice. Bitterman's own interest in this field is partly polemic and arises from his frequently expressed impatience with laws of behavior established solely from work with the rat.

The advantage of the kind of comparative research recommended by Bitterman is that the functional relationships (as he calls them) on which it concentrates have been thrown up by behavior itself. One of the reasons why it is unlikely that we shall find important differences between species in their performance on the oddity problem, or on avoidance learning, is that these are the names for experimental situations that we as experimenters have devised. In many cases they have been devised to tell us if our theories are right rather than to tell us more about behavior. On the other hand, such things as increased resistance to extinction with partial reinforcement have been brought to our attention by the behaving animal.

It would be foolish ever to expect that we should find a one-to-one relationship between treatments and tests—that the only effect of treatment X would be to change the animal's performance on task Y. Our behavioral tests are not pure in this way. The best we can hope for is that for any one treatment there will be one test that is particularly sensitive and will carry an important part of the effects of the treatment. We cannot draw a definite distinction between the features of behavior Bitterman recommends for attention and others we might have chosen. All we can say is that there seems a certain inherent probability that tests concerned with phenomena thrown up by the study of behavior itself will reveal the effects of treatments more directly than tests based on categories imposed on behavior by the experimenter.

Partial Reinforcement and Extinction

The phenomenon studied most fully by Bitterman is the partial-reinforcement effect (PRE). It is perhaps worth reviewing this work in some detail, as it raises some problems of general interest. It is clearly established for the rat that habits established under continuous reinforcement extinguish faster than habits established under one of the schedules of periodic reinforcement. Now this effect—PRE—occurs in the rat over a wide range of conditions. It seems to be independent of the apparatus used and to occur with different schedules of partial reinforcement, under massed and distributed practice, and so on. Any treatment that abolished PRE without having any effect on acquisition, could be said to have produced a major change of some generality. Similarly, any phylogenetic discontinuity in the occurrence of PRE would be interesting. Wodinsky and Bitterman (1959) report two experiments with fish—African mouthbreeders—in which PRE fails to occur. One group of fish received partial reinforcement (50 percent), and the other received continuous reinforcement. Both groups were extinguished to the same criterion. There was no significant difference between the two groups in extinction, and what difference there was, was in the opposite direction to PRE. The behavior of the two groups during acquisition (lower latencies for the continuously reinforced group) was, on the other hand, sufficiently close to what we should expect from two similarly treated groups of rats to suggest that there was nothing obviously inadequate about the testing situation.

Now, one possible objection to an isolated finding like this has been anticipated and partly answered by Bitterman. It could be suggested that the failure of PRE to occur in this situation has in fact no general interest and that it is merely a function of the particular value of, say, deprivation or effortlessness of response used in this experiment. Over the range of deprivation used for the rat there is no evidence that it interacts with PRE, but we have nothing but common sense to tell us whether or not the level of deprivation chosen for the fish falls within a comparable range. Bitterman points out that, although we cannot control such variables as deprivation across species by "equation," we can control them by what he calls "systematic variation." Thus, the suggestion that the mouthbreeders in Wodinsky and Bitterman's experiment failed to show PRE because of the particular deprivation schedule used carries the implication that at some level of deprivation the effect *would* appear. This can be tested, and an experiment by Longo and Bitterman (1960) compares fish trained at high and low levels of deprivation. Here the conventional effect of partial reinforcement was clearly reversed: partially reinforced fish extinguished faster. Both partial groups extinguished faster than either consistent group, and there is no evidence that Wodinsky and Bitterman's results can be explained as a result of the particular deprivation schedule used: the effects of partial reinforcement do not seem to interact with those of deprivation. A curious feature of this experiment by Longo and Bitterman is that the fish had only one training trial every 24 hours, although this training schedule has been shown (Weinstock, 1958) to produce PRE in the rat.

In principle, Bitterman's technique of control by systematic variation has something to recommend it, but it is doubtful whether it has much practical value. The difficulty is that there are too many possible factors for us ever to be able to vary them all systematically. Deprivation is obviously one of the easiest, but, as there was no evidence at all that it would turn out to be relevant, one has the feeling that Longo and Bitterman were setting up a straw man.

There are, however, a number of other experiments in which fish fail to show PRE. Wodinsky and Bitterman (1960) show that their previous finding can probably not be explained by suggesting that the processes producing PRE in the fish are simply slower to develop than those in the rat. In their first experiments they had given two-hundred

training trials; here they give eight hundred. Again the partially reinforced group extinguished faster.

The most important question about these experiments—given that
we accept that, for the range of situations studied, there is a difference
between rat and fish and that it is not the result of any obvious lack
of control—is what kind of conclusion we are to draw from them. To
say simply that fish fail to show PRE tells us very little until we understand more about PRE in the species that show it. Bitterman appeared
to be suggesting in his early work that it followed from these studies
that because rat and fish behave differently with regard to PRE in
similar situations, the rat must possess some structure or at least some
specialized capacity that the fish does not share. This provided him
with a stick for beating learning theories that claim to derive the whole
range of learning phenomena from a single set of rules established in
work with the rat. In fact, this kind of objection was anticipated by
Hull (1945), who, although he admitted that his theory had not had
much to say about individual or species differences, pointed out that
the differences could almost certainly be accommodated to it by adjusting the values of constants in his equations.

Put less formally, this amounts to saying that the difference in PRE
between fish and rat does not require us to think of some specialized
capacity possessed by one species but not by the other: it is at least
as likely that the difference arises from some difference in balance
between processes common to both species. Indeed a more recent paper
from Bitterman's laboratory (Gonzalez, Eskin, and Bitterman, 1962)
acknowledges this: "Resistance to extinction in any given species probably is determined by a variety of interrelated factors whose relative
weights at the very least vary considerably from species to species."

It would help us to understand the nature of the difference between
fish and rat if we knew more about PRE in the rat. This has received a
great deal of attention, and a brief review of some of the explanations
put forward can be found in Lawrence and Festinger (1962). The
theories differ not merely in detail, but in the kind of explanation they
offer. Thus Amsel's (1958; 1962) is essentially an explanation in terms
of motivation—the animal's frustration generated on unreinforced
trials. Early theories like Sheffield's (1949) preserve the language of
stimulus-response theory and speak in terms of sensory after-effects:
the partially reinforced animal learns during acquisition to respond
after unreinforced trials. Other theories, like Bitterman's, insist that
relatively complex cognitive processes are necessary to explain the
effect. This is not the place to attempt a review of these theories;
they are mentioned simply to emphasize the point that to say that
the fish fails to show PRE becomes interesting only when we understand the effect in the rat.

In fact, Bitterman's later work on PRE has shown a refusal to be
content with any simple conclusion and a determination to analyze the
difference between rat and fish more closely. In the process, his original
and striking demonstration is shown not to be generally valid—there
are circumstances in which the fish shows PRE—but these experiments
show well how a single finding (the failure of the fish to show PRE
over the conditions of the early experiments) gives us a starting point
for an interesting analysis. It turns out that not only do our behavioral
tests tell us something about the difference we are concerned with but
also the difference tells us something about the tests. Thus, Bitterman's
work, starting from an apparent interspecies difference in PRE, leads

us on to some interesting conclusions about the nature of PRE in the rat.

Gonzalez, Eskin, and Bitterman (1962), using a free operant test with fish, found that when they compared a continuously reinforced group with groups reinforced on either variable or fixed interval schedules, the two partially reinforced groups extinguished more slowly (PRE). Why should PRE have been found here but not in the previous experiments? The authors suggest three differences that might be important. First of all, it might be that PRE in fish appears in free-operant situations but not in experiments consisting of discrete trials. Second, whereas in the earlier experiments the percentage of reinforcement for partially reinforced groups had always been 50, in this experiment (with fixed or variable intervals between reinforcements of 1 minute) the ratio of reinforcements to responses was much lower. It might be that, in the fish, PRE appears only with relatively severe schedules. Third, in PRE experiments it is possible to equalize for partial and continuous groups either the total number of trials or the total number of reinforcements, but not both. The first arrangement is more usual, but with interval schedules the second must be used, and this could be important.

Gonzalez, Eskin, and Bitterman report a second experiment in the same paper. An attempt is made to choose among these alternatives by using discrete trials, a 50 percent schedule for the partial group, and equal numbers of reinforcements rather than trials. Here the familiar PRE effect is found again. One explanation of this result would be that both fish and rats are capable of showing PRE but that with fish the total number of reinforcements (regardless of the ratio of reinforced to unreinforced trials) is an important variable in deciding resistance to extinction. The suggestion would be that in the earlier experiments of the series (when trials were equated rather than reinforcements) any tendency for PRE to appear was masked by the fact that continuously reinforced animals received twice as many reinforcements as partially reinforced animals. When the number of *reinforcements* is equated, PRE is able to appear.

However, a simpler explanation would be that the total number of *trials* is an important variable and that the reason for the slower extinction of the partially reinforced group in the experiment just mentioned is that, in addition to receiving primary reinforcement on "reinforced" trials, they received secondary reinforcement on "unreinforced" trials. This possibility is considered and dismissed in an experiment by Gonzalez, Eskin, and Bitterman (1963) where the behavior of two partially reinforced groups is compared. For both groups the proportion of reinforced trials is the same (half) and so is the total number of trials (and therefore the numbers of reinforced and unreinforced trials). The variable manipulated here is the maximum number of successive unreinforced trials allowed by the schedule. It is found that, although the resistance to extinction of the partial group reinforced according to a Gellerman schedule that never allowed more than three unreinforced trials in succession is not significantly different from that of a continuously reinforced control group, a partially reinforced group whose schedule included longer runs of unreinforced trials does show greater resistance to extinction. Despite the lack of difference between the "Gellerman" and continuous groups, it does seem possible to argue from this experiment that there are circumstances in which partial reinforcement can increase resistance to extinction in the fish even when number of trials rather than number of reinforcements is equated.

It is suggested by Gonzalez, Behrend, and Bitterman (1965) that two variables determine resistance to extinction in the fish. (1) It appears to increase (regardless of the proportion of reinforced to unreinforced trials) with the total number of reinforced trials. (2) It increases (regardless of the total number of reinforcements) with the length of the runs of unreinforced trials. In the original experiments with fish the continuously reinforced subjects received more reinforcements, and the runs of unreinforced trials were too short for this handicap to be overcome.

This conclusion raises an interesting point about PRE in the rat. In the conventional experiment on PRE, where the total number of trials rather than reinforcements is equated, the difference between partial and continuous schedules is usually described as a difference in the percentage of reinforcement. But, in fact, as Gonzalez and Bitterman (1964) point out, two variables are confounded with this: total number of unreinforced trials and length of runs of unreinforced trials. Lawrence and Festinger (1962, Expt. 5) have claimed that the first of these is critical and that resistance to extinction increases with the number of unreinforced trials in acquisition, regardless of the ratio of reinforcement. But, following the findings of Gonzalez, Behrend, and Bitterman (1965) with the fish, it might be that the length of runs of unreinforced trials is also a relevant variable. Gonzalez and Bitterman show that when percentage of reinforcement and total number of trials are held constant but the length of runs of unreinforced trials is varied, animals who experience longer runs extinguish more slowly.

It is particularly interesting to notice that the suggestion that this factor might influence resistance to extinction in the rat came from work with the fish, and this is a good example of the two-way traffic that can exist between treatments and tests. Established findings with the rat provided an initial point of contact with the difference between rat and fish: rats show PRE under some conditions where fish fail to show it. In a sense, of course, we should not speak as if PRE were a single, unitary phenomenon, occuring sometimes under one set of conditions and sometimes under another. PRE can hardly be defined except by reference to the conditions that produce it. All we can say is that extinction in the rat is retarded after certain schedules of reinforcement, and in fish after certain other schedules. What is of interest is to ask what different factors or what different balance among the same factors is responsible. The answers to this tell us something not only about the difference between rat and fish but also about PRE in the rat.

We have discussed this work on PRE at some length because it is the most fully developed example of its kind. Bitterman's work on serial reversal and on probabilistic behavior, reviewed by Bitterman (1965), makes essentially the same point. In these cases, too, an established regularity in the behavior of the rat provides us with a point of departure for studying differences between species.

Interproblem Learning

All the tests we have been concerned with so far have involved training animals on single problems, and we have pointed out serious obstacles to drawing meaningful behavioral distinctions among species from their behavior on single problems. But learning occurs not only within individual tasks but also between successively learned tasks, and it has been suggested that the two kinds of learning are independent and that they might be differently affected both by phylogenetic status and by treatments. The attraction of this point of view is that if we can maintain that interproblem learning—"learning to learn"—is really a special capacity, independent of intraproblem learning, we might expect it to answer our requirements for a measure of behavior not tied to any particular set of testing conditions.

By interproblem learning we mean an improvement in the performance of single problems that occurs during the learning of a series of similar problems. Despite the ingenious arguments of Reese (1964), who has attempted to reconcile the data on learning-set formation with Hull-Spence behavior theory, I shall take the view that this improvement is independent of the stimulus items used in the problems that have produced it and that it represents an ability to deal successfully with an unlimited set of problems of a similar kind. Miller has recently (1964) suggested that human language behavior is best described in terms of its obedience to certain rules: the language user, possessing a "dictionary" and a "grammar" can generate and understand any grammatical utterance, even though he may never have encountered it before. Miller has claimed that the capacity for displaying rule-governed behavior is distinctively human—that it separates man from, say, the anthropoid apes. We shall see that there is reason to believe that some of the data on interproblem learning contradicts this claim for uniqueness.

Interproblem learning has been studied in animals in a number of situations. The simplest case—and the one where the rule-governed character of the behavior is most open to question—is serial-reversal learning. Here the animal is presented with a choice between two responses (the responses may be to position or to cues independent of position) only one of which is reinforced. After training the animal for a certain number of trials or to a certain performance criterion, the problem is reversed: the previously unreinforced response is now reinforced. This sequence is repeated. It is found that performance within individual problems in the series of reversals improves (after an early deterioration) and approaches the stage of one-trial reversal, where, as soon as response A fails to be reinforced, the animal switches to response B. We can describe this kind of behavior as a simple application of the rule "win, stay—lose, shift."

There is some evidence that the rate of improvement in learning successive reversals of a problem is independent of the rate of learning on the first problem, although, for reasons that we shall consider more fully shortly, we should be cautious about coming to this conclusion. The evidence is from two sources. The first is phylogenetic: rats have frequently been shown to improve with successive reversals under a considerable variety of conditions, and one-trial reversal is frequently achieved (Stretch, McGonigle, and Rodger, 1963; Stretch, McGonigle, and Morton, 1964). Bitterman (1965) has recently reviewed the evidence for lower species, and he discerns an orderliness in it. There is no evidence for significant improvement in the fish. Bitterman, Wodinsky, and Candland (1958) report the results of a series of fourteen reversals of a spatial habit for the mouthbreeder, and also of a series of sixty reversals of a discrimination habit (i.e., a simultaneous discrimination with position irrelevant). No improvement occurs in either case, although there is clear evidence of learning within problems. Rats run by the same authors in an apparatus and under conditions designed to be as closely comparable as possible show the familiar improvement. Similar failures to find improvement are reported for the paradise fish by Warren (1960), for the octopus by Mackintosh (1962), and for the crab by Datta, Milstein, and Bitterman (1960). Reporting two experiments on position reversal in the turtle, Kirk and Bitterman (1963) find equivocal signs of improvement in one case. For the pigeon, however, despite an earlier failure by Reid (1958) to find improvement, Bullock and Bitterman (1962), using an automated testing apparatus, find improvement over a set of reversals of a spatial problem, and of a simultaneous color discrimination. For a color discrimination, when the stimuli were presented successively, only one bird out of four showed reliable improvement. In their discussion of the results of this experiment, Bullock and Bitterman conclude, "The fact that progressive improvement in habit reversal appears only under certain specialised conditions in the pigeon suggests again the possibility that the negative results obtained with simpler animals may be due only to the inadequacy of the experimental conditions employed." It should be noted that this cautious conclusion is apparently rejected in Bitterman's more recent summary of the comparative evidence, where he suggests that the results fit a very orderly scheme. According to this, proficiency in reversal learning increases with phylogenetic status. Thus the fish shows improvement neither on spatial nor on visual discrimination problems; the turtle improves on spatial but not on discrimination problems; and pigeons, rats, and primates improve on both. It is most doubtful from the published data whether the turtle at least can hold its place in this table. Kirk and Bitterman themselves, in discussing the results in their original paper, speak of a "hint" of improvement. The number of turtles is small (5) and the series of reversals is long (70); by the end of training the turtles had not achieved one-trial reversal. It seems legitimate in this case to ask whether the small improvement that did occur might be attributed to increasing familiarity with the testing situation or to some such factor.

The work we have considered so far has all been concerned with improvement in performance over a *series* of reversal problems. Recently it has been suggested (Rajalakshmi and Jeeves, 1965) that a simple measure based on the relationship between performance on the original problem and performance on a *single* reversal may be useful for making comparisons between species. What Rajalakshmi and Jeeves call the reversal index is the ratio of the number of trials to criterion on the first reversal to the number of trials to criterion on the original problem. One advantage of the measure is that it can be calculated independently of differences in the absolute difficulty of individual problems. Rajalakshmi and Jeeves present interesting data showing a considerable measure of agreement between the reversal index and the phylogenetic level.

It is certainly true that discrimination problems where the number of trials required for initial learning varies over a wide range may yield the same reversal index. Indeed, for rats, Rajalakshmi and Jeeves present data of their own showing that this is so. However, it is not difficult to think of cases where, within a single species, two discrimination problems might be made to yield very different reversal indexes. As long as we can assume that the number of trials taken for the original learning of a discrimination reflects in some sense its intrinsic difficulty, there is no problem. But the original learning may take a large number of trials not because the discrimination is intrinsically difficult but because, for example, it is presented in such a way that it is some time before the animal begins to attend to its relevant features or because the animal comes to it with an inappropriate set. Factors like these (which would be expected to affect the difficulty of initial learning but not the difficulty of reversal) would yield a spuriously low reversal index. Perhaps one experimental example will make the point. Bitterman and McConnell (1954) trained rats in a jumping stand either on two successive discriminations or on two simultaneous discriminations. The first successive discrimination was markedly more difficult than the first simultaneous, but the second successive was not more difficult than the second simultaneous. They suggest that the reason for the initial difficulty of successive problems is that their solution requires a special perceptual set, that it takes the animal some time to acquire. If in Bitterman and McConnell's experiment the second problem for each set of animals had been a *reversal* of the first (rather than a new problem) and they had calculated a reversal index, it seems likely that the successive problem would have yielded a lower index than the simultaneous problem.

There is also a certain amount of evidence that has been interpreted as suggesting that *treatments* may affect the ability to show improvement with successive reversals but not the rate of learning single problems. Gonzalez, Roberts, and Bitterman (1964) report that rats with extensive cortical lesions made early in life are reduced to the status of the turtle: they show improvement on position reversals but not with discrimination problems. Thompson and Langer (1963), working with the rat, report that lesions of the limbic system produce a deficit in serial position reversal. Their paper fails to report the performance of their animals on any control task, and it is therefore not legitimate to conclude that the loss they report is in any way specific to reversal learning. In any case, their claim that the limbic system exercises an important control over the course of reversal learning agrees oddly with Bitterman's claims on behalf of the cortex.

Even if it were possible to conclude from either of these pieces of evidence that the effects of the treatments in question were specific to reversal learning, we should still need to ask the kind of question that needed to be asked about the results with partial reinforcement: What is it about reversal learning that makes it sensitive to treatments? Bitterman is inclined to stress the intellectual demands it makes of the animal, but the results of an experiment by Gonzalez and Ross (1961), showing that, in the rat, chlorpromazine improves reversal performance (spatial and discrimination problems), might incline us to think that reversal learning includes an important emotional component.

Harlow (1949) introduced a new paradigm for the study of inter-problem learning: the learning-set situation. Full descriptions of the procedures involved can be found in Harlow (1949; 1950; 1959). The animal is given a series (in some cases more than 1000) of two-choice discrimination problems, where the individual problems are assumed to be of approximately equal difficulty. The data can be presented in several different ways to demonstrate the formation of a learning set (LS).

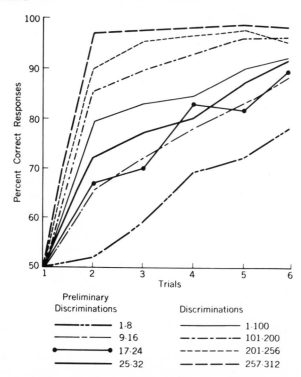

Fig. 7-1. Learning set: correct choices per trial for successive problem blocks. (Redrawn from Harlow, 1949, in *Psychol. Rev.*, 56, by permission of American Psychological Association.)

If we divide the series of problems into equal blocks of problems and plot correct choices per trial for successive problem blocks, we find a family of curves like that illustrated in Fig. 7-1. The most sensitive single index of performance is provided by the data from trial 2: obviously the animal's performance on the first trial of a new problem cannot be better than chance, but obedience to the rule "win, stay—lose, shift" produces perfect performance on trial 2. Alternatively we can display the improvement across problems more directly by plotting some measure of performance on individual problems against successive problem blocks. This typically produces a negatively accelerated curve (see Fig. 7-2).

Harlow (1959) offers four reasons for suggesting that the formation of LS is independent of intraproblem learning. It is important that we should examine them.

1. The typical intraproblem learning curve for the early problems in a series is sigmoid, whereas the curve for later problems—after the formation of an LS—is very different. Harlow suggests that this difference is important evidence in favor of the view that the solution of early and late problems involves different kinds of learning. But, although it would be possible to define LS not simply as any degree of improvement in learning with successive problems but as the appearance of a particular kind of learning curve or as the achievement of a particular level of trial 2 performance, this is not in practice what is done.

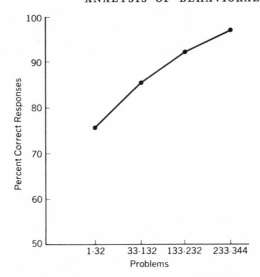

Fig. 7-2. Learning set: correct choices per problem for successive problem blocks. (Redrawn from Harlow, 1949, in *Psychol. Rev.*, 56, by permission of American Psychological Association.)

LS seems more often to be thought of simply as interproblem improvement of which, of course, there may be many different levels. We do not normally point to a particular stage in the interproblem improvement as that at which an LS was formed. Subprimate species have not so far been shown to be capable of the high level of trial 2 performance shown by some primates. If we were to present the data from LS experiments with rats (Koronakos and Arnold, 1957; Wright, Kay, and Sime, 1963) in the way that the data from monkeys is shown in Fig. 7-1, we should never find intraproblem learning curves of the kind that Harlow seems to require if the term LS is to be used. But in practice workers in this area have not spoken of rats as being unable to form learning sets or as showing a degree of interproblem learning that falls short of qualifying as LS; they have simply said that monkeys are better at LS formation than rats, by which they mean that they show a higher degree of improvement across problems. If we use the term in this way, Harlow's distinction between two kinds of intraproblem curves is irrelevant.

2. There is developmental evidence, for the monkey at least (Mason, Blazek, and Harlow, 1956; Harlow, Akert, and Schiltz, 1964), that the ability to develop learning set varies with age.

3. Harlow also suggests that the ability to form LS correlates well with phylogenetic status and that LS information really can be used as a "marker" in a way that no single problem can.

4. He suggests that studies of the effects of brain lesions on LS performance support the view that it is independent of performance on individual tasks.

These last two points demand further inquiry. We have argued previously that a behavioral measure may distinguish between species without telling us anything interesting about the difference between them. It is true that, for the species so far tested, the LS results correlate fairly well with phylogenetic status. It does not follow from this that we are entitled to make any general statement of the kind: the level of interproblem learning or of rule-governed behavior increases with phylogenetic development. Before we could say this, we should need evidence that differences between species with respect to LS formation hold independently of the nature or difficulty of the tasks involved. We do not have this evidence, and indeed we have evidence that such is not the case.

The difficulty is that the level of LS performance achieved is not independent of the difficulty of the individual problems. Harlow and Warren (1952) gave to 8 rhesus monkeys a series of 450 discriminations involving planometric stimuli. A moderately efficient LS was established, but, when the monkeys were switched to a series of 144 problems with stereometric stimuli, not only did the LS transfer but also the level of performance rose. Blazek and Harlow (1955) studied the effects on LS of the difficulty of the individual tasks more thoroughly. In a series of 768 6-trial problems, there were equal numbers of each of 4 levels of difficulty (the difficulty was manipulated by varying the size of the relevant part of the cues). The hypothesis was that, although initially there would be differences in performance on the 4 kinds of problem, as training proceeded these differences would disappear. The prediction was not confirmed. For each level of problem difficulty there was clear evidence of LS formation, but the curves representing improvement across problems for the 4 levels of difficulty remained separate and appeared to have reached asymptotes. It is clear, then, that within a single species LS performance is not independent of problem difficulty. It has also been shown (Schrier and Harlow, 1956) that the size of the reinforcement affects LS performance, independently of difficulty.

This raises serious problems about comparison of species. We have already decided that it is not possible to compare, say, rat and monkey on any single problem because of the impossibility of controlling the large number of variables (irrelevant to our formal description of the problem) that may affect performance. The advantage of LS is that it is supposed to transcend the individual problem. But if we can show that within a single species problem difficulty affects LS formation comparisons between species are of no value until we can find some way of giving equally difficult sets of problems to the two species.

Most of the experiments comparing species for their ability to form LS fail to meet this requirement. Miles and Meyer (1956) compared the performance of 3 marmosets and 3 rhesus monkeys on 1000 6-trial problems. The marmosets showed unmistakable improvement between problems, but they were clearly inferior to the rhesus. In a later study, Miles (1957) showed that the performance of squirrel monkeys on a similar range of problems fell between the performance of the rhesus monkeys and the marmosets. These performance relationships are what the relative phylogenetic status of the three species leads us to expect. But unfortunately the relationships are also what we should expect if there were differences in the difficulty of the individual problems for the three species. The difference between, say, marmoset and squirrel monkey on the same series of problems is of precisely the same form as that for rhesus (in Harlow and Warren's experiment) between problems using planometric and stereometric stimuli. Neither of these studies makes any attempt to answer this objection. Indeed it is difficult to see how it could ever be answered satisfactorily.

What precisely does it mean to speak of equally difficult problems for two different species? We might go to the length of testing large numbers of animals from each species on individual problems until we had, for each species, a set of problems where each individual problem was solved in the same number of trials and where the number of trials required to solve members of the 2 sets of problems was also the same. But it is doubtful, even if we could do this, whether it would help. Even with such relatively similar species as the rhesus and the marmoset Miles and Meyer had to test their animals in somewhat different pieces of apparatus. The greater the difference between 2 species, the greater the difference between the conditions under which they would have to be trained, and the less meaningful it becomes to say that problems are equally difficult just because they need the same number of trials for solution. It is, for example, very doubtful what we could conclude about the relative difficulty of 2 sets of problems from the fact that rats solved members of one set in 50 trials (in the jumping-stand) and monkeys solved members of the other set also in 50 trials (in the WGTA). But, until we have dealt with this problem, there does not seem to be any point in comparing the species for their ability to form LS.

A more satisfactory approach might be to vary the level of difficulty of different LS series over as wide a range as possible. If we found that the difference between two species in the capacity for forming LS held over a wide range of difficulty and over many different testing conditions, we could be more confident that it was important. But we could never be completely confident. Such attempts as have been made in this direction emphasize the need for caution. Wright, Kay, and Sime (1963) found poor LS performance in rats using two-dimensional stimuli. But Kay and Oldfield-Box (1965) showed that with three-dimensional stimuli there was a great improvement, and there is no reason to believe that their testing situation was the best possible for the rat. It is quite possible, as the matter stands, that the apparent inferiority of rats in forming LS arises from the fact that they have been tested with difficult problems or under unsuitable conditions. It would be perfectly possible, by choosing the conditions carefully enough, to conduct a comparative experiment to show that the rat is superior to the monkey.

These arguments about drawing conclusions from LS performance apply equally to the case where the difference is between treated and untreated members of a single species. Chow (1954) tested 3 rhesus monkeys for retention of LS after bilateral temporal lesions; both object and pattern LS's had been established. All 3 animals showed a complete loss of pattern LS and failed to reestablish it. Only two of the three showed any loss in object LS, and they soon reestablished it. Chow's hypothesis was that the well-known temporal deficit in visual-discrimination learning consists of an inability to grasp the essential principle of a problem, and he suggests that an index of this inability ought to be provided by LS performance. He finds that his results support his hypothesis. But there are several difficulties. If he is right, we must conclude that the formation of LS for different kinds of stimulus materials (here patterns and objects) is served by independent capacities. One might have thought that the ability to grasp the principle of a problem was independent of the stimulus materials used, but here LS for patterns is affected, whereas LS for objects is not. (It is

worth noticing that this contradicts a statement of Harlow and Warren
[1952], who, in discussing the transfer they found between stereometric
and planometric stimuli say that "learning set is not specific to a particular class of stimuli.") A further difficulty, as Chow acknowledges,
is that, even before operation, pattern discriminations were harder than
object discriminations and that this difference would almost certainly
be exaggerated by the operation. We could therefore explain the deterioration in pattern LS as a result of the increased difficulty of the
individual problems.

The objections we have been discussing are not intended to suggest
that LS cannot be useful for investigating treatments or phylogenetic
differences. It is simply that LS does not measure some capacity whose
efficiency is independent of individual problems. We cannot argue that
the differences in interproblem learning between rhesus and marmoset,
or between normals and temporals represent a difference in any unitary
capacity. But whatever reservations we must have about the value of
LS capacity as a phylogenetic marker, certain features of the experimental technique remain valuable. Clearly the activity of learning to
learn is important and bears some relationship to the kind of behavior
we call insightful, and the LS experiment is a sensitive and objective
technique for studying it. Other approaches to this sort of problem have
either been too qualitative and informal, like Köhler's (1925), or they
have been (as Harlow says of Maier's work with rats) "an intellectual
tour de force independent of the data."

A most important development of the LS technique is Harlow's demonstration (Harlow, 1950) that the data from an LS series can be made
to yield more than just a measure of improvement between problems.
Harlow shows that there are interesting changes in the kinds of error
an animal makes as the experiment proceeds, and there is evidence that
different patterns of error occur with different treatments. He takes the
view that the establishment of LS consists in the suppression of tendencies to respond incorrectly rather than in the formation of positive
reaction tendencies. He calls these tendencies error factors (EF's) and
shows that they operate independently. Any simple measure of the
course of learning in which responses are counted either as right or
wrong and all wrong responses are counted together may well conceal
incorrect but highly systematic patterns of response. This had been
suggested by Krechevsky (1932) for the rat. He showed, for instance,
that a rat's behavior within a single insoluble problem was by no means
random: there were times when the rat appeared to be responding
in terms of position and times when it appeared to be responding in
terms of a preference for one of the cues. Harlow's position is similar
in that he is suggesting that on each trial there are a number of aspects
of the situation competing to determine the animal's response: the
formation of LS requires the suppression of most of these tendencies
and can be described in terms of their progressive disappearance.

Harlow points out that the course of learning for individual problems gives us severely restricted opportunities for observing the changing balance among these EF's and that they do not reveal themselves
fully until we can observe performance over the problems of a series.
He originally suggested four EF's (Harlow, 1950) and illustrated them
by reference to data from a series of 200 LS problems. *Stimulus perseveration errors* are defined as "the excess of consecutive errors following first trial error beyond those which would be predicted from the

obtained frequencies of all errors." *Differential cue errors* arise from the fact that, in one sense, even after the first (informative) trial of each problem, the situation is still ambiguous. The position of the discriminanda on trial 2 may be the same as on trial 1, or it may be the reverse. It is possible that the animal may respond on trial 2 not to the *cue* reinforced on trial 1 but to the *position* reinforced on trial 1. If this were happening, we should expect accuracy of performance on trial 2 to depend on whether or not the position of the cues had been reversed. *Response shift errors* represent the tendency, after a run of reinforced responses to the correct cue, for the animal to respond to the other cue. *Position habit errors*, so noticeable in the rat, are the consistent choice of a single position, regardless of which cue occupies it. Each of these error factors can be given an unequivocal operational definition, and their frequency can be shown as a function of successive problem blocks. Harlow finds that the proportion of the total errors contributed by each of the error factors changes with training. Stimulus perseveration is fairly common at first, but its contribution declines rapidly; no sign was found of position-habit errors. On the other hand, differential cue and response shift remain important sources of error. The proportion of the total contributed by response shift actually increases, and the differential cue is as important during problems 101–200 as during 1–100.

There are a number of other experiments with normal monkeys that show the fruitfulness of this approach and show that we can think of the different sources of error as independent. If they are, it ought to be possible to affect the balance among them by changes in experimental procedure. There are several examples of this. Schrier and Harlow (1956) gave monkeys 432 problems, on equal numbers of which each of three different reward sizes was used. The general level of performance varied with incentive, but so did the relative contribution of error factors. Differential cue and position-preference errors were unaffected, but response-shift errors were much less frequent with the largest incentive. In LS problems it is possible to ensure that the first choice is reinforced (by baiting both cups) or unreinforced (by baiting neither). The normal procedure is for equal numbers of problems to be of each kind, and in this case no reliable difference between levels of performance on the two kinds of problem appears. However, King and Harlow (1962) showed that a difference was produced—and that it took the form of a systematic change in behavior—if the proportion of the two kinds of problem was varied. If 75 percent of the problems started with trial 1 positive, response-shift errors were reduced in frequency; with 75 percent of the problems starting with trial 1 negative, response-shift errors were increased. This is an elegant demonstration of the lawfulness of errors.

Further evidence that animals can learn to suppress specific kinds of response tendency is provided by an experiment by Riopelle (1953). In an LS series, monkeys had 6 6-trial problems each day. Five of these were completely new, but the sixth was the reversal of one of these five (either the first or the fourth). Riopelle asks what is transferred from one problem to another in LS formation. If it is, even in part, a tendency to select stimuli according to their similarity to those stimuli previously reinforced, it would be expected that animals would perform worse on reversed problems than on the new ones. This was so, but only in the earlier stages of training; by the end of the series, trial 1 performance on new and reversed problems was indistinguishable. Riopelle interprets this as showing that monkeys can learn not to respond to a specific kind of error-producing stimulus.

Harlow's original suggestions about EF's have been formalized and elaborated by Levine (1959), who develops a mathematical model applicable to the first three trials of each problem in a series. Levine's analysis speaks of the relative strength of nine "hypotheses": position preference; position alternation; stimulus preference; stimulus alternation; "win, stay—lose, shift" with respect to position, and with respect to object; "lose, stay—win, shift" with respect to object, manifested either on trial 2 or trial 3; and random behavior. Levine himself shows that his model can be applied to LS data, and Oxbury and Weiskrantz (1962) have made use of it.

There is also good evidence that treatments affect LS formation by changing the balance among EF's. This has the great advantage that, where two treatments affect LS to approximately the same extent (if we count all errors together), it may be possible to show that their effects are different by showing that they change the pattern of errors in different ways, even though they produce the same total numbers of errors. When testing is confined to a single fairly difficult visual discrimination, monkeys with frontal lesions show no loss, whereas temporal monkeys are seriously impaired. However, it has been shown that with a series of object discriminations both groups show approximately equal loss in the formation of LS. Brush, Mishkin, and Rosvold (1961) report two experiments from which they conclude that the two deficits, although apparently equal, are qualitatively different. In the first experiment 200 10-trial problems were given, and a crude score showed that both operated groups (frontal and temporals) were impaired significantly but equally in contrast to normals. Of these 200 problems, 100 were trial 1 positive, and 100 trial 1 negative. If the course of LS formation for the 2 kinds of problem is shown separately, we find that normals do equally well and that temporals do equally badly on both. On the other hand, frontals did as well as normals on trial 1 positive problems but significantly worse on trial 1 negative problems.

Brush, Mishkin, and Rosvold suggest that the reason for this is that frontals have no discrimination loss but do have great trouble in reversing aversions or preferences. They tested this with a series of two-stage problems. For the first 5 trials one member of the pair of stimuli to be used at stage 2 was presented alone, reinforced or unreinforced. Then a pair of stimuli, including the original, was presented; here the original stimulus could be positive or negative (regardless of what it had been previously). This gave 4 possible relationships between the value of the single stimulus in the first stage of the problem and its value later: positive-positive, negative-negative, positive-negative, and negative-positive. It was predicted that frontals would show a high proportion of stimulus-perseveration errors: that is, they would perform worse than normals on positive-negative and negative-positive problems but that they would be unimpaired on positive-positive and negative-negative ones. This was confirmed. Close examination of error patterns here allows us to draw a distinction between two grossly similar levels of performance by frontals and temporals. The temporals' loss seems to be purely in discrimination: in the first experiment, temporals did equally well (or badly) on both kinds of problem, whereas in the second experiment, where the single-stimulus training made the discrimination very easy, they showed no loss. For the frontals, however, the loss appears to be independent of discrimination: it seems to stem from an inability to overcome preferences and aversions. This finding for frontal animals is confirmed by Miles (1964), working with squirrel monkeys. There was a significant difference between frontal and normal animals on 6-trial problems, in the probability that they would make 1, 2, 3, 4, or 5 consecutive choices of the same object within a problem. The difference appears for positive and negative objects.

Mishkin, Prockop, and Rosvold (1962) report an experiment similar to the second part of Brush, Mishkin, and Rosvold's study. Here, only one pretraining trial with a single stimulus was given. It was predicted that positive-positive and negative-negative problems would be easier for frontals than positive-negative or negative-positive problems. In fact, however, where the single stimulus had been positive during pretraining (positive-positive, and positive-negative problems) all animals —frontals, temporals, and normals—were better on the reversal problem (positive-negative) than the nonreversal (positive-positive). The difference for the frontals was larger than for normals and temporals. On problems where the single stimulus is negative during pretraining all animals do better on the nonreversed problems than on the reversed (better, that is, on negative-negative than on negative-positive). Again the difference for the frontals is significantly larger. This result apparently contradicts Brush, Mishkin, and Rosvold, but it is suggested that all animals have a strong tendency on trial 2 to select the novel object and that it is this tendency that the frontals have difficulty in overcoming. Mishkin, Prokop, and Rosvold suggest that in Brush, Mishkin, and Rosvold's experiment, the longer pretraining period (5 trials) was sufficient to establish learned preferences and aversions that masked the appeal of novelty. They reconcile the findings with the conclusion "The analysis suggests that frontal lesions produce abnormal difficulty in suppressing whatever response normally prevails in a situation." The important thing for our purposes is that again this experiment emphasizes the usefulness of looking closely at patterns of error. An experiment reported briefly by Oxbury and Weiskrantz (1962) consists of a series of 1600 3-trial problems, in which for half the trials the object chosen on trial 1 was positive and for the other half negative. Here there is no simple difference between frontal performance on trial 1 positive and trial 1 negative problems, and this appears to contradict Brush, Mishkin, and Rosvold. This is not the place to discuss possible resolutions of this contradiction, and this series of experiments has been discussed in some detail mainly to demonstrate how EF analysis has been used.

This work illustrates particularly clearly one of the points we have been trying to make throughout this chapter. Instead of assuming that the effects of a treatment will fit into one of our predetermined categories (like "learning to learn") we should always be looking for techniques that allow us to analyze behavior in, as it were, its own terms. The original interest in LS experiments for studying the effects of a treatment was based on the assumption that they would reflect differences in a special and significant learning capacity. But what emerges most usefully from them is something rather different. Analysis by means of EF's is sometimes able to take us beyond the statement that a treatment affects a particular kind of learning to a more satisfactory understanding of its effect, and the analysis is performed in terms of categories that have arisen from the close examination of behavior itself.

Summary

It is difficult to imagine an active treatment that could not in some sense be said to affect learning. For the purposes of preliminary screening—for taking a rough-and-ready measure of the potency of a treatment—this lack of selectivity is an advantage, but it has been the main concern of this chapter to argue that for any more sophisticated analysis it is a disadvantage. Simply to choose a learning situation at random and to show that treated and untreated animals perform differently in it, tells us very little about the precise effect of the treatment.

What is needed is that we should be able to break down the area we conventionally call learning into units that respond differentially to treatments. The difficulty, we have suggested, is to know along which lines the breaks are likely to occur. It is possible that clues might be provided by some of the learning differences between species of different evolutionary status, and the problem of analyzing these differences is very similar to that of analyzing the differences between treated and untreated members of a single species. Two approaches to this problem and some of the difficulties arising from them were discussed in some detail. Neither approach offers any straightforward solution to the problem of describing treatment effects. An incidental advantage of this kind of analysis is that we may gain fresh insights into familiar learning tasks.

REFERENCES

AMSEL, A. 1958. The role of frustrative nonreward in noncontinuous reward situations. *Psychol. Bull.*, **55**, 102–119.

AMSEL, A. 1962. Frustrative nonreward in partial reinforcement and discrimination learning: Some recent history and a theoretical extension. *Psychol. Rev.*, **69**, 306–328.

BITTERMAN, M. E. 1960. Towards a comparative psychology of learning. *Amer. Psychologist*, **15**, 704–712.

BITTERMAN, M. E. 1965. The evolution of intelligence. *Scient. Amer.* (January), 92–100.

BITTERMAN, M. E., & McCONNELL, J. V. 1954. The role of set in successive discrimination. *Amer. J. Psychol.*, **67**, 129–132.

BITTERMAN, M. E., WODINSKY, J., & CANDLAND, D. K. 1958. Some comparative psychology. *Amer. J. Psychol.*, **71**, 94–110.

BLAZEK, N. C., & HARLOW, H. F. 1955. Persistence of performance differences in discriminations of varying difficulty. *J. comp. physiol. Psychol.*, **48**, 86–89.

BRUSH, E. S., MISHKIN, M., & ROSVOLD, H. E. 1961. Effects of object preferences and aversions on discrimination learning in monkeys with frontal lesions. *J. comp. physiol. Psychol.*, **54**, 319–325.

BUGELSKI, B. R. 1956. *The Psychology of Learning.* London: Methuen.

BULLOCK, D. H., & BITTERMAN, M. E. 1962. Habit reversal in the pigeon. *J. comp. physiol., Psychol.*, **55**, 958–962.

CHOW, K. L. 1954. Effects of temporal neocortical ablation on visual discrimination learning sets in monkeys. *J. comp. physiol. Psychol.*, 47, 194–198.

DATTA, L. G., MILSTEIN, S., & BITTERMAN, M. E. 1960. Habit reversal in the crab. *J. comp. physiol. Psychol.*, 53, 275–278.

FORGAYS, D. G., & FORGAYS, J. W. 1952. The nature of the effect of free-environmental experience in the rat. *J. comp. physiol. Psychol.*, 45, 322–328.

GARDNER, L. P., & NISSEN, H. W. 1948. Simple discrimination behavior of young chimpanzees. Comparison with human aments and domestic animals. *J. genet. Psychol.*, 72, 145–164.

GONZALEZ, R. C., BEHREND, E. R., & BITTERMAN, M. E. 1965. Partial reinforcement in the fish: Experiments with spaced trials and partial delay. *Amer. J. Psychol.*, 78, 198–207.

GONZALEZ, R. C., & BITTERMAN, M. E. 1964. Resistance to extinction in the rat as a function of percentage and distribution of reinforcement. *J. comp. physiol. Psychol.*, 58, 258–263.

GONZALEZ, R. C., ESKIN, R. M., & BITTERMAN, M. E. 1962. Extinction in the fish after partial and consistent reinforcement with number of reinforcements equated. *J. comp. physiol. Psychol.*, 55, 381–386.

GONZALEZ, R. C., ESKIN, R. M., & BITTERMAN, M. E. 1963. Further experiments on partial reinforcement in the fish. *Amer. J. Psychol.*, 76, 366–375.

GONZALEZ, R. C., ROBERTS, W. A., & BITTERMAN, M. E. 1964. Learning in adult rats with extensive cortical lesions made in infancy. *Amer. J. Psychol.*, 77, 547–562.

GONZALEZ, R. C., & ROSS, S. 1961. The effects of chlorpromazine on the course of discrimination reversal learning in the rat. *J. comp. physiol. Psychol.*, 54, 645–648.

GRICE, G. R. 1948. The relation of secondary reinforcement to delayed reward in visual discrimination learning. *J. exp. Psychol.*, 38, 1–16.

GRINDLEY, G. C. 1965. Personal communication.

GROSS, C. G., CHOROVER, S. L., & COHEN, S. M. 1965. Caudate, cortical, hippocampal and dorsal thalamic lesions in rats: Alternation and Hebb-Williams maze performance. *Neuropsychologia*, 3, 53–68.

GUTTMAN, N. 1953. Operant conditioning, extinction, and periodic reinforcement in relation to concentration of sucrose used as reinforcing agent. *J. exp. Psychol.*, 46, 213–224.

HARLOW, H. F. 1949. The formation of learning sets. *Psychol. Rev.*, 56, 51–65.

HARLOW, H. F. 1950. Analysis of discrimination learning by monkeys. *J. exp. Psychol.*, 40, 26–39.

HARLOW, H. F. 1951. Primate learning. In Stone, C. P. (Ed.), *Comparative psychology*. Englewood Cliffs, N.J.: Prentice-Hall.

HARLOW, H. F. 1959. Learning set and error factor theory. In Koch, S. (Ed.), *Psychology: A study of a science*. Vol. II. New York: McGraw-Hill.

HARLOW, H. F., AKERT, K., & SCHILTZ, K. A. 1964. The effects of bilateral prefrontal lesions on learned behaviors of neonatal, infant and pre-adolescent monkeys. In Warren, J. M., & Akert, K. (Eds.), *The Frontal granular cortex and behavior*. New York: McGraw-Hill.

HARLOW, H. F., UEHLING, H., & MASLOW, A. H. 1932. Comparative behavior of primates: 1. Delayed reaction tests on primates from the lemur to the orang-outan. *J. comp. Psychol.*, 13, 313–343.

HARLOW, H. F., & WARREN, J. M. 1952. Formation and transfer of discrimination learning sets. *J. comp. physiol. Psychol.*, 45, 482–489.

HEBB, D. O., & WILLIAMS, K. 1946. A method of rating animal intelligence. *J. gen. Psychol.*, 34, 59–65.

HILGARD, E. R., & MARQUIS, D. G. 1961. *Conditioning and learning.* (Rev. ed.) London: Methuen.

HILLMAN, B., HUNTER, W. S., & KIMBLE, G. A. 1953. The effect of drive level on the maze performance of the white rat. *J. comp. physiol. Psychol.*, 46, 87–89.

HONZIK, C. H. 1936. The sensory basis of maze learning in rats. *Comp. Psychol. Monogr.*, 13., No. 64.

HULL, C. L. 1945. The place of innate individual and species differences in a natural-science theory of behavior. *Psychol. Rev.*, 52, 55–60.

HYMOVITCH, B. 1952. The effects of experimental variations on problem solving in the rat. *J. comp. physiol. Psychol.*, 45, 313–321.

IVERSEN. S. D., & WEISKRANTZ, L. 1964. Temporal lesions and memory in the monkey. *Nature*, 201, 740–742.

KAY, H., & OLDFIELD-BOX, H. 1965. A study of learning-sets in rats with an apparatus using 3-dimensional shapes. *Anim. Behav.*, 13, 19–24.

KIMBLE, D. P. 1963. The effects of bilateral hippocampal lesions in rats. *J. comp. physiol. Psychol.*, 56, 273–283.

KING, J. E., & HARLOW, H. F. 1962. Effects of ratio of trial I reward to non-reward on the discrimination learning of macaque monkeys. *J. comp. physiol. Psychol.*, 55, 872–875.

KIRK, K. L., & BITTERMAN, M. E. 1963. Habit reversal in the turtle. *Quart. J. exp. Psychol.*, 15, 52–57.

KÖHLER, W. 1925. *The mentality of apes.* New York: Kegan, Paul, Trench, Trubner & Co.

KORONAKOS, C., & ARNOLD, W. J. 1957. The formation of learning sets in rats. *J. comp. physiol. Psychol.*, 50, 11–14.

KRECHEVSKY, I. 1932. "Hypotheses" in rats. *Psychol. Rev.*, 39, 516–532.

KRECHEVSKY, I. 1937. Brain mechanisms and variability. I. Variability within a means-end-readiness. *J. comp. Psychol.*, 23, 121–138.

LANSDELL, H. C. 1953. Effect of brain damage on intelligence in rats. *J. comp. physiol. Psychol.*, 46, 461–464.

LASHLEY, K. S. 1929. *Brain mechanisms and intelligence.* Chicago: University of Chicago Press.

LAWRENCE, D. H. 1949. Acquired distinctiveness of cues: I. Transfer between discriminations on the basis of familiarity with the stimulus. *J. exp. Psychol.*, 39, 770–784.

LAWRENCE, D. H., & FESTINGER, L. 1962. *Deterrents and reinforcement.* London: Tavistock.

LEVINE, M. 1959. A model of hypothesis behavior in discrimination learning set. *Psychol. Rev.*, 66, 353–366.

LONGO, N., & BITTERMAN, M. E. 1960. The effect of partial reinforcement with spaced practice on resistance to extinction in the fish. *J. comp. physiol. Psychol.*, 53, 169–172.

MACKINTOSH, J. 1962. An investigation of reversal learning in Octopus vulgaris Lamarck. *Quart. J. exp. Psychol.*, 14, 15–22.

MACKINTOSH, N. J. 1962. The effects of overtraining on a reversal and a nonreversal shift. *J. comp. physiol. Psychol.*, 55, 555–559.

MACKINTOSH, N. J. 1963a. The effect of irrelevant cues on reversal learning in the rat. *Brit. J. Psychol.*, 54, 127–134.

MACKINTOSH, N. J. 1963b. Extinction of a discrimination habit as a function of overtraining. *J. comp. physiol. Psychol.*, 56, 842–847.

MACKINTOSH, N. J. 1964. Overtraining and transfer within and between dimensions in the rat. *Quart. J. exp. Psychol.*, 16, 250–256.

MACKINTOSH, N. J. 1965. Overtraining, reversal, and extinction in rats and chicks. *J. comp. physiol. Psychol.*, 59, 31–36.

MACKINTOSH, N. J., MACKINTOSH, J., SAFRIEL-JORNE, O., & SUTHERLAND, N. S. 1966. Overtraining, reversal and extinction in the goldfish. *Anim. Behav.*, 14, 314–318.

MASON, W. A., BLAZEK, N. C., & HARLOW, H. F. 1956. Learning capacities of the infant rhesus monkey. *J. comp. physiol. Psychol.*, 49, 449–453.

MAYER, B. A., & STONE, C. P. 1931. The relative efficiency of distributed and massed practice in maze learning by young and adult albino rats. *J. gen. Psychol.*, 39, 28–49.

MILES, R. C. 1957. Learning-set formation in the squirrel monkey. *J. comp. physiol. Psychol.*, 50, 356–357.

MILES, R. C. 1964. Learning by squirrel monkeys with frontal lesions. In Warren, J. M., & Akert, K. (Eds.), *The frontal granular cortex and behavior.* New York: McGraw-Hill.

MILES, R. C., & MEYER, D. R. 1956. Learning sets in marmosets. *J. comp. physiol. Psychol.*, 49, 219–222.

MILLENSON, J. R., & HURWITZ, H. M. B. 1961. Some temporal and sequential properties of behavior during conditioning and extinction. *J. exp. anal. Behav.*, 4, 97–106.

MILLER, G. A. 1964. Lecture before the University of Cambridge.

MISHKIN, M., PROCKOP, E. S., & ROSVOLD, H. E. 1962. One-trial object-discrimination learning in monkeys with frontal lesions. *J. comp. physiol. Psychol.*, 55, 178–181.

MONTPELLIER, G. DE 1933. An experiment on the order of elimination of blind alleys in maze learning. *J. genet. Psychol.*, 43, 123–139.

MOWRER, O. H. 1960. *Learning theory and behavior.* New York: Wiley.

MUNN, N. L. 1950. *Handbook of psychological research on the rat.* Boston: Houghton Mifflin.

OXBURY, J. M., & WEISKRANTZ, L. 1962. Effects of frontal cortex lesions on object discrimination learning by monkeys. *Nature,* 195, 310–311.

PERIN, C. T. 1943. The effect of delayed reinforcement upon the differentiation of bar responses in white rats. *J. exp. Psychol.*, 32, 95–109.

POLIDORA, V. J. 1963. A sequential response method of studying complex behavior in animals and its application to the measurement of drug effects. *J. exp. anal. Behav.*, 6, 271–277.

RABINOVICH, N. S., & ROSVOLD, H. E. 1951. A closed field intelligence test for rats. *Canad. J. Psychol.*, 5, 122–128.

RAJALAKSHMI, R., & JEEVES, M. A. 1965. The relative difficulty of reversal learning (Reversal Index) as a basis of behavioural comparisons. *Anim. Behav.*, 13, 203–211.

RAZRAN, G. H. S. 1933. Conditioned responses in animals other than dogs. *Psychol. Bull.*, 30, 261–324.

REESE, H. W. 1964. Discrimination learning set in rhesus monkeys. *Psychol. Bull.*, 61, 321–340.

REID, L. S. 1953. The development of noncontinuity behavior through continuity learning. *J. exp. Psychol.*, 46, 107–112.

REID, R. L. 1958. Discrimination-reversal learning in pigeons. *J. comp. physiol. Psychol.*, 51, 716–720.

RIOPELLE, A. J. 1953. Transfer suppression and learning sets. *J. comp. physiol. Psychol.*, 46, 108–114.

ROSENTHAL, R., & FODE, K. L. 1963. The effect of experimenter bias on the performance of the albino rat. *Behav. Sci.*, 8, 183–189.

SCHRIER, A. M., & HARLOW, H. F. 1956. Effect of amount of incentive on discrimination learning by monkeys. *J. comp. physiol. Psychol.*, 49, 117–122.

SHEFFIELD, V. F. 1949. Extinction as a function of partial reinforcement and distribution of practice. *J. exp. Psychol.*, 39, 511–526.

SIDMAN, M. 1960. *Tactics of scientific research.* New York: Basic Books.

SKINNER, B. F. 1950. Are theories of learning necessary? *Psychol. Rev.* 57, 193–216.

SMITH, C. J. 1959. Mass action and early environment in the rat. *J. comp. physiol. Psychol.*, 52, 154–156.

STRETCH, R. G. A., McGONIGLE, B., & MORTON, A. 1964. Serial position reversal-learning in the rat: Trials per problem and the inter-trial interval. *J. comp. physiol. Psychol.*, 57, 461–463.

STRETCH, R. G. A., McGONIGLE, B., & RODGER, R. S. 1963. Serial position reversal-learning in the rat: A preliminary analysis of training criteria. *J. comp. physiol. Psychol.*, 56, 719–722.

SUTHERLAND, N. S. 1959. Stimulus analysing mechanisms. In *Mechanization of thought processes.* Vol. 2. London: HMSO.

SUTHERLAND, N. S., & MACKINTOSH, J. 1964. Discrimination learning: Nonadditivity of cues. *Nature*, 201, 528–530.

TEEL, K. S. 1952. Habit strength as a function of motivation during learning. *J. comp. physiol. Psychol.*, 45, 188–191.

THOMPSON, R., & LANGER, S. K. 1963. Deficits in position reversal learning following lesions of the limbic system. *J. comp. physiol. Psychol.*, 56, 987–995.

THOMPSON, R., & MALIN, C. F., JR. 1961. The effect of neocortical lesions on retention of a successive brightness discrimination in rats. *J. comp. physiol. Psychol.*, 54, 326–328.

TOLMAN, E. C., & NYSWANDER, D. B. 1927. The reliability and validity of maze measures for rats. *J. comp. Psychol.*, 7, 425–460.

WARREN, J. M. 1960. Reversal learning by Paradise Fish (macropodus opercularis). *J. comp. physiol. Psychol.* 53, 376–378.

WATSON, J. B. 1907. Kinaesthetic and organic sensations: Their role in the reactions of the white rat to the maze. *Psychol. Rev. Monogr. Suppl.*, 8, (Whole No. 33).

WECHKIN, S., ELDER, R. F., JR., & FURCHTGOTT, E. 1961. Motor performance in the rat as a function of age and prenatal X-irradiation. *J. comp. physiol. Psychol.*, 54, 658–659.

WEINSTOCK, S. 1958. Acquisition and extinction of a partially reinforced running response at a 24-hour intertrial interval. *J. exp. Psychol.*, 56, 151–158.

WODINSKY, J., & BITTERMAN, M. E. 1959. Partial reinforcement in the fish. *Amer. J. Psychol.*, 72, 184–199.

WODINSKY, J., & BITTERMAN, M. E. 1960. Resistance to extinction in the fish after extensive training with partial reinforcement. *Amer. J. Psychol.*, 73, 429–434.

WRIGHT, P. L., KAY, H., & SIME, M. E. 1963. The establishment of learning sets in rats. *J. comp. physiol. Psychol.*, 56, 200–203.

ZEAMAN, D. 1949. Response latency as a function of the amount of reinforcement. *J. exp. Psychol.*, 39, 466–483.

CHAPTER 8

Memory

L. WEISKRANTZ

M EMORY has always been one of the central problems of psychology. It has been attracting more interest in recent years, particularly among those persons working in the border country between psychology and physiology. Although we seem to be on the verge of understanding what physiological changes are responsible for the phenomena of memory, genuine difficulties arise in defining precisely just what we are looking for in such a quest. These difficulties are not solved simply by dressing up our discussion in the garb of modern jargon. As with all our categories of behavior, it is difficult to make a definition that is very sharp, but this in itself is no cause for alarm. Indeed, this difficulty is more or less inevitable, and, at any rate, definitions are usually best formulated after, rather than before, the phenomena start to become clear. Nevertheless, the type of techniques that we consider profitable to analyze and review in this chapter depend on questions of definition to a certain extent, and some preliminary attention to this matter is therefore warranted.

What conditions must be met in order for us to say that an organism remembers? It is obvious that a current event involving a single organism must be influenced by an event that took place in the past. But this, while a necessary condition, is certainly insufficient because all sorts of present events are affected by past events without our wishing to say that memory is involved; e.g., if someone's leg was amputated when he was an infant, it would affect the manner in which he presently walks. Even those very restricted instances prove awkward when the occurrence of an event leads to a different outcome precisely because that same event (or a similar one) had occurred previously. Although these would include the commonplace case of recognition, there are many situations when the same stimulus occurs on two occasions and when the response to the second stimulus is different because the stimulus has occurred previously, and yet normally we would not wish to say that memory has been demonstrated. An obvious case is that of muscle fatigue. Exactly comparable is the case of sensory adaptation, or any of any of the phenomena subsumed under "sensitization" or "desensitization." The issue is arbitrary, and the reader might want to insist that such cases involve memory—after all, it might be said that noting the degree of bleaching in a visual pigment is one method of recording its recent history. But most readers probably will find so broad a definition much too inclusive because we would be forced to say that many physical systems subject to similar modification will be said to possess memory, e.g., metal fatigue or soil erosion. In fact, the requirement merely that there be some sort of recording of past events (or some method of inferring the past history from the current state) would seem to be insufficient. At any rate, we think it more in accordance with everyday usage and more profitable to apply the term *memory* to those cases when a present event can be *related* to a past event by the organism (or system) itself. Thus, an organ such as the eye may demonstrate sensory adaptation, but, until successive stimuli can be compared and an output *made contingent on that comparison*, we do not normally talk about memory. For such a comparison, the eye requires an attachment to a brain. The most basic (but not the only) relations between present and past events are identity and nonidentity: the operations are *matching* and *mismatching*. William James used the language of an earlier age of psychology, but, as usual, expressed the point admirably:

> The successive editions of a feeling are so many independent events, each snug in its own skin. Yesterday's feeling is dead and buried; and the presence of today's is no reason why it should resuscitate. A farther condition is required before the present image can be held to stand for a past original. That condition is that the fact imaged be expressly referred to the past. But how can we think a thing as in the past, except by thinking of the past together with the thing, and of the relation of the two? (James, 1890, vol. I, p. 650.)

The original event must leave some change in the nervous system that permits a present event to be related to it. We will follow convention and call this change a *trace*, without committing ourselves as to its nature or properties.

General Approaches to Study of Memory in Animals

In studying memory in animals, it is obvious that we must have a response by which we assess whether the two events, past and present, have been related by the subject. Typically we associate the first event with reward or punishment. Such conditioning techniques provide by far the most common method by which memory is studied in animals. We will see that they involve certain difficulties, when memory is the special object of the inquiry, that encourage us to use either special cases of conditioning or, rather, different sorts of tests altogether.

Often an inborn response of arousal or orientation is used to infer a mismatch between a current event and the trace of the earlier event. This inference is permissible only when repetition of the same event gives rise to no such response. The waning of the arousal response, or indeed of any response, with repeated stimulation, is often called *habituation*. But it must be pointed out that it is very difficult operationally to distinguish habituation from sensory adaptation, and we have already confessed to a certain reluctance to admit adaptation as a demonstration of memory. It is true that by *adaptation* we generally refer to peripheral processes and by *habituation* to central processes, but whether a process is peripheral or central in itself is scarcely reason for postulating a difference in kind, and, in any case, some of the phenomena generally classified as adaptation appear to have central components (e.g., after-effect of movement, Pickersgill & Jeeves, 1964; negative after-images, Weiskrantz, 1950; Oswald, 1957). Habituation is generally said to follow a different time course than adaptation, but this is not sufficient to permit a qualitative distinction, and the time courses for different examples of sensory adaptation and habituation are so variable as to make the generalization a dangerous one. Sensory adaptation generally involves only a change in sensitivity, repeated stimulation leading to an increased threshold, whereas habituation to a stimulus of a given intensity still permits a response to several types of deviation, including one of *decreased* intensity. This difference is an important one, even though it is probably difficult to characterize all cases of sensory adaptation as simple threshold changes (e.g., color adaptation, particularly in view of the recent rescuscitation of an "opponent processes" type of theory; cf. also, De Valois, 1965). Still, it may be doubted whether even this difference is one in kind, but rather one in complexity of discrimination. If we assume, say, that discriminable differences of any degree of sophistication of which an organism is capable (say, between four-legged and five-legged donkeys) leads to activity in different neural circuits somewhere in the c.n.s., then repeated use of the circuit specific to one of the discriminanda may be said to lead to a rise in threshold for that specific circuit (if no important consequences follow). A five-legged donkey may be said to cause arousal not because it is being "mismatched" with four-legged donkeys but because its circuit has a relatively low threshold. A somewhat simpler instance of an analogous change, except that it is sometimes irreversible, might be the effect of the repeated sounding of an intense pure tone, which is known to decrease the sensitivity of a specific region of the basilar membrane, thereby increasing the threshold for that tone but leaving responses to tones of higher and lower frequencies unaltered.

These comments should not be taken to imply that the mechanisms of habituation are not of fundamental importance in their own right nor that there are not a few instances that cannot be dealt with easily in terms of specific neuronal fatigue, e.g., habituation to a specific rhythm, with dishabituation caused by a change in rhythm or the omission of a beat. One's decision as to whether to consider habituation of interest for the study of memory will depend on whether modifications akin to those of sensory adaptation will be treated as relevant; the present argument merely points out that an operational distinction is difficult and that a matching operation is not necessarily involved in either.

A final approach to the study of matching or mismatching between a current event and a trace of a past event is to make matching the direct object of the study by rewarding the animal for making a match. There are two techniques that do so, the first is "delayed matching from sample"; the other is Konorski's "recent memory" test and is similar to the other test except that the sample stimuli are presented successively rather than simultaneously. Both these techniques will be discussed later in this chapter.

It must be pointed out that by stressing matching we do not wish to imply that this always involves inputs from the environment. The performance of motor skills also involves the matching of a present response sequence with a past one. Their performance involves the interaction of feedback from within the body with environmental stimuli produced by the responses themselves. But skills have been studied hardly at all in animals, particularly in the context of the study of memory, and we will not treat them at all in this chapter.

Finally, the study of animal memory differs from that of human memory in that there is no easily measurable phenomenon of "free recall" in animals: the typical animal studies are of "recognition." Free recall cannot be said to involve matching in any simple sense.

Learning vs. Memory

It has already been pointed out that not only are the behavioral categories of this book broad but that no single technique can be said to be a pure measure of any single category. So much, in our view, is inevitable. Therefore, we should not be unduly alarmed by discovering that so-called tests of memory involve relationships that do not fall within our definition and that, furthermore, tests of categories other than memory involve relationships that do fall within our definition. But the study of learning lies so close to that of memory that some special attention must be paid to the relation between the two.

If we assume that learning is concerned with the *establishment* of "what goes with what," i.e., with associations, then it is obvious that we cannot study learning unless the organism can remember. If the conjoint events require several repetitions before an association can be formed, then the point is obvious enough. But even if learning takes place in one trial, we would not know this unless we could administer a test at a later point in which we presented at least one component of the stimulus complex involved in the original trial. Therefore, memory is inevitably bound up in the study of learning, and it follows that any treatment that produces a change in efficiency of learning as measured in a standard learning test may be doing so because it is interfering with memory; that is, it may not be interfering with the formation of an association but with the storage of this association and its retrieval on a subsequent occasion. Nevertheless, it is clear that if we are interested in the study of learning rather than memory our strategy is to keep the memory requirements relatively easy and constant (e.g., we would not normally have an intertrial interval of 5 years), while varying the nature and relations of events to be associated.

Although it would be theoretically possible to study memory without involving associative learning (as in some cases of human recall), for all practical purposes in animal research it may be said to be impossible. The reason for this is clear: in order to know whether an event can be stored and retrieved (more strictly, can produce a change within the organism that permits a subsequent repetition of the event to be related to the original) we must have a response that we can measure. We obtain such a response by associating our event with another that is known to control behavior in a predictable manner, i.e., a reward or punishment. Learning enters into the picture merely in providing us with a measurable output—but enter it does. (The study of habituation may be said to be an exception to this rule, but we have already seen that there is a question as to its relevance, and, at any rate, the issue is partly semantic because it might be said that habituation is learning that *no* event of any consequence follows the event in question.) In the study of memory we try to keep the learning requirements constant and usually relatively easy while varying the interval between test and retest and the nature and relationship between the events at these two stages (e.g., degree of similarity).

Learning, then, is bound up with the study of memory as a matter of practical necessity. A treatment that impairs performance on a "memory test" may be doing so because it interferes with the original learning. An animal cannot remember what it never learned. But it will be seen immediately that a method presents itself for dissociating the two, because the treatment can be, and, indeed, very often is, introduced *after* the learning session. Independent evidence can be obtained that a learned association was adequately formed either by running a control group with no treatment and demonstrating an adequate association on a subsequent retest or by ensuring that the experimental group had reached a "criterion of learning" before the treatment is ever applied. If the treatment subsequently affects performance on retest, inferences can be drawn about changes in memory independent of those on learning.

So, one conclusion that appears to hold is that the precise point at which treatments are introduced is important in dissociating one type of effect from another. We will later in this chapter discuss this matter in somewhat more detail. The only point to consider here is that an impairment in a "learning task" cannot, by itself, permit inferences to be drawn that discriminate between effects on learning or memory, whereas an impairment on a "memory task" under some circumstances can do so.

But there are some serious difficulties in interpreting results of treatment effects when an animal has first been run until it achieves a criterion of learning, because this will in itself involve repeated trials between which an operation of matching will have taken place. When the retention test is ultimately given, it will not be clear with what it is being matched. Especially when the time course of inferred traces is the object of the study, interpretation will be particularly awkward. This object, in fact, is a very important and popular one because research appears to have revealed that (as will be seen later) the very first traces set up by inputs to the nervous system are especially vulnerable. Because of these difficulties we will not consider here memory tests involving prior learning to a criterion. This is not to say that they are not often useful, as when the temporal life history of the trace is not the main interest or when very long temporal intervals are used between criterion and retention testing (e.g., "Over how many years can monkeys remember specific testing situations"), when retention is studied directly as a function of the number of trials required to reach criterion (Iversen, 1964), or when retention is studied as a function of the number of extra or "overtraining" trials given in the learning session (Orbach and Fantz, 1958). But the general points that we will make about alternative forms of memory tests can easily be extended to such criterion situations by the reader himself if he so wishes.

Standard learning situations involving repeated trials are of great importance when parallel changes are being *sought* in the nervous system, as in the biochemical studies of Hydén, although the situation there was far from standard (Hydén, 1964). Such studies might be instrumental in uncovering what neural changes correspond to the laying down of traces. But although in this chapter we are considering the studies that are best suited for the analysis of *treatment* effects on memory, similar problems of analysis arise when the nervous system is the dependent variable in behavioral studies and a simple correlation between changes in the nervous system and learning is not, in itself, sufficient to demonstrate that the changes have anything to do with traces.

There is a further practical point favoring the use of one-trial learning situations when treatment effects on retention are being studied, which is that in general they are far more sensitive to treatments than tasks based on multitrial learning (unless, in the latter case, the treatment follows each trial—which makes interpretation very messy and, which, anyway, is impossible for treatments such as brain lesions). For instance, pharmacological agents such as anaesthetics have little effect on habits based on repeated experience, whether in man, honeybee (Ribbands, 1950), or octopus (Boycott and Young, 1955). Even such a drastic treatment as lowering the body temperature of the animal to a point that respiration, heart activity, and electrical activity of the brain cease need not be detrimental to retention upon return to normal body temperature (Andjus *et al.*, 1956; Mrosovsky, 1963). Brain lesions in the posterior association cortex do produce modality-specific retention decrements for discrimination tasks acquired preoperatively (Chow, 1952; Mishkin and Pribram, 1954), but the decrement is frequently slight and nowhere as impressive as the effect of similar lesions upon initial learning. And it has been shown that overtraining of the problem preoperatively causes the effect of the posterior lesions on retention to disappear (Orbach and Fantz, 1958).

A more useful situation, then, is one that involves retesting after only a single experience and an analysis of such techniques will follow directly. We have already committed ourselves to discussing the question of the precise positioning of the treatment with respect to training and also to the question of the time course of memory traces, which will take us into a discussion of "short-term" versus "long-term" memory. Finally, we will consider the problems of distinguishing the effects of treatments on "storage" versus "retrieval." These topics will follow directly in order.

One-Trial Learning Situations and Problems Involving "Unique" Relationships

In recent years a few tests have been evolved that are very effective in producing learning in one trial. The tests most commonly involve relatively strong electric shock, associated with a particular position or a particular response. The response occurs spontaneously prior to the shock, as when an animal simply wanders about an open field-type of situation (Bureš and Burešová, 1963) or steps down from one platform to another (Jarvik and Essman, 1960; Chorover and Schiller, 1965), but the response may first be established by a training procedure, as with bar pressing in a Skinner box (Pearlman, Sharpless, and Jarvik, 1961). A single shock is then delivered in conjunction with the response, and the response either fails to occur on the next testing occasion, say 24 hours later, or is at least attenuated; or it appears in a smaller proportion of animals than was the case prior to the delivery of shock. These tests have been designed for use with rats, but there is no reason why they should not also be suitable with a wide range of species.

Learning in one trial using food reinforcement was reported for primates by Jarvik (1953; 1956) who used food itself as the discriminanda. Pieces of bread were dyed with vegetable colors, the negative stimuli having been soaked in a distasteful solution of red pepper extract, bile extract, and quinine. Similarly, discriminations of colored peanut shells (the negative stimulus having had the kernel removed) and of colored plaques with the food placed within a depression on the underside of the plaques were learned in one trial.

These important experiments by Jarvik (see Chapter 9 for a further discussion) have not been used for memory testing, nor has anyone reported results for nonprimates. Nor has any dimension other than color been shown to produce one-trial learning. Iversen (1964) found that monkeys required something of the order of 100 trials to learn a size discrimination between large versus small peanut shells, the negative shells having had the kernels removed.

There are two possible drawbacks to the use of these simple one-trial learning situations for the study of memory. First, only a limited number of tests are available, and it is therefore difficult to use a single animal more than once or to use him as his own control; consequently a large number of animals are required for typical treatment studies. Second, if a memory impairment is only partial, such tests are insensitive for determining the degree of impairment within the *single organism*, because upon retesting, a single experience is sufficient for relearning. Fortunately, a number of tests are available that permit us to overcome both these difficulties, which we will designate as tests involving "unique relationships."

By a *unique relationship*, we mean one that applies among a set of events only on a single occasion. Either the events themselves are presented only once or the significance of the events changes from occasion to occasion. Contrasted to a unique relation is one that is *constant*, by which we mean that the same relation applies among the events on every occasion. Suppose, for example, we have two containers placed side by side. The experimenter might always place food (without the animal seeing him do so) under the left-hand cup. When the animal solves the problem correctly, he is doing so because of the constant relationship between position and food reward.

But the experimenter could, on each occasion, place the food under the cup opposite to the one under which it was placed on the previous occasion. Here the relationship between position and food reward would be a unique one—the correct solution cannot be obtained without reference to one specific event. The reader will no doubt recognize this situation as the delayed-alternation test, which is one example of a test employing a unique relation. Similarly, when a human subject is shown a series of digits and then asked to repeat them, he must solve his problem with reference to a unique set of digits and make no reference to any earlier set of digits he might have encountered.

In every testing situation in which a unique relationship obtains, there is also a constant relationship. The animal must know a rule. In the delayed-response problem, it is "go to the cup just baited"; in delayed alternation, it is "go to the cup opposite to the one just baited." These relations obtain throughout the entire task. In fact, in attempting a classification of various types of situations employing unique relations actually in common use, it is most convenient to classify them in terms of the constant relation associated with them.

There appear to be four principal types of constant relations into which unique relations may be introduced. These may be characterized in terms of the question that the unique event is intended to answer. These are: *Where* ? *Which* ? *Whether* ? and *How* ?. The present classification of unique relations is based simply on convenience. With a bit of sophistry, one can easily claim that the typical "where" or "which" problem is really a combination of two "whether" problems or that the "whether" problem is really a complex "where" problem. Many alternatives are open, especially when theoretical issues are in dispute, but the present classification is used largely for convenience.

Where ?

DELAYED RESPONSE. The spatial delayed-response task is perhaps the one that fits most obviously into this category. As it is commonly carried out, the experimenter places food under one of two or more containers in the presence of the animal. The animal is prevented from obtaining the food, however, until several seconds later. During this interval, an opaque screen is usually lowered between the animal and the containers. When the screen is raised, the animal is permitted to lift any one of the containers. If the animal is to be consistently successful, it must remember the position of the baited container. Hence, the constant relation is based on position—the animal learns to go to the position that was previously baited—and the unique relation is what instructs the animal which position is correct on any specific occasion.

There are, of course, a very large number of variations on the delay-response theme, some of which will be considered later. But anyone who has used any of the usual forms as an experimental test soon discovers one element of uncertainty in its administration. It is obvious that the animal will do no better than chance if it happens to be facing away from the containers whenever the experimenter baits one of them. In fact, just this sort of interpretation of the deficit in delayed response caused by frontal-lobe lesions in monkeys has been offered by Nissen *et al.* (1938), who claim that the animals do not attend to the baiting events and therefore cannot be expected to remember what they did not learn. It is essential that the animal "see" the experimenter baiting the container, but this is a difficult response to control, and in any case the intrusion of the experimenter into the experiment itself leaves open the possibility of a bias of which the experimenter need not be aware. He might, for instance, wiggle the bait back and forth slightly more vigorously for one animal than for another. The only way of ensuring that the animal is responding to the baiting stimulus is to require that he makes a response to the baiting stimulus itself. One technique is to allow the animal to obtain the food immediately following the baiting. After food is obtained, the screen is lowered for the usual period of delay, and then the animal must respond in the usual manner after the delay period. This procedure was adopted by Finan (1942) in a study of frontal lobe function and is called "predelay reward." (As might be expected, animals perform more successfully with predelay reward than with the conventional procedure. One reason, no doubt, is that, in addition to the stimulation the animal gets from the baiting, it is also providing stimulation by actually making a response toward a definite position.) This technique ensures that the animal has perceived the baiting; it still does not ensure that adequate control has been exercised over the baiting or that a bias has not been unwittingly introduced.

It is possible to introduce a greater degree of baiting control by using the so-called indirect method of baiting. Instead of using food as the baiting cue, a stimulus is paired with food and used as the signal. The simplest and most frequent stimulus is a light placed close to the appropriate container. This, in fact, was the technique used in the classic study of delayed response by Hunter (1913). (It should be noted, parenthetically, that the term *indirect method* has been used with several different connotations by different authors). Thus, Maier and Schneirla [1935] appear to restrict the term to those situations in which preliminary training is required. This, however, is not entirely satisfactory because even with food used as the baiting stimulus some minimal preliminary training must usually be employed. Harlow, Uehling, and Maslow [1932] used the term *indirect method* in a quite different way—to refer to the case when the experimenter was not visible at the time of test but may be visible at the time of baiting. Probably the most widely accepted distinction between *direct* and *indirect* is whether food is used as the baiting stimulus [direct] or another stimulus is paired with food [indirect].) It will also be appreciated that "predelay reward" can be used with indirect baiting to control for perception of the baiting stimulus. In fact, with indirect baiting the response to the baited position need not be rewarded with food: one may arrange simply for the response to terminate the baiting stimulus and to initiate the delay period. It will be seen that the indirect baiting can also be adapted to automatic test situations quite readily, whereas the direct method could be adapted only very clumsily. When the experimenter is interested in nonvisual baiting stimuli, he is more or less forced to use the indirect method. For an example of an auditory delayed-response situation, see Blum (1952).

Thus although the indirect method offers certain advantages for stimulus control, unfortunately it usually involves a much lengthier training procedure. In fact, automatic testing of delayed response often appears to extinguish the experimenter rather than to train the animal. Köhler (1925) placed great stress on the more "meaningful" character of direct baiting method.

DELAYED ALTERNATION. The delayed alternation situation is one in which no problem arises about adequacy of perception of the baiting stimulus and in which the experimenter is not as likely to be a biasing factor as in the conventional direct-method delayed response. Because of these features, delayed alternation is perhaps a more popular situation than delayed response, although it is also generally a more difficult problem for animals to master. In this situation only two containers are presented; the animal must alternate his choice from trial to trial, with the interval between trials controlled by the experimenter's lowering an opaque screen.

Two general questions about delayed response and/or alternation have concerned experimenters and theorists alike. On reflection, it will be obvious that these questions apply equally to all of our categories of unique relation problems, but, because they have been discussed primarily in the present context, we will take them up here. (1) How long a delay interval can be imposed without reducing the organism's behavior to chance, and is such a delay related to the phylogenetic status of the organism? (2) In what kinds of activities does an organism indulge during the delay period, and do these have any bearing on how well the animal succeeds in performing the task? Unfortunately, to neither of these questions is a definitive answer available.

1. *Length of delay and phylogenetic status.* Even the most superficial consideration of the delayed response or alternation situation will reveal that any claim for an *absolute* delay limit is virtually meaningless because a whole host of factors will affect an animal's performance (cf. Harlow, 1951). The superiority of the predelay reward technique over the conventional procedure has already been mentioned. In addition, the number of containers and the separation between are important. The role of spatial separation was ingeniously studied by Nissen, Carpenter, and Cowles (1936). They showed that, for chimpanzees at least, spatial separation was more important a factor at the time of baiting than at the time of response. Stimulus factors during the delay also appear to be important. Malmo (1942), for example, showed that monkeys perform better when they are in darkness during the delay period than when in the light. The amount of incentive and the period for which it is exposed would presumably be important variables, although Harlow, Davis, and Meyer (1952) found that keeping the stimulus tray moving throughout the delay period did not produce an improvement in frontal monkeys' performance (which is generally seriously deficient). Gross (1963a) found that increased food deprivation improved delayed response performance of both normal and frontal monkeys, whereas it had no effect on delayed alternation performance by any group.

Various investigators (e.g., Wade, 1947) have found sodium pentobarbitol (a central depressant) improves the performance of frontal monkeys on delayed response. The investigators interpreted this as due to a reduction in hyperactivity during the delay, but Pribram (1950) interprets the result in terms of the effects of the drug on appetite. Weiskrantz, Gross, and Baltzer (1965) give yet another interpretation of the effects of this and similar drugs on frontal delayed-response performance, viz., that their effect on frontals is due to a change in sensory input. The fact that so many disparate interpretations of the effects of treatments on delayed response are possible in itself points to the difficulties of making unequivocal interpretations unless certain conditions are met. These conditions are discussed in Chapter 15. ·

The spacing of trials would appear to be particularly important. Gleitman *et al.* (1963) have shown clearly that massing of trials leads to poorer performance by monkeys in delayed response than does spacing of trials. They comment that, "on the whole, investigators who found successful performance on very large delays have used fewer trials per day (e.g., Adams, 1929; Maier, 1929; Tinklepaugh, 1928), the reverse being true for those reporting rather short delay limits (e.g., Cowles and Nissen, 1937; Harlow, Uehling, and Maslow, 1932; Hunter, 1913)." The spacing of trials is of interest with regard to interactions with particular treatment effects. Spaet and Harlow (1943), for example, claimed that a baboon who was unable to solve delayed response with 25 trials per day solved it when given one trial per day. Wilson, Oscar, and Gleitman (1963), however, found that frontal monkeys still showed the classical defect when given one trial per day. The scheduling of delay intervals and reward would also appear to be important. Harlow, Davis, and Meyer (1952) were able to improve the performance of frontal monkeys in delayed response by inserting visual discrimination trials or free food between delayed-response trials. Gleitman *et al.* (1963) report delayed-response performance deteriorated more after a series of long-delay trials than after a series made up of an equal number of short-delay trials.

The point need not be labored that the whole question of an absolute delay period is clearly anchored to specific situations; precisely the same considerations apply here as to the meaning of "threshold" in conventional psychophysics. Even so, the enormous *range* of delay limits that have been reported comes as a bit of a shock. As routinely administered by investigators of the effects of cortical lesions in the monkey, delayed-response and alternation tasks have limits in the region of 1 minute. Indeed, even 10 seconds is sometimes too great a delay. Yet, Tinklepaugh (1928) found monkeys could perform successfully with delays up to 15 to 20 hours in a situation superficially quite similar! Maslow and Harlow (1932) reported maximum delays for the chimpanzee of about 2 minutes, whereas Yerkes and Yerkes (1928) found delays of 48 hours. Similar considerations apply to other species. An interesting case is described by Thorpe (1956, p. 88) as follows:

> Within the winter territory the exactness of memory for a particular spot may be astonishing. Thus, Swanburg (1951) showed that the Nutcracker bird is dependent during the northern winter on its hazel nuts, and that even when the young are being fed in spring these still constitute the main source of food. This implies great precision and reliability in finding the nuts, and Swanburg found that up to a half a metre of snow did not affect the birds' success in nut-finding. Thus out of 351 diggings observed during the snowy months of January, February and March, 80 to 85% were immediately successful. Since the percentage of success does not drop with the passage of the winter months, it seems necessary to suppose that each bird retains a memory of the sites it has exploited as well as the sites of the caches it has made in the autumn.

Additional control procedures would be essential before such a conclusion could be accepted, but this type of situation differs in one important characteristic from the laboratory delay-response situation, namely, that in the latter the *same* location can sometimes contain food and sometimes not, each particular occasion being determined by the prior occurrence of a single baiting event. Many experimental and naturalistic observations are based on situations where the food is buried on a single or on a few occasions in the animal's view, and the animal subsequently is given a single retention trial. In the conventional delayed-response situation, hundreds of trials are presented involving only two possible baiting positions, and, in fact, some experimenters consider the conventional situations to be a one-trial reversal problem (e.g., Harlow, 1951). In the single occasion food-burying type of observation, the animal must merely remember where the food was buried, not where it was *last* buried. The enormity of the range of delay limits is made quite clear in Maier and Schneirla's (1935) discussion of the problem, and there is nothing to indicate that the overall picture has changed since then. Many of the factors discussed above are important in accounting for the large range of delay limits. Meanwhile, it is clear that the whole subject of delay limits would benefit from systematic investigation. Such an investigation would be of particular value in helping to consider phylogenetic comparisons. For example, Harlow, Uehling, and Maslow (1932) have reported an increased capacity from lemur and South American monkeys to Old World monkeys to the Apes—as indicated by maximum delays and speed of original learning. Large variations in maximal delays within a species as a function of situational factors, however, suggests that these differences are really small in perspective. But without systematic data such assertions are vapid. It is still possible, if factors were rigidly controlled between species as they were in Harlow's experiments, that a fairly reasonable phylogenetic scale of maximum delays could be constructed, despite the great difficulties that are to be encountered in attempting to equate situations for animals with quite different perceptual and motor capacity. Fortunately, the investigator concerned merely with treatment effects on delayed response is not likely to have to enter the doubly sticky quagmire of cross-species comparisons and determination of maximum delays.

2. *Kinds of activity in the delay period.* The question of the type of activity in which the animals engage during the delay period is difficult if one is attempting an exhaustive account. But, because delayed response and alternation involve "positional" relations, orientation responses during the delay may be correlated with degree of success in performing these tasks. An oriented response made at the time of baiting and maintained throughout the delay period would provide an excellent cue at the time of response. Precisely the same type of possibility applies in the analysis of any of the situations involving unique relationships—the animal's own behavior might serve as a mediating response in such a way as to invalidate an interpretation in terms of memory. In many of the situations already discussed, particularly those that antedate automatic testing techniques, experimenters have customarily observed their animals carefully in the delay intervals. But the only safe method of guaranteeing that behavior during the delay is not serving to bridge the gap is to put the delay behavior directly under experimental control. One could require that the animal perform a particular response of a constant nature and could so rule out bodily orientation. Because the delayed-response situation has been used frequently for frontal-lobe analysis in monkeys, it is strange that control of interval behavior has not been attempted more seriously. It is true that various indirect methods have been used, such as drugs, but this is a far cry from a deliberate attempt to control interval behavior, and in any case the side effects of drugs complicate the picture considerably. The study of monkeys with interval behavior under direct control would appear to be a missing but vital step in the analysis of frontal-lobe function.

The issue of mediating responses in delayed response, therefore, is not entirely clear-cut. There seems to be no question that animals can perform delayed response without the help of orienting responses (see Maier and Schneirla, 1935, for review). In one experiment, for example, Tinklepaugh (1932) removed his monkey and chimpanzee subjects from the experimental room during the delay period. Chimpanzees performed at roughly 90 percent accuracy with one pair of containers in each of 10 rooms, all 10 pairs having been individually baited prior to testing. Clearly, an orientation response could not possibly have been utilized.

In fact, many if not most observers of primates in the conventional delayed-response situation would seem to feel that, even when conditions readily permit oriented responses, they are not reliably produced. Monkeys merely sit relatively still or engage in activity that seems to have no orientational aspect. The matter was put to a much more rigid examination by Gleitman *et al.* (1963), who kept careful records of the positions of monkeys at the time of baiting and at the time of choice. They found that the animals generally responded to the side on which they were located at the time of choice but that this position was not consistently related to the position the animal adopted at the time of baiting. In addition, it was "evidently irrelevant whether the positional pattern was continuous or not, a fact which throws some doubt on the bridging function of spatial responses" (p. 450). Evidently, in primates, continuously maintained orientational responses are neither necessary nor preferred. And yet, when Nissen, Carpenter, and Cowles (1936) set up conditions deliberately to encourage chimpanzees to make such a response, the animal's performance improved. "Forcing the animal to go to the correct side of the restraining cage before initiation of the delay provides a superior and perhaps unique cue of which chimpanzees do not, as far as our observation shows, spontaneously avail themselves" (p. 135).

In Hunter's early study of delayed response (1913), he reported definite and consistent orientation responses in rats and dogs, occasional orientation responses in raccoons, but no orientation responses in children. He commented that "some intraorganic factor" is necessary to account for the successful performance of raccoons and children. However, Hunter's training procedure definitely encouraged orientation responses, because he started introducing the delay after animals had first been trained to run toward a lighted door. It has been reported subsequently (see Maier and Schneirla review, 1935; MacCorquodale, 1947; Ladieu, 1944) that rats are capable of delayed response or alternation without producing orientation responses, and the results of spontaneous alternation experiments with rats would also help reject any view of mediation by the rat purely in terms of its bodily orientation.

Very little information is available on this question from research with inframammalian organisms. One study of delayed response in the octopus (Schiller, 1949) is clearly relevant. Schiller allowed the octopus first to detect the presence of a crab. The octopus could reach the bait, however, only by entering a "runway" from which he could enter either the compartment containing the crab or another empty compartment. While in the runway, the octopus could not directly perceive the bait, and his choice upon leaving the runway could be determined only by memory of its location. The delay interval could be varied by altering the length of the runway or by closing the exit for a fixed period of time. Schiller observed that octopuses generally traveled through the runway by proceeding along either of the walls and that they generally were more often correct when they proceeded along the wall closer to the bait. With one animal, when a small hole was placed at the far end of the runway through which the octopus had to travel to effect its exit and which forced the animal to relinquish its usual orientation, its success fell to chance levels. The increased time required to squeeze through the hole was probably not a factor because confinement of a comparable period of time in the original situation did not produce a decrement. Schiller concludes that "a delay of one minute does not interfere with the correct choice. The same amount of delay, however, if it involves disorganisation of the bodily posture while in locomotion, prevents a successful delayed choice" (Schiller, 1949, p. 224). Using a very similar apparatus, Schiller also obtained delays in the minnow of approximately 5 seconds, but states that the fish did not use orientational cues but that it, rather, spent the delay interval in "free swimming" (Schiller, 1948).

Interesting as these observations on a single octopus are, they do not demonstrate that an octopus is incapable of delayed response without the use of orienting responses but merely that in a situation that favors a particular type of "thigmotactic" progression, delayed response behavior deteriorates when the animal is required to change its usual response. Substantiation and extension of Schiller's work with the octopus and other invertebrates would obviously be a great interest in this connection (cf. Wells' [1964] study of the importance of vision for performance by octopus in a Schiller type situation).

Hunter (1913) strongly advocated the use of the "double alternation" maze precisely so that orientation responses could not be used as an adequate explanation of successful performance. But, whereas it is possible to train rats and cats to perform the double alternation once, extending the problem beyond this appears to be difficult (Karn, 1939). For example, in Karn's experiment, the cats could master RRLL but could not extend the series to RRLLRRLL successfully. (See also Yamaguchi and Warren, 1961.)

SPONTANEOUS ALTERNATION. The delayed-alternation situation is one in which the animal is constrained to alternate on each successive trial if it is to be maximally rewarded. But it is known that some species will tend, if given a choice situation (e.g., a T maze) with reward in both goal boxes, to alternate between the two positions on successive occasions. Such alternating is typically far from maximal but, nonetheless, is significantly greater than chance expectation. A number of factors have been found to influence the level of spontaneous alternation, such as motivational level and spacing of trials. These are discussed in a review by Dember and Fowler (1958). Using such a technique, greater than chance alternation with intertrial intervals of up to 90 minutes has been reported in rats (Walker, 1956). Evidently, using "forced trials"—i.e., requiring that the animal go to a particular position before allowing him a free choice—will produce alternation on the free choice after an interval of several hours in rats (Still, 1966). Because of the far from maximal level of spontaneous alternation, it would seem to offer less scope as a sensitive test of treatment effects on memory than the delayed-alternation technique, when the animal is deliberately trained to alternate, although certain subcortical lesions have been reported to cause a decrease in the level of spontaneous alternation (Roberts, Dember, and Brodwick, 1962), whereas neocortical lesion appears to have little if any effect. For example, Still (unpublished) has found that the maximum intertrial interval for spontaneous alternation by rats (several hours in his situation) was not altered by frontal or posterior neocortical lesions (For a comparison with the effects of lesions on *trained* alternation in rats see Gross, Chorover, and Cohen, 1965.).

Which ?

It is a simple matter to change the delayed response situation described above so that the two containers are clearly different and to require that the animal respond to the *same* container that was baited regardless of its position following the delay period. The alternation situation, similarly, could be changed so that the animal is required to respond to the container to which it did not respond previously, again without respect to the positions of the containers. These are called *nonspatial* delay tasks. The question being answered by each unique event is *which* object is to be responded to on the next occasion.

According to Harlow (1951), no subprimate had ever been reported as being able to solve a nonspatial delayed response, although it is doubtful that subprimates have really been given a fair chance. At any rate, Blough (1957) subsequently trained pigeons successfully on delayed matching from sample, which is formally very similar. Clearcut evidence of adequate performance in chimpanzees was provided by Yerkes and Yerkes (1928) and later by Nissen, Riesen, and Nowlis (1938). Harlow (1951) reports successful performance by monkeys. Generally speaking, it would be fair to say that most investigators found the nonspatial problem to be more difficult than the spatial delayed response. Thus, in the study of Yerkes and Yerkes (1928), chimpanzees were found to respond correctly with delays of up to 3 hours in the spatial situation, although the animals in the nonspatial situation tended to break down at the 30-minute limit. The authors comment that the animals tended to go to the earlier position of the baited container rather than to the baited container. Nissen, Riesen, and Nowlis (1938) also found similar relative difficulty of the nonspatial as compared with the spatial delay situations. Harlow argues cogently (1951) against the extension of such findings into a general assumption that nonspatial learning is more difficult than spatial learning and shows that in some situations monkeys can be shown to be "object-oriented" rather than "position-oriented."

> The data show at the least that, if there is a natural preference for position, it can be completely obscured by training. And, one might ask, has differential space and object training ever been controlled in any experiment with rats and monkeys? To control such training would demand immobilizing the animal from birth, if not before. Until such procedures are effected, natural preferences are a philosophical, not a psychological, concept (p. 230).

Philosophical considerations aside, using animals with varied and uncontrolled experience, most investigators would probably agree that spatial delayed response empirically appears to be somewhat simpler than nonspatial delayed response. Nonspatial delayed alternation appears to be even relatively more difficult than spatial delayed alternation and has only infrequently been used (e.g., Pribram and Mishkin, 1956).

Upon reflection it will be seen that the nonspatial delayed-response task is formally related to a number of other "which" tasks, all of which depend for their correct solution upon reference by the animal to a single unique prior event but which operate on different rules. The experimenter has at least three independent variables at his disposal: (1) the number of alternative stimuli present during the original trial as compared with the "retention" trial, (2) whether the same stimuli are used throughout all pairs of exposure and retention trials or whether new ones are introduced for each pair of trials, and (3) whether or not the animal is rewarded during the original exposure trial.

If, for example, the animal is presented with two stimuli during the original trial and is allowed to respond to one of them, thereby receiving reward or nonreward, and then subsequently is presented with the same two stimuli, and if new stimuli are presented for each original trial, then we are using the situation generally called one-trial discrimination learning, which primates can solve in one trial if they have sufficient experience with this general type of task. The rule for correct solution here is "win-stay, lose-shift" (Levine, 1959), as in any discrimination learning situation. (It is obvious that one could insist on the opposite rule, "win-shift, lose-stay," and this was also employed by Brush, Mishkin, and Rosvold, 1961). Most often, in fact, the animal is given more than a single retention trial, as in the "learning set" studies first introduced by Harlow (1949; see also Chapter 7), but Brush, Mishkin, and Rosvold (1961) have used the paradigm just outlined and have systematically evaluated the importance of stimulus preference in normal and brain-operated monkeys by controlling whether or not the selected stimulus was rewarded in the original trial. There is no need, of course, to present both stimuli during the original trial. A single stimulus suffices to enable a rule to be followed. Again, Brush, Mishkin, and Rosvold (1961) have used something quite close to this paradigm (except that the single stimulus was presented five times before the retention trial was presented). New stimuli were used after each retention trial.

If the same population of stimuli are kept throughout repeated series of trials, we have the "delayed matching from sample" paradigm. That is, the animal is presented on the original trial with a single stimulus out of a possible n stimuli. The animal responds and may be rewarded. Subsequently he is presented with all n stimuli, and he must respond to the previously presented stimulus to obtain reward. Usually reward is not presented for the response to the single original stimulus except early in the training phase. But the response requirement is generally retained and is used to terminate the single stimulus and to initiate the delay period.

But as similar as these various situations are to each other, note that a situation involving but a *single* stimulus on the original trial, with reward *never* presented on that trial, can operate on a simpler rule than the others. Both one-trial discrimination learning and delayed response (or alternation) involve an operation of associating two events on the original trial and an operation of matching the original and retention trials. Spelled out more literally, for example, the rule for the subject for one-trial discrimination learning may be: "To win now, stay with the stimulus with which I just won previously or shift from the stimulus with which I just did not." In delayed matching from sample, however, no operation of association is required in the original trial—just the operation of matching between original and retention trials. In this sense, as anticipated earlier in the chapter, this test is one in which matching itself is the object of study.

Details of the delayed matching from sample procedure can be found in Blough (1957) and Harlow (1951), who also discusses rather more complex "which" problems (such as delayed Weigl-principle task). One highly instructive study by Buffery (1964) is relevant to the use of delayed matching from sample to study treatment effects. Buffery varied the population of stimuli and response positions systematically, combined with a "titration procedure" in which the maximum delay interval for sucessful matching was continuously measured. (Schekel [1965] had previously used such a titration technique, which is based on Békésy's, [1947] similar technique in audiometry.) It was found, for example, that not only did frontal baboons have the expected much shorter maximum-delay interval but also that *without* delay they nevertheless were impaired relative to controls when the stimulus population became large. These animals appear to have an impairment in the operation of matching per se. Further differences between frontal and temporal operated and unoperated controls emerged from the analysis of the latency of response to the single sample stimulus and the subsequent matching stimuli. Frontal operates took significantly longer to respond to the single stimulus and temporals took longer to respond to the matching stimuli, which suggested that the former's difficulty lay at the initial stage and the latter's at the retrieval stage. The delayed matching from sample situation would appear to be an especially powerful one for uncovering treatment effects.

Whether?

Just as certain of the "where" and "which" types of problems can be considered as one-trial simultaneous discrimination tasks, so a successive discrimination can be converted into a "whether" type of unique relation. A simple example would be where the baiting of a single container indicates *response* after delay and where nonbaiting of the container indicates withholding of response (i.e., no reward for responding after delay). This procedure can be used either with direct or indirect baiting stimuli.

This type of situation was used by Mishkin and Pribram (1956) in an analysis of the effects of frontal-lobe lesions in monkeys. A comparison was made between two types of "whether" problems: (1) peanut: go; no peanut: no-go and (2) peanut on left: go; peanut on right: no-go. These were compared with two types of "where" problems: (1) peanut: go left; no peanut: go right and (2) peanut on left: go left; peanut on right: go right. They reported that frontal animals had a greater deficit on the "where" type problems than the "whether" type problems.

An interesting variation on the delayed matching from sample theme has been proposed by Konorski (1959). A single stimulus is presented on the original trial, and a single stimulus on the retention trial. If the two stimuli are identical, the animal is rewarded for making a response; if they are different, the animal is unrewarded for making that response. As described by Konorski and used by Stepien, Cordeau, and

Rasmussen (1960), the test falls into the "whether" category, although if two alternative "go" responses were used (e.g., go-left; go-right) it would fall in the "where" category. It is extremely unlikely, however, that animal subjects could solve the latter without great difficulty. The situation has special advantages with auditory stimuli, because these cannot be presented conveniently in the conventional delayed matching from sample situation. Stepien, Cordeau, and Rasmussen (1960) have reported that visual and auditory versions of the task can be affected differentially by different temporal-lobe lesions in the monkey. But the present author and Mingay (unpublished) have been unable to confirm the visual effects and have also found incidentally that the task is not particularly sensitive to frontal-lobe lesions. This insensitivity is of particular interest in view of the marked sensitivity of delayed matching from sample and delayed response to frontal lesions. A possible explanation stems from Buffery's finding that the number of stimulus alternatives in the retention trial of the delayed matching from sample test is an important variable for frontal operates. Frontal-lobe function, as such, is not the object of our attention in this chapter, but the results illustrate the strengths and limitations of particular techniques in a concrete context.

"Whether" type problems, with or without delay, suffer from an inherent defect in that the two responses (go and no-go) are not equally likely and, furthermore, that any changes in motivation or distraction will alter the balance between them. The imbalance can be reduced but not overcome by use of "symmetrical" reward (Weiskrantz, 1956) in which correct "no-go" responses are rewarded.

How?

There is a type of unique relation that is not properly covered in our former categories in which an event signals the *patterning* of responses. For example, signal A might indicate, following a delay, rapid responding; signal B, slow responding. The Skinner box lends itself to the establishment of such differential response patterns, but, because Skinnerian schedules are considered elsewhere, the present discussion will be brief.

The so-called multiple schedule is one example that has been put to use in the analysis of possible memory defects following frontal-lobe lesions in the monkey by Pribram (1958) and Oxbury (1961). These investigators established an alternation between two schedules (with Pribram, between fixed interval and fixed ratio; with Oxbury, between variable ratio and DRL), and they compared the behavior when the schedules were always accompanied by a cue (e.g., red light always present with one schedule, green light with the other) with the situation where no cues were present and the animal had only the prior schedule to indicate to him which schedule was to be operative. Both these authors reported a deficit in frontal monkeys when the cues were absent and reported no deficit when the cues were present.

By and large, however, the category of "how" type problems, in the context of the study of memory, is largely an academic one, as it has not been much exploited. No doubt much of the ethological research centered around the definition of stimulus properties and ancillary conditions for the determination of response patterning could be considered from the present point of view (Thorpe, 1956).

Temporal Discrimination

Still another category of unique relationships, and one that has been used in the analysis of memory changes in animals, is that of temporal discrimination. Temporal discriminations usually have been established in animals in two ways. First, the *preference* of an animal for the shorter of two delays in obtaining access to a food compartment is exploited. An example of this technique can be taken from Finan's study (1939) on frontal-lobe lesions and temporal discrimination by monkeys. The animal is released from a starting box with the doors to two other compartments in an open position. The animal is allowed to pass under either door, the chosen door being closed immediately to form a closed "detention chamber." If, say, the animal chooses the left compartment, he is detained for 30 seconds; if he chooses the right, he is detained for 120 seconds. At the end of the detention period, the animal is released into a food chamber. Since the animal's preference is the dependent variable, prior to the formal experiment it must be established that the animal has no preexisting preference for either side. Furthermore, the preferences of animals in this type of "detention situation" have been hardly studied systematically, and one could easily imagine that rats, say, would rather like being closed up in a dark space. There is another question, moreover, which is whether it is fair to call this kind of test one of "temporal discrimination." If being confined is unpleasant, the animal feels greater displeasure just before it is released from one compartment than from the other, without necessarily being able to discriminate temporal intervals as such. In order to be certain of that, one must place the response of the animal with respect to temporal interval directly under the control of reward or punishment, and such techniques comprise our second (and more legitimate) method.

For example, an avoidance situation can be established in a shuttle box such that the animal is shocked unless it transfers from one compartment to another within a certain specified time interval. The interval can be initiated by a definite signal, such as raising the screen between the compartments, a visual flicker, a buzzer, such that the animal must transfer not earlier than, say, 10 seconds and not later, say, than 20 seconds after the initiation of the signal (Finan, 1939). The interval can also be initiated by the animal's previous response, or the "safe" interval can occur cyclically. Once the actual contingencies are established, the shuttle box is not necessarily the most convenient situation in which to study them. The Sidman avoidance procedure is one form of temporal discrimination carried out with a single response lever in a Skinner box (see Chapter 3), and any one of the three types of contingencies just mentioned—response-initiated, stimulus-initiated, or cyclical—can be established in a Skinner box.

Similar considerations exist with the use of positive reinforcement. The cyclical case is simply the well-known "fixed interval" schedule with "limited hold." The response-initiated case is also widely used, generally known as "differential reinforcement of low rate," or DRL. In this situation, the animal is rewarded for lever pressing only if he waits at least x seconds after the last response was made. Any response that occurs less than x seconds following the previous response "resets" the apparatus timer to zero. The technique has proved to be sensitive both to drug treatment (Segal, 1962) and to frontal-lobe lesions (Oxbury, 1961; but see Stamm, 1963).

From quite another approach, temporal discrimination calls to mind the multiplicity of "biological clocks" that have been described and analyzed with elegance by zoological research workers (cf. Chapter 5). Harker (1964) for example, has found that the activity of ascent and descent of the mayfly nymph will show a rhythmic activity after a single experience to a light-dark alternation over a single 24 hour period. Rhythmic activity in bees and other arthropods has also been analyzed in detail (cf. Thorpe, 1956, pp. 251 ff.). Such rhythmic behavior, although perhaps depending on environmental change for its initial establishment, can often be sustained in a subsequently uniform environment. It is clear in many instances that the behavior parallels a rhythmic metabolic process. It is doubtful if we would wish to term all these examples of "memory" in the sense in which we have used the word heretofore, although they are obviously of great interest. There are, however, numerous examples of mnemonic processes in animals observed under nonlaboratory conditions that would make them excellent candidates for the analysis of treatment effects. Many invertebrate species in particular demonstrate instinctive patterns that are steered by isolated events that must be remembered. Conditions affecting the behavior of the digger wasp, for example, in burying captive honeybees that it paralyzes, for storage as food for the larvae, have been analyzed in some detail. The digger wasp also demonstrates quite rapid learning of general features of the surroundings of its nest hole, which can be retained for many hours without further practice. Tinbergen found that a 9 second flight was sufficient for learning of landmarks in a new situation. Such instances of rapid learning make them ideal candidates for the study of memory function. (See Thorpe for general review.) The dancing behavior of the honeybee also demonstrates to us memory processes of an impressive order, particularly when we learn that the honeybee can convey, through its dancing pattern, information of the distance of food up to 11 kilometres from the hive (see Thorpe, 1956). Other examples of relevant ethological observations could be offered, e.g., the retrieval of food by the nutcracker bird and the homing behavior of salmon and trout.

The selection of species and type of test will be determined by many different considerations, many of them in conflict with each other. By and large, investigators of treatment effects of, e.g., pharmacological agents or neurological manipulations, will prefer mammals as opposed to lower forms because of the interest in extrapolating to man, and often they will wish to exert such control over the behavior under consideration that the distinction between "natural" and "unnatural" becomes pointless.

Positioning of Treatments and Short-Term Vs. Long-Term Memory

We have already pointed out that a treatment introduced following the original learning trial allows somewhat simpler inferences to be drawn than when it is introduced during learning. It is important to examine somewhat more precisely the implications of the position of a treatment in the total sequence of testing.

In order to refer to the various stages of testing more conveniently, we can set out the following sequence and can label various positions at which treatments might be introduced by the letters A through F.

A	B	C	D	E	F
	Learning			Retention	Retention
———	(Exposure	———————————————		Trial	Trial
	Trial)				

When the situation is a one-trial learning one, the effect of a treatment at any one of these stages will usually be compared with a control group that either has no treatment or some alternative treatment.

Sometimes it will be possible to use the animal as its own control by running a number of sequences of exposure and retention trials involving different problems and with varying treatments. For the sake of the present analysis, which procedure is used is not relevant to the discussion that follows. Although it is fairly easy to define the point at which the treatment is introduced, it is much more difficult to say when the treatment is no longer in force.

When a treatment such as electroconvulsive shock (ECS) is introduced at C, with C occurring immediately after the exposure trial, there is usually an impairment on the retention trial given at E say, 24 hours afterwards. If the treatment is given after a longer interval, say 6 hours, at D, then generally no impairment is found or it is significantly less than the impairment found with treatment at C (Hudspeth, McGaugh, and Thomson, 1964; Chorover and Schiller, 1965). A large number of treatments, such as brain concussion (Russell, 1959), anaesthetics (Pearlman, Sharpless, and Jarvik, 1961), spreading depression (Bureš and Burešová, 1963), and brain stimulation (Bickford, *et al.*, 1958), are all said to have this retrograde "amnesic" effect, and certain treatments such as that of strychnine have a facilitating effect (Lashley, 1917; McGaugh, *et al.*, 1962). One is naturally led to the idea that the traces set up by the exposure trial gradually change their state so that they are very vulnerable to disturbance immediately after they are initiated but so that they become gradually "consolidated." This idea, in turn, has been linked somewhat superficially to the speculation that there are two kinds of traces: a short-lasting one, susceptible to disrupting treatments, and a long-lasting and insusceptible one. These, in turn, have been linked to the speculation that the former is electrical in nature and that the latter involves a structural change within the nervous system. These, in turn, have been linked to a distinction between "short-term" and "long-term" memory, based inferences from purely behavioral research with such material as recall of sequences of digits in dichotic listening experiments (Broadbent, 1957). This is not the place to discuss these speculations in detail, but the relevance of treatment effects of ECS to them obviously depends in large part on the question of what legitimate inferences can be drawn from the treatment effects. The only thing that is clear is that different authors use quite different implicit assumptions and definitions when referring to short-term memory. Some of the issues have been discussed by Weiskrantz (1966), who concluded that no analysis merely of the retrograde effects of ECS or other treatments is able to specify the limits of a hypothetical short-term trace.

More immediately, three questions of a somewhat less speculative nature can be ventilated. First, what consistency is there in the relationship between the interval between the exposure trial and a treatment at C, and the degree of impairment on the retention trial at E. A cursory glance at the literature will convince the reader that the critical interval within which the treatment is effective is extremely variable, ranging from a second or so with ECS (Mayer-Gross, 1943; Chorover and Schiller, 1965) to months or even years in the case of brain damage (Russell, 1959). The only statement that can be made with any reliability is that retention of recent events is more susceptible to interference than less recent events. It is true that the modal figure from animal work appears to be of the order of 45 minutes, but it is, nevertheless, so variable that it is extremely difficult to argue for a consolidation period possessing any uniformity of time course (cf. Weiskrantz, 1966). The alternatives are to say that different traces have different time courses or that additional factors other than consolidation complicate the issue. What sort of additional factors need we consider?

This brings us to our second question: can the treatment itself be considered as constituting additional exposure trial and, therefore, as having an effect on retention not because of any retroactive effect but because it introduces new associations.

Variables such as ECS may be aversive in their own right and so be capable of punishing a response that has just previously been made. Such a position has been put forward by Coons and Miller (1960), who convincingly demonstrated that ECS can have aversive properties in its own right quite independently of any amnesic effects (see also a similar position by Adams and Lewis, 1962a & b). The empirical issue is still under investigation, but it has become apparent that the contingencies in the original exposure trial must be so arranged as to yield one outcome if the treatment at C is producing an amnesic effect and to yield another outcome if it is producing a learning effect because of its punishing or reinforcing properties. Thus, in an exposure trial delivering strong shock for stepping down from a platform to the floor, if the ECS is delivered immediately after the animal has stepped down and while the animal is on the floor, any aversive properties it possesses should summate with the experimental shock to yield a greater resistance to stepping down, whereas an amnesic effect should yield an opposite result. The latter result is obtained, although, if the experiment is then repeated several times with the same animal, it has been reported that the tendency to make the punished response gradually diminishes (Hudspeth, McGaugh, and Thomson, 1964). Thus an aversive effect is not necessarily completely attentuated by the ECS.

Third, in what sense might E.C.S. or any other treatment be interfering with "consolidation" of a trace rather than with the subsequent availability of the trace? This is an extremely important question to which we will return at a later point. For the moment, one way, which is illuminating, of putting the question is to ask how permanent the retention impairment is. If, for example, there is an impairment at E but not at F, it is obvious that the same trace must have been present but inaccessible at E. Many clinicians, for example, refer to a gradual shrinkage with time of retrograde amnesia by brain damage, and there appears to be a rough correlation between the degree of posttraumatic confusion and the period over which retrograde amnesia extends backwards in time (Russell, 1959). This type of question has hardly been put to the test with treatments such as ECS, although Chevalier (1965) did vary the interval between exposure trial and retention over a wide range of several days, holding the interval between exposure trial and ECS constant at a brief value of seconds, and he found no recovery from amensic effects. What is required is a systematic examination of this type for a wide range of intervals between learning trial and ECS. One recent study (A. Miller, unpublished) partly fulfills such a requirement and, together with other material (Zinkin and Miller, 1967), makes it clear beyond any reasonable doubt that retention tested at 48 hours after ECS is much better than retention *by the same rats* at 24 hours, even when no retention is detectable at 24 hours. The improvement is a function of the interval between exposure trial and ECS.

A most instructive study indicating a failure of accessibility rather than destruction of traces has been provided by Bickford *et al.* (1958), who stimulated human patients via deep electrodes in the temporal lobe. They found that the period over which the resulting retrograde amnesia extended backwards in time varied directly with the length of stimulation (up to several days for stimulation of about 10 seconds). Furthermore, the amnesia gradually disappeared with time following stimulation. Clearly, we are dealing here with inaccessibility rather than with destruction; it is as if the stimulation adds noise to the storage system, gradually dissipates, and that older traces produce stronger signals than younger traces and are more likely, therefore, to be detected. The detectability will depend both on the noise level (the longer the stimulation, the greater the noise level) and the age of the trace. Whether or not this is a useful model remains to be seen (cf. Weiskrantz, 1966, for a more complete elaboration).

So far we have considered only brief treatments presented at *C* or *D* in our sequence. When we consider introduction of the treament at *E*, and when no retention is found at *E* while the treatment is still being applied, then no reasonable experimenter could fail to consider the hypothesis of inaccessibility by going on to study retention at *F* without the treatment. Some of the older studies showing "dissociation" of memory under curare (Girden, 1940) may be taken as examples of this type of effect (see also the more recent work with sodium pentobarbital, Overton, 1964), whereas claims that sodium amytal or hypnosis make certain otherwise inaccessible events available may be taken as an example of the same type of effect but of one that is opposite in direction. Given the ease with which the hypothesis of inaccessibility is formulated with treatments at *E*, it is surprising that the same hypothesis is so rarely tested in precisely the same manner when the treatment is introduced earlier at *C* or *D*.

Earlier in this chapter we attempted to justify the importance that we have attached to one-trial learning situations, and now we retract somewhat and point out that, in animal experiments, at least, they may have certain disadvantages, particularly when the treatments are of long duration or are permanent, such as brain lesions. All of our treatments heretofore discussed have been introduced following the learning trial. Suppose, however, that none of these, even with exhaustive study, is found to have any effect on retention for events exposed to the subject prior to the treatment—can we thereby conclude that we have eliminated all the possibility of effects of the treatment on memory? Consider a brain operation that has no effect on retention of *past* events but interferes with the retention of events presented *after* the operation. But, one may say, that is impossible to demonstrate because the animal will be unable to learn following the operation and because the failure to show retention may be due to a variety of causes, such as blindness. It is impossible to demonstrate a specific impairment in retention unless some evidence can be produced that the animal detected events in their appropriate relationship in the first place. That is true enough, but there may be impairments of the kind that allow the animal to retain information for much shorter time than is true of the normal animal. In fact, precisely such impairments do arise commonly with brain pathology and/or as the result of specific lesions. Penfield and Milner (1958) and Scoville and Milner (1957) have reported that bilateral temporal lobe lesions in man (or lesions inferred to be bilateral) allow the patients to perform satisfactorily on tasks that they can bridge a short interval without distraction but that subsequently they have no retention for these tasks. The state can sometimes be induced temporarily in patients with unilateral temporal abnormality by anaesthetizing the normal hemisphere by the technique of Wada and Rasmussen (1960). Similar defects, although different in detail, occur in Korsakoff psychosis and various forms of brain pathology and also in senility. The commonness of this type of defect suggests that they have considerable importance for the drawing of inferences about memory mechanisms in the nervous system. How can we study these defects in animals?

The general form of the result that is required is as follows: treatment is introduced at A, and retention is found to be unimpaired at E but impaired at F (without specifying here the time intervals between B, E, and F). If the learning situation is simply a one-trial learning situation, then the sensitivity of our measure of retention will be small, because in the retention trials the appropriate response will either occur or it will not. To determine the shape of the transition from E to F will require either large numbers of subjects, which is often inconvenient or impossible, or large numbers of repeated tests on the same animal, which will be very time consuming and, if there are slow changes in the effect of the treatment occurring over time, will be difficult to interpret. An alternative type of testing has been evolved that has turned out to be extremely useful for studying the type of defect in question. When results are of the proper type, it is possible to draw the startling conclusion that animals can learn but not remember or, put more cautiously, that they can remember long enough to demonstrate learning but not long enough to demonstrate retention at some subsequent point.

The technique involves teaching the animal a very simple task requiring, e.g., 10 to 15 trials to reach a criterion of 9 out of 10 correct. Monkeys, particularly if they have been trained on a "learning set" procedure (see Chapter 7), can quickly solve discrimination problems based on pairs of small three-dimensional objects, such as toys, that vary markedly from each other in color, size, shape. At some later point the animal can be retrained, and the trials required for relearning can be compared with the original learning scores. Iversen and Weiskrantz (1964) have used the following schedules:

Day 1   Problems A and B
Day 2   B and C
Day 3   C and D
Day 4   D and E
                                   etc.

and

Day 1   Problems A and B and C
Day 2   B and C and D
Day 3   C and D and E
Day 4   D and E and F
                                   etc.

and

Day 1   Problems A and B and A
Day 2   B and C and B
Day 3   C and D and C
Day 4   D and E and D
                                   etc.

In this way, retention between days and within a day can be assessed. A large number of permutations are available, and Iversen (1964) has used some of them to investigate the effects of temporal lobe and other lesions. Buffery (1964) has used a highly similar approach except that he varied the numbers of discriminanda systematically between two and eight. Buffery's study in particular allows one to draw the conclusion that temporal lobe monkeys can learn such simple tasks at a normal rate but are markedly impaired on retention 24 hours later. Quite interestingly, he also found that frontal monkeys were slower to learn when the number of discriminanda was large but were perfectly normal in their retention 24 hours later.

A somewhat similar approach was also used by Gross (1963b) with the paradigm

Day 1   A and B
Day 2   B and A
Day 3   A and B
Day 4   B and A

with frontal monkeys where B is a single *reversal* of A, and he concluded that the monkeys were normal in retention between days but defective in reversing within a day. He also suggested that the degree of impairment in reversal should be an inverse function of the number of trials given prior to reversal. Weiskrantz, Mihailović, and Gross (1962) have also reported that frontal-lobe stimulation produced impaired learning when the tasks were relatively simple but produced normal learning when the tasks were relatively difficult. The results are consistent with the view (Gross and Weiskrantz, 1964) that recent but not distant events are relatively inaccessible for frontal monkeys. Other interpretations of the frontal defect remain possible (and, indeed, are necessary), but the point is that, with thought, paradigms can be constructed that test the effectiveness of retention of events *following* a treatment in such a way as to dissociate effects occurring at different stages of the gap between original exposure of the material and subsequent retesting.

Storage vs. Accessibility

We have already seen that certain treatments can be shown to affect retention because of failure of retrieval rather than destruction of traces. Given a retention impairment with a particular treatment, the demonstration that it is specifically a retrieval failure always requires that the impairment be undone—either by another treatment or simply by the passage of time. It follows that a retention failure can never conclusively be shown to depend on the destruction of traces, because it is always possible that some circumstance would be found in which retention would be unimpaired. The demonstration of trace destruction is, then, tantamount to proving the universal negative.

Treatments that are irreversible are at a particular disadvantage in helping to decide whether a retention failure is a retrieval failure. Stable memory impairments resulting from brain lesions are doomed to be indecisive until such time as reversible lesions can be made. Certain stimulation techniques (Stamm, 1963; Chow, 1961; Weiskrantz, Mihailović, and Gross, 1962) are promising in this regard because they can produce reversible states that closely resemble, in their behavioral effects, the effects of the surgical removal of tissues. "Reversible lesions" both of frontal cortex and temporal cortex have been made in the monkey, but the feature of reversibility has not been particularly exploited to help make the distinction being drawn here. It is clearly evident from Chow's study, however, that temporal-lobe stimulation in the monkey produces an impairment in accessibility, because animals performed at chance levels on visual discrimination tasks learned prior to the stimulation sessions but performed at high levels during control sessions. But the effect of the stimulation on the establishment and durability of traces is much less clear-cut; Chow's animals were unable to learn visual discrimination during stimulation, but no control data are available to determine whether the animals' subsequent learning showed any benefit from their experience under stimulation. The fact that higher-than-chance performance was seen even in the first 15 poststimulation learning trials suggests that there may have been some savings. But without more data it is impossible to draw any conclusions about whether the so-called learning impairment in temporal monkeys is due primarily to a retrieval difficulty.

Other useful reversible treatments developed in recent years in connection with alteration of brain activity are the spreading-depression technique of Bureš and Burešová (1963), and the unilateral cerebral anaesthetization technique of Wada and Rasmussen (1960). In the former, cortical tissue is temporarily depressed by electrical or chemical stimulation, and usually it is found that a rat trained with unilateral cortical depression is unable to demonstrate retention when the other cortical hemisphere is depressed and when the original is allowed to recover. Russell and Ochs (1963) have reported very rapid relearning of a simple bar-pressing response under such circumstances, which suggests a degree of savings.

The Wada and Rasmussen technique (1960) has been used to determine speech lateralization and also to investigate memory disorders of the type found in patients with bilateral temporal pathology. Evidently such a disorder can be established temporarily by anaesthetizing the contralateral hemisphere in patients with unilateral temporal pathology (Milner, Branch, and Rasmussen, 1962). The task involved a series of pictures, including some that were presented while the patients were under amytal, and they showed errors of recognition. The interesting question in the present context is whether the unrecognized pictures were recognized after the amytal state, and the answer appears to be that they were not (Milner, personal communication).

In an earlier study (Penfield and Milner, 1958) patients with bitemporal pathology were not aided in their recall by "therapy" with sodium amytal. Thus, to date, the bitemporal impairment in man appears to involve the durability of traces rather than their accessibility, but as has been pointed out, such a view is impossible to prove. As with any attempt to prove the universal negative, one simply continues the search diligently, trying to make the conditions for finding a positive effect optimal.

No doubt, information about neural changes associated with "traces" revealed by the biochemist, electrophysiologist, and electron microscopist will someday aid in the interpretation of treatment effects on memory. Just as certainly such treatment effects will themselves guide these research workers in their search.

REFERENCES

ADAMS, D. K. 1929. Experimental studies of adaptive behavior in cats. *Comp. Psychol. Monogr.*, 6, 168.

ADAMS, H. E., & LEWIS, D. J. 1962a. Electroconvulsive shock, retrograde amnesia and competing responses. *J. comp. physiol. Psychol.*, 55, 299–301.

ADAMS, H. E., & LEWIS, D. J. 1962b. Retrograde amnesia and competing responses. *J. comp. physiol. Psychol.*, 55, 302–305.

ANDJUS, R. K., KNÖPFELMACHER, F., RUSSELL, W. R., & SMITH, A. U. 1956. Some effects of hyperthermia on learning and retention. *Quart. J. exp. Psychol.*, 8, 15–23.

BÉKÉSY, G. VON 1947. A new audiometer. *Acta otolaryngol*, 35, 411–422.

BICKFORD, R., MULDER, D. W., DODGE, H. W., SVIEN, H. J., & ROME, H. P. 1958. Changes in memory function produced by electrical stimulation of the temporal lobe in man. *Res. Publs. Ass. Res. nerv. ment. Dis.*, 36, 227.

BLOUGH, D. S. 1957. Effects of drugs on visually controlled behavior in pigeons. In Garattini, S., & Ghetti, V. (Eds.), *Psychotropic drugs*. Amsterdam: Elsevier.

BLUM, R. A. 1952. Effects of subtotal lesions of frontal granular cortex on delayed reaction in monkeys. *Arch. Neurol. Psychiat.* (Chicago), 67, 375–386.

BOYCOTT, B. B., & YOUNG, J. Z. 1955. A memory system in *Octopus vulgaris* Lamarck. *Proc. R. Soc. B.*, 143, 449–480.

BROADBENT, D. E. 1957. Immediate memory and simultaneous stimuli. *Quart. J. exp. Psychol.*, 9, 1–11.

BRUSH, E. S., MISHKIN, M., & ROSVOLD, H. E. 1961. Effects of object preferences and aversions on discrimination learning in monkeys with frontal lesions. *J. comp. physiol. Psychol.*, 54, 319–325.

BUFFERY, A. W. H. 1964. The effects of frontal and temporal lobe lesions upon the behaviour of baboons. Unpublished doctoral dissertation, University of Cambridge.

BUREŠ, J., & BUREŠOVÁ, O. 1963, Cortical spreading depression as a memory disturbing factor. *J. comp. physiol. Psychol.*, 56, 268–272.

CHEVALIER, J. A. 1965. Permanence of amnesia after a single post trial electroconvulsive seizure. *J. comp. physiol. Psychol.* 59, 125–127.

CHOROVER, S. L., & SCHILLER, P. H. 1965. Short-term retrograde amnesia in rats. *J. comp. physiol. Psychol.*, 59, 73–78.

CHOW, K. L. 1952. Further studies on selective ablation of association cortex in relation to visually mediated behavior. *J. comp. physiol. Psychol.*, 45, 109–118.

CHOW, K. L. 1961. Effect of local electrographic after-discharge on visual learning and retention in monkey. *J. Neurophysiol.*, 24, 391–400.

COONS, E. E., & MILLER, N. E. 1960. Conflict versus consolidation of memory traces to explain "retrograde amnesia" produced by ECS. *J. comp. physiol. Psychol.*, 53, 524–531.

COWLES, J. T., & NISSEN, H. W. 1937. Reward-expectancy in delayed responses of chimpanzees. *J. comp. Psychol.*, 24, 345–358.

DEMBER, W. N., & FOWLER, H. 1958. Spontaneous alternation behavior. *Psychol. Bull.*, 55, 412–428.

DEVALOIS, R. L. 1965. Behavioral and electrophysiological studies of primate vision. In Neff, W. D. (Ed.), *Contributions to sensory psychology*, Vol. I. New York: Pergamon. Pp. 137–178.

FINAN, J. L. 1939. Effects of frontal lobe lesions on temporally organized behavior in monkeys. *J. Neurophysiol.*, 2, 208–226.

FINAN, J. L. 1942. Delayed response with pre-delay reinforcement in monkeys after the removal of the frontal lobes. *Amer. J. Psychol.*, 55, 202–214.

GIRDEN, E. 1940. Cerebral mechanisms in conditioning under curare. *Amer. J. Psychol.*, 53, 397–406.

GLEITMAN, H., WILSON, W. A., Jr., HERMAN, M., & RESCORLA, R. A. 1963. Massing and within-delay position as factors in delayed-response performance. *J. comp. physiol. Psychol.*, 56, 445–451.

GROSS, C. G. 1963a. Effect of deprivation on delayed response and delayed alternation performance by normal and brain operated monkeys. *J. comp. physiol. Psychol.*, 56, 48–51.

GROSS, C. G. 1963b. Discrimination reversal after lateral frontal lesions in monkeys. *J. comp. physiol. Psychol.*, 56, 52–55.

GROSS, C. G., CHOROVER, S. L., & COHEN, S. M. 1965. Caudate, cortical, hippocampal and dorsal thalamic lesions in rats: Alternation and Hebb-Williams maze performance. *Neuropsychologia*, 3, 53–68.

GROSS, C. G., & WEISKRANTZ, L. 1964. Some changes in behavior produced by lateral frontal lesions in the macaque. In Akert, K., & Warren, J. M. (Eds.), *Frontal cortex and behavior.* New York: McGraw-Hill.

HARKER, J. E. 1964. *The physiology of diurnal rhythms.* Cambridge: Cambridge University Press.

HARLOW, H. F. 1949. The formation of learning sets. *Psychol. Rev.*, 56, 51–65.

HARLOW, H. F. 1951. Primate learning. In Stone, C. P. (Ed.), *Comparative psychology.* London: Staples Press. Pp. 183–238.

HARLOW, H. F., DAVIS, R. T., & MEYER, D. R. 1952. Analysis of frontal and posterior association syndromes in brain-damaged monkeys. *J. comp. physiol. Psychol.*, 45, 419–429.

HARLOW, H. F., UEHLING, H., & MASLOW, A. H. 1932. Comparative behavior of primates. I. Delayed reaction tests on primates. *J. comp. Psychol.*, 13, 313–343.

HUDSPETH, W. J., McGAUGH, J. L., & THOMSON, C. W. 1964. Aversive and amnesic effects of electroconvulsive shock. *J. comp. physiol. Psychol.*, 57, 61–64.

HUNTER, W. S. 1913. The delayed reaction in animals and children. *Behav. Monogr.*, 2, 86.

HYDÉN, H. 1964. RNA—A functional characteristic of the neuron and its glia. In Brazier, M. A. B. (Ed.), *Brain function*, Vol. 2. Berkeley: University of California Press.

IVERSEN, S. D. 1964. The effect of temporal lobe lesions on the behaviour of primates. Unpublished doctoral dissertation, University of Cambridge.

IVERSEN, S. D., & WEISKRANTZ, L. 1964. Temporal lobe lesions and memory in the monkey. *Nature*, 201, 740–742.

JAMES, W. 1890. *Principles of psychology.* New York: Holt, Rinehart, and Winston.

JARVIK, M. E. 1953. Discrimination of colored food and food signs by primates. *J. comp. physiol. Psychol.*, 46, 390–392

JARVIK, M. E. 1956. Simple color discrimination in chimpanzees: Effect of varying contiguity between cue and incentive. *J. comp. physiol. Psychol.*, 49, 492–495.

JARVIK, M. E., & ESSMAN, W. B. 1960. A simple one-trial learning situation for mice. *Psychol. Rep.*, 6, 290.

KARN, H. W. 1939. The behavior of cats on the double alternation problem in the temporal maze. *J. comp. Psychol.*, 27, 201–208.

KÖHLER, W. 1925. *The mentality of apes*, Winter, E. (trans.). New York: Harcourt, Brace & World.

KONORSKI, J. 1959. A new method of physiological investigation of recent memory in animals. *Bull. Acad. pol. Sci. II. Sér. Sci. Biol.*, 7, 115.

LADIEU, G. 1944. The effect of length of delay interval upon delayed alternation in the albino rat. *J. comp. Psychol.*, 37, 273–286.

LASHLEY, K. S. 1917. The effect of strychnine and caffeine upon rate of learning. *Psychobiology*, 1, 141–170.

LEVINE, M. 1959. A model of hypothesis behavior in discrimination learning set. *Psychol. Rev.*, 66, 353–366.

MACCORQUODALE, K. 1947. An analysis of certain cues in the delayed response. *J. comp. physiol. Psychol.*, 40, 239–253.

McGAUGH, J. L., THOMSON, C. W., WESTBROOK, W. H., and HUDSPETH, W. J. 1962. A further study of learning facilitation with strychnine sulphate. *Psychopharmacol.*, 3, 352–360.

MAIER, N. R. F. 1929. Delayed reaction and memory in rats. *J. genet. Psychol.*, 36, 538–550.

MAIER, N. R. F., & SCHNEIRLA, T. C. 1935. *Principles of animal psychology.* New York: McGraw-Hill.

MALMO, R. B. 1942. Interference factors in delayed response in monkeys after removal of frontal lobes. *J. Neurophysiol.*, 5, 295–308.

MASLOW, A. H., & HARLOW, H. F. 1932. Comparative behavior of primates. II. Delayed reaction tests on primates at Bronx Park Zoo. *J. comp. Psychol.*, 14, 97–107.

MAYER-GROSS, W. 1943. Retrograde amnesia. *Lancet*, 2, 603.

MILNER, B., BRANCH, C., & RASMUSSEN, T. 1962. Study of short-term memory after intracarotid injection of sodium amytal. *Trans. Amr. neurol. Ass.*, 87, 224–226.

MISHKIN, M., & PRIBRAM, K. H. 1954. Visual discrimination performance following partial ablation of the temporal lobe: I. Ventral vs. lateral. *J. comp. physiol. Psychol.*, 47, 14–20.

MISHKIN, M., & PRIBRAM, K. H. 1956. Analysis of the effects of frontal lesions in monkey: II. Variations of delayed response. *J. comp. physiol. Psychol.*, 49, 36–45.

MROSOVSKY, N. 1963. Retention and reversal of conditioned avoidance following severe hypothermia. *J. comp. physiol. Psychol.*, 56, 811–813.

NISSEN, H. W., CARPENTER, C. R., & COWLES, J. T. 1936. Stimulus- versus response-differentiation in delayed reactions of chimpanzees. *J. genet. Psychol.*, 48, 112–136.

NISSEN, H. W., RIESEN, A. H., & NOWLIS, V. 1938. Delayed response and discrimination learning by chimpanzees. *J. comp. Psychol.*, 26, 361–386.

ORBACH, J., & FANTZ, R. L. 1958. Differential effects of temporal neocortical resections on overtrained and non-overtrained visual habits in monkeys. *J. comp. physiol. Psychol.*, 51, 126–129.

OSWALD, I. 1957. After-images from retina and brain. *Quart. J. exp. Psychol.*, 9, 88–100.

OVERTON, D. A. 1964. State-dependent or "dissociated" learning produced with pentobarbital. *J. comp. physiol. Psychol.*, 57, 3–12.

OXBURY, J. M. 1961. An analysis of the effects of frontal cortex lesions in rhesus monkeys by means of tests involving time estimations. Unpublished doctoral dissertation, University of Cambridge.

PEARLMAN, C. A., Jr., SHARPLESS, S. K., & JARVIK, M. E. 1961. Retrograde amnesia produced by anaesthetic and convulsant agents. *J. comp. physiol. Psychol.*, 54, 109–112.

PENFIELD, W., & MILNER, B. 1958. Memory deficit produced by bilateral lesions in the hippocampal zone. *A.M.A. Archs. Neurol. Psychiat.*, 79, 475–497.

PICKERSGILL, M. J., & JEEVES, M. A. 1964. The origin of the after-effect of movement. *Quart. J. exp. Psychol.*, 16, 90–103.

PRIBRAM, K. H. 1950. Some physical and pharmacological factors affecting delayed response performance of baboons following frontal lobotomy. *J. Neurophysiol.*, 13, 373–382.

PRIBRAM, K. H. 1958. Neocortical function in behavior. In Harlow, H. F., & Woolsey, C. N. (Eds.), *Biological and biochemical bases of behavior.* Madison: University of Wisconsin Press. Pp. 151–172.

PRIBRAM, K. H., & MISHKIN, M. 1956. Analysis of the effects of frontal lesions in monkey: III. Object alternation. *J. comp. physiol. Psychol.*, 49, 41–45.

RIBBANDS, C. R. 1950. Changes in the behavior of honeybees following their recovery from anaesthesia. *J. exp. Biol.*, 27, 302–310.

ROBERTS, W. W., DEMBER, W. N., & BRODWICK, M. 1962. Alternation and exploration in rats with hippocampal lesions. *J. comp. physiol. Psychol.*, 55, 695–700.

RUSSELL, I. S., & OCHS, S. 1963. Localization of a memory trace in one cortical hemisphere and transfer to the other hemisphere. *Brain*, 86, 37–54.

RUSSELL, W. R. 1959. *Brain, memory and learning.* Oxford: Oxford University Press, p. 71.

SCHEKEL, C. L. 1965. Self-adjustment of the interval in delayed matching: limit of delay for the rhesus monkey. *J. comp. physiol. Psychol.*, 59, 415–418.

SCHILLER, P. VON 1948. Delayed response in the minnow (*Phoxinus laevis*). *J. comp. physiol. Psychol.*, 41, 233–238.

SCHILLER, P. VON 1949. Delayed detour response in the octopus. *J. comp. physiol. Psychol.*, 42, 220–225.

SCOVILLE, W. B., & MILNER, B. 1957. Loss of immediate memory after bilateral hippocampal lesions. *J. Neurol, Neuros. Psychiat.*, 20, 11–21.

SEGAL, E. F. 1962. Effects of dl-amphetamine under concurrent VI DRL reinforcement. *J. exp. anal. Behav.*, 5, 105–112.

SPAET, T., & HARLOW, H. F. 1943. Problem solution by monkeys following bilateral removal of the prefrontal areas. II. Delayed reaction problems involving use of the matching-from-sample-method. *J. exp. Psychol.*, 32, 424–434.

STAMM, J. S. 1963. Function of prefrontal cortex in monkeys in timing behavior of monkeys. *Exp. Neurol.*, 7, 87–97.

STEPIEN, L. S., CORDEAU, J. P., & RASMUSSEN, T. 1960. The effect of temporal lobe and hippocampal lesions on auditory and visual recent memory in monkeys. *Brain*, 83, 470–489.

STILL, A. W. 1966. Repetition and alternation in rats. *Quart. J. exp. Psychol.*, 18, 103–108.

SWANBERG, P. O. 1951. Food storage, territory and song in the thick-billed nutcracker. *Proc. 10 Int. Congr. Orn. Upsala.* 545–554.

THORPE, W. H. 1956. *Learning and instinct in animals.* London: Methuen.

TINKLEPAUGH, O. L. 1928. An experimental study of representative factors in monkeys. *J. comp. Psychol.*, 8, 197–236.

TINKLEPAUGH, O. L. 1932. Multiple delayed reactions with chimpanzees and monkeys. *J. comp. Psychol.*, 13, 207–243.

WADA, J., & RASMUSSEN, T. 1960. Intracarotid injection of sodium amytal for the lateralization of cerebral speech dominance. Experimental and clinical observations. *J. Neurosurg.*, 17, 266–282.

WADE, M. 1947. The effect of sedatives upon delayed response in monkeys following removal of the prefrontal lobes. *J. Neurophysiol.*, 10, 57–61.

WALKER, E. L. 1956. The duration and course of the reaction decrement and the influence of reward. *J. comp. physiol. Psychol.*, 49, 167–176.

WEISKRANTZ, L. 1950. An unusual case of after-imagery following fixation of an "imaginary" visual pattern. *Quart. J. exp. Psychol.*, 2, 170–175.

WEISKRANTZ, L. 1956. On some psychophysical techniques employing a single manipulandum. *Brit. J. Psychol.*, 48, 190–199.

WEISKRANTZ, L. 1966. Experimental studies of amnesia. In Whitty, C. W. M., & Zangwill, O. L. (Eds.), *Amnesia*. London: Butterworth.

WEISKRANTZ, L., GROSS, C. G., & BALTZER, V. 1965. The beneficial effects of meprobamate on delayed response performance in the frontal monkey. *Q. J. exp. Psychol.*, 17, 118–124.

WEISKRANTZ, L., MIHAILOVIC, L., & GROSS, C. G. 1962. Effects of stimulation of frontal cortex and hippocampus on behavior in the monkey. *Brain*, 85, 487–504.

WELLS, M. 1964. Learning and movement in octopuses. In Thorpe, W. H., & Davenport, D. (Eds.), *In Learning and associated phenomena in invertebrates. Animal behavior* (Supplement 1). London: Baillière, Tindall and Cassell.

WILSON, W. A., Jr., OSCAR, M., & GLEITMAN, H. 1963. The effect of frontal lesions in monkeys upon widely spaced delayed-response trials. *J. comp. physiol. Psychol.*, 56, 237–240.

YAMAGUCHI, S., & WARREN, J. M. 1961. Single versus double alternation learning by cats. *J. comp. physiol. Psychol.*, 54, 533–538.

YERKES, R. M., & YERKES, D. N. 1928. Concerning memory in the chimpanzee. *J. comp. Psychol.*, 8, 237–271.

ZINKIN, S., & MILLER, A. J. 1967. Recovery of memory after amnesia induced by electroconvulsive shock. *Science*, 155, 102–103.

CHAPTER 9

Discrimination

A. COWEY

S OME DEFINITIONS epitomize a subject; they reveal exactly what will be discussed. *Discrimination* eludes a definition that is both concise and informative, probably because it represents too large a segment of behavior. For the sake of brevity, *discrimination* is here defined as "the behavioural detection of a difference between stimuli," when *behavioral* refers to an "observable motor response." The definition of discrimination excludes purely physiological responses, which may be used to explain or predict discriminative behavior but which are not, in terms of the definition, examples of it.

This broad definition of discrimination embraces more than can be discussed in a chapter. It is like, and about as useful as, a suburban signpost pointing to the city center. It gives a general direction without indicating precisely what lies ahead. But some additional directions can be given. Studies of discrimination are concerned with one or more of five things:

1. The ability to distinguish between two things, e.g. triangles and circles, with no attempt to measure a difference threshold. Many early experiments were of this kind as are numerous recent investigations whose purpose is to test some model or hypothesis of discriminatory behavior.

2. The absolute and difference thresholds, e.g., visual acuity.

3. The relative ease or difficulty with which a discrimination is acquired, reversed, or extinguished. In this category also the primary interest may lie in theories or models of learning and discrimination.

4. The phylogeny of discrimination or its ontogeny, e.g., experiments that test the roles of maturation, critical periods, or perceptual deprivation.

5. Critical reviews of reasoning and experimental design.

This chapter is primarily concerned with the last category. Furthermore, it examines the results and methodology of experiments in categories 3 and 4 only insofar as these experiments employ interesting and novel ways of measuring discrimination, or show that an animal's final performance depends on the manner in which a discrimination problem is presented; i.e., these experiments may be relevant to categories 1 and 2. In discussing category 3 we enter the territory of Chapter 7, but the trespass is slight.

There are several comprehensive summaries of the results of discrimination experiments, and they will not be paraphrased. However, it is often meaningless to discuss methods without considering results, and this makes some reiteration of results inevitable. Criticisms of methodology are less common and often fragmentary, being devoted to one particular problem or type of experiment. It seemed useful to assemble such criticisms in one place where they might be more effective, even at the risk of being too frequently unoriginal.

The account is subdivided as follows: it examines first the contributions of anatomy and physiology to studies of discrimination. There follows a comparison of the use of innate and learned responses. The section on learned responses is devoted to the effects of various ways of presenting cues and is principally illustrated by examples from primate vision. Certain principles emerging from these sections are then applied to the study of audition. Other modalities are not considered. To do so would extend an already lengthy account, and the reader can, in any case, himself consider the relevance of the principles to other modalities.

Indirect Methods of Studying Discrimination

Behavioral experiments with animals are often lengthy. For instance, it requires several months to measure minimum separable visual acuity in monkeys (Weiskrantz and Cowey, 1963), it may take a year to train them in a perimeter and to plot any field defects they have as a result of striate cortex lesions (Cowey and Weiskrantz, 1963), and it can take even longer to measure a stable flicker fusion threshold (Mishkin and Weiskrantz, 1959). It would be attractive if we could dispense with behavioral measures on occasions and decide, on other grounds, what an animal's abilities are. For example, few people would disagree that eyes and ears indicate sight and hearing, even if we have not specifically tested them. There are two reasons why we are confident about this. (1) It can readily be shown that these organs resemble in essential features the eyes and ears of other animals with whom a relationship between structure and behavioral function has been demonstrated. (2) We are making a very coarse-grained statement about function. To say that an animal sees is to assert the minimum about its vision. This is like saying that a camera will take photographs. It is when we become more specific about the quality of an animal's discrimination on the basis of anatomical or physiological evidence that the indirect inferential method can be unreliable, as the next two sections show.

1. Inferences from Anatomy

It has sometimes been argued that rats and guinea pigs must be color blind because they lack cones in the retina, an argument smacking of phrenology. In fact, rats do have cones (Walls, 1934), but it would be similarly false to infer from this that they possess color vision. After all, hue discrimination is absent in cone monochromats, who possess functional cones (Weale, 1953).

A similar example involves visual acuity. "The squirrels . . . are also the only Mammals to possess a pure cone retina. This enables them to see clearly without the necessity for eye movements, for their whole retina is as efficient from this point of view as our fovea . . ." (Tansley, 1950). This, like the similar and commoner assertion that snakes see acutely because they have a pure cone retina, is a prediction masquerading as a fact and is made despite the early discovery that in man the diminution in acuity with increasing eccentricity from the fovea resembles but does not parallel the reduction in linear or areal cone density from fovea to periphery (Polyak, 1941, fig. 99; Ludvigh, 1941). It is a prediction because the circuit diagram for an acuity mechanism is incomplete; we need to know the interconnections between cones and ganglion cells, the structure of the lateral geniculate body, and the pathways to the visual cortex before the squirrel's sight begins to be determinable without behavioral measures. And, at present, adequate circuit diagrams exist for only the simplest features of discrimination; for example, the results of the anatomical examination of the distribution of optic nerve fibres from the nasal and temporal halves of the retina in primates demand rather than predict that unilateral damage to the visual cortex will produce contralateral field defects.

These cautionary remarks about inferences from anatomy may be thought gratuitous, either because statements of the kind questioned are usually recognized for what they are worth or because they are rare. One doubts that the former is true, and the latter is certainly false. The ethologists have shown very clearly how misleading it can be to infer how and what an animal will discriminate by examining its sense organs (Tinbergen, 1951; Thorpe, 1956).

2. Inferences from Physiology

Physiology, like anatomy, may indicate that certain discriminations are impossible. For example, a demonstration that two lights of different wave length always evoke identical neural activity is sufficient to prove that the organism cannot discriminate between them. Put into more general terms, physically different stimuli will be indiscriminable if they produce indistinguishable physiological responses *at any stage* prior to the point at which a difference is translatable into behavior. Of course, we need to be confident of two things before this statement is of much help. (1) The physiological activity being recorded must be the relevant activity; and it is conceivable, for instance, that spike discharge is not the only means by which neurones code differences. (2) We must know that the physiological activity is being recorded peripherally to the point at which any differences begin to govern discriminatory behavior. Very often these two conditions will not be fulfilled, but in general the more peripheral the physiological recording the more convincing any statement that discrimination is impossible. For example, if the eye fails to distinguish between physically different lights, then the brain can hardly do so, but a similar result when recording in the striate cortex would indicate little, because other structures, like superior colliculus and optic tectum, receive optic inputs. Confidence also depends on the complexity of the region in which recordings are made; for, as the complexity increases, our ability to record the entire activity evoked by even a simple stimulus diminishes. And, when stimuli appear to evoke identical responses, it can be objected that the differences were missed. For instance, it is probably impracticable to record simultaneously from every ganglion cell connected to a single mammalian retinal receptor. But one can probably display the entire activity of optic nerve fibres following stimulation of an ommatidium in Limulus.

So far I have mentioned only the negative kind of statement about discrimination that can be made from physiological studies. Positive statements, i.e., that an animal can discriminate A from B because he has the physiological equipment to do so, are much less secure. Although the idea that an organism might discard information about stimulus differences is unpalatable because we tend to regard organisms as efficient, we can never be certain, using only physiological measures, that the information is used. For example, experiments that reveal differential physiological responses to lights of different wave lengths (See Ingvar, 1959 for review) are by themselves insufficient evidence of color discrimination. Behavioral tests have often failed to reveal color discrimination, and, although there is good reason to suspect the adequacy of many of them, we should not assume that they are inadequate simply because physiology predicts a different result.

Three examples will emphasize and illustrate some of these points. The first concerns the Purkinje phenomenon, which, as first described in man, is a shift in the point of maximum subjective brightness of a spectrum from the yellow-green to the blue-green region with a respective change from photopic to scotopic vision. It is now more usually described as a shift in the point of maximum sensitivity, which can be investigated by both behavioral and physiological methods. In man, the two sensitivity curves almost certainly reflect the activity of cone and rod vision, the former chromatic, the latter achromatic. From here, it is a short but unjustified step to the conclusion that animals having a Purkinje shift possess color vision (Tansley, 1950; E. Hess, 1960), and that color blindness is indicated by the absence of any shift (C. Hess, 1909). Conceivably, an animal may possess duplex vision in which both systems are achromatic. For example, cone monochromats have the customary bipartite dark-adaptation curve and show a Purkinje shift—relative sensitivity to blue-green being greatly increased in scotopic vision (Baumgardt, 1955), yet color discrimination is absent.

Hess (1909, and see Walls, 1942, for further discussion) equated color blindness with the absence of a Purkinje shift. He used behavioral methods to determine relative brightness of spectral lights in fish, but his argument has since been repeated with physiological findings in a variety of animals. But an animal may possess different pigments whose peak absorption does not vary under conditions of light and dark adaptation—precluding any shift in peak sensitivity, the absence of which is therefore not evidence for achromatic vision.

The second example is taken from Tansley, 1950, who discusses the critical fusion frequency (cff) of a variety of animals, relating it to their type of eye and to their mode of life. However, the methods of measuring cff vary among electroretinogram, optic nerve discharge, and behavioral response, which variety makes the behavioral comparison somewhat dubious, for, although the brain cannot distinguish a frequency that the sense organ is unable to follow, the reverse is not necessarily true. So the electroretinogram or the response in the optic nerve reveals only the extremes of a range within which the behavioral cff might lie anywhere.

The last example concerns taste. When rats are deprived of the adrenal glands, they excrete too much sodium chloride, but they compensate by consuming more. Adrenalectomized rats will detect and consume weak salt solutions that normal rats show no preference for with respect to water (Richter, 1939). "It has been suggested that the lowered preference threshold results from an increased gustatory sensitivity. . . . The animal is said to prefer the weaker concentrations because it can now *taste* (italics added) the more dilute salt solutions . . . this hypothesis was tested by a direct comparison of the gustatory sensory thresholds of normal and adrenalectomized rats" (Pfaffmann and Bare, 1950, p. 320). These authors found that the weakest salt solution to which the chorda tympani nerve responded was the same in normal and in adrenalectomized rats, and concluded that the results "do not substantiate the hypothesis that the taste thresholds are lowered in a state of increased salt need," p. 323). Instead, they concluded that the normal rat simply stopped preferring salt solution to water before it ceased to detect a difference between them, whereas the adrenalectromized rat was prepared to accept a smaller difference. The latter conclusion was subsequently confirmed by two behavioral studies when rats of both kinds were encouraged to discriminate by punishing them for an incorrect response (Carr, 1952; Harriman and MacLeod, 1953). The important point here is that the conclusion based on entirely physiological evidence is unjustified even though, as we now know, it is correct. It is unsound because (1) the chorda tympani nerve does not contain all the taste fibers, and (2) we do not know where in the CNS the threshold for salt detection is based or how it is set. Gustatory sensitivity and taste threshold are not necessarily the same thing. It could well be that the receptors and chorda tympani nerve respond equally to a given salt concentration in normal and in adrenalectomized rats but that a centrally determined threshold mechanism is set differently in the two groups. Recordings made peripherally to the mechanism may reveal nothing about its properties.

These critical comments are restricted to certain *interpretations* made from physiological experiments. Besides being important in their own right, the experiments provide a reasonable explanation for what we already know about discrimination, and they suggest things worth measuring behaviorally, like color vision in cats. There is probably no better summary of the problem just discussed than that given by Granit (1955, p. 142).

> The question as to whether or no any given experimental animal is capable of utilizing its retinal mechanism of wave-length discrimination is, therefore, not of immediate interest. Still less is it claimed that the theory (of dominators and modulators) can give any information as to whether, or to what extent, an animal may possess colour vision. This does not mean that one should wholly abstain from interpretation of the physiological cues . . . nothing can be gained by refusing to consider evidence obtained with methods other than psychological ones. The task of physiology is to detect cues for behavior based on our "internal measuring instruments" and to do so at all levels where such cues might be had.

Learned vs. Innate Discriminatory Responses

By a *learned*, or *operant*, *response* is meant one that an animal is taught to produce in the presence of a particular stimulus. *Innate responses*, or *respondents*, are those that the experimenter finds ready-made, and it will not be the business of this chapter to discuss whether they are really inborn or self-taught. This section examines some general principles associated with the way the two kinds of response are used in studying discrimination and gives detailed examples of the use of innate responses. Detailed methodological points concerned with learned responses are illustrated in later sections.

Many tests of discrimination involve teaching the animal to respond to the cues in a distinctive and measurable way. But an animal may fail to discriminate in such a situation for more than one reason. His nervous system may be unable to register the stimulus difference; he may be physically incapable of producing the appropriate motor responses, like a curarized person who can consciously perceive but can not communicate his understanding; or he may be unable to relate perception and action, like dogs, which can move left or right and can distinguish (as we know from other experiments) between the sounds of a buzzer and a metronome but which find it exceedingly difficult to make a directional response contingent upon a particular sound when the source of the noise is always in the same place (Konorski, 1964). Or the animal may be unable to remember what he learns for more than a short while. It is not easy, when faced with negative or poor evidence for discrimination, to know which of these various factors is limiting performance. One can discount the animal's inability to perform the necessary motor response if he can display it to other stimuli. But it is not possible to exclude a learning difficulty by showing that the organism can perform the same learned responses to stimuli of a different modality presented in a similar way. For example, Battig, Rosvold, and Mishkin (1962) showed that rhesus monkeys easily learn a "go, no-go" visual discrimination when the stimuli are spatially diffuse, as they were in an auditory discrimination that the monkeys found difficult. But this kind of finding is of little help here for two reasons. (1) The animal's ability to relate stimulus and response may not be identical for all modalities (Konorski, 1964). (2) If there is a genuine difficulty in detecting a stimulus difference in one modality, the animal may alter its response strategy with respect to the stimuli such that the learning process becomes more complicated. Stimulus detection and learning may be interacting in a manner that precludes a simple interpretation of their respective roles.

These drawbacks assume even greater importance if one is interested in the effect on discrimination of an independent variable, which might affect chiefly the animal's ability to learn or to remember what he has learned. An example of this problem concerns the study of the effects on visual discrimination of bilateral inferotemporal ablation in monkeys (Mishkin and Pribram, 1954; see also Chapter 8). The operation impairs visual pattern and object discrimination; the animals perform less well than unoperated controls when given either new patterns or patterns that they learned to criterion beforehand. Is it a sensory impairment? It has been suggested that the operation affects the sensory side of vision; perhaps the animal sees less clearly in some way. For example, the animals are impaired on form discriminations if the forms differ little in size (Pasik, et al. 1958), and the difference limen for the discrimination of square versus triangle is raised at low levels of illumination although not at high (Valciukas and Pasik, 1965). Despite the latter findings, the impairment could be a learning deficit, for even normal animals show some forgetting of a problem between periods of testing, and it could be argued that the inferotemporal monkey is impaired after operation because he has difficulty in relearning what he has to some extent forgotten. Mishkin and Weiskrantz (1959) found that the flicker fusion threshold was lower in infero-temporal monkeys than in two control groups, one unoperated and the other having frontal cortex lesions. This also seems to support the idea of a sensory impairment. But it will be shown later that, by making a discrimination more difficult to learn, we can influence the threshold measurement. As Mishkin and Weiskrantz point out, the inferotemporal animal may take longer to master the ever in-creasing difficulty of the task, and the performance scores suggest that no group had reached its asymptote after a year of testing but that the inferotemporal group was improving less quickly. Given time, all animals may have reached the same threshold.

There is evidence that in certain respects the inferotemporal animal has no sensory loss. Visual acuity is unaffected (Weiskrantz and Cowey, 1963) and the animals' visual fields are normal (Cowey and Weiskrantz, 1963, and further unpublished observations). Yet animals with striate-cortex lesions do have an acuity loss and defective visual fields without having the deficit in visual pattern discrimination shown by inferotemporal animals.

Is it learning or memory? Iversen and Weiskrantz (1964) attempted to distinguish between these two possibilities by measuring learning and retention between daily testing sessions. They found that infero-temporal and normal animals learned object discrimination problems almost equally well to a criterion of 9 out of 10 correct but that the former group was significantly impaired on retention the following day. So the deficit does involve visual memory but of course does not necessarily exclude sensory deficits.

By using tests involving innate responses, it is possible to avoid some of these difficulties of interpretation, both in studying the discrimina-tion of normal animals and in evaluating treatment effects. There are many such tests, and only a few are presented here. They have been selected for their simplicity and ingenuity even though they have not always been applied with appropriate controls. It is their potentiality that is important.

Orienting Reflex

The orienting reflex is an alerting inquisitive response to a novel stimulus. Because it habituates rapidly, it can be used to measure an ani-mal's ability to discriminate between a stimulus to which the orienting response has weakened and any other stimulus. If the new stimulus resuscitates the response; the old and the new must be discriminable. It is very much like studying discrimination by plotting generalization curves to a conditioned stimulus, without having to condition the ani-mal first. But, despite this apparent simplicity, the orienting reflex is little used in behavioral studies (for examples, see Sharpless and Jasper, 1956; and Thompson and Welker, 1963, whose study of head orienta-tion to sound in cats showed that the effects of removing auditory neocortex on sound localization could be demonstrated without formal and lengthy discrimination training), probably because its electro-physiological signs, like GSR and EEG, are not easily measured in ani-mals and partly too because the intertrial interval may have to be lengthy as, for instance, in the study of the arousal from sleep in animals or man (Sharpless and Jasper, 1956; Oswald, 1962). Nevertheless, it remains a potentially powerful and simple tool for anyone who can reliably detect when an animal pricks up its ears in response to sound and when it does the equivalent for other modalities.

Optokinetic Response

Many animals, when surrounded by a rotating drum lined with vertical stripes, attempt to follow the moving contours with their eyes, head, or entire body. This optokinetic response (OKR) provides a ready means of studying contour discrimination both in animals like insects and larval amphibians, to which training methods are difficult to apply even to the intact organism (Birukow, 1939, 1949; Reichardt, 1961) and in mammals which have had the striate cortex removed, making it difficult for them to orient properly in most testing situations (Smith, 1951; Smith and Warkentin, 1939). Smith, for instance, was able to show that the threshold OKR of normal and destriated cats was barely different, indicating an adequate nonstriate mechanism that mediated movement perception.

But the most illuminating application of the OKR has been made by Birukow (1939; 1949) in studying color vision of frogs. Birukow argued that if the frog is color blind he will confuse a particular color with some shade of gray and cease to follow the alternating colored and grey striations at that point. He could not find a shade of gray that, when paired with red or blue stripes, failed to produce OKR. But there was clear evidence of a large neutral region in the spectrum where yellow and green were indistinguishable from certain grays. At scotopic intensities any colour could be matched with gray.

Using the OKR, it should be possible to study visual acuity with different colored stripes by gradually reducing their width. No one has yet studied this fascinating problem in normal or destriated mammals despite the fact that monkeys retain a clear OKR to black and white stripes after striatectomy (ter Braak and van Vliet, 1963). Birukow (1939) found with frogs that the threshold angle for red and blue stripes was twice that for black and white, but he neglected to control for the difference in percentage of incident light reflected by the various stripes and, thus, for their contrasts.

Although the OKR can be used to measure certain aspects of vision, it has one major technical disadvantage. Walls (1942) points out that, even if two colors can be independently matched for subjective brightness, there may be sufficient chromatic aberration to introduce a perceptible difference in the grayness of the edges of the stripes for an achromatic animal, which might therefore appear to possess color vision. This possibility could be tested with a monochromatic human subject, or the effects of aberration could be independently evaluated. For instance, the greater the difference in wave length between two spectral lights, the larger the artifact produced by chromatic aberration. If an animal can discriminate red from green but not red from blue, he can hardly be doing so on the basis of chromatic aberration, for its possible effects are slighter with the first stimulus pair. Logically, the possible artifactual effect of chromatic aberration applies to any test of color vision where the stimuli have distinct borders, but an animal is most likely to detect the effect where contours are frequent, as in the striated drum.

Color Preferences

Many animals avoid certain colors or show a preference when pre-sented with two or more. This natural behavior provides an excellent means of studying color vision, provided that certain controls are used to ensure that the preference is not based on luminosity. Unfortunately, a great number of experiments lack the control, although in other respects they are attractively simple.

For example, Reighard (1908) found that certain coral-reef fishes preferred blue bait to red, and white bait to blue. He concluded that the discrimination was not based on luminosity, for the physical bright-ness of the baits was in the order white-red-blue, which does not parallel the preference order of white-blue-red. There are three possible objec-tions to such a conclusion from this and innumerable similar experi-ments.

1. It should never be presumed that the rank order of subjective brightness of two or more stimuli of different wave lengths is the same as the rank order for physical intensity, even when the physical inten-sities are very different. Reighard's fish could be color blind yet display the behavior he observed if they selected the brighter of two colored stimuli and if they were relatively insensitive to red light.

2. Even if the rank orders of physical and subjective brightness cor-respond, it is wrong to assume that preference will be a monotonic function of subjective brightness. If the preference curve is U shaped, an animal may prefer white and blue to red because he prefers bright and dim lights to one of intermediate intensity. Of course, in order to behave in this way the animal must judge the absolute rather than the relative brightness of the stimuli, and one way of overcoming the objection is to show that he cannot do this. Another and simpler method would be to show that the preference curve is monotonic, using only white stimuli over a range from very intense to absolute threshold, or to demonstrate that the animal shows no preference for either of two white stimuli whatever their intensities. The latter method was success-fully used by Bauer (1910) in establishing that red-shy fish were dis-criminating on the basis of wave length.

3. Reighard also found that his fish avoided all shades of red bait when it was offered with bait of any other color. He assumed that some of the other colors must have matched certain of the reds with respect to subjective brightness. This, too, is a dangerous assumption; for, if the spectral sensitivity curve is greatly depressed at the red end of the spectrum, a red stimulus may be subjectively dimmer than any other, especially when the stimuli are all illuminated by the same inci-dent light, as was the case with Reighard's colored bait. Indeed, Hess (1909) was able to reverse the preference of so-called red-shy fish by illuminating one end of their aquarium with intense red light and the other with weak blue light. This suggested that in other experiments energies of the colored stimuli were not varied sufficiently. Mello and Peterson (1964) were aware of this problem in studying color vision in cats, and varied the brightness of the coloured stimuli in the correct fashion by taking account of the photopic spectral sensitivity curve for the cat (Gunter, 1954b). Theirs is the only published study that dem-onstrates color vision in cats and that includes this essential control.

It can also be argued that the spectral sensitivity to red light is so high that a red stimulus tends to be subjectively brighter than any other, and, therefore, discriminable and avoidable on the basis of luminosity. This is unlikely in view of the shape of the absorption spectrum for all photolabile pigments that have been tested, but it can conclusively be disproved in another way. Reeves (1919) found that Dace avoided a dim red light no matter what the intensity of the alternative white light. The most intense white lights must have contained more red than the red stimulus and must therefore have appeared brighter. The lights should accordingly have been avoided if the fish were bright-shy. And, incidentally, white light near threshold should also have been avoided if the fish were dim-shy. Reeves' experiment, using only a preference technique, conclusively demonstrates color vision in Dace, but its elegance has not often been repeated.

One further attempt to control for brightness has been used improperly. Having found two intensities of white light between which Dace could not discriminate in a training situation, Reeves (1919) reduced the intensity of the brighter light with a red filter. The fish promptly avoided this light. Reeves argues that the brightness difference must now be even less than before, indicating that the fish are responding on the basis of wave length. But is it less? If the fish are relatively insensitive to red, a red filter may *reverse* the subjective stimulus brightness *and* raise it above threshold.

Color mimicry and a dependent color preference were together used by Mast (1915) in an ingenious demonstration of color vision in flounders. He noted that the fish slowly changed color to match their surroundings and that the eyes were necessary for this. Furthermore, fish preadapted to a particular color would swim toward it if subsequently placed on a boundary between it and another color. The only exception was red, which the fish avoided even if they had acquired it. Mast did not control adequately for brightness in his preference demonstration, but his method of relating preference and skin color is excellent.

One disadvantage of the color-preference technique is that it likely reveals only the coarsest features of hue discrimination. For instance, red avoidance shows that all other colors are treated as equal but not that they are indiscriminable. But it is possible to vary the technique and to say something about the other colors. For instance, Moericke (1950) showed that the peach aphid normally inserts its proboscis only into green material. But, if first placed on a red background, it will subsequently attempt to penetrate a grey substrate, presumably because of a complementary green after-image. Other colors failed to induce this behavior, indicating that they are discriminable from red, as red is from green. This technique could also be used to study simultaneous color induction, for example by observing the response to gray paper placed on a large red background.

It should be stressed that many of the points raised in this section apply also to tests of color vision that employ training techniques. Some of the criticisms are considered by Bernstein (1961) in a paper that also is instructive in that it describes how conditional cardiac deceleration may be used to study color discrimination. Bernstein shows that, when brightness cues are controlled, goldfish in which the forebrain has been removed fail to discriminate on the basis of wave length, contrary to what had been reported in earlier studies that lacked adequate control of subjective brightness.

Form and Pattern Preferences

The use of unlearned responses has led to the solution of a seemingly intractable problem with regard to visual perception. The characteristics, or even presence, of form discrimination in infant primates has been disputed by both philosophers and psychologists. By recording the eye movements and the fixation duration of newly born chimpanzees and of human infants, differential responses (and, therefore, discrimination) were found to members of various sets of patterns presented simultaneously above the infant's crib (Fantz, 1957, 1958; Fantz, Ordy, and Udelf, 1962). These experiments are important and uncontroversial. They provide positive evidence of discrimination. And the method can also be used to show that a particular treatment, such as dark-rearing in chickens, does not impair certain aspects of discrimination and that, because it does not do so, the contrary results reported by other investigators may be caused by the effect of the treatment on the animal's ability to learn a complex response to visual stimuli or caused by emotional disturbances because of the subject's being first exposed to light at a late stage in development (see Fantz, 1957, for discussion).

Depth and distance perception have also been investigated with the "visual cliff," which involves no formal training. Walk and Gibson (1961) found that a variety of animals, when placed on a narrow, flat platform, consistently descended on the side where the drop was shallow in preference to the other side where it was deep. A sheet of glass overlay the stimulus on the shallow side and extended into space on the deep side, preventing any real fall if the animal stepped off on the latter. With this apparatus Walk and Gibson have studied the ability of animals and human infants to discriminate various depth cues at different ages and have studied this to assess the effects of dark-rearing on this ability. For example, the researchers were able to show that chickens tested a few hours after birth displayed excellent depth discrimination, no bird attempting to descend on the deep side. Lambs tested 24 hours after birth behaved similarly. Kittens and monkeys were tested, with similar results, as soon as they could crawl. But of course they had been able to see for some time. When two of the possible cues to depth, viz., motion parallax and pattern density, were studied independently, day-old chicks showed no preference between the deep and the shallow side when the only cue was pattern density but almost always chose the shallow side when guided by motion parallax (and perhaps by accommodation). Young goats and lambs behaved likewise, but infant rats showed a consistent preference when either cue was available. However, the rats could not be tested until 30-days-old, so we cannot be sure that the effectiveness of the cues is unlearned. Certainly the cues are not equivalent; for, when pattern density and motion parallax are placed in opposition, rats descend on the side that motion parallax indicates to be shallower.

The effects of dark-rearing and restricted depth perception were studied in cats and rats. Rats deprived of light from birth, or reared in illuminated cages where no object was further than 4 inches from the animal, chose the shallow side when the cue was motion parallax. In this respect, they were like normal rats. Unlike normal rats, they showed no preference when the only difference on the two sides of the cliff was texture density. These two results are related in an important way; for the first, where animals behaved normally, indicates that the second, where they did not, is almost certainly not attributable to factors like emotional disturbance, poor motor coordination, or a reliance on nonvisual cues, any of which might be responsible for this kind of treatment effect. It is an example of the single dissociation paradigm that one rarely finds in experiments on visual deprivation. Dark-reared kittens showed no preferential responses on the visual cliff even when both cues were present and, lacking this dissociation, the result is more difficult to interpret.

The experiment with dark-reared rats is an illustration of the particular usefulness of a respondent in studying discrimination, for it resolves an old dispute arising from the demonstration by Lashley and Russell (1934) that dark-reared rats can jump accurately across gaps of various widths when subsequently tested in light and that distance perception must therefore be unlearned. Unfortunately, the animals had to be *trained* to jump in the light, and it has been suggested that depth perception was acquired during the brief period of training. The results of the visual cliff are not open to this objection.

Pupilloscopy

Changes in pupil size can be used to investigate spectral sensitivity without training procedures, for there is evidence that contraction of the pupil correlates with perceived brightness, at least in some animals (see Walls, 1942, p. 500). For example, Abelsdorff (cited in Walls, p. 501) found that spectral lights of equal subjective brightness in a monochromatic human subject exerted equal effects on the pupil. But pupilloscopy does not establish the presence or absence of color vision; for it is wrong to assume, as Hess (1917) did, that, because the spectral sensitivity curve of certain animals, as determined by pupilloscopy, coincides with that of the monochromatic or dark-adapted human being, the animals are color blind (see Reeves, 1919, for extended discussion). But pupilloscopy has an important and, as far as the writer is aware, unused application in a study of color vision. If the pupil contracts much more vigorously to light of certain wave lengths than to all others of equal physical energy, as it does in the cat to blue light (Walls, 1942), indicating that the animal perceives that light as brighter than the others, we can use this information to select the appropriate range of energies in order to (1) make subjective brightness an irrelevant cue and (2) make the pupil response itself an ineffective cue in discrimination. For instance, in testing the color vision of cats, some of the red stimuli must be made physically very intense if they are to appear subjectively brighter than blue stimuli and are to produce a greater pupillary change. Walton (1933) overlooked this control in his study purporting to demonstrate color vision in rats.

Limitations of Tests Involving Innate Responses

The outstanding feature of these tests is that the animal displays a response with which he is naturally equipped. Their chief weakness is that the response indicates a preference between stimuli. They can never be used, therefore, to indicate the limits of discrimination; for an animal may cease to prefer one stimulus to another while still perceiving a difference between them. For example, a preference may be seasonal as in the reproductive cycle of fish. And it has already been pointed out that preference measures in normal rats do not reveal the threshold for salt discrimination and that red-shyness in animals does not imply that all other colored stimuli appear identical. Similarly, a lack of preference on the visual cliff does not indicate that both drops appear alike; the point at which an animal ceases to respond to a colored object as it is slowly desaturated (Hess and Gogel, 1954) does not necessarily reveal spectral sensitivity at that wave length; and, when the human infant ceases to inspect a striated card in preference to a plain gray card, we have not necessarily discovered his visual acuity (Fantz, 1961; Fantz, Ordy, and Udelf, 1962). Furthermore, any changes in performance with age or with some kind of treatment may reflect variations in preference as well as in the ability to discriminate. For these reasons, tests involving innate responses can never replace training methods, where one stimulus acquires aversive or unrewarding properties to such an extent that we are confident the animal will discriminate between it and others as long as he can detect their differences.

The Problem of Controlling or Identifying the Relevant Cue

In many of the examples given so far it has been shown that factors like preference, learning, and memory can affect discrimination and make it difficult to determine whether performance is being limited by the animal's detection system. Yet certain difficulties remain when the others we have mentioned are eliminated or controlled. The chief of these is the property of many stimuli to change in more than one discriminative aspect when we attempt to vary them in only one way. For example, the apparent hue of all but three wave lengths alters along with the intensity of the light (Bezold-Brucke effect); the *relative* perceived brightness of different wave lengths varies with intensity (Purkinje shift); perceived pitch, which chiefly depends on frequency, also varies with intensity; loudness is similarly affected by frequency, as well as by intensity (see Teuber, 1960, for extended discussion). In other words, any psychological dimension is a function of more than one physical variable, and any physical variable is likely to affect more than one psychological dimension. This creates certain problems in studying discrimination, as the following example shows. Discrimination is often considered to be the opposite of generalization. A generalization curve may therefore indicate the relative discriminability of a whole range of stimuli varying (supposedly) along one dimension, without having to perform a lengthy experiment in which an animal attempts to discriminate between various pairs of stimuli selected in turn from the continuum. For instance, pigeons trained to peck a key when a particular wave length is presented "should" transfer the response to other wave lengths according to the degree of similarity between the training wave length and the new wave length. Such an experiment has been done by several workers (see Guttman, 1963, for review) most of whom were surprised and puzzled to find that the generalization curve (plotting response rate against wave length) was

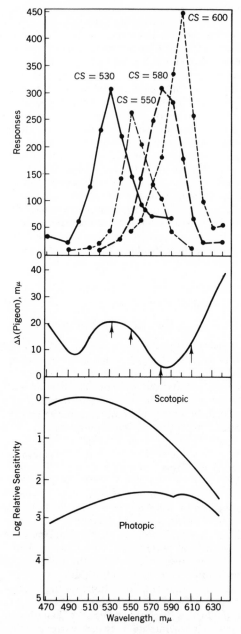

Fig. 9-1. Top: generalization gradients for four groups of pigeons trained at four different wavelengths. Note the similarity of the four generalization gradients. Center: the wave-length discrimination curve for the pigeon. Bottom: the scotopic and photopic sensitivity curves of the pigeon. (Top and center, after Guttman, 1963, in Koch: *Psychology: A Study of a Science*, Vol. V. Used by permission of McGraw-Hill Book Company. Bottom, after Blough, 1957, in *J. opt. Soc. Amer.*, **47**, by permission.)

not the inverse of the difference threshold curve (where the threshold discrimination between neighboring wave lengths is plotted against wave lengths). The pigeon does not show any steep changes in its response rate when the training wave length and new wave length occupy a part of the spectrum where discrimination between wave lengths is most sensitive (see Fig. 9–1, top and center).

We have already mentioned that perceived brightness, as well as the hue, varies with the wave-length, and indeed the pigeon's generalization curve corresponds more closely to the spectral sensitivity curve (see Fig. 9–1, bottom). But the correspondence is still far from perfect, indicating that the pigeon is not responding only to change in apparent brightness. What is more, Blough (1961) cleverly attempted to eliminate any possible response to subjective brightness by adjusting the luminance of each wave-length in accordance with the spectral sensitivity curve for the pigeon, the spectral sensitivity curve being an equal brightness curve at threshold intensity. The generalization curves were still essentially similar to those obtained when this precaution had not been taken. What are we to make of this? The spectral sensitivity curve employed by Blough to make his correction was presumably obtained with luminances well below those used to study the generalization curve. How can we be sure that the curve of equal brightness preserves its shape at the greater luminances used to study generalization? If it does not retain its shape (and with human subjects we know it does not, for, as intensity is increased, the apparent brightness of different spectral bands does not change at the same rate; e.g., red appears to grow brighter faster than green [Stevens, 1958]), Blough's correction is insufficient.

We are left with the possibility that the pigeon could be responding to changes in hue or in apparent brightness as the wave length is changed. And because we do not know the curve relating apparent brightness to wave-length at the luminances used, the generalization curve will not tell us which psychological diversion is used; nor should we expect it to. Moreover, what if the pigeon uses both cues (hue and brightness) at once, or switches from one to another, depending on which most clearly signifies a difference from the wave length to which the animal has been trained? Furthermore, there is a third cue; saturation also varies with wave length and intensity. If the pigeon has three possible ways of distinguishing his training wave-length from all others, we should not be surprised at the smoothness of the generalization curve, which is now seen to be a very imperfect measure of hue discrimination. It is hardly necessary to add that, if we are studying the effects of some treatment on hue discrimination, alterations, or lack of them, in a generalization curve will be no less misleading.

Learned Responses

The Problem of Contiguity

This section is concerned with established training methods of testing discrimination and with the important effects of spatial contiguity between cue, response, and reward. Some of these effects have been suspected for many years, but only in the last 10 years have they been studied systematically. The results have great practical and theoretical importance, but the stress here is on the former.

The first widely used piece of apparatus for testing discrimination learning, the Yerkes-Watson box, varied in size with the species of animal being tested, but, otherwise, it was fairly standardized. After leaving a starting box, the animal encountered two doorways, with or without doors, each of which led by a long reflexive alley to a reward cup. Visual stimuli could be placed above or alongside the doorways but were often not even immediately adjacent to them. If doors were used, the one next to the negative stimulus was locked. Punishment could be given by an electric shock if the animal entered the wrong doorway or pushed the wrong door. Some striking results were obtained with this apparatus; for example, Johnson (1914) established that the visual acuity of cebus monkeys is close to that of man when tested under similar conditions. Subsequent experimenters, using what are now acknowledged to be superior methods, have found nothing to challenge this result (Weinstein and Grether, 1940; Spence and Fulton, 1936; Weiskrantz and Cowey, 1963). However, there were failures too. Rats needed several hundred trials to learn a brightness discrimination, and Lashley (1912) found no evidence of form discrimination in rats after 1000 trials. Size discrimination was possible but difficult.

These frustrations led Lashley to modify the apparatus rather than to conclude that the rat is visually unperceptive. He trained the rat to jump at the discriminanda, one of which was locked, causing the animal to fall if he responded to it. The other stimulus was free to swing back, revealing a reward. Rats now discriminated where their predecessors had failed, and, in general, their learning was much swifter (Lashley, 1930).

Why is the Lashley jumping-stand superior to the Yerkes-Watson box? There is a minimum delay between responding and being rewarded or punished, and the spatial contiguity between cue and response, cue and reward, and response and reward is maximal. The effects of the temporal delay have been exhaustively investigated by learning theorists, and we know that delays of only a few seconds hinder discrimination. The role of the several possible spatial factors has been relatively neglected until recently and is still imperfectly understood. Accordingly, it is described in some detail here. A very brief account is given by Riopelle (1960).

The first observations on this topic arose from experiments devoted to other matters, but they illustrate the problem and the course of its long development. Köhler (1925, p. 37) noted that chimpanzees failed to use a stick to capture food if it was not already pointing in the direction of the reward. Seemingly, the significance of a cue is best appreciated if it adheres in some way to the reward. Gellerman (1933) found that chimpanzees would not learn a form discrimination if the stimuli were attached to the front of the food boxes, but did so easily when they were mounted immediately adjacent to the lids. Jenkins (1943) attempted to teach four chimpanzees form discrimination involving plywood squares of different sizes. The food wells were covered by large lids such that a stimulus placed at the front of the lid lay directly above the food well; a stimulus at the back was 6 inches from the well. The animals responded by grasping the front of the lid. After 250 trials with the stimuli distant, the animals had reached only 66 percent correct responses. On moving the stimuli to the front, performance improved to 97 percent correct during the first 256 trials, but 3 animals fell to 58 percent correct over 600 trials when the stimuli were replaced to their first position. Jenkins observed that his result could be attributed to either cue-response or cue-reward spatial separation. His study does show that proximity of response and reward is not sufficient to permit learning, a result that everyone since has confirmed, leaving only two factors to be investigated.

One of the first studies that systematically studied and varied the degree of contiguity was performed by McClearn and Harlow (1954). They used a vertical display board with two food wells at the base, each covered by identical blocks. The stimuli were coterminous with the blocks or were 1, 2, or 4 inches above them. The performance curves of 4 rhesus monkeys for the 4 conditions showed no overlap, but all reached better than 90 percent correct eventually. Difficulty was directly proportioned to separation, but, as the separation of response from cue and of reward from cue varied equally, little can be said about their relative significance.

In 1955, Murphy and Miller carried out a similar study with a group of monkeys and reported more striking effects. A 6-inch vertical displacement of cue from reward in an object learning-set situation entirely prevented the animals from learning the discrimination. Furthermore, the excellent performance score of the control group, which had not experienced a spatial separation, fell to chance levels when it was introduced, even though the same objects were being used. One might ask why the effects were so much more severe in this study, and two possibilities are evident. (1) The spatial separation was 6 inches compared with the maximum of 4 inches used by McClearn and Harlow. (2) The monkeys used by McClearn and Harlow were trained on all the possible degrees of spatial separation throughout the experiment. There were no lengthy training periods when a large discontiguity was suddenly introduced and retained.

The title of the paper by Murphy and Miller and their discussion indicate that they consider the relevant discontiguity to be cue from reward. However, they also speak of "the significant effect of a 6 inch separation between the stimulus cue and the *site of the rewarded response*" (p. 222, italics added), and this is a less specific but more justifiable conclusion.

The first successful attempt to maximize the contiguity between cue and reward, by making them identical, is due to Jarvik (1953; 1956). He used artificially colored and flavored bread with rhesus monkeys and chimpanzees. Three naive rhesus monkeys made no more than one error in 25 trials. They were then given various transfer tests. When the bread was obscured by large colored plaques, performance fell to chance levels and remained there when colored but transparent covers were used instead. Performance abruptly recovered when small colored squares were pasted onto the bread, but strikingly subsided when similar colored squares were placed 1 millimeter in front of the bread. There were no errors in the final condition, when small colored squares were placed but not pasted on the reward. It may seem surprising, in view of McClearn and Harlow's finding, that the animals were so bad under the discontiguous arrangement, even though they received training meanwhile with maximum contiguity. But it must be remembered that Jarvik gave only 25 trials on each condition, whereas McClearn and Harlow used several hundred trials on each of their conditions.

In Jarvik's second study (1956), chimpanzees were tested with artifically colored peanut shells, only certain of which contained nuts. He also used colored blocks into which a peanut could be inserted via a hole in the base. Once again the animals mastered the discrimination with impressive speed. They were much slower if the colored block simply covered a food well.

Jarvik attributed the proficiency of his animals to the complete contiguity between cue and reward. The chief evidence for rejecting cue-response contiguity as the most important variable in the first study is that the animals failed to discriminate when the cues were opaque or when transparent colored covers overlay the food wells, despite the fact that they had to respond to the colors by displacing them. But it can be argued that a monkey swiftly sweeps aside a cover, whereas its response to colored food is more protracted, for it involves picking it up and transferring it to its mouth. We may therefore be dealing with two different cue-response relationships, one more favorable than the other to discrimination. The same objection can be leveled at Jarvik's second study when the animals would spend more time handling a colored block if the reward was concealed within it.

A reply to Jarvik appeared in 1959. Riopello and Guyant (1959) trained five rhesus monkeys to discriminate between cubes of different colors. Either the edges or the center of each face of the otherwise white cubes were colored, and the animal rotated the cubes to reveal food impaled on a nail protruding from the far side (see Fig. 9–2).

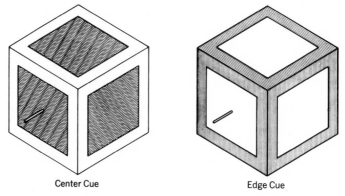

Center Cue   Edge Cue

Fig. 9-2. Stimulus and reward arrangements used by Riopelle and Guyant, 1959. The cubes rotated on a shaft through the base.

Discrimination was best when the stimuli formed the edges of the cubes. The authors conclude that stimulus-reward contiguity has the lesser influence. However, their experimental design is not flawless, for, by impaling the reward on the nail, they conceal part of the center-face cue (which was 1 inch square) but leave the edge cue unobscured. Their conclusion is, therefore, no more convincing than Jarvik's, which it was thought to refute.

The effects of even slight separation of a cue from the response and reward position appear also in a testing situation when the animal is responsible for presenting the cues (Polidora and Fletcher, 1964). Pattern or color cues were projected automatically onto two panels after the animal had pressed its face into a viewing mask. Beneath the panels and in apposition with them were shallow food trays. One group of monkeys pressed the panels to obtain a reward from the already open trays. The trays were closed and locked with the second group, which could unlock the tray beneath the positive stimulus by pulling the tray; there was no need to press the panel. In doing this, the animal's fingers were only ½ inch below the stimuli. There were no significant differences between the scores of the two groups with respect to color discrimination, but, with patterns, only group I responded significantly above chance. When conditions were reversed for the groups, the experimenters noticed that any one animal's performance depended on whether it had maintained its old response strategy. Animals that had first learned to press the panels continued to discriminate well only if they maintained the now unnecessary panel press. Animals that had learned only to pull open a tray still performed poorly if they continued to touch the tray before the panel above it. If this indicates, as the authors suggest, that a monkey derives its information from the region of its initial response, then we must allow that cue-response contiguity is more important than cue reward. Polidora and Fletcher make one other important point. Monkeys can solve delayed response problems, when cue and response are temporally disunited, more easily than a nondelay problem, when cue and response are spatially separated. So an animal does not need to touch the stimuli to discriminate them; he can sample from something he only sees. This observation is also consistent with the view that the conjunction of cue and reward is important, for in delayed response the stimuli are customarily spatially contiguous with the reward site.

In 1964 Miller and Murphy made a deliberate attempt to investigate the relative importance of the two spatial factors, and in doing so revised their earlier conclusion that separation of cue and reward has the greater consequence. The animal was presented with two horizontal shelves 7 inches apart (see Fig. 9–3). Two response blocks were placed

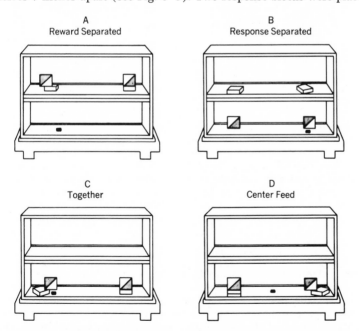

FIG. 9-3. Spatial arrangement of stimuli used by Miller and Murphy, 1964. Each drawing shows the appearance of the apparatus following a correct response. The dark spot is the open food well. The black-and-white blocks are the stimuli. (From *J. exp. Psychol.*, **67**, by permission of American Psychological Association.)

on the top shelf, with food wells below on the bottom shelf. The lid
of each food well could be retracted by the experimenter. Seventeen
rhesus monkeys were divided into four groups as follows:

Group 1. Cue response contiguous, i.e., stimuli on the response
blocks.

Group 2. Cue reward contiguous.

Group 3. Cue response reward contiguous, and all on bottom shelf.

Group 4. Cue response contiguous, single central remote reward.
All on bottom shelf.

The four conditions are shown in Fig. 9–3.

The learning curves for the first 1200 trials showed that group 3
was significantly superior to the others (see Fig. 9–4). Group 1 reached
85 percent correct after 2700 trials, group 2 achieved only 60 percent
at the same point. Group 4 reached 85 percent correct after 1500
trials. The results show that both cue-response and cue-reward discontiguity hamper discrimination, but the former more so. If the reward
has to be remote, it is better to have one food well rather than two,
but one would like to see this demonstrated with cue and response on
one shelf and the reward on the other shelf *in both cases* before accepting this result. Groups 1 and 4 did not differ with respect only to the
number of food wells.

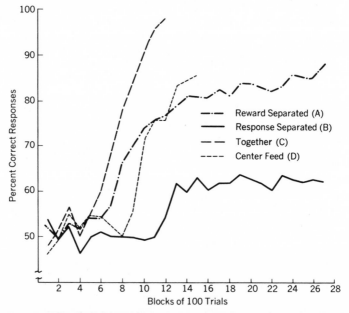

FIG. 9-4. The learning curves of the four groups of monkeys used
by Murphy and Miller, 1964. (From *J. exp. Psychol.*, 67, by permission of American Psychological Association.)

To date, the study by Miller and Murphy (1964), is the only published study that clearly separates and evaluates the effects of the two
important modes of discontiguity. But it would be premature to conclude that a cue-reward discontiguity is of relatively minor importance,
for Cowey and Weiskrantz (unpublished), in an experiment that is
remarkably similar in aims and design to that of Miller and Murphy
(1964), have found that the two types of spatial separation may re-

tard discrimination learning equivalently. Thirty-five experimentally naive juvenile rhesus monkeys were used with a stimulus display consisting of 4 identical white panels, one pair 8 inches above the other, mounted in a vertical board. Each panel was hinged at the top. For the two experimental groups, one pair of panels served as the response site; the other as the reward site. When a response panel was pushed, the reward panel on the same side of the apparatus automatically unlocked, swinging back slightly to allow the animal to reach a concealed food well immediately beneath and behind it. The stimuli, a black cross and a black square, were mounted on the response panels for the cue-response contiguous group (14 animals), and on the reward panels for the cue-reward contiguous group (12 animals). With 9 control animals, for whom cue response, and reward were all contiguous, only one pair of panels was used. These relationships are shown in Fig. 9-5. Two

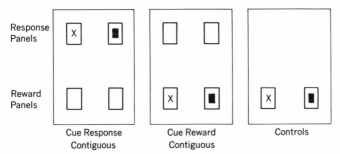

FIG. 9-5. Apparatus used by Cowey and Weiskrantz to vary the spatial relationships of cue, response, and reward.

further variations were investigated with each of the three main groups. The screen used to expose the display was moved in a different direction with half the animals in each group, and the position of response and reward panels was reversed with half the animals. The latter arrangement can be envisaged by turning Fig. 9–5 upside down. Because these variations affected each main group, their influence is not considered here, and the results of the subgroups are considered together. Criterion was 90 percent correct in 100 consecutive trials. The results are illustrated and statistically analyzed by the Mann-Whitney U test in the same way as those of Miller and Murphy (1964) to facilitate comparison. The response-separated and reward-separated animals did not differ significantly with respect to trials to criterion; the control animals differed significantly from both other groups (see Table 9–1, and Fig. 9–6a).

TABLE 9–1

Group Comparisons for Trials to Criterion.

(All analyses made by Mann-Whitney U test.)

Groups	P. 2-tailed
Cue-response contiguous vs. cue-reward contiguous	>.20
Cue-response contiguous vs. control	<.02
Cue-reward Contiguous vs. control	<.01
Switched to cue-response contiguous vs. original control	>.10
Switched to cue-reward contiguous vs. original control	>.10

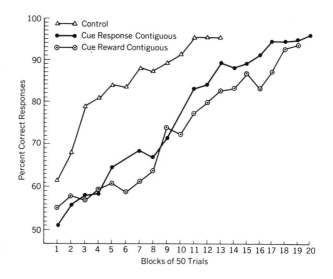

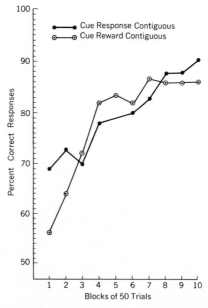

Fig. 9-6. Top: the learning curves of three groups of monkeys—controls, cue-response contiguous, and cue-reward contiguous. Bottom: the relearning curves for certain animals of the two experimental groups after they were switched from one type of spatial discontiguity to the other type.

This experiment does not confirm Miller and Murphy's finding that a cue-response separation has the more serious effect on discrimination learning, and the reason is not obvious. But the two experiments show that discrimination is influenced by apparently trivial and as yet undetected differences in the way stimuli are presented.

There is a rider to the experiment by Cowey and Weiskrantz (unpublished). Once an animal has mastered a discrimination problem involving one form of spatial separation, will he maintain his performance if the other form of discontiguity is introduced? Apparently not, even with the same stimuli. Eight animals from the cue-response contiguous group and six animals from the cue-reward contiguous group were switched to the alternative condition after reaching criterion. Their learning scores are shown in Fig. 9–6b. The two groups are not significantly different, and each required several hundred trials to regain criterion.

Summary and Conclusions

1. Very few experiments clearly evaluate the relative effects on discrimination learning of cue-response and cue-reward spatial separation, but several investigators discount the latter. The most reasonable conclusion is that both factors may produce measurable and serious effects.

2. Although a few animals in any large group may be unaffected by spatial discontiguities (Stollnitz and Schrier, 1962), the latter are best avoided. But apparatus used in testing discrimination is not always so designed and often reflects the point of view of the experimenter rather than of the animal. It may test the animal's intelligence rather than its discriminative capacity. For this reason, as Klüver (1933, p. 310) points out, we should always suspect negative results. In this connection, it would be very instructive to test the color vision of cats under conditions where stimulus and reward are identical, as in Jarvik's study with monkeys. Two of the few experiments that claim to demonstrate color vision in cats have done this (Kalischer, 1909; Buchholtz, 1952), but the latter lacks adequate controls for brightness and size, and the former for brightness and odor. Very young infant rhesus monkeys have mastered visual form discriminations (Zimmerman, 1961) and the success of this study is very likely attributable to the fact that the teat containing the milk reward was embedded in the discriminanda, making cue, response, and reward spatially conjoined.

3. Even if an animal learns to discriminate in a particular experiment, we should not be confident on these grounds alone that we have a suitable stimulus arrangement. For instance, Gunter (1954a) found no evidence of hue discrimination in cats and concluded that they are incapable of this discrimination because they did succeed in mastering a brightness discrimination in the same apparatus. The evidence already cited from Polidora and Fletcher (1964) shows that monkeys will learn a color discrimination under conditions of cue-response discontiguity, but not pattern discrimination. Yet we know that monkeys discriminate these patterns when they are presented in other ways.

4. In determining sensory thresholds, the design of an apparatus is very important, and any slight differences must be evaluated in comparing the results of different investigators. We know now that the effect of spatial discontiguity is related to the difficulty of the discrimination itself. Because discrimination becomes more difficult as the threshold is approached, we might expect slight differences in the ar-

rangement of stimulus response and reward to produce greater differences in a particular discrimination threshold. The present author (together with L. Weiskrantz) has one unpublished experience of this effect in testing the visual acuity of rhesus monkeys. The test fields occupied two windows, one with stripes on it, cut in the front of two trolleys. When the top of the reward cup was level with the bottom of the test field, 5 animals learned the initial discrimination very slowly and reached a mean stable threshold of 0.97 minutes of arc (range 0.82–1.09). When the reward cups were altered so that they were suspended in front of the test field, obscuring part of it, 10 other animals learned the discrimination much more rapidly, and the threshold acuity was 0.6 minutes of arc (range 0.54–0.72). In neither case did the animals ever touch a test field.

5. Even if animals discriminate successfully when cue response and reward are contiguous, their performance is likely to deteriorate and remain poor if a discontiguity is subsequently introduced (Murphy and Miller, 1955; Jenkins, 1943; Jarvik, 1953; Polidora and Fletcher, 1964). There is no study that clearly distinguishes the effect of cue-response and cue-reward separation after initial contiguity of all three variables. There are indications that monkeys can overcome spatial discontiguity if training with each degree of discontiguity is given *throughout* an experiment (McClearn and Harlow, 1954) or if the discontiguity is gradually increased (Stollnitz and Schrier, 1962). However, both results were obtained with a very simple black-white discrimination; a monkey might not master more difficult discrimination involving spatial discontiguity if trained in this manner.

6. The influence of spatial contiguity has been studied exclusively with visual discrimination. It is worth while to consider its influence on auditory discrimination. Monkeys respond to certain auditory cues very quickly, but they are surprisingly poor at discriminations involving different responses to two different auditory stimuli. One of several possible reasons for this may lie with the testing procedure where the stimulus source, from one or more loud speakers, is customarily remote from both the response and the reward sites. This is discussed fully in a later section dealing with audition.

7. Sometimes it is necessary that an animal should not know where a stimulus is to be presented on any trial, for example, in plotting visual field defects in monkeys by using a small, briefly presented, spot of light (Cowey and Weiskrantz, 1963). In this experiment, the animal had to discriminate between the click of a buzzer and the same click plus a visual stimulus. The spatial relationships between the light of the paired stimulus and the response lever for that stimulus varied continually, and a lengthy training period is probably inevitable in such cases.

8. In conditional discriminations, the sign of a particular stimulus is contingent upon some other variable feature of the testing situation, e.g., the color of the surroundings or the quality of the background noise. If these are spatially remote from the site of the rewarded response, their relevance may not be readily appreciated by an animal, which accounts for the difficulty of many conditional discriminations.

The Size and Mounting of Cues

Where to place discriminanda with respect to response and reward is not the only important consideration in designing the physical features of a testing situation; "How large?" and "How mounted?" are other important questions that this section considers.

Klüver (1933) reported that two Java macaques suddenly lost their ability to discriminate between two white squares of different sizes when the stimuli were mounted in identical black backgrounds instead of being presented in isolation. Klüver concluded that in the second condition, the animals were responding to the complete figure and ground, which were, of course, equal in size. Similarly, Harlow (1945a), studying visual form perception in rhesus monkeys with wooden blocks, found that the objects were more easily discriminated when they alone covered the food wells than when they were mounted on identical white bases. Moreover, the superiority that three-dimensional forms possessed over planometric patters was lost when the forms rested on a background like the patterns (see also Harlow, 1951).

Warren (1953c) constructed various pairs of patterns in six different sizes, all mounted on identical cards. He found that discrimination was significantly easier the larger the patterns. Furthermore, the differences in difficulty of discrimination with this kind of problem are not reduced by extensive practice or by varying the incentive (Blazek and Harlow, 1955; Schrier and Harlow, 1957). The effect that Warren reported is almost certainly due to the proximity of the larger cue to the border of the card, for he went on to show (Warren, 1953b) that the size effect could be largely overcome by placing a small cue off-center and therefore close to the edge of its mount. Riopelle, Wunderlich, and Francisco (1958) confirmed and extended Warren's finding, again using rhesus monkeys. They found that colored discs on white plaques were more difficult to discriminate if surrounded by identical colored rings that were themselves irrelevant to the solution of the problem. This alone is hardly surprising, for the addition of the rings makes the entire range of plaques more alike. However, the discrimination became more difficult as the irrelevant rings receded from the colored discs (which ought to make the latter more isolated and therefore more discriminable) and approached the edge of the plaques. All these experiments indicate that a pedestal or mount, particularly its edges, impedes discrimination learning because the animal regards it as a relevant part of the stimulus.

But what if the mount is so flat as to be two-dimensional and immovable? Schrier and Harlow (1957) investigated this by teaching monkeys to discriminate between colored cards that were either mounted on larger white cards or laid directly over food wells surrounded by a white square painted on the testing board. The appearance of the testing board was almost identical in both cases, but one group of animals had to touch the relevant cue itself in order to move it, whereas the other group could displace it by moving the white mount. The authors found that the cues on painted immovable squares were discriminated more easily than those on a movable base, suggesting that the "edge" effect is at least partially dependent on the animal's having to touch the edge of the base in order to move it.

We might note that the authors provide a different interpretation of their results that is related to the contiguity problem discussed earlier. The spatial contiguity between the reward and a small colored card lacking a base is maximal; when the card has a base, the reward is not revealed until the base has been displaced, and the color cue is now a minimum of 1 inch from the reward.

Schrier and Harlow also used large cards that were completely filled by the colored stimulus; i.e., the stimulus did not rest on a base. There was no significant difference between the large cue and the small cue without a base, but the small cue on a base was significantly inferior to both. Here we have additional evidence that there is no intrinsic advantage in using large stimuli; they are effective because they abolish an irrelevant border. It seems unlikely that anyone could use a large cue on an even larger base, but it is not known whether the base would impair discrimination learning in such a case.

Unfortunately, Schrier and Harlow had no control group without even a painted square surrounding the stimulus card, and so we cannot say that the edge effect is entirely abolished by providing a painted and immovable surrounding to a cue. But this problem has been clearly settled by two papers that show that border cues are effective because monkeys usually respond there and not because of any intrinsic superiority. Schuck (1960) found that monkeys discriminated border cues readily when the cues occupied the near border, which the animal had been trained to push, but not when they lay along the far edge. Unfortunately the control group, which had to pull the cards, did not demonstrate the opposite effect, but Schuck noted that these animals tended to manipulate the nearer edges first, and he concluded that this habit was a disturbing carry-over from the prior training that all his animals had with an earlier discrimination. If Schuck is correct, this is further evidence for the view of Polidora and Fletcher (1964) that a monkey samples only from the region of its first response.

The clearest evidence for the respective roles of position of cue *per se* versus position with respect to response is given by Schuck *et al.* (1961). Monkeys learned to press a small button in the center of each response panel in an automatic testing apparatus. The cues were projected either onto the borders of each panel, which measured only 3 inches square or onto the center. More than 800 color discriminations were used in a learning-set situation. The animals discriminated the center cues much more readily, and the difference between performance on center and edge cues increased, not decreased, with extended training.

One further characteristic of a cue needs considering. Very often an animal obscures part or all of a cue with its arm while responding. Does this affect discrimination? Apparently not, for Horel, Schuck, and Meyer (1961) found no difference in performance on a difficult horizontal-vertical discrimination when the small stimuli (measuring ¾ inch in diameter) were placed either above the central response button, or below them, where the animal's outstretched arm covered the cue to which it had responded. One might have expected this result in any case from the fact that monkeys often look away when responding and easily master delayed response problems where the cues have been removed before any overt response can be made.

Summary and Conclusions

1. Monkeys attend chiefly to things they touch first. If stimuli are to be displayed on a plaque or screen, they should appear as close to the edge as possible if the animal tends to respond by touching the edge rather than the center, which it usually does. But there is nothing intrinsically superior about the border of a cue; its prominence is almost certainly related to the spatial contiguity of cue and response, as discussed in an earlier section.

2. Nor is there anything inherently superior about large cues; they are effective because of their proximity to the border of their support and, presumably, because some part of the cue will be contiguous with an animal's response no matter which part of the support it touches. The best arrangement is probably a small manipulandum entirely occupied by the cue.

3. The effects of displaying a stimulus in an unfavorable way are not easily overcome by extensive training.

4. Most experiments concerning the best manner of presenting stimuli have been performed with monkeys, and it would be foolhardy to assume that less intelligent animals could overcome an arrangement that a monkey finds difficult. We do know that rats tend to attend to the lower edge of cards at which they jump (Ehrenfreund, 1948); perhaps this animal's notoriously poor form-discrimination could be improved by teaching it to press a button in the center of the stimulus.

The Problem of Stimulus Complexity

If stimuli differ in more than one respect, e.g., color, size, shape, length of contour, and total luminous flux, how many of the dimensions does the animal use when discriminating? If an animal does use more than one stimulus quality, does this help him? The numerous experiments explicitly designed to answer these questions, or carried out for different reasons but quoted by others in support of their views, often seem contradictory. If divided into the following two groups their interpretation is clearer.

1. *Experiments attempting to show that animals presented with multidimensional cues react to more than one dimension.* Lashley (1938, p. 167–169) taught rats to discriminate between three circles, differing with respect to linear dimensions, area, and total luminous flux, and then studied performance when the animals were presented with stimuli differing in only one or two of these qualities. The results showed that the rats had attended chiefly to total area of the training stimuli but that some had responded also to total luminous flux.

Nissen and Jenkins (1943) reported similar results with chimpanzees. Eight animals were taught a problem combining size and brightness cues before being tested with stimuli varying along only one of these dimensions. If the animals had responded initially to only one of the two possible cues, we should expect their performance on the second problem to remain at better than 90 percent correct or to fall to 50 percent correct. This was not found. Five animals performed about as well with brightness alone as with size and brightness, but their mean score on size alone was 65 percent (range 55 to 81), not 50 percent. Similarly, three animals that performed almost perfectly with size alone recorded 60 percent correct (range 50 to 70) with brightness.

A similar result was obtained in an experiment with rats (Sutherland and Mackintosh, 1964). After learning to discriminate between a horizontal white rectangle and a vertical black rectangle, the animals were given four transfer tests (see Fig. 9–7), in each of which only one of the original cues (brightness or orientation) was present. Retraining on the original discrimination was interspersed between successive transfer tests. Animals scored a mean of 96 percent correct on the retraining trials but selected the horizontal rectangle on 86 percent of the transfer tests with the orientation cue and chose the white stimulus on 72 percent of the transfer tests with the brightness cue

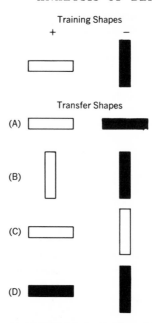

FIG. 9-7. The stimuli used by Sutherland and Mackintosh, 1964, in a study of the effects of subtraction of a cue.

present. These group means are less informative than results for individual rats, which are unfortunately not given, but they indicate that some animals must have utilized both cues in the initial discrimination. However, there was a negative correlation between the number of times individual animals chose brightness when it was the only relevant cue and the frequency with which they chose the horizontal rectangle when orientation was relevant, suggesting that the more a rat utilizes one cue, the less he learns about the other.

The fourth, and most detailed, experiment to be mentioned was performed by Warren (1954). Monkeys were trained with discriminanda differing in color, size, and shape. The animals were given 6 trials on each of 96 problems, each batch of 6 being followed by 9 trials where one or two cues had been subtracted. The removal of color and form or of color and size produced clear and approximately equal disruptive effects. Subtraction of color alone produced less impairment. Subtraction of only form or size, or both, caused only a slight but significant disturbance. Unfortunately, only group mean scores are given, and one can not be certain that every animal was affected by the removal of a cue.

The last and rather different study of this kind used pigeons. Jones (1954) taught six birds a discrimination involving color, size, and position as possible cues (green, circle, right, all positive; red, triangle, left, all negative). The stimuli were then rearranged in various ways so that each positive stimulus was now in opposition to the other two. Four trials were given on each new arrangement. Four birds responded consistently to color and two to position. Form was not chosen. This seems to show that pigeons, unlike rats and monkeys, attend only to one cue when several are present in the initial learning situation. But such a conclusion is unjustified, for experiments on substraction and rearrangement of cues are not equivalent. The birds may have noticed and utilized all three cues during initial training, but they responded to a preferred cue when the stimuli were recombined in various ways.

The first four experiments illustrate the effect of stimulus subtraction, and they answer the first of our two questions, but they leave unanswered the second problem about whether discrimination is easier on *initial* training if more than one cue is present.

2. *Experiments attempting to show that multiple cues assist discrimination.* Harlow (1944) presented naive rhesus monkeys with twenty object-discrimination problems followed by 10 tests of discrimination reversal. The animals mastered all the problems with impressive speed, often by the second or third trial. Hitherto, no one had demonstrated such swift discrimination with monkeys, and the only obvious reason was that objects are potent stimuli because they vary along several stimulus dimensions (see also Harlow, 1951). This was followed by a direct demonstration (Harlow, 1945b) that objects are superior to patterned cards as discriminative stimuli with monkeys. However, it is not clear from this, and from similar experiments, whether objects are more easily discriminated because of their multidimensional stimulus quality or because an animal tends to touch an object more often than the pattern on a card while responding; i.e., cue-response contiguity may be maximal with objects.

The latter interpretation is supported by three experiments (Harlow, 1945c; Meyer and Harlow, 1949; Warren, 1953a), where it was found that cues differing only in color are superior to those varying only in form, size, or form plus size but that cues differing along all dimensions are no better than color alone; i.e., there is no additivity.

Now, it could be said that color is such an easy discrimination for monkeys (they often solve the problem in one trial) that we cannot improve the performance by adding cues. But if we use only cues that in isolation are more difficult, do they summate and quicken discrimination? Warren (1956) applied this reasoning and finally succeeded in demonstrating additivity of stimuli with monkeys by using colors that were not easily discriminable, together with form and size.

Further evidence that multiple cues assist discrimination learning is provided by Eninger (1952), who found that rats learned a simple maze much faster when the correct turn was indicated by both visual and auditory cues than when one or the other cue was present. And the cues were presented in such a way that the compound stimulus had no greater cue-response contiguity.

Summary and Conclusions

Experiments on subtraction of cues indicate that animals can learn something about more than one stimulus in a multidimensional cue. Yet many experiments on additivity of cues fail to demonstrate summation as defined by quicker learning. These findings are reconcilable if we accept the following points.

1. Animals prefer, or are more attentive to, or influenced by, certain types of stimulus; e.g., color seems to be potent[1] with monkeys, orienta-

[1] "Potent" may be a more apt description than "preferred" for Butler (1958) presents evidence that monkeys prefer certain meaningful sounds over visual stimuli in exploratory situations, yet there is no doubt that auditory discriminations are more difficult than visual.

tion seems to be potent with rats (Sutherland and Mackintosh, 1964), and cats can certainly perceive colors but tend to ignore differences in hue (Mello and Peterson, 1964). If a potent cue is present, the addition of a less effective one may not assist discrimination. This explains the results already mentioned (Harlow, 1945c; Meyer and Harlow, 1949; Warren, 1953a). It will also account for the finding of Peterson and Rumbaugh (1963) that there is no deterioration in the perform-ance of squirrel monkeys on object learning-sets when the animals are prevented from palpating the cues and have to rely solely on vision.

2. If we select cues of comparable and preferably not very great potency, so that the animal does not very successfully discriminate be-tween them in a few trials, we do find evidence for additivity (War-ren, 1956).

3. Experiments on summation and subtraction of cues may not al-ways be comparable. Let us assume that in an experiment on summa-tion three cues are present and that each animal utilizes only one of them, although different animals choose different cues. The mean learn-ing score may be no different from that of control animals with only one or two cues present if we further assume that the animals im-mediately select a relevant cue however many are present. The experi-ment would not indicate a summation effect. But if we now subtract a cue, the animals who selected it originally must learn afresh. Subtract two cues, and even more animals are likely to be affected. We would have our evidence for subtraction. We ought to detect this kind of effect if we look at the individual scores for each animal (as did Nissen and Jenkins, 1943), but with combined scores it remains obscure.

4. One last point about simple and complex cues. If animals are looking for differences along a particular dimension (i.e., they are not behaving as in the hypothetical example given in 3), a complex cue will be superior to a simple one, for it is more likely to possess the stimulus qualities sought by the animal. This is the kind of stimulus anyone interested in rapid discrimination will want to use. If, on the other hand, an experimenter is studying discrimination along a par-ticular dimension, "irrelevant" cue differences should be eliminated, for many may be potent cues occupying the animal's attention without helping it to solve the problem. For instance, because it is so difficult to equate the subjective brightness of different hues, most experiments deliberately vary brightness and make it an irrelevant cue when testing hue discrimination in cats. This is a necessary control, but it may dis-suade the cat from attending to color rather than brightness, especially if the latter is preferred by the animal.

Simultaneous and Successive Discrimination Procedures

On each trial in a two-choice discrimination experiment, both stim-uli, or only one of them, may be presented. These are the methods of simultaneous and successive discrimination respectively, and it is important to know which favors faster learning in an experiment where the same stimuli are used throughout and which yields finer discrim-ination in a threshold experiment where differences between the stimuli are continually varied until the animal cannot detect them.

It is commonly stated that simultaneous discrimination is superior because it permits many and direct comparisons between the two stim-uli on each trial and because successive discrimination requires exactly twice as many trials for the animal to perceive each stimulus. But these reasons are often presumptive rather than empirical, and, as Sutherland (1961) has shown, the actual evidence is confusing. Sutherland has reviewed and interpreted the relevant experiments in considerable detail, which allows us to concentrate on certain methodological points.

Simultaneous and successive discrimination procedures are often compared as if they differed in only one respect, namely, two types of stimuli or one type on each trial. But they may differ in several ways as follows:

A. *Simultaneous.*

A1. The stimuli are arranged so that the animal learns to touch one and not the other; e.g., he displaces it, pushes it, presses it, or he may pass through it if it is a colored alley. This is the commonest simultaneous procedure, and, as cue and response are contiguous, it will be called *simultaneous-direct.*

A2. The animal responds not to the stimulus, but in some particular direction with respect to it; for example, he may jump through, or press, an adjacent door. Cue and response are not contiguous. Moreover, a different response is often required to one particular stimulus depending on its position, e.g., positive stimulus on the left—jump to the left of it; positive stimulus on the right—jump to the right of it. A2 will be called *simultaneous-indirect.*

B. *Successive.*

B1. A single stimulus is present on each trial.

B1a. The animal manipulates one stimulus to obtain a reward and has to refrain from touching the other. This is an approach-avoidance or "go, no-go" technique. But two differing reward schedules are common. In symmetrical reward, all correct responses are rewarded. With unsymmetrical reward, correct no-go responses are unrewarded.

B1b. The same as for B1a, but cue and response are discontiguous as, for instance, in auditory discriminations. This will be called *go, no-go indirect.*

B2. A *pair* of identical stimuli is present on each trial. (Both B2a and B2b are sign-differentiated position responses, the former direct, the latter indirect.)

B2a. The animal is trained to manipulate the left stimulus of one pair and the right stimulus of the other. Cue and response are contiguous.

B2b. The same as for B2a, but cue and response are spatially separated; e.g., the animal responds to the left of one stimulus pair and to the right of the other.

Bearing the previous classification in mind, we can state the following conclusions about the relative merits of simultaneous and successive discrimination procedures.

1. If the stimuli are highly similar, as they must be at some stage in a threshold discrimination experiment, simultaneous discrimination is superior to successive. Saldanha and Bitterman (1951) found that rats could discriminate between different shades of gray or between stripes of different widths much faster when the stimuli were presented simultaneously, whereas the two different testing procedures yielded indistinguishable learning curves with a horizontal-vertical or a large circle–small circle discrimination. This was confirmed by MacCaslin

(1954). The present writer (unpublished observation) found that rhesus monkeys trained on a visual acuity discrimination showed a much higher threshold if the stimuli were presented successively than if they appeared together. These observations suggest that simultaneous-direct is superior to "go, no-go direct" with threshold discrimination, but they do not reveal the reason for the difference between the two methods. Presumably, immediate stimulus comparison is helpful when the stimuli are alike.

2. Many attempts to compare the efficiency of simultaneous and successive procedures are confounded by the effects of cue response contiguity and the number and type of responses to be made. For instance, Wodinsky, Varley, and Bitterman (1954) trained rats to jump at the outer of four doors arranged in a semicircle about the jumping platform. The rats were divided into four groups, and each group learned two visual discrimination problems with testing procedures corresponding to A1; A2; and B2a and B2b in our classification, i.e., to simultaneous-direct and indirect and to successive sign-differentiated-direct and indirect. The rats learned A1 fastest, followed by B2a, B2b, and A2 in that order, except that the difference between B2b and A2 disappeared on the second problem. We can make the following points about their results.

a. If animals jump at the stimuli (A1 and B2a), they will learn faster than if they jump elsewhere (A2 and B2b), irrespective of simultaneous or successive procedures. Experiments that are designed to evaluate simultaneous versus successive discrimination and that neglect the contiguity factor are therefore invalid. See Sutherland (1961) for examples.

b. Equating for cue-response contiguity, we see that simultaneous-direct is superior to successive sign-differentiated-direct. However, as Sutherland (1961) points out, in the former, all an animal needs to learn is to approach one stimulus; in the latter, he must learn to jump one way to one stimulus pair and the other way to the second pair. So the type of response may be making the successive discrimination more difficult. Similarly, we can compare simultaneous-indirect with successive sign-differentiated-indirect. Here the successive discrimination was easier with the first pair of patterns but not with the second, and so we should perhaps not stress this result. However, Sutherland (1961) again points out that in the sign-differentiated condition an animal can learn by following the rule "stimulus pair x go left, pair y go right," whereas in the simultaneous-indirect condition the animals may be learning the more complex rule "stimulus x-on-left y-on-right, go left; stimulus y-on-left x-on-right, go right." That is, as well as discriminating between the stimuli, they must take note of their *relative* positions. Sutherland concludes that, when an animal does not respond directly to the stimulus, the simultaneous method has no advantage over successive. But it does not follow from this that neither procedure is preferable. For reasons already given, it is better to train animals to respond directly to the stimuli, and here the simultaneous method is definitely preferable.

Experiments comparing simultaneous and successive procedures are also confounded by (1) the difficulty of keeping certain cues distinct, (2) the number of discriminatory choices made in any one trial, and (3) stimulus preferences. An example of the possible operation of all three factors is provided by Weise and Bitterman (1951). A maze with four choice points had a pair of lights at each T junction. Rats had to choose the light or dark alley at each junction (simultaneous group) or to turn one way when both lights were on and the other way when neither was on (successive group). The simultaneous group required twice as many trials to reach criterion. Calvin and Siebel (1954) point out that the stimuli for the successive group may be more distinctive than for the simultaneous group where some of the light from one alley escapes into the other. They repeated Weise and Bitterman's experiment but placed the lights 8 inches into the alleys. They obtained the same results, and therefore discarded their objection. However, as the alleys were only 12 inches long, light from the first illuminated alley could project into the dark alley at the second choice point, from the second to third, and third to fourth. The objection is therefore not overruled.

Calvin and Williams (1956) consider that Weise and Bitterman's result may be a product of multiple-choice apparatus. They suggest that the goal gradients and alternation that are a feature of multiple-choice mazes may act in different ways on simultaneous and successive discrimination procedures. They repeated Weise and Bitterman's experiment but used only one choice point. There was then no difference in the performance scores of the simultaneous and successive groups.

Calvin and Williams also provided data on the third point. The animals in the simultaneous group for whom the dark alley was positive had a mean error score of 47, whereas the animals for whom the light alley was positive made 105 errors. Animals in the successive group made only 78 errors, and, although the authors do not state it explicitly, they implied that there were no differences in the two subgroups. The results indicate that stimulus preference can hinder a simultaneous discrimination, but not a successive discrimination where the animal cannot exercise its preference on any one trial, where both alleys are either light or dark. Of course, if animals in one subgroup of a simultanous discrimination are hindered to the same extent that those of the other subgroup are assisted, the effects cancel. But we cannot be certain of this. For example, if a hypothetical animal with no preference learns a simultaneous discrimination in thirty trials, the greatest possible reduction in another animal for whom the positive stimulus is preferred is thirty trials. A third animal for whom the preferred stimulus is negative may persist in choosing it for more than sixty trials. The overall result would be to make simultaneous discrimination more difficult. Of course, the confounding effect of stimulus preferences is chiefly of interest to someone comparing *learning* in different testing procedures. The fact that the preference exists indicates that the animal can discriminate the stimuli. Spence (1952) has drawn attention to these confounding effects and presents good evidence that, when they are removed simultaneous testing procedures are superior to successive.

No testing method mentioned so far has employed the "go, no-go" direct and indirect procedures, but the former has been used extensively and successfully to test shape discrimination in the octopus (see Sutherland, 1961, for review). Sutherland and Muntz (1959) compared the "go, no-go" direct procedure with simultaneous-direct and found it to be superior with the octopus, perhaps because it does not permit the animal to develop position preferences. Many animals do develop position preferences with a difficult discrimination involving two distinct response positions, and this may in part explain why the only convincing demonstration of hue discrimination in cats utilizes a "go, no-go" procedure (Mello and Peterson, 1964). Animals were trained to press a panel when the latter was red, irrespective of luminance, and were rewarded on a variable interval schedule for doing so. They were not rewarded if the cue panel was green, yellow, or blue, again irrespective of luminance. However, the animals took 1½ years to master the color discriminations, and one suspects that learning would have been much faster had they used a direct rather than an indirect response.

The "go, no-go" method may also be superior in testing auditory discrimination (see the section on audition), but it also has one disadvantage, especially in investigating the effect of some treatment on discrimination. The animal must learn to withhold a response on no-go trials, and the treatment may affect this. For instance, Battig, Rosvold, and Mishkin (1962) found that frontal and caudate lesions produced an impairment in visual and auditory discrimination, using a "go, no-go" procedure with asymmetrical reward, between 90 percent and 100 percent of all errors being made on no-go trials. But the same animals were unimpaired on a simultaneous-direct visual discrimination (Battig, Rosvold, and Mishkin, 1960), suggesting that the operations prevented the animals from withholding their response rather than disturbing their ability to discern differences in the stimuli. (But see Gross and Weiskrantz, 1964, for further discussion of this point.)

Errorless Discrimination Training

One of the most promising recent developments in discrimination training is the discovery of a method by which errors are minimized or altogether abolished and by which the number of trials to criterion is reduced. Two conditions appear to be necessary, namely, the introduction of the negative stimulus after a response to the positive stimulus has been established, and an initial large difference between the two stimuli that is thereafter reduced. For example, Terrace (1963b) rapidly taught pigeons to discriminate between red and green lights by rewarding key presses to a 5-second red light and by then introducing a very dim 1-second green light which was gradually increased in duration and intensity until these matched the positive red stimulus. Most birds learned the discrimination without ever responding to the negative stimulus. A further orientation discrimination was mastered without error by superimposing a horizontal or vertical white line on the colored key and by then fading out the color on successive trials.

It remains to be seen whether Terrace's methods will be successful with a wide variety of species and with all the various testing procedures described earlier, but one important point is already clear: Terrace has gone on to show that whether the pigeon learns a discrimination with or without errors can influence the effect of subsequent treatment. For example, chlorpromazine and imipramine, which impair performance if the animal learns a discrimination in the conventional manner where errors are initially common, are without effect if an errorless training method is used (Terrace, 1963a). Similarly, when pigeons are taught to discriminate between two wave lengths of light and are then presented with several wave lengths in a generalization test, a shift in the peak of the generalization gradient away from the negative stimulus is observed only if the animals have been trained initially with a procedure that allows errors to occur (Terrace, 1964). Terrace proposes that the negative stimulus does not acquire aversive properties when errorless training methods are used. If that is so, the different treatment effects that he has described in discrimination tasks with and without errors may well be widespread.

Auditory Discrimination

Thus far the discussion has been illustrated almost exclusively by examples from visual discrimination, and it has been left to the reader to consider the relevance of the various conclusions to other modalities. This section deals specifically with audition, which follows vision in being the most popular subject in the study of discrimination in mammals.

The study of auditory discrimination is often divided into four sections, dealing with localization of sound and with discrimination of frequency, intensity, and pattern. This classification is followed here, but without implying that these four sensory qualities have nothing in common.

Sound Localization

Many animals can successfully localize the source of a continuously or intermittently emitted sound, but this alone indicates little about an animal's spatial acuity, for just as certain insects locate a moist environment by moving as long as it is dry and by changing direction whenever it gets drier, so too an organism with very poor spatial auditory acuity could change direction whenever a sound became fainter. Of course, the speed with which an animal reached the source, or, better still, the course he followed in doing so, might indicate how accurately it could localize the sound, but these are tedious measures that have the further possible disadvantage of being sensitive to treatments that affect gait and speed of movement rather than hearing. For these reasons, auditory localization is usually studied by presenting a brief noise behind one of two panels and by allowing the animal to move toward the panels when the noise has been extinguished. The angular separation of the panels is then reduced and increased systematically to find the discrimination threshold. This has been done with several species, and tables of comparative auditory spatial acuity are available (Maier and Schnierla, 1935; Smith, 1951). Ought we to be satisfied with this method, and in particular can we be confident that any treatment effects that it reveals really reflect alterations in hearing? Although no one has demonstrated any flaw in the procedure, there are two possible candidates. If I walk across a room toward two telephones, one of which rang briefly before I moved, I must remember which one it was in order to pick up the correct receiver. If I forget which one rang, I may still be correct if I can continue to walk in a straight line toward my original target. But if I have both a bad memory and unstable gait I may be incorrect, and my chances of being so will increase the smaller the angular separation of two instruments. If a drug or brain lesion produces this kind of affliction, neither would need to be present to any great extent to raise the spatial threshold slightly, which is the effect of certain cortical lesions of the auditory projection areas in cats (Neff and Diamond, 1958). There is no evidence for either disability in cats that have sustained this lesion, but it would be possible to eliminate their effects by arranging that the animal's response could not be altered once initiated, just as a bullet, once fired, is no longer controlled by any change in the marksman's behavior. Response levers in front of the animal are hardly satisfactory because of the cue-response-reward spatial relationships already discussed, but a pull-in technique, whereby the animal hauls the appropriate stimulus carrier toward him, is suitable for many animals. But perhaps the best arrangement, especially for animals unable to manipulate cords, is to place a partition, with a mesh construction that will allow sound to pass through it, from a point midway between the two response panels, to the start box. In this way, the animal would reach the panel of his original choice, even if he steered badly and forgot which it was en route.

One further point about auditory localization should be considered. If some form of treatment impairs localization, it is likely to affect performance on intensity, frequency, and pattern discrimination if these are tested in a manner where the animal must identify the spatial location of the stimuli. Fortunately, this is usually not so, but certain experimenters, e.g., Konorski (1964), have described the advantages of using spatially separated stimuli, and other reasons for doing so will be suggested below.

Reviews of the effects of brain lesions on auditory localization are given by Neff (1961a; 1961b) and Neff and Diamond (1958), but we might note here that no study clearly shows which of the three possible cues to the spatial position of an auditory stimulus, viz., differential intensity, phase, and time of arrival at the two ears, is affected by a particular treatment. It is probably not the intensity difference, for cortical lesions that seriously impair auditory localization have no effect on intensity discrimination (see Neff, 1960; 1961a; 1961b for review).

Intensity Discrimination

This is probably the most easily measured attribute of audition. By teaching an animal to respond in some way whenever it hears a tone, wave-length sensitivity curves have been obtained with monkeys, chimpanzees, dogs, and cats (see Ades, 1959; Wegener, 1964 for reviews). These curves are potentially very useful in the design of experiments on frequency and pattern discrimination when it is necessary to make intensity irrelevant by varying it through a range appropriately chosen so that no particular frequency or pattern will be consistently softer or louder than another. Nevertheless, some investigators still attempt to equate loudness by adjusting pure tones until they appear equally loud to the human ear or attempt to make it irrelevant by varying the physical intensity about the point of subjective equality for the human ear. Of course we cannot be certain that the wave-length sensitivity curve retains its shape at the much higher intensities used in frequency and pattern discrimination experiments, but it is the best we have until someone devises a method of assessing relative loudness at high intensities and ensures that the response is not based on frequency.

The differential sensitivity to tones varying in intensity, with wave length held constant, has also been studied, chiefly in cats and using an avoidance conditioning procedure (see Neff, 1961a, for review). As mentioned earlier, both perceived pitch and loudness vary when only the physical intensity of a pure tone is changed, and we cannot be certain from these experiments alone that the animal is responding entirely to perceived changes in loudness. We could be sure if a lesion that severely impaired frequency discrimination (frequency being the principal determinant of pitch) failed to affect performance on absolute or differential intensity discriminations, but removal of the auditory cortex in cats permanently impairs neither discrimination, and cortical plus inferior collicular lesions impair both discriminations (Kryter and Ades, 1943; Neff, 1961a; Goldberg and Neff, 1961). The only exception is provided by Meyer and Woolsey (1952), who describe frequency discrimination deficits without impairment on an intensity task. Neither task was tested at threshold, but the former was tested with a frequency difference four times above threshold, the latter at an intensity difference only twice the difference limen. There was therefore a weighting against the intensity discrimination, which was nevertheless unimpaired.

Frequency Discrimination

The study of auditory frequency discrimination is an excellent example from a modality other than visual of the fact that whether or how easily an animal learns a discrimination depends as much on the testing procedure as on the animal's sensory capacities. For instance, the extensive experiments of Hunter from 1914 to 1927 (see Maier and Schnierla, 1935, for review) indicated that rats could barely discriminate between pure tones and silence, although they were able to respond selectively to the more complex noises provided by buzzers and whistles. The demonstration that, as with vision, certain classes of stimuli are more readily discriminable than others is important, but, in other respects, the chiefly negative results are questionable on the grounds already raised in discussing vision. Indeed, it was soon found that rats could discriminate between pure tones and silence if the auditory stimulus was continuously emitted during a trial instead of being briefly presented, as by Hunter, while the animal was in the start box (Meunzinger and Gentry, 1931), or if the loudspeaker was placed at the end of one of the alleys instead of being suspended above the center of the apparatus (Thuma, 1932). Herington and Gundlach (1933) succeeded in teaching guinea pigs (which also failed to discriminate tones when tested by Hunter's methods) to discriminate between pure tones by placing loudspeakers near *each* end of an E shaped maze, by presenting the stimuli in rapid alternation before the animal was released, and by presenting the appropriate tone again when it reached a goal box. These three experiments indicate the importance of temporal and spatial contiguity in auditory discrimination, yet in none of them are these relationships optimal, using *optimal* in the sense derived from visual discrimination studies. For instance, in a maze the choice is still far removed temporally and spatially from the reward. Furthermore, the stimuli were given successively, although Herington and Gundlach (1933) approached a simultaneous presentation.

Unlike the study of visual discrimination, the *systematic* examination of the factors controlling the ease or difficulty of auditory discrimination in a two-choice apparatus virtually stops at this point. Instead, most investigators have used an avoidance conditioning procedure in which it was shown, even while Hunter was reporting extreme insensitivity to pure tones, that rats, guinea pigs, dogs and cats have excellent frequency discrimination, in many cases superior to man's (for reviews, see Anrep, 1920; Neff, 1961a).

The characteristics of the cat's frequency discrimination are well known and undisputed, but the effects of various cortical lesions are not nearly as clear, and they provide an interesting example of how different testing techniques can influence a treatment effect. Neff and Diamond (1958) reported that cats could relearn a frequency discrimination following bilateral removal of areas AI, AII, Ep, and SII, whereas Meyer and Woolsey (1952) found that apparently identical lesions permanently impaired the ability of the cat to discriminate between a very similar selection of pure tones. The first study used a double-grill avoidance box, the second a rotating wheel that the animal had to turn when the stimulus frequency changed. But the testing box was not responsible for the difference, for Thompson (1958) confirmed Neff and Diamond's results despite using a rotating wheel. Nor was the difference in lesion-size responsible, for Goldberg and Neff (1961) reproduced the negative effect with even larger ablations, including insular, temporal, and suprasylvian cortex. The negative results were obtained with a stimulus arrangement where a continuously pulsating neutral stimulus, lasting an average of 1 minute, was followed by an avoidance signal lasting 14 seconds and with no silent period between trials. The impairments were obtained when a relatively short neutral stimulus preceded a single brief tone signaling shock within 1 second of its offset, and with a silent period between trials. When Thompson (1960) tried both stimulus arrangements in a rotating wheel apparatus, he found relearning with the former and not with the latter, even though the same animals were used. He also found that punishment of false positive-avoidance responses prevented relearning and further emphasized the importance of superficially trivial procedural differences.

Pattern Discrimination

The only animal that has been extensively tested on auditory pattern discrimination is the cat. In general, cats find auditory patterns more difficult to discriminate than frequency or intensity, and cortical lesions to AI, AII, and Ep, which seriously disturb the former, leave the simpler discriminations unimpaired (Diamond and Neff, 1957; Neff and Diamond, 1958; Diamond, Goldberg, and Neff, 1962). It is important to know whether the lesion selectively impairs pattern discrimination or whether it simply affects more difficult tasks. The experiment by Diamond, Goldberg, and Neff (1962) indicates that the latter may well be true and also demonstrates that, when a frequency discrimination is presented in such a way that it includes a feature normally only present in pattern discrimination, it too may be impaired. Figure 9–8 (adapted from Diamond, Goldberg, and Neff, 1962) shows three possible paradigms for testing frequency or pattern discrimination. Arrangement *a* is commonly used to test frequency discrimination and *b* to study pattern discrimination. In *a* the avoidance signal contains a unique frequency, in *b* it consists of a rearrangement of frequencies already presented in the neutral stimulus. Arrangement *c* is also a frequency discrimination, but, in common with b, the avoidance signal includes no unique frequency. The authors tested cats preoperatively and postoperatively in a double-grill avoidance box using paradigm c and compared the results with those obtained in their own previous studies using paradigms a and b. Postoperative testing was also given with paradigm a. They report that normal animals find a much easier to learn than c, by an average of 11 sessions to 36. After removal of cortical areas AI, AII, and Ep, cats fail to relearn frequency discrimination c, as they do pattern discriminations, whereas they can still learn the customary frequency discrimination as presented in a. The results of this experiment are suggestive but still inconclusive. One needs a study of the effects of cortical lesions on frequency and pattern discrimination when the two are tested according to paradigms a and b and are equated for test difficulty beforehand. Until then it is not certain that any cortical lesion selectively impairs auditory pattern discrimination.

Neff has proposed a model or auditory discrimination that helps to reconcile some of the discrepant results of experiments involving intensity, frequency, and pattern (Neff, 1961b; Diamond, Goldberg, and Neff, 1962). The three assumptions in the model that are most relevant here are:

1. Tones of different frequencies excite different populations of fibers, and the higher the sound intensity the more fibers are excited.

2. As long as the tone of an avoidance signal excites fibers that are unaffected by the neutral signal, discrimination is possible even after destruction of the auditory cortex *if in addition* the avoidance signal evokes a relatively larger neural response.

3. The neural response habituates, habituation being negligible for intervals much shorter than a minute, but considerable when a tone is repeatedly presented for about a minute.

In both pattern discrimination (paradigm b in Fig. 9–8), and frequency discrimination tested according to paradigm c in Fig. 9–8, requirement 2 is not met, and in both cases destruction of auditory cortex abolishes the discrimination. In many studies of frequency discrimination tested according to paradigm a in Fig. 9–8, the neutral stimulus

	Neutral signal	Avoidance signal	Neutral signal
a	**LLL**	LHL	**LLL**
b	HLH	LHL	HLH
c	LHL	**LLL**	LHL

FIG. 9-8. Temporal stimulus arrangements used in testing auditory frequency and pattern discriminations.
H = high frequency tone; L = low frequency tone.

is presented for upwards of 1 minute. If assumption 3 is correct, the neural response to the neutral stimulus will have waned, and the avoidance signal will, besides stimulating different fibers, evoke a relatively larger neural response. In these studies, frequency discrimination is still possible following removal of the auditory cortex.

In two studies of frequency discrimination, the neutral and avoidance signals were separated by an interval of silence (Allen, 1945) or the duration of the stimulus was only 12 seconds (Meyer and Woolsey, 1952). Habituation will be negligible according to assumption 3; the neutral and avoidance signals will stimulate different fibers, but not to greatly differing extents. It was found in these studies that removal of the auditory cortex does impair frequency discrimination.

Perhaps the most interesting feature of this analysis is the proposal that the *size* of the neural response is important in the frequency discrimination of operated animals. It is as if the animal discriminates frequency partially on the basis of perceived intensity, the intensity difference resulting from habituation to the stimulus first presented. An analogy in vision would be a demonstration that two spectral lights, first adjusted to appear equally bright, subsequently appear unequally bright if one of them is exposed to the subject for about a minute.

The Perplexing Difficulty of Auditory Discrimination

At present the swiftest way to teach auditory discriminations to animals is probably to use an avoidance conditioning technique. But a wide variety of testing techniques is useful and desirable in analyzing treatment effects. It is for this reason doubly disappointing that almost everyone who has tried other methods of testing auditory discrimination with, for instance, monkeys, is chiefly impressed by the difficulty that the animals have in learning the discrimination. The remainder of this chapter is devoted to an analysis of the possible reasons why chiefly monkeys, chosen because so many experimenters use them and because their performance on visual and auditory tasks can be compared, appear to find auditory discrimination so difficult. There are four broad categories, first suggested by Wegener (1964), to whom the reader is referred for a detailed account and somewhat different conclusion, under which the reasons for the difficulty may be sought.

SENSORY CAPACITY. The difficulty does not lie here. There are several studies of absolute and differential frequency threshold that show that in this respect the auditory sensory capacity of the monkey is very much like man's (see Wegener [1964] for references). Moreover, the performance of monkeys and cats in a differential frequency discrimination is quite similar when both species are tested with a shock avoidance procedure, which has been used in most of the experiments showing rapid learning of auditory discriminations in cats.

MOTIVATION. The kind of stimuli usually used in auditory discrimination are pure tones, buzzers, and bells. If the animals find these aversive and require considerable experience to overcome their fear, we might expect discrimination learning to be slow. There is some evidence that suggests certain sounds are aversive. Chow (1951) reported that monkeys solved a "go, no-go" discrimination problem (silence vs. bell) in a mean of 120 trials, the go cue being silence, whereas Stepien and Cordeau (1960) report that monkeys required six times as many trials to learn buzzer versus silence when the no-go cue was silence. And Wegener (1964) found that rhesus monkeys trained in an auditory localization experiment (buzzer vs. silence) required about three times as many trials to reach criterion when they had to approach the sound source as when they had to retreat from it.

It seems that the aversiveness of some auditory stimuli may contribute to the difficulty of discrimination, and one way of testing this would be to use amydalectomized animals that lose their aversion to noxious stimuli. But this can hardly be a sufficient explanation, for the author has abundant personal experience that squirrel monkeys have the usual difficulty in learning a "go, no-go" auditory discrimination (buzzer vs. 2000 cps tone) and that the majority of incorrect responses are made on no-go trials, even though the loudspeaker formed the base of the covered food well. Why should an animal advance directly toward a stimulus of which he is afraid? There is good evidence (Butler, 1958) that monkeys depress a lever more often to present the noises of other monkeys' feeding or an interrupted white noise, than they do to listen to a barking dog that is presumably aversive.

REINFORCEMENT. As mentioned earlier, auditory discriminations are acquired relatively easily when a conditioned avoidance procedure is used. For instance, Wendt (1934) and Harris (1943) found very similar wave length sensitivity curves in a variety of monkeys, but in the first study, where a "go, no-go" procedure was used, the thresholds were established only after more than 100 testing sessions, whereas in the second experiment, where a conditioned avoidance of shock in a rotatable cage, was used a maximum of three training sessions was needed. These and similar experiments (see Wegener, 1964, for review) suggest that learning might be rapid in other testing situations if incorrect responses are punished with electric shock. Unfortunately, there is no study that expressly examines the role of shock in other procedures, nor can its effects be ascertained with certainty by comparing results of different investigators, some of whom have used shock and others not. Wegener in 1964 has attempted a comparison, but the several experiments he discusses differ in so many points of procedure that even his cautious acceptance of the beneficial effects of shock is a trifle optimistic.

STIMULUS PRESENTATION. It has been stressed in this chapter that the ease with which monkeys learn visual discrimination is greatly influenced by small differences in the way the cues are presented. Comparable evidence with audition is scanty, but, if the results from vision have any general application it seems worthwhile to speculate about features of auditory displays that are likely to make discrimination difficult. And some of the conclusions can be tested quite easily.

Spatial Contiguity of Cue, Response, and Reward. Unlike visual stimuli, auditory cues are usually pervasive, occupying no discrete position in an animal's spatial environment. He cannot touch a noise in the way he can push aside or press a visual pattern. But we know from experiments of sound localization that the source of the stimulus is identifiable. It might, therefore, be profitable to improve cue-response contiguity in tests of frequency, pattern, and intensity by using two loudspeakers, each placed as close as possible to the response site, instead of using the conventional single loudspeaker suspended above the animal. Now, there is a little evidence that appears to show that the proposed arrangement would not be beneficial, but it is far from conclusive. For instance, sound localization should be much easier than other auditory discrimination because the stimulus is spatially close to the response. Wegener (1964) has tested both sound localization and a frequency-intensity discrimination in the same apparatus, and the learning curves were not significantly different. But the loudspeakers in the localization experiment lay behind curtains some distance behind the response panels. Because even slight separation of cue and response may impair visual discrimination, the experiment is not a fair test of the hypothesis; a satisfactory arrangement would be to conceal the reward in the loudspeaker itself that had to be touched by the animal.

The second relevant experiment is by Battig, Rosvold, and Mishkin (1962). Puzzled by the fact that rhesus monkeys required many more trials to learn an auditory discrimination than to learn a visual discrimination, both tested according to a "go, no-go" procedure, the researchers subsequently tested the animals on a color discrimination, where the cues were diffusely presented from above as in the preceding auditory experiment. This visual discrimination was, nevertheless, learned rapidly. But the result does not prove the inevitable superiority of vision to audition for two reasons. (1) All animals had mastered the preceding auditory discrimination and may have therefore learned to overcome a cue-response discontiguity. (2) The diffuse colored stimuli may have imparted their quality to the gray cards covering the food wells in a way that remote auditory stimuli cannot. Contiguity of cue, response, and reward could therefore be better in the visual discrimination. The same conclusion can be drawn of several other experiments in which auditory discrimination was more difficult than visual and in which it is alleged (Wegener, 1964) that the stimuli from the two modalities were presented in essentially identical manner.

Attention to Cues. It is easy to be confident that monkeys attend to visual stimuli before responding to them. The animals often look from one stimulus to another. It is difficult to be certain that the same is true of auditory stimuli, and, if the animal is not consistently attending, the discrimination will be difficult. Burton and Ettlinger (1960) attempted to maximize attention to the stimuli. They used two trolleys (each containing a light source, loudspeaker, and food well) and a modified pull-in technique whereby a stimulus was presented when the animal pulled the cord attached to a trolley. Despite this observing response, monkeys failed to learn any of the auditory discriminations, including a frequency discrimination, whereas they did solve a visual frequency discrimination. The experiment indicates that self-presentation of auditory cues is of little help, but the experiment is no more than an indication, for the visual discrimination was learned in a mean of 1178 trials but the auditory frequency discrimination was stopped after 1000 trials when the animals were scoring above chance. Furthermore, there was a general difficulty in learning with this apparatus, for the animals failed *both* a visual and an auditory rhythm discrimination, although they were given 3000 trials. And Polidora and Fletcher (1964) have shown that simple visual pattern discrimination become difficult, even when the animal is responsible for presenting the cues, if cue and response are separated by ½ inch. A study of auditory discrimination is needed in which the animal presents cues that are spatially contiguous with the response.

One final point about attention to cues is not amiss. Experiments by Ettlinger (1960) show that, when monkeys learn a shape discrimination exclusively by vision, there is no evidence of cross-modal transfer when they are subsequently given the same shapes to discriminate by touch in the dark. Furthermore, animals that first learn the discrimination in the dark show no transfer when tested in the light and are yet allowed to palpate the cues as before. It seems that monkeys attempt to solve a discrimination problem visually when in the light. If they have to learn not to use vision in auditory tests, which are customarily given in illuminated surroundings, discrimination will be slow. This possibility could be tested by presenting auditory discriminations in total darkness, as tactile discriminations often are.

Simultaneous and Successive Procedures. It was concluded in an earlier section that visual discrimination learning is faster with the simultaneous-direct procedure than with most of the various successive methods. Simultaneous presentation is presumably avoided in auditory testing because of the interaction of the stimuli, but there is no evidence that it would not assist discrimination. Moreover, the interaction effects could be avoided by presenting two spatially separated sounds in rapid alternation, in the manner of Herington and Gundlach (1933).

The most illuminating analysis of the influence on auditory discrimination of different successive procedures has been made by Konorski and his colleagues (Konorski, 1964). The results of four different testing procedures and stimulus arrangements are shown in Table 9–2, all the results being obtained with dogs. Procedure 4 in Table 9–2 is commonly used to test auditory discrimination, but is clearly inferior to procedure 3. Procedure 1 is inferior to 2 despite the spatial separation of the stimulus sources, but one would like to know if this is still true when response and reward are contiguous with the loudspeaker emitting the positive stimulus. Procedure 2 is commonly used with monkeys but is usually used with symmetrical reward, i.e., both correct go and no-go responses are rewarded. According to Konorski (personal communication) the task is much more difficult under these conditions, his explanation being that the animal confuses "advance" and "remain" when both are associated with reinforcement. By a withholding of the reward when the animal correctly refrains from responding, the two types of response are always distinct.

One might ask how dogs will perform localization plus other auditory cues, and the answer is contained in a further experiment by Konorski (1964, and personal communication). He used the following three conditions in a discrimination of buzzer versus metronome, stimuli which differ in intensity, frequency, and pattern.

A. *Go left; go right.* The animals were trained to lift the left foreleg in response to the buzzer from behind them and to lift the right foreleg in response to a metronome placed in front of them. They were then given a transfer test with the positions of buzzer and metronome reversed. The paradigm is:

$$\left.\begin{array}{c} \text{Buzzer Posterior} \rightarrow \text{Left leg} \\ \text{vs.} \\ \text{Metronome Anterior} \rightarrow \text{Right leg} \end{array}\right\} \text{Train}$$

$$\left.\begin{array}{c} \text{Buzzer Anterior} \\ \text{vs.} \\ \text{Metronome Posterior} \end{array}\right\} \text{Transfer, with all responses rewarded}$$

This problem resembles 3 in Table 9–2 except that the stimuli differ in intensity and frequency as well as in location. After learning the initial problem (no scores were given), the animals responded on the transfer test by lifting the left leg to the metronome and the right leg to the buzzer; i.e., they were responding to the directional quality of the stimuli. Of course this does not prove that frequency and intensity components are ignored (but see C below).

B. *Go, no-go with unsymmetrical reward.* The paradigm is:

Buzzer Posterior   ⎫   Buzzer Anterior   ⎫
        vs.   ⎬ Train   vs.   ⎬ Transfer
Metronome Anterior ⎭   Metronome Posterior ⎭

This problem resembles 1 in Table 9–2 with the exception that frequency cues are available in addition. After learning the problem, the dogs maintained their behavior to the *sounds* of the buzzer and the metronome on the transfer tests; i.e., they were responding on the basis of auditory quality and not localization, which is the reverse of A.

C. *Go left; go right with stimuli adjacent.* Experiment A was repeated with the buzzer and the metronome adjacent. The animals failed to learn the discrimination; they cannot utilize intensity and frequency cues when the latter originate from contiguous spatial positions, confirming 4 in Table 9–2.

TABLE 9–2
Examples of Stimulus and Response Arrangements Used in Testing Auditory Discriminations.

Test procedure	Stimulus arrangement	Trials to criterion
1. "Go, no-go." Unsymmetrical reward.	Direction cue. Identical tone from loudspeaker up or down.	Chance after 360 trials.
2. "Go, no-go." Unsymmetrical reward.	Single loudspeaker. 1000 vs. 700 cps.	180
3. Go-left, go-right.	Direction cue. Identical tone from loudspeaker up or down.	180
4. Go-left, go-right.	Single loudspeaker. 300 vs. 900 cps.	Barely above chance after 360 trials.

The reason why dogs and monkeys appear unable to use directional cues in a "go, no-go" situation and to use auditory quality with a "go-left, go-right" procedure is not fully clear, and the reader is referred to Konorski (1964) for an account of the possible importance of the orienting response. But, if the reasons are obscure, the lesson is clear. The difficulty of auditory discrimination depends to a large extent on the testing method, and, until the factors that have been implicated are tried in all their possible combinations, it should not be assumed that auditory discrimination learning is inferior to visual. For instance, an obvious procedure to try would be to use spatially distinct cues that are contiguous with response and reward, which alternate rapidly to approach a simultaneous discrimination and which are presented, in total darkness, by a hungry animal that is punished with mild electric shock for incorrect responses. Twenty years ago it was unthinkable that monkeys could learn visual pattern discrimination in a Wisconsin General Test Apparatus in fewer than ten trials. If we could make as much progress in audition, we may yet study learning sets and short-term memory in that modality.

REFERENCES

ADES, H. W. 1959. Central auditory mechanisms. In Field, J., Magoun, H. W., & Hall, V. E. (Eds.). Handbook of physiology, Vol. 1. Washington, D.C.: American Physiological Society. Pp. 585–61.

ALLEN, W. F. 1945. Effect of destroying three localized cerebral cortical areas for sound on correct conditioned differential responses of the dog's foreleg. Amer. J. Physiol., 144, 415–428.

ANREP, G. V. 1920. Ditch discrimination in the dog. J. Physiol., 53, 367–385.

BATTIG, K., ROSVOLD, H. E., & MISHKIN, M. 1960. Comparison of the effects of frontal and caudate lesions on delayed response and alternation in monkeys. J. comp. physiol. Psychol., 53, 400–404.

BATTIG, K., ROSVOLD, H. E., & MISHKIN, M. 1962. Comparison of the effects of frontal and caudate lesions on discrimination learning in monkeys. J. comp. physiol. Psychol., 55, 458–463.

BAUER, V. 1910. Über das Farbenunterscheidungsvermögen der Fische. Arch. ges. Physiol., 133, 7–26.

BAUMGARDT, E. 1955. Un cas d'achromatopsie atypique. J. Physiol. (Paris), 47, 83–87.

BERNSTEIN, J. J. 1961. Loss of hue discrimination in forebrain-ablated fish. Exp. Neurol., 3, 1–17.

BIRUKOW, G. 1939. Purkinjesches Phänomen und Farbensehen beim Grasfrosch (Rana temporaria). Z. vergl. Physiol., 27, 41–79.

BIRUKOW, G. 1949. Die Entwicklung des Tages—Und des Dämmerungsehens im Auge des Grasfrosches (Rana temporaria). Z. vergl. Physiol., 31, 322–347.

BLAZEK, N. C., & HARLOW, H. F. 1955. Persistence of performance differences on discriminations of varying difficulty. J. comp. physiol. Psychol., 48, 86–89.

BLOUGH, D. S. 1957. Spectral sensitivity in the pigeon. J. opt. Soc. Amer., 47, 827–833.

BLOUGH, D. S. 1961. The shape of some wavelength generalization gradients. J. exp. anal. Behav., 4, 31–40.

BRAAK, J. W. G. TER, & VAN VLIET, A. G. M. 1963. Subcortical optokinetic nystagmus in the monkey. Psychiat. Neurol. Neurochir., 66, 277–283.

BUCHHOLTZ, C. 1952. Untersuchungen über das Farbensehen der Hauskatze, Felis domestica. Z. Tierpsychol., 9, 462–470.

BURTON, D., & ETTLINGER, G. 1960. Cross-modal transfer of training in monkeys. Nature, 186, 1071–1072.

BUTLER, R. A. 1958. The differential effects of visual and auditory incentives on the performance of monkeys. Amer. J. Psychol., 71, 591–593.

CALVIN, A. D., & SIEBEL, L. J. 1954. A further investigation of response selection in simultaneous and successive discrimination. J. exp. Psychol., 48, 339–342.

CALVIN, A. D., & WILLIAMS, C. M. 1956. Simultaneous and successive discrimination in a single-unit hollow-square maze. J. exp. Psychol., 52, 47–50.

CARR, W. J. 1952. The effect of adrenalectomy upon the NaCl taste threshold in rat. J. comp. physiol. Psychol., 45, 377–370.

CHOW, K. L. 1951. Studies of the posterior associative cortex in monkeys. Comp. Psychol. Monogr., 20, 187–217.

COWEY, A., & WEISKRANTZ, L. 1963. A perimetric study of visual field defects in monkeys. *Quart. J. exp. Psychol.*, 15, 91–115.

DIAMOND, I. T., GOLDBERG, J. M., & NEFF, W. D. 1962. Tonal discrimination after ablation of auditory cortex. *J. Neurophysiol.*, 25, 223–235.

DIAMOND, I. T., & NEFF, W. D. 1957. Ablation or temporal cortex and discrimination of auditory patterns. *J. Neurophysiol.*, 20, 300–315.

EHRENFREUND, D. 1948. An experimental test of the continuity theory of discrimination learning with pattern vision. *J. comp. physiol. Psychol.*, 41, 408–422.

ENINGER, M. U. 1952. Habit summation in a selective learning problem. *J. comp. physiol. Psychol.*, 45, 604–608.

ETTLINGER, G. 1960. Cross-modal transfer of training in monkeys. *Behavior*, 16, 56–65.

FANTZ, R. L. 1957. Form preferences in newly hatched chicks. *J. comp. physiol. Psychol.*, 50, 422–430.

FANTZ, R. L. 1958. Pattern vision in young infants. *Psychol. Rec.*, 8, 43–47.

FANTZ, R. L. 1961. The origin of form perception. *Sci. Amer.*, 204, No. 5, 1–8.

FANTZ, R. L., ORDY, J. M., & UDELF, M. S. 1962. Maturation of pattern vision in infants during the first six months. *J. comp. physiol. Psychiol.*, 55, 907–917.

GELLERMAN, L. W. 1933. Form discrimination in chimpanzees and two-year-old children. I. Form triangularity per se. II. Form vs. background. *J. genet. Psychol.*, 42, 3–27, 28–49.

GOLDBERG, J. M., & NEFF, W. D. 1961. Frequency discrimination after bilateral ablation of cortical auditory areas. *J. Neurophysiol.*, 24, 119–128.

GRANIT, R. 1955. *Receptors and sensory perception.* New Haven, Conn.: Yale University Press.

GROSS, C. G., & WEISKRANTZ, L. 1964. Some changes in behavior produced by lateral frontal lesions in the macaque. In Warren, J. M., & Akert, K. (Eds.), *The frontal granular cortex and behavior.* New York: McGraw-Hill. Pp. 74–101.

GUNTER, R. 1954a. The discrimination between lights of different wave lengths in the cat. *J. comp. physiol. Psychol.*, 47, 169–172.

GUNTER, R. 1954b. The spectral sensitivity of light-adapted cats. *J. Physiol.*, 123, 409–415.

GUTTMAN, N. 1963. Laws of behavior and facts of perception. In Koch, S. (Ed.), *Psychology: A study of a science*, Vol. V. New York: McGraw-Hill. Pp. 114–178.

HARLOW, H. F. 1944. Studies in discrimination learning by monkeys: 1. The learning of discrimination series and the reversal of discrimination series. *J. gen. Psychol.*, 30, 3–12.

HARLOW, H. F. 1945a. Studies in discrimination learning by monkeys: III. Factors influencing the facility of solution of discrimination problems by rhesus monkeys. *J. gen. Psychol.*, 32, 213–227.

HARLOW, H. F. 1945b. Studies in discrimination learning by monkeys: V. Initial performance by experimentally naive monkeys on stimulus-object and pattern discrimination. *J. gen. Psychol.*, 33, 3–10.

HARLOW, H. F. 1945c. Studies in discrimination learning by monkeys: VI. Discriminations between stimuli differing in both color and form, only in color, and only in form. *J. gen. Psychol.*, 33, 225–235.

HARLOW, H. F. 1951. Primate learning. Stone, C. P. (Ed.), *Comparative psychology*, Englewood Cliffs, N.J.: Prentice-Hall. Pp. 183–238.

HARRIMAN, A. E., & MacLEOD, R. B. 1953. Discriminative thresholds for salt for normal and adrenalectomized rats. *Amer. J. Psychol.*, 66, 465–471.

HARRIS, J. D. 1943. The auditory acuity of preadolescent monkeys. *J. comp. Psychol.*, 35, 244–265.

HERINGTON, G. B., & GUNDLACH, R. H. 1933. How well can guinea pigs and cats hear tones? *J. comp. Psychol.*, 16, 287–303.

HESS, C. VON. 1909. Untersuchungen uber den Lichtsinn bei Fischen, *Arch. F. Augenheilk*, 64, 1–38.

Hess, C. von. 1912. Vergleichende Physiologie des Gesichtssinnes. In Winterstein (Ed.), *Handbuch der vergleichenden Physiologie*, Vol. 4. Jena: Fischer. Pp. 1–290.

Hess, C. von. 1917. New experiments on the light reactions of plants and animals. *J. Anim. Behav.*, 7, 1–10.

Hess, E. H. 1960. Sensory processes. In Waters, R. H., Rethlingshafer, D. A., & Caldwell, W. E. (Eds.), *Principles of comparative psychology*. New York: McGraw-Hill. Pp. 74–101.

Hess, E. H., & Gogel, W. C. 1954. Natural preferences of the chick for objects of different colors. *J. Psychol.*, 38, 483–493.

Horel, J. A., Schuck, J. R., & Meyer, D. R. 1961. Effects of spatial stimulus arrangements upon discrimination learning by monkeys. *J. comp. physiol. Psychol.*, 54, 546–547.

Ingvar, D. H. 1959. Spectral sensitivity as measured in cerebral visual centers *Acta. physiol. Scand.*, 159, 1–105.

Iversen, S. D., & Weiskrantz, L. 1964. Temporal lobe lesions and memory in the monkey. *Nature*, 201, 740–742.

Jarvik, M. E. 1953. Discrimination of colored food and food signs by primates. *J. comp. physiol. Psychol.*, 46, 390–392.

Jarvik, M. E. 1956. Simple color discrimination in chimpanzees: Effect of varying contiguity between cue and incentive. *J. comp. physiol. Psychol.*, 49, 492–495.

Jenkins, W. O. 1943. A spatial factor in chimpanzee learning. *J. comp. Psychol.*, 35, 81–84.

Johnson, H. M. 1914. Visual pattern discrimination in the vertebrates: II. Comparative visual acuity in the dog, the monkey and the chick. *J. Anim. Behav.*, 4, 340–361.

Jones, L. V. 1954. Distinctiveness of color, form, and position cues for pigeons. *J. comp. physiol. Psychol.*, 40, 363–374.

Kalischer, O. 1909. Weitere Mitteilung über Ergebnisse der Dressur als physiologischer Untersuchungsmethode auf den Gebeiten des Gehör—Gerucks—und Farbensinns. *Arch. f. Anat. u. Physiol., Physiol. Abt.*, 303–322.

Klüver, H. 1933. *Behavior mechanisms in monkeys*. Chicago: University of Chicago Press.

Köhler, W. 1925. *The mentality of apes*. New York: Harcourt, Brace & World.

Konorski, J. 1964. Some problems concerning the mechanisms of instrumental conditioning. *Acta. Biol. Exper.* (Warsaw), 24, 59–72.

Kries, J. von. 1896. Über die Funktion der Netzhautstäbchen. *Zeit. Psych. Physiol. Sinnesorg*, 9, 81–123.

Kryter, K. D., & Ades, H. W. 1943. Studies on the function of the higher acoustic nervous centers in the cat. *Amer. J. Psychol.*, 56, 501–536.

Lashley, K. S. 1912. Visual discrimination of form and size in the albino rat. *J. Anim. Behav.*, 2, 310–331.

Lashley, K. S. 1930. The mechanism of vision. I. A method for rapid analysis of pattern vision in the rat. *J. genet. Psychol.*, 37, 453–460.

Lashley, K. S. 1938. The mechanism of vision. XV. Preliminary studies of the rat's capacity for detail vision. *J. genet. Psychol.*, 18, 123–193.

Lashley, K. S., & Russell, J. T. 1934. The mechanisms of vision. XI. A preliminary test of innate organization. *J. genet. Psychol.*, 45, 136–144.

Ludvigh, E. 1941. Extrafoveal visual acuity as measured by Snellen test letters. *Am. J. Opth.*, 24, 303–310.

MacCaslin, F. F. 1954. Successive and simultaneous discrimination as a function of stimulus similarity. *Am. J. Psychol.*, 67 308–314.

McClearn, G. E., & Harlow, H. F. 1954. The effects of spatial contiguity on discrimination learning by rhesus monkeys. *J. comp. physiol. Psychol.*, 47, 391–394.

Maier, N. R. F., & Schneirla, T. C. 1935. *Principles of animal psychology*. New York: McGraw-Hill.

MAST, S. O. 1915. Changes in shade, color and pattern in fishes and their bearing on certain problems of behavior and adaptation. *Proc. Nat. Acad. Sci.*, 1, 214–219.

MELLO, N. K., & PETERSON, N. J. 1964. Behavioral evidence for color discrimination in cat. *J. Neurophysiol.*, 27, 323–333.

MEUNZINGER, K. F., & GENTRY, E. 1931. Tone discrimination in white rats. *J. comp. Psychol.*, 12, 195–205.

MEYER, D. R., & HARLOW, H. F. 1949. The development of transfer of response to patterning by monkeys. *J. comp. physiol. Psychol.*, 42, 454–462.

MEYER, D. R., & WOOLSEY, C. N. 1952. Effects of localized cortical destruction upon auditory discriminative training in cat. *J. Neurophysiol.*, 15, 149–162.

MILLER, R. E., & MURPHY, J. V. 1964. Influence of the spatial relationships between the cue, reward, and response in discrimination learning. *J. exp. Psychol.*, 67, 120–123.

MISHKIN, M., & PRIBRAM, K. H. 1954. Visual discrimination performance following partial ablations of the temporal lobe. I. Ventral vs lateral. *J. comp. physiol. Psychol.*, 47, 14–20.

MISHKIN, M., & WEISKRANTZ, L. 1959. Effects of cortical lesions in monkeys on critical flicker frequency. *J. comp. physiol. Psychol.*, 52, 660–666.

MOERICKE, V. 1950. Ueber das Farbensehen der Pfirsichblattlaus, Myxodes persical. *Z. Tierpsychol.*, 7, 265–274.

MURPHY, J. V., & MILLER, R. E. 1955. The effect of spatial contiguity of cue and reward in the object-quality learning of rhesus monkey. *J. comp. physiol. Psychol.*, 48, 221–224.

NEFF, W. D. 1960. Sensory discrimination. Field, J., Magoun, W. H., & Hall, V. E. (Eds.). *Handbook of physiology*, Vol. 3. Washington, D.C.: American Physiological Society. Pp. 1447–1470.

NEFF, W. D. 1961a. Discriminatory capacity of different divisions of the auditory system. Brazier, M. A. B. (Ed.). *Brain and behavior*, Vol. 1. Washington, D.C.: Amer. Inst. Biol. Sci.

NEFF, W. D. 1961b. Neural mechanisms of auditory discrimination. In Rosenblith, W. A. (Ed.). *Sensory communication*. New York: Wiley. Pp. 259–278.

NEFF, W. D., & DIAMOND, I. T. 1958. The neural basis of auditory discrimination. In Harlow, H. F., & Woolsey, C. N. (Eds.). *Biological and biochemical bases of behavior*. Madison, Wisc.: University of Wisconsin Press. Pp. 101–126.

NISSEN, H. W., & JENKINS, W. O. 1943. Reduction and rivalry of cues in the discrimination behavior of chimpanzees. *J. comp. Psychol.*, 35, 85–95.

OSWALD, I. 1962. *Sleeping and waking*. Amsterdam: Elsevier.

PASIK, P., PASIK, T., BATTERSBY, W. S., & BENDER, M. B. 1958. Visual and tactual discriminations by macaques with serial temporal and parietal lesions. *J. comp. physiol. Psychol.*, 51, 427–436.

PETERSON, M. E., & RUMBAUGH, D. M. 1963. Role of object-contact cues in learning set formation in squirrel monkeys. *Per. Mot. Skills.*, 16, 3–9.

PFAFFMANN, C., & BARE, J. K. 1950. Gustatory nerve discharges in normal and adrenalectomized rats. *J. comp. physiol. Psychol.*, 43, 320–324.

POLIDORA, V. J., & FLETCHER, H. J. 1964. An analysis of the importance of S-R spatial contiguity for proficient primate discrimination performance. *J. comp. physiol. Psychol.*, 57, 224–230.

POLYAK, S. L. 1941. *The retina*. Chicago: University of Chicago Press.

REEVES, C. D. 1919. Discrimination of light of different wave-lengths by fish. *Behav. Monogr.*, 4, No. 3, 1–106.

REICHARDT, W. 1961. Autocorrelation and the central nervous system. In Rosenblith, W. A. (Ed.). *Sensory communication*. New York: Wiley. Pp. 303–317.

REIGHARD, J. E. 1908. An experimental study of warning coloration in coral-reef fishes. *Pap. Tortugas Lab., Carnegie Inst.*, 2, 257–325.

RICHTER, C. P. 1939. Salt taste threshold for normal and adrenalectomized rats. *Endocrinol.*, **24**, 367–371.

RIOPELLE, A. J. 1960. Complex processes. In Waters, R. H., Rethlingshafer, D. A., & Caldwell, W. E. (Eds.). *Principles of comparative psychology.* New York: McGraw-Hill. Pp. 208–249.

RIOPELLE, A. J., & GUYANT, J. L. 1959. Absence of stimulus-reward contiguity effects in discrimination learning by monkeys. *U.S. Army Med. Research Lab.*, Report No. 412, 1–7.

RIOPELLE, A. J., WUNDERLICH, R. A., & FRANCISCO, E. W. 1958. The discrimination of concentric-ring patterns by monkeys. *J. comp. physiol. Psychol.*, **51**, 622–626.

SALDANHA, E. L., & BITTERMAN, M. E. 1951. Relational learning in the rat. *Am. J. Psychol.*, **64**, 37–53.

SCHRIER, A. M., & HARLOW, H. F. 1957. Direct manipulation of the relevant cue and difficulty of discrimination. *J. comp. physiol. Psychol.*, **50**, 576–580.

SCHUCK, J. R. 1960. Pattern discrimination and visual sampling by the monkey. *J. comp. physiol. Psychol.*, **53**, 251–255.

SCHUCK, J. R. POLIDORA, V. J., McCONNELL, D. G., & MEYER, D. R. 1961. Response location as a factor in primate pattern discrimination. *J. comp. physiol. Psychol.*, **54**, 543–545.

SHARPLESS, S., & JASPER, H. 1956. Habituation of the arousal reaction. *Brain*, **79**, 655–680.

SMITH, K. U. 1951. Discriminative behavior in animals. In Stone, C. P. (Ed.). *Comparative psychology.* Englewood Cliffs, N.J.: Prentice-Hall. Pp. 316–362.

SMITH, K. U., & WARKENTIN, J. 1939. The central neural organization of optic functions related to minimum visible acuity. *J. genet. Psychol.*, **55**, 177–195.

SPENCE, K. W. 1952. The nature of the response in discrimination learning. *Psychol. Rev.*, **59**, 89–93.

SPENCE, K. W., & FULTON, J. F. 1936. The effects of occipital lobectomy on vision in chimpanzee. *Brain*, **59**, 35–50.

STEPIEN, L. S., & CORDEAU, J. P. 1960. Memory in monkeys for compound stimuli. *Amer. J. Psychol.*, **73**, 388–395.

STEVENS, S. S. 1958. Some similarities between hearing and seeing. *Laryngoscope*, **68**, 508–527.

STOLLNITZ, F., & SCHRIER, A. M. 1962. Discrimination learning by monkeys with spatial separation of arc and response. *J. comp. physiol. Psychol.*, **55**, 876–881.

SUTHERLAND, N. S. 1961. The methods and findings of experiments on the visual discrimination of shape by animals. *Exp. Psychol. Soc. Monogr.*, No. 1, 1–68.

SUTHERLAND, N. S., & MACKINTOSH, J. 1964. Discrimination learning: Non-additivity of cues. *Nature*, **201**, 528–530.

SUTHERLAND, N. S., & MUNTZ, W. R. A. 1959. Simultaneous discrimination training and preferred directions of motion in visual discrimination of shape in *Octopus vulgaris* Lamarck. *Pubbl. Staz. zool. Napoli*, **31**, 109–126.

TANSLEY, K. 1950. Vision. In *Physiological mechanisms in animal behaviour.* Cambridge: Cambridge University Press. Pp. 19–33.

TERRACE, H. S. 1963a. Errorless discrimination learning in the pigeon: Effects of chlorpromazine and imipramine. *Science*, **140**, 318–319.

TERRACE, H. S. 1963b. Errorless transfer of a discrimination across two continua. *J. exp. anal. Behav.*, **6**, 223–232.

TERRACE, H. S. 1964. Wavelength generalization after discrimination learning with and without errors. *Science*, **144**, 78–80.

TEUBER, H.-L. 1960. Perception. In Field, J., Magoun, W. H., & Hall, V. E. (Eds.). *Handbook of physiology*, Vol. III. Washington, D.C.: Amer. Physiol. Soc. Pp. 1595–1668.

THOMPSON, R. F. 1958. Function of auditory cortex of cat in frequency discrimination. *Fed. Proc.*, 17, 645.

THOMPSON, R. F. 1960. Functions of auditory cortex of cat in frequency discrimination. *J. Neurophysiol.*, 23, 321–334.

THOMPSON, R. F., & WELKER, W. I. 1963. Role of auditory cortex in reflex head orientation by cats to auditory stimuli. *J. comp. physiol. Psychol.*, 56, 996–1002.

THORPE, W. H. 1956. *Learning and instinct in animals.* London: Methuen.

THUMA, B. D. 1932. The response of the white rat to tonal stimuli. *J. comp. Psychol.*, 13, 57–86.

TINBERGEN, N. 1951. *The study of instinct.* London: Oxford University Press.

VALCIUKAS, J. A., & PASIK, P. 1965. Influence of illumination on pattern discrimination thresholds in monkeys with temporal lobe lesions. *Fed. Proc.*, 24, No. 2, Part I, 274.

WALK, R. D., & GIBSON, E. J. 1961. A comparative and analytical study of visual depth perception. *Psych. Monogr.*, 75, No. 519, 1–44.

WALLS, G. L. 1934. The visual calls of the white rat. *J. comp. Psychol.*, 18, 363–366.

WALLS, G. L. 1942. *The vertebrate eye.* Bloomfield Hills, Mich.: Cranbrook Press.

WALTON, W. E. 1933. Color vision and color preference in the albino rat. *J. comp. Psychol.*, 15, 359–394.

WARREN, J. M. 1953a. Additivity of cues in visual pattern discrimination by monkeys. *J. comp. physiol. Psychol.*, 46, 484–486.

WARREN, J. M. 1953b. Effect of geometrical regularity on visual form discrimination by monkeys. *J. comp. physiol. Psychol.*, 46, 237–240.

WARREN, J. M. 1953c. The influence of area and arrangement on visual pattern discrimination by monkeys. *J. comp. physiol. Psychol.*, 46, 231–236.

WARREN, J. M. 1954. Perceptual dominance in discrimination learning by monkeys. *J. comp. physiol. Psychol.*, 47, 290–292.

WARREN, J. M. 1956. Some stimulus variables affecting the discrimination of objects by monkeys. *J. genet. Psychol.*, 88, 77–80.

WEALE, R. A. 1953. Cone-monochromatism. *J. Physiol.*, 121, 548–569.

WEGENER, J. G. 1964. Auditory discrimination behavior of normal monkeys. *J. aud. Res.*, 4, 81–106.

WEINSTEIN, B., & GRETHER, W. F. 1940. A comparison of visual acuity in the rhesus monkey and man. *J. comp. Psychol.*, 30, 187–195.

WEISE, P., & BITTERMAN, M. E. 1951. Response selection in discrimination learning. *Psychol. Rev.*, 58, 185–195.

WEISKRANTZ, L., & COWEY, A. 1963. Striate cortex lesions and visual acuity of the rhesus monkey. *J. comp. physiol. Psychol.*, 56, 225–231.

WENDT, G. R. 1934. Auditory acuity of monkeys. *Comp. Psychol. Monogr.*, 10, 1–51.

WODINSKY, J. V., VARLEY, M. A., & BITTERMAN, M. E. 1954. Situational determinants of the relative difficulty of simultaneous and successive discrimination. *J. comp. physiol. Psychol.*, 47, 337–340.

ZIMMERMAN, R. R. 1961. Analysis of discrimination learning capacities in the infant rhesus monkey. *J. comp. physiol. Psychol.*, 54, 1–10.

CHAPTER 10

Some Aspects of Attention

L. WEISKRANTZ

ATTENTION is at once one of the most important and yet most elusive of topics in the study of behavior. Both these features stem, perhaps, from the fact that the methods by which one supposes it is studied overlap very largely with the study of perception, learning, and vigilance, and it is difficult to discover any particular residue that is to be assigned uniquely to "attention" when these other categories are excluded. As in the case of all our categories, the classification is more a matter of emphasis and convenience than of mutual exclusiveness. There is no doubt that there has been a dramatic awakening of interest in physiological mechanisms said to be related to "attention," and therefore indirectly in treatments said to affect "attention." But, when one speaks of the "physiology of X," it is just as well to try to discover just what *special* emphasis is implied by "X." This chapter will be more an outline of an approach to the problem rather than exhaustive analysis. In any case, an exhaustive account would not be helpful here because many of the relevant methods are to be found in other chapters in this book.

Our approach to the question will be to consider the organism as a detector of signals originating in its environment. The problem of attention is the problem of determining which stimuli are detected and the laws controlling the detection. A useful analogy is the wireless receiver. Out of a very large set of possible signals, the receiver limits its selection to a very narrow range. So with biological organisms. Most wireless receivers have at least two independent controls. One control sets the "gain" or "sensitivity" of the set independently of which signal happens to be selected, and the other control selects the particular wave length independently of the "gain." It is doubtful that the analogy with biological organisms is usefully extended to the assumption of independence of the two types of controls, sensitivity and selection, but it happens to be convenient to discuss these two aspects of stimulus detection separately.

From a practical point of view, especially in connection with assessing the effects of treatments, one is interested in determining which particular stimuli are detected and with what sensitivity and, further, in the factors that *control* the detection. It is difficult to give an exhaustive account of the latter, but, in general, we can say that learning, particularly discrimination learning situations, are among those that are designed to *guarantee* that particular stimuli will be detected. Discrimination learning experiments are typically concerned with the rate at which detection is reliably established, and psychophysical experiments are typically concerned with the capacity for sensitivity or fineness of detection of particular stimuli, again preselected by the experimenter. While the description of the factors controlling stimulus selection have been dressed up, from time to time, in language with suggestive causal connotations, such as with accounts of the "filtering" of information, we have not really progressed beyond a simple empirical listing of relevant factors on which concepts such as "filters" depend circularly for their specification. Crudely speaking, we can say that certain stimuli can be guaranteed to be detected innately, such as the "releasers" much studied by the ethologists, and also including stimuli normally called reinforcers, many of which are also detected without learning, provided certain motivational conditions prevail. In addition, we can specify certain situations under which detection can be modified, and these include the typical learning experiments and also experiments involving novelty of stimulation and exploratory behavior. The subject matter of many of these relationships is dealt with at length in Chapters 6, 7, and 9. Those chapters obviously do not give anything like an exhaustive account, but we will not deal further here with factors that can be exploited more or less to guarantee detection of stimuli that either experimenters or genes have preselected. Nor can we treat one of the common methods by which detection is modified in human subjects, namely, by external verbal instruction and by self-instruction. This is not to deny the importance or effectiveness of such processes, but we know very little about their development in man and even less about comparable types of control in animals.

We will restrict ourselves in this chapter to the treatment of topics covered only slightly, if at all, in other sections of this book. The main emphasis will be on asking how we can determine the effectiveness of signal detection at any particular moment. Is an organism likely to detect a signal, and, if so, which signal is it likely to detect? In typical discrimination and learning experiments we are certain that stimulus detection is taking place because certain environmental stimuli exercise a reliable control over behavior. Of course, even within that familiar territory, there are difficult questions, because a demonstration of stimulus control does not necessarily tell us which particular aspect of the stimulus is controlling the behavior nor the class of stimuli that would be equally effective. For these questions, we require transfer techniques, such as the "method of equivalent stimuli" (Klüver, 1933). But, nevertheless, the detection is a by-product of the experimenter's deliberate "shaping up" procedure (or of his use of "innate releasers," but these are relatively restricted in number, particularly with higher organisms). Suppose we put the animal in a relatively unrestricted environment and do not use stimuli with deliberately established or innate "meanings." Can we say anything about the manner in which the animal samples the stimuli with which it is presented? The emphasis in this chapter will be not on how we can make an animal "attend" to a particular stimulus, but on how we can find out whether the animal is "attending," and to what, when we have not especially attempted to bias the animal's selection in advance. With such an emphasis in mind, it is obvious that we will tend to concentrate on responses, including physiological responses, that require little or no history of "shaping up." As stated above, we will discuss stimulus detection by analogy with the two types of control found on wireless detectors, namely, "gain" or "sensitivity," and "tuning" or "selectivity."

Sensitivity

It is easy to admit that there are two extreme states of arousal, one of deep sleep or coma in which no detection occurs and one of wakeful alertness in which one is sensitive to stimulation, but the characterization and scaling of the dimension on which these extremes fall is far from simple. No doubt, the most successful index, for mammals at least, is in terms of gross EEG activity, but any physiological index of this type requires validation in terms of behavioral states of which it is supposedly an index.

There appears to be quite good agreement that behavioral deep sleep (itself defined in terms of threshold for behavioral response to stimulation) is correlated with "stage 4" type EEG activity (see following) and that behavioral alertness is correlated with low voltage and variable high frequency EEG patterns. Lindsley (1960) has somewhat optimistically presented a table listing the various behavioral states along a continuum ranging from strong, excited emotion to death, together with the EEG pattern associated with each. But the criteria for discriminating neighboring stages of EEG from each other are far from precise, and the behavioral criteria for discriminating degrees of alertness are even less precise. We can ask a more restricted question, the answer to which would suffice for present purposes. Is there any indication from the EEG as to the likelihood that a signal will be detected? Because one of the ways in which the depth of sleep itself is defined is in terms of the strength of stimulus required to rouse the subject, one might obtain a partial answer to the question so far as various stages of sleep are concerned. That some rough correlation does exist between depth of sleep and EEG patterns cannot be denied. This has been described by many workers, and Dement and Kleitman's (1957) classification of EEG sleep patterns into four stages is widely used:

Stage 1. Somewhat irregular low-voltage alpha, slightly slower than the normal waking alpha (10 cps).
Stage 2. Spindling (trains of waves of 14–15 cps superimposed on an irregular pattern of slower waves) with low-voltage background activity.
Stage 3. Delta waves (about 1 cps) with spindling.
Stage 4. Slower delta without spindling.

Various additional complexes of waves have also been identified, such as K-complex (Kleitman, 1963). The four stages are generally said to correspond to different depths of sleep, stage 4 being deepest.

But even restricting the EEG to indicate depth of sleep produces some difficulties. Jouvet (1961) for example, has described a so-called paradoxical phase of sleep in the cat, consisting of a "waking" type of EEG record in association with rapid eye movements and marked muscular relaxation. During this phase, however, the cat is difficult to rouse, its auditory awakening threshold being about as high as during stage 4 "deep sleep." The "paradoxical" or "activated" phase of sleep appears to be similar to states that are associated with dreaming in man, similarly characterized by an activated EEG, rapid eye movements, and increased respiratory rate. In one other important respect the two phenomena resemble each other: they do not appear until after the cat or person has shown a period of deep-sleep EEG activity, that is, high-voltage, low-frequency activity. For that reason Kleitman calls the state in man "emergent stage 1," distinguishing it from the "initial stage 1," seen just as a person is going to sleep. Thus, not only the immediately evident EEG pattern but also the preceding state is important in using EEG as an index. Again, the auditory arousal threshold is moderately higher in emergent state 1 than in initial stage 1 sleep. Kleitman comments on the "paradoxical" sleep pattern as being "an excellent example of the non-reliability of the EEG pattern as a sole criterion of sleep, let alone the depth of sleep" (1963, p. 212).

Another example of the breakdown between EEG and a behavioral sleep is seen under the influence of drugs. Atropine, for example, produces EEG sleep patterns in dogs without producing behavioral sleep (Wikler, 1952). Reserpine, on the other hand, produces a sustained EEG waking pattern (Rinaldi and Himwich, 1955), even though the animal is behaviorally markedly unresponsive to external stimulation (Weiskrantz, 1957).

One is tempted, naturally, to seek other physiological indexes of depth of sleep, possibly to be used in combination with EEG. It is interesting to note that, along with the EEG, periodic oscillations in circulation, respiration, electrical skin resistance, and motility can be seen during a night's sleep, each period being about 1½ hours in length (Kleitman, 1963, p. 113). But, unfortunately, there are similar inconsistencies to those seen with the EEG. For example, respiratory and cardiac rates *increase* during emergent stage 1 sleep, despite the heightened threshold for awakening by external stimuli. Furthermore, as Kleitman points out, "it so happens that the fluctuations of the several concomitants of sleep do not run synchronously in the course of a night's sleep, and the curves of the depth of sleep vary with the concomitant measured" (p. 108). Malmo (1959) has shown a good correspondence between low-frequency EEG (through a band-pass filter), palmar conductance, heart rate, and respiratory rate throughout the course of sleep. But no cycles were reported, nor any indication of depth of sleep as measured behaviorally.

There is no question that the EEG has proved a useful instrument, more useful probably than any other single device, for predicting the organism's depth of sleep, as measured by behavioral responses to external stimuli. But we have seen that neither it, nor any other existing index, is entirely adequate. The possibility of the EEG providing an adequate index of varying states of "attentiveness" in the *waking condition* appears, on the face of it, therefore, to be somewhat unlikely, because neither the various behavioral states nor the EEG patterns admit of easy discriminations among them. It is true that the "alpha" EEG of the "relaxed" subject is easily discriminated from the low-voltage fast activity EEG of the "aroused" subject, but it appears to be difficult to admit of any gradations between "alpha" and an "activated" EEG. Moreover, the depth of sleep is measured relatively reliably, depending as it does for its definition upon the strength of the stimulus that produces awakening. But such reliable (albeit complex) anchor points for different states of "attentiveness" in the waking condition are difficult to isolate.

All the same, many claims have been made that changes in wakeful attentiveness can be monitored by EEG and by measurements of other bodily changes. Because any such measure must be validated in terms of behavioral criteria of attention, we must turn to an analysis of the types of situations in which one behaviorally studies attention in the waking organism. The reader is reminded that we are treating in this section only those aspects of signal detection that relate to the sensitivity of the organism to respond to signals, not the question of signal selection, even though, as will be seen, it is difficult to maintain this distinction sharply without considerable empirical evidence at hand. The object in reviewing the behavioral situations is twofold: (1) These are the situations with which treatment effects will, by and large, be studied. (2) The discovery of concomitants of behavioral changes, particularly when they are easily measured, will obviously be helpful not only in predicting behavioral states and, consequently, in predicting the effects of treatments upon them but also in analysis of physiological mechanisms underlying these states. We cannot here give an exhaustive review of research on concomitants, particularly because it is a rapidly developing field, but we will mention research on EEG, evoked potentials, body temperature, and other autonomic nervous system activity when these seem relevant.

Although we pressed the analogy of the "gain" control of the wireless receiver and the sensitivity to stimuli of the biological organism, it is obvious that analogy breaks down in one important respect. The gain control of the ordinary wireless set is not itself affected by the signals being detected, whereas living organisms often change their sensitivity directly as a result of signal detection. One falls asleep in a "boring" situation or is roused in an "exciting" situation. This change in sensitivity as a result of signal detection (or lack of it) is itself a clue to the measurement of sensitivity behaviorally, and some of the situations we will describe depend critically on it. We will call these "reactive sensitivity" situations, as distinct from "passive sensitivity" situations in which signal detection does not drastically affect the subsequent sensitivity of the organism. The distinction is, of course, relative rather than absolute and depends largely on the time scale over which one wishes to measure changes in sensitivity.

Passive Sensitivity Situations

In general, passive sensitivity situations are most usefully exploited as "probes" to detect changes in sensitivity induced by various treatments or inherent in slow endogenous rhythms. Ideally, therefore, they should be relatively short in duration on each occasion of testing, and the subjects should have habituated to them sufficiently to make reactive sensitivity phenomena minimal.

PROBABILITY OF DETECTION SITUATIONS. The so-called vigilance situation, which has been extensively used with human subjects, is a typical one in which the dependent variable is the probability of detecting an irregularly occurring standard signal, e.g. as in radar watching. A major part of interest has been in the gradual decline in performance with time (i.e., their reactive sensitivity aspect), as well as in the variables that control performance—such as rate of presentation and knowledge of results (Broadbent, 1958). But it has also been used in the sense of a probe to study the effects of various treatments, such as high temperature and sleep deprivation (Wilkinson, 1960). In the case of sleep deprivation, on which there is an extensive literature, the main phenomena seem to be of the "reactive sensitivity" type, because usually subjects deprived of sleep can perform well if the task is of brief duration, but they decline drastically as tasks are prolonged (Kleitman, 1963, p. 224). But the changes induced by sleep deprivation appear to be complex, and there is still considerable disagreement as to whether it produces increased or decreased "activation" or "arousal"—by whatever criteria one wishes to define such a dimension (Kleitman, 1963, p. 229).

Surprisingly, very few animal studies have deliberately used a "vigilance" type situation as a tool for the study of treatment effects, although, in principle, it would be simple to do so. A closely related type of situation, however, has been used promisingly by Chow and Orbach (1957), and by Fuster (1958) with monkeys. In this situation the probability of correct discrimination is measured as a function of the duration for which visual stimuli are presented. It is a tachistoscopic discrimination task. Chow and Orbach used such a situation with brain-operated and control animals and found that inferotemporal lesions were without effect. Fuster (1958) found a significant improvement in performance when a monkey received electrical stimulation in the brain-stem reticular formation as compared with control nonstimulation conditions; i.e., the animal could perform at above chance levels with shorter stimulus exposures during stimulation. When the intensity of reticular-formation stimulation was increased, a decline in performance from control levels was reported, suggesting that performance is an inverted U shaped function of intensity of reticular activity (Malmo, 1959). The results of Fuster's study are open to more than one interpretation, but it is a rare illustration of a nice attempt to relate brain manipulation to relevant behavioral capacity, quantitatively assessed. We still do not know whether similar changes in tachistoscopic thresholds would occur in association with spontaneous as well as with induced EEG arousal.

A somewhat similar situation had been used earlier by Harlow and Johnson (1943), although not with a sufficient range of presentation times to determine a tachistoscopic threshold. In this experiment the food itself served as the stimulus, and the dependent variable was the success of monkeys in obtaining the food by reaching for it directly. Various exposure times were used, from 1 second to 10 seconds. It was reported that monkeys with frontal-lobe lesions made significantly more failures at the lowest exposure time (1 second) than control animals, but there was no difference at other exposure times.

REACTION TIMES AND SPEED OF STIMULUS PROCESSING. The last study described, by Harlow and Johnson, could equally well be considered as a reaction-time experiment as a probability of detection experiment. We do not know whether the monkey failed to detect the brief stimuli or could not respond quickly enough to secure it within the time limit. Harlow and Johnson themselves inclined toward the latter interpretation, because "errors were frequently made even though the prefrontal animals were oriented towards the correct food platform" (p. 499). They suggested that the prefrontal animal suffers from a failure to "initiate behavior."

The typical reaction-time experiment has no imposed maximum— the stimulus is presented and the time is measured for response to occur. But, equally, it is difficult to know in the reaction-time experiment whether changes are due to an increase in signal-detection time or to response-initiation time (including so-called decision time). In the context of the present chapter, we are interested only in the former, but we will consider reaction-time experiments even when it is not possible to say whether the change is in detection time or in response time, or both. Indeed, it is the rare study of treatment effects that enables the distinction to be drawn satisfactorily.

Reaction times have a possible bearing on signal-detection probability for two reasons. (1) If a signal is processed more quickly, then more signals can be processed per unit time, and hence the probability of detection may be altered. (2) It is possible to interpret slower reaction times in certain situations not simply as damping, continuous in time, but as the intrusion of brief "blocks" or "pauses." According to Bills (1931), prolonged performance in a vigilance task tends to affect the number and length of "blocks" much more than performance in between the blocks. Insofar as changes in reaction times admit of a possible interpretation along these lines, they give us information directly on probability of stimulus detection (cf. Broadbent, 1958).

Fuster (1958), in the tachistoscopic exposure experiment mentioned earlier, measured not only probability of correct response but also reaction time. He found that the conditions of brain-stem reticular-formation stimulation that led to a lower tachistoscopic threshold also led to faster reaction times. Quite interestingly, the shorter reaction times cannot be accounted for wholly in terms of the higher probability of correct response, because, even when the stimulation performance is matched to the control performance (by selecting a control exposure that yields the same probability of correct response as a shorter stimulation exposure), the stimulation reaction times are nevertheless faster over most of the range of exposures used. Therefore, it cannot be decided where in the input-output sequence the change has occurred. But, evidently, artificially induced "arousal" patterns of the brain lead to faster reaction times.

An interesting attempt to relate changes in reaction times of human subjects to the state of the EEG has been made by Lansing, Schwartz, and Lindsley (1959). These workers found that the reaction time to a visual stimulus was lowered directly as a function of the length of an auditory "warning signal" just preceding the visual stimulus, up to about 400 msec, beyond which the reaction time was level at a minimal value. EEG records were made simultaneously, and the authors plotted the curve for the "percent of alpha blocking" at the time of the visual stimulus. That curve shows a remarkable similarity in shape to the reaction-time curve, suggesting a functional dependence of the one on the other. But, unfortunately, reaction times, *without the warning signal*, although longer than with the warning signal, did *not* vary according to the presence or absence of alpha. Therefore, the most parsimonious conclusion is that the warning signal, rather than the state of the alpha, was the controlling variable, causing a simultaneous change in reaction time and a blocking of alpha. One could certainly not take the results of the experiment to indicate that the spontaneous blocking of alpha in the human EEG will enable one to predict reaction times.

On the other hand, a different feature of the human EEG, namely, the mean period of the EEG between the stimulus and the response, has been found by Surwillo (1963; 1964) to correlate highly with reaction time. He found, further, a high correlation between age and brainwave period and found that the increased reaction-time associated with greater age could be accounted for entirely in terms of the longer brain-wave period. The results held true not only for groups of subjects but also for variations within individual subjects. This type of approach would appear to be quite promising, at least when the mean period can be measured reliably, which is probably not the case for highly "activated" EEG patterns.

The results of Fuster's study (1958), already mentioned, are, unfortunately, open to a similar interpretation as that of Lansing, Schwartz, and Lindsley. Fuster's most striking results appeared when the onset of reticular-formation stimulation occurred consistently 2 seconds prior to the onset of the trial—that is, the stimulation may have served as a warning signal and had its beneficial effect because of its informational rather than its arousing properties. When the interval between the onset of stimulation and the trial was lengthened the beneficial effect declined to control levels at about 8 seconds (Fuster and Uyeda, 1962). Fuster is inclined to discount this interpretation because the trial was always preceded, in all conditions, by an auditory warning signal 2 seconds earlier, which he said appeared "invariably" to direct the animal's attention to the area of the visual display, and also because some nonreticular stimulation points were ineffective. But these facts cannot be taken as conclusive evidence against the "warning signal" interpretation—the only experimental evidence that would be sufficient for that purpose would be the case where reticular stimulation was deliberately arranged to be uncorrelated with the onset of the trial, e.g., if the stimulation were delivered in continuous trains throughout the whole experimental session.

One of the most significant studies of reaction time is that of Kleitman (1963), who used it (and other tasks) to investigate variations in performance throughout the course of the day. Kleitman found clear evidence that reaction times (both simple and choice) to visual auditory stimuli vary inversely with body temperature in human subjects and also that this relationship holds both for spontaneous, naturally occurring changes in body temperature as well as for changes induced by changes in posture. One of Kleitman's situations was deliberately set up to measure the intrusion of "Bills' blocks," and he found that both the number of blocks per minute and their mean length were inversely related to body temperature. So here we have quite good evidence of body temperature being a predictor of signal detection. Kleitman also showed that performance on a number of other tasks yielded a similar inverse relationship with body temperature. Whether these same relationships would still hold for more extreme changes in body temperature is unclear, but, within the limits of variation studied by Kleitman, body temperature emerges as a quite powerful predictor.

Changes in body temperature are a good index of metabolic rate, and, therefore, it might be expected that a host of physiological variables might be suitable predictors of reaction times. We have already considered EEG patterns, but there is a considerable literature on the correlations among such variables as muscle tension, skin conductance, heart rate, respiratory rate, blood pressure, and various forms of performance. The issues that emerge from these studies are both pragmatic and theoretical. Pragmatically, it might be asked what is gained by multiplying the number of possible indexes when any one of them will suffice. The answer is not merely that one increases reliability by so doing but that the relative ranges differ widely over which the physiological variables can vary. Body temperature is under the control of homeostatic mechanisms that normally keep it within fairly narrow limits, whereas heart rate and respiratory rate, for example, can undergo much greater change. In addition, EEG patterns represent not so much a dimension as a qualitative classification. If one is interested in "alpha rhythm," it is true that one can measure "alpha percentage seen in total record," but even this nominal scale leads to paradoxes such as the demonstration that an alerting stimulus, which typically blocks alpha in an awake but relaxed subject, will *augment* alpha in a drowsy person (Stennet, 1957). The question of range of variation is as important in another context, namely, the performance of subjects at extreme values of physiological indexes. There has long been a claim that performance is an inverted U function of variables such as skin conductance and heart rate. Thus, Freeman reported (1940) that reaction time in a single subject was an inverted U function of skin resistance. Various authors have reviewed the matter (Duffy, 1957; Malmo 1959; Hebb, 1955; Freeman, 1948), and although the number of converts per demonstration seems remarkably high, the hypothesis appears reasonable. The reason Freeman found the inverted U function between reaction times and skin resistance, while Kleitman found a monotonic relation between reaction times and body temperature, may be due to the limited range over which body temperature can vary except in pathological states.

It is, of course, extremely tempting to relate various correlated physiological indexes to a single theoretical dimension, such as arousal, activation, or "energy mobilization." The concept was proposed some years ago by Duffy (1932) and has cropped up in similar forms repeatedly (Freeman, 1948; Hebb, 1955; Lindsley, 1951). It is a short step to draw the hypothetical inverted U function of "performance" against "arousal." It was natural that the concept of arousal should find its supposed embodiment in the activity of the brain-stem reticular formation. There is no question that the theory is heuristically attractive, particularly as it can account—if one adds the assumption that the organism tends to alter his own arousal level towards the value that yields optimal performance—for some of the puzzling phenomena induced by sensory deprivation (Hebb, 1955). But, in a rigidly practical context, "activation theory" still has many inadequacies, the main one being in the difficulty in assigning actual values to the scale of arousal. If we wish to predict the probability of signal detection from some indicant of "arousal," we have seen that we are likely to get different functions depending on which indicant we use. Furthermore, those indicants (such as skin resistance and muscle tension) that have the advantage of showing the widest range of variation within a single subject are also likely to show wide interindividual variation. Conversely, those indicants (such as body temperature) that show little interindividual variation do not possess sufficient intraindividual variation, evidently, to reveal the inverted U functions. Malmo, a strong advocate of activation theory, has admitted that "it is true that *inter*-individual correlations (among physiological indicants of activation) are low" but goes on to add that this fact is irrelevant insofar as using these measures to gauge activation is concerned. "The important question is whether significant *intra*-correlations are found in a sufficiently high proportion of individuals, and the answer appears to be yes" (Malmo, 1959, p. 377). But the difficulty with this reply is that, if one has to go to the length of calibrating each individual subject before one can "gauge activation," little practical advantage is gained in using indicants to predict one's performance, although, no doubt, the exercise is interesting enough for theoretical purposes.

From the point of view of predictability, the indicant one chooses is going to depend on very practical issues. If there is no opportunity for advance calibration, one would be well advised to use an indicant that shows quite good intersubject correlation, such as body temperature, and that, as we have seen, is a good predictor of reaction times and many other types of performance. On the other hand, if one is going to carry out intensive examination of a small number of subjects under a large range of conditions, then using a battery of more "free-ranging" indicants might in fact enable one to predict from certain conditions to other conditions quite effectively.

Reactive Sensitivity Situations

The situations we have been considering until now are those in which the stimuli themselves do not seriously affect the level of detection sensitivity of the organism, at least, not more than temporarily. Thus, in Kleitman's experiments we have no reason to believe that a subject's body temperature was much altered by performing the reaction-time tasks. But on a much shorter time scale almost any "probe" has measurable effects on sensitivity, and indeed sometimes the time scale is not always short. If, for example, we are measuring the "depth of sleep" by determining the strength of the stimulus that produces behavioral awakening, sensitivity is thereby changed for as long as the person remains awake—perhaps a matter of hours.

In general, we might expect that rewards and punishments would serve as effective stimuli for changing the sensitivity of organisms, and with such stimuli, we can, by definition, find behavioral responses that they can be made to control. In addition, rewarding and punishing stimuli usually evoke easily detected consummatory or defensive responses, as well as longer lasting emotional states (see Chapter 4). There is no difficulty, in principle, therefore, in measuring a subject's sensitivity to these specific stimuli (or to stimuli associated with them) or changes in sensitivity to these stimuli with repeated presentation. But such information is insufficient in at least two respects.

1. The information is insufficient in the sense that one cannot tell from such information alone whether there has been a change in sensitivity per se or whether the subject is "tuned" more effectively to the particular stimuli in question. We will see later that this question lies at the heart of many investigations of employing specific responses to evocative stimuli and that it is often left unresolved, particularly in

physiological investigations. It is obvious, once formulated in this manner, that the answer can be obtained only by sampling responses to a range of stimuli—the larger the better—but we will return to this question when we deal with the question of selective detection. The same issue, of course, has been with us all the time in discussing the so-called passive situations, but it is just because the sensitivity changes referred to there were reflected in so many concurrent behavioral measures that one felt relatively safe in referring to changes in sensitivity per se. For example, Kleitman's reaction time experiments involved two modalities and both simple and choice reactions. His reported body-temperature correlation held not only with reaction time but also with other performances.

2. The information is insufficient in that it limits us to too narrow a range of stimuli. It is true that stimulus change per se can be said to be rewarding in the sense that animals will perform instrumental responses to produce it. The behavior, indeed, can be quite strong, as can be seen in Chapter 6. But in our own experience we obviously spend a great deal of time detecting stimuli that are not particularly rewarding or punishing, or that are only weakly so or only very temporarily so. In addition, certain stimuli changes can be said to be both rewarding and punishing in the sense that they produce both approach and withdrawal in oscillation, and behavior under their control is often complex (e.g., see Hinde, 1960). In all these instances a purely behavioral response may have severe shortcomings. It is true that we can *make* stimuli control behavior by establishing them as discriminative stimuli. But we have pointed out that, especially with animals, such discriminative control usually involves lengthy training procedures, and it is difficult to overcome a kind of Heisenberg dilemma—the measuring procedures affect the very variable we wish to measure.

The discovery that even mild and behaviorally relatively neutral stimuli produce physiological changes, broadly subsumed under the rubric of the "orienting reflex," represents a possible breakthrough. In the present context, these are of special interest, because these physiological responses precisely involve variables that might be expected, from what we have already seen, to serve as rough indicants of sensitivity. Hence, the physiological orienting response holds out the extremely attractive possibility that it can serve not only as a measure of detection where behavioral measures might fail but also as an indicator of the sensitivity as such. The use of purely physiological indicants in such a context is obviously tempting, but they have inherent serious handicaps so far as validation is concerned. These are perhaps best considered after an examination of the type of situation in which the "orienting reflex" has been used and some of the properties of the reflex, as well as the properties of other physiological "reflexes."

ORIENTING REFLEX TO A CHANGE OF A NEUTRAL STIMULUS. It is probably a bit misleading to refer to the "orienting reflex" as a "reflex," but if we adopt this terminology loosely for the moment, then we can ask what is the unconditioned stimulus that evokes it. The essential property of the situation that defines the unconditioned stimulus for the orienting reflex is that there must be a change from the value of a previously constant stimulus. The clearest instances occur when the constant stimulus itself is of no ultimate consequence to the animal, so that with repetition it sooner or later becomes behaviorally neutral. When the stimulus is first changed, there is usually a mild behavioral response—the subject might prick up its ears and in general orientate towards the source of the stimulus—but there need be no detectable behavioral manifestation. Physiologically a set of complex changes can be recorded. With repetition of the altered stimulus, both the behavioral response, if any, and the physiological responses habituate. The unconditioned stimulus is stimulus *change*; with absence of change the reflex gradually fails to occur.

The physiological changes generally subsumed under the orienting reflex have been elucidated at length by Sokolov (1960), who is mainly responsible for the modern use of a concept that originated with Pavlov. The physiological changes admitted by Sokolov are quite broad and include

> somatic components in the form of eye movements, body movements, and change of position of the body. There are vegetative responses in the form of changes of respiration, vascular responses, heart rate, and the GSR (galvanic skin response). There are EEG components, which include alpha-rhythm depression or arousal or the change of driving response of the cortex. There are sensory components, in the form of a change of responsitivity of the analyzers and the change in their threshold. (Sokolov, 1960, p. 227).

In fact, many of these changes are ones with which we have become familiar in our earlier discussion. (See also Chapter 4.) The particular responses that Sokolov has exploited uniquely stemmed from his discovery that stimulus change produces vasodilation of blood vessels in the head (generally recorded from the scalp in the temporal region), and concurrently vasoconstriction of blood vessels of the finger. This pattern of responding is both convenient, because it is easily recorded, and discriminatory because nonneutral stimuli such as electric shock, warmth, and cold produce vascular changes going in the same direction in both the head and the finger.

A typical example of the elicitation of orienting reflex can be seen if a person is presented with a 1000 cps tone once a minute, each tone lasting, say, 5 seconds. The first few presentations produce vasodilation in the head electrode, vasoconstriction in the finger electrode; the EEG shows an increase in fast low-voltage activity, heart rate increases, and so forth. After 10 presentations or so, these responses fail to occur.

But this situation is one that admits of several variations both in the temporal parameters of stimulus presentation and in the pattern of resulting changes. One has to consider not only the changes induced by the repetitive stimulus on each occasion but also the base line from which the changes are observed. In addition, one is interested in the change in the changes induced by the stimulus as a function of repetition, the process generally called *habituation*. Moreover, there are long-term effects such as are involved in repeated daily sessions, each of which may involve, perhaps, more and more rapid habituation. And, in all these possible relationships, one is interested in whether the changes are in sensitivity or gain, per se, or in tuning. These various complexities have not been investigated exhaustively, but a few relevant and hopefully representative findings can be cited. It should be clear that many of the same considerations apply logically to any situation that is broadly classed as "habituation."

Some changes induced by the stimulus on each occasion are of the type that might lead us to expect, from earlier evidence, a change in gain per se. Sokolov produces quite clear evidence that this is the case. For example, he allowed the orienting reflex to a light flash to habituate. When a loud sound was produced that itself yielded an orienting reflex, the response to the light could again be elicited. As the response to the sound habituated, so the response to the light followed suit. The change in gain can be seen even at peripheral loci. For example, Sokolov found that the electroretinogram of a rabbit's eye showed habituation to a flashing light. When a sound was presented that itself produced an orienting reflex the ERG showed a clear response to the light stimulus. In other words, the effect of producing the orienting reflex by one stimulus can increase the probability that another stimulus in another modality will also produce it. Conversely, habituation of one stimulus can reduce the probability of a response to the other stimulus.

The base-line level from which the physiological changes are measured introduces questions both of practical and theoretical importance. One naturally wishes to measure the response of the stimulus on each occasion from the same base line. If that base line corresponds to low "activation" one may have to wait for varying periods of considerable duration for the activity to return to that level. Sharpless and Jasper (1956) have referred to a long-lasting or "tonic" arousal, and short-lasting or "phasic" arousal, but no doubt there is a continuum rather than a dichotomy. At any rate, the repetition rate for stimulus presentation is not entirely under the experimenter's control, and this means that the situations involving frequent stimulus presentation (say, once a minute) must perforce be carried out when the subjects show only a short-lasting arousal response. Moreover, the nature of the response itself depends on the particular base-line level chosen, and this varies for the particular response under consideration. As Sokolov points out, "if the subject is in a state of excitation and the alpha-rhythm is absent with only beta-waves being present, no marked change in the EEG can be observed. But, at this time, the vascular response and the GSR's can nevertheless be very marked. It does not mean that there is an absence of response in the brain, only that we cannot, in this case, observe the changes by the particular method we are using" (1960, p. 233). But it is to be doubted whether the vascular responses, for example, vary in sensitivity as a simple monotonic function of the base line level; it is also likely that the direction of the change itself is a function of the base line. Quite striking evidence to this effect has been produced by Bridger on newborn human babies (1960), in studying the effects of an air puff to the abdomen on change of heart rate. The stimulus produces in the same individual an *increase* in heart rate if the base-line heart rate is low, but a *decrease* in heart rate if it is high. The size and direction of the change depend on the rate just prior to delivery of the stimulus. Indeed, the issue is even more complex, although in a highly interesting way. Bridger reports that an air puff to the baby's mouth can produce either behavioral startle or a sucking response. The changes in heart rate associated with the first case as a function of the base-line level are of the type just described— an increase in heart rate from low base-line levels and a decrease in heart rate from high base-line levels. But changes associated with sucking were an inverted U function of base-line level!

Finally, the very fact of habituation of the orienting reflex with repeated trials, coupled with the fact that a change in the repetitive stimulus will evoke an orienting reflex anew, implies a degree of tuning as habituation ensues. The tuning is, of course, of a negative type —the repeated stimulus is not responded to, but other stimuli are. Sokolov, among others (e.g., Sharpless and Jasper, 1956), has shown that the tuning can become quite sharp. At this point we wish to draw attention to the fact that the typical orienting reflex experiment involves *both* a change in gain and a change in selectivity. (A similar point is made by Woodworth and Schlosberg [1955, p. 151] in their discussion of habituation of GSR.) Probably these changes have different time courses; Sokolov states that, with the first presentation of a novel stimulus, there is a generalized response seen throughout the brain, and we can conceive of this being largely an increase in gain. With repetition, the response becomes more localized to the region of the projection area of the stimulus, and we can conceive of this as the development of tuning such that only the stimulus itself is detected. Finally, with further repetition, the response disappears altogether, and we can view this as the beginning of negative tuning, which becomes sharper as repetition continues, together with a decrease in gain. The course of events is like what we ourselves would apply to a wireless set over which we suddenly heard a faint new signal, possibly one of interest to us. We would first turn up the gain, then sharpen up the tuning. As we discovered that the signal was of no interest to us, we would turn down the gain a bit and start tuning elsewhere. If, after a long spell, no new signals were picked up, we might switch the gain down drastically and go and have a nap.

In any situation in which a response gradually declines, questions of interpretation inevitably arise as to whether the decline represents fatigue of the response itself or fatigue of the sensory receptors that initiate the sequence (sensory adaptation) or a process akin to adaptation in pathways central to the receptors (see Chapter 8). Peripheral fatigue is clearly ruled out as a universal explanation of habituation of the orienting reflex, because Sokolov showed that, after habituation, a *decrease* in intensity of stimulation would produce a new orienting reflex. In another example, he showed that a change in the duration of a repetitive signal (to which habituation had taken place) produced an orienting reflex. These types of controls are unfortunately not always included in studies of habituation.

RESPONSES TO NONNEUTRAL STIMULI. By a *nonneutral stimulus* we mean one that reliably evokes behavioral responses. Just as we considered neutral stimuli as unconditioned stimuli eliciting the orienting reflex, so we can consider various behavioral and physiological responses to nonneutral stimuli as measures by which we might make inferences about gain and selectivity. The point about our so-called neutral stimuli was that neutrality was defined in terms of the eventual habituation of the response to them—when they are first presented as novel stimuli they are not physiologically neutral because they elicit the orienting reflex, and behaviorally there might also be indications of response. Here we consider stimuli that do not habituate, at least not completely, or only slowly, and, for reasons we will come to soon, we also wish to insist for the moment that there be clear behavioral manifestations. But, in keeping with our original aim, we do not want elaborate and lengthy training procedures by which the behavior is brought under control.

The class of stimuli that will elicit behavioral responses reliably is large, and it is paradoxical that more systematic work on "attention" has been carried out with stimuli whose effects are transitory, as is the case with the orienting reflex experiments we have just considered, than with stimuli whose effects are stable with repetition. Such nonneutral stimuli have been used, however, in many studies of the electro-physiology of learning, with which this chapter is not concerned, but we will be able to exploit some of those facts because one of the appropriate (but, alas, infrequently conducted) controls for conditioning, namely, the "pseudo-conditioning" control, produces evidence of direct relevance. First, however, we will consider instances where clearly evocative stimuli have been used more directly in a way that might allow us to make statements about sensitivity and selectivity.

Perhaps the best-known experiment using evocative stimuli is that of Hernández-Peón, Scherrer, and Jouvet (1956), who presented cats with various attractive stimuli, such as mice (in a jar) and sardine odor, and studied their effect on the evoked potentials produced by repetitive neutral stimuli, such as an auditory click. When the animal was relaxed, prior to the introduction of an evocative visual stimulus (mice), the evoked potential to the click (recorded in the cochlear nucleus) was moderately large. With the introduction of the mice, the response to the click was reported to be much reduced or to be absent. When the mice were removed, the response to the click was seen once again. (Also, cf. Hernández-Peón et al. [1957] for analogous effects on visual evoked potentials.)

The interpretation that often has been drawn from these experiments is that channels carrying unimportant, neutral information are suppressed while channels carrying important information are boosted. But, as we have seen, in the early stages of the orienting reflex experiments of Sokolov, one effect of an arousing stimulus is to boost the gain generally to all inputs. This, superficially, appears not to be the case in the present experiments because the evoked electrical responses to the neutral clicks were reduced when the mice were presented. But, alas, the amplitude of evoked potentials is a poor guide to their significance, as we shall see. At any rate, an important control that is missing from this experiment is the effect of evocative stimuli on the evoked responses of stimuli in the *same* modality. A control of this kind has been provided by Horn (1960), who found that the cat's evoked cortical responses to light flashes were *reduced* in amplitude when mice were presented. This result is not surprising, because evoked responses are seen least clearly in an "activated" EEG and seen most clearly, in fact, under anaesthesia. So all we are really free to conclude from Hernández-Peón, Scherrer, and Jouvet (1956) is that the evocative stimuli produced an arousal pattern in which evoked responses generally were reduced. The fact that the reduction was seen at a peripheral station (cochlear nucleus) is interesting from the viewpoint of possibly demonstrating efferent pathways in sensory systems, but other controls are needed for a conclusive demonstration.[1]

In fact, one might ask why the cochlear nucleus evoked potentials to auditory clicks were of such high amplitude when the cat was in the relaxed state before being confronted with the mice, because it has been reported that the evoked responses to clicks in that nucleus habituate (Hernández-Peón, Jouvet, and Scherrer, 1957; Galambos,

---

[1] Since this chapter was written, an excellent and fully-documented review of these and other electrophysiological experiments has appeared by Horn (1965).

Sheatz, and Vernier, 1956). But an account of some of the difficulties encountered in these studies can be seen from a report by Worden and Marsh (1963), who tried in vain for six years to repeat the earlier habituation findings. The researchers' very thorough investigation indicated considerable variation in the size of evoked responses, so that chance sampling might have led one to conclude that habituation had taken place. The only consistent finding was that evoked potentials were larger when the animal was in an alert state than when it was sleeping. This is surprising considering what we have just said above, but the researchers point out that the results may have something to do with the fact that the animal tended to have its ears on the floor or to have them covered with its paws when in a drowsy state! They comment that the increasing tendency to do this with repetition of the stimulus may be responsible for reports of habituation of the response. This report is instructive in many respects, such as in showing the importance of careful statistical control over sampling procedures and of maintaining constancy of the physical stimulus prior to its impact upon the receptors, but it does not strengthen the claim that changes in evoked potentials of the type reported reflect changes in selectivity.

Another reliably evocative stimulus is electric shock, which has been used in a number of conditioning studies when concomitant physiological activity was being recorded. For example, Galambos, Sheatz, and Vernier (1956) paired auditory clicks (to which habituation had supposedly already occurred in the cochlear nucleus evoked response) with electric shock and reported that, as a result, the electrically evoked response to the clicks was augmented. The cats also showed clear signs of behavioral classical conditioning—they crouched, twitched, etc. to the clicks. This experiment by itself, however, is insufficient to demonstrate whether the specific association of click with shock was responsible for the electrical change or whether the shocks simply increased the gain so that clicks would produce a larger response even without a history of association with shock. Behaviorally, such a phenomenon can readily occur in classical conditioning situations and is known as "pseudoconditioning." That something of this sort might have been happening is suggested by the finding in the Galambos, Sheatz, and Vernier experiment that after an extinction procedure, when the response to clicks (without shock) had habituated, "applied shocks promptly changed the records of responses to those typical of the conditioned state." A very careful study has been reported by Gerken and Neff (1963), in which definite "pseudoconditioning" effects were found with evoked potentials recorded from the cat's auditory cortex. Here, then, we have clear evidence that an evocative stimulus (electric shock) produces a change in the responses to other stimuli in other modalities, and this is most simply interpreted as a change in gain per se. (We do not wish to imply that all reported changes in neural responses to stimuli associated with electric shock are unspecific. A clear example of a specific change can be seen in the report by Hearst et al. [1960] in which it was shown that the response at several points in the C.N.S. to a tone associated with shock was more altered than the response to another tone not associated with shock.)

We have been talking about evocative stimuli, defined behaviorally, and also about evoked responses in the nervous system. If we include the latter as a criterion of a nonneutral stimulus, then the range of stimuli is infinite. But there are serious reasons, both empirical and logical, for not allowing ourselves this liberty. Empirically, as we have seen, the amplitude of the evoked response does not correlate highly with the behavioral status of the animal. For example, it sometimes decreases with arousal (Horn, 1960; 1965), but it is also said to decrease with habituation (Hernández-Peón, Jouvet, and Scherrer, 1957; Galambos, Sheatz, and Vernier, 1956). It is also said to increase with arousal (Worden and Marsh, 1963; Gerken and Neff, 1963). It is sometimes not detectable when the animal is obviously responding behaviorally to the stimulus (unless elaborate "averaging" techniques are used), and it is sometimes obviously present when the animal is not behaviorally responding to the stimulus, as in sleep or under barbiturate anaesthesia.

A logical point is introduced by this last observation, namely, the question of the definition of *detection*. An evoked response, or any other physiological response to a stimulus, tells one something about the properties of receptors and neurones located earlier in the chain of events giving rise to the response, but it can tell one nothing about the processing of events subsequent to the point at which the responses are recorded, or in parallel pathways. The closer one is to the effector in one's recording, then, the better, and it is for this reason that a behavioral definition of detection is to be preferred. There are, of course, a multiplicity of effectors that may be brought into action by a single stimulus event, and the decision as to which effectors are best monitored is entirely pragmatic at this stage of knowledge, although most people will feel dissatisfied, say, with recordings restricted to autonomic effectors, because they will say that these can respond to stimuli even when a person is "unaware" of the stimulus. But we do not wish to get into the quicksand of a behavioral definition of awareness. The point is merely to show the limitations of a purely electrical response recorded from the nervous system. These points are not altered by recording with microelectrodes from single cells, although some may feel that such recordings might be preferable for other reasons.

Of course, if one's interest lies in unraveling the chain of events within the nervous system, one will depend heavily on electrical recordings of various types of neural activity, but there are grave dangers of extrapolating from such recordings to the properties of the whole behaving organism. Our interest here lies not with mechanism per se but with measures that might be relevant to treatments affecting sensitivity of detection. But, in any case, the study of details of mechanism can scarcely be carried out fruitfully in the absence of knowledge of the input-output relationships of the organism as a whole to which those details are to be related. So, in any case, we must give priority to the behavioral measures, and, after this consideration of evoked responses, we now return to the behavior to which they and other physiological responses must be related in our so-called reactive sensitivity situations.

We have already seen an example of evocative stimuli being used to alter the electrical responses of neutral stimuli, e.g., the presentation of mice altering the cat's chochlear response to clicks. But there is no reason why in principle the measuring probe itself should not be behavioral rather than electrical, although it is surprising how rarely this procedure has been carried out. If one had concurrent physiological records in such a case, one would obviously be in a very strong position both to uncover indexes and to throw light on mechanism.

Some experiments on the physiological correlates of learning are possibly relevant to such a design, because the "neutral" stimuli gradually come to evoke behavioral responses (John and Killam, 1959; Gerken and Neff, 1963; Hearst *et al.*, 1960), but, from the point of view of our current interest, they do not hit the nail directly on the head, because our interest is in changes in gain independent of the establishment of new associations.

The evocative stimulus itself could be used both to change sensitivity and, as a probe, to measure that change in sensitivity. For example, a behavioral response to electric shock—latency of response or the strength of shock required to produce a barely detectable response to shock—could be used to gauge sensitivity (response can be variously defined: crouching, twitching, and other unconditioned effects of the shock, or a simple operant can be established, such as movement from one position to another or pressing a key, etc.). The question of changes in gain produced by the shock boils down to the question of the independence of the responses to successive shocks as a function of the interval between them, e.g., if an animal is drowsy, the response to a shock will probably have a long latency, and one which follows soon afterwards will have a short latency. There are statistical techniques for handling such relationships (Frick and Miller, 1951). Even in situations generally thought to be passive, according to our earlier definition, as in standard psychophysical experiments, nonindependence has been reported (Howarth and Bulmer, 1956). In general, any pattern of effects where one talks of "priming" or "warm-up" effects is likely to demonstrate just the effect to which we are referring; e.g., the fact that intracranial stimulation sometimes requires a "priming stimulus" before the animal treats the stimuli as strongly reinforcing, leads one to talk of a "motivating" effect of the stimuli (Deutsch and Howarth, 1963) independent of their reinforcing effects. Similarly, a smaller quanity of food delivered just before the performance of a food-directed response will sometimes have the effect of increasing the speed of response (Bruce, 1938) and one talks again of "drive induction" or "appetite whetting."

But sooner or later the question will arise with such a procedure whether changes in sensitivity are limited to the evocative stimulus, i.e., whether the phenomenon is selective, or whether the change is a general nonspecific one. Therefore, another behavioral task is required with which to assess the effects of the evocative stimulus. Because we have so little actual experimental evidence bearing on such situations, we can only speculate about the best practical arrangements. It would appear simplest to use a nonevocative stimulus situation for this purpose to minimize the complexity of two-way interactions. Some of the experimental arrangements already discussed under the heading of passive-sensitivity situations would appear to be reasonable in this context—reaction-time experiments of the type used by Kleitman, tachistoscopic threshold situations as used by Fuster. Indeed, it would be very surprising if Fuster's results could not be repeated using electrical stimulation to the skin instead of to the reticular formation as the "arousing stimulus." But whatever the second situation, some obvious behavioral response will have to be measured, and with non-evocative stimuli this will almost certainly have to be established through training or through verbal instruction, and one may therefore find that the "probe" stimuli assume evocative effects through association with other stimuli used in the training procedure. This is the Heisenberg dilemma, on which we have already remarked briefly. Because we already have a behavioral response to our deliberately chosen evocative situation, the two-way interactions could, in principle, always be assessed. By analogy with Hernández-Peón's experiment with clicks and mice, it would be interesting to establish some clear behavioral response to the click itself and to determine the effect of the presentation of the mice upon some feature of the click response, such as latency or intensity of click required to elicit the response. One would have to take obvious precautions to minimize the possibility that the responses to the click and the mice were mutually incompatible. The click could be made the discriminative stimulus in a food-reinforcement operant situation, such as key-pressing, or the conditioned stimulus in a classical conditioning situation, such as conditioned salivation.

It can be seen that the behavioral situation approaches closely to one in which the effects are studied of "distracting stimuli" on the detection of control stimuli. If the distracting stimuli have the effect of making detection of the control stimuli less efficient, one can generally be safe in assuming that there has been a change in selectivity. Logically, however, it is possible that the "distracting stimuli" simply decrease the gain without altering selectivity. We have seen that this sometimes happens in the case of the orienting reflex, in that habituation to one stimulus can reduce the probability that another stimulus will evoke an orienting reflex (Sokolov, 1960, p. 199). And, clearly, if the distracting stimuli have no effect on detection of control stimuli, it cannot be concluded that the distracting stimuli have not been detected. So, logically, the minimum data we require are independent measures of detection of both the distracting and the control stimuli. The interaction of the responses to the two sets of stimuli constitute the data from which we can conclude whether or not changes in detectability are specific or general and can conclude which stimuli are producing the change. Given two independent measures, whether we call one set of stimuli "distracting" and the other one "control" is trivial. The problem of assessing stimulus-induced changes in detection behaviorally resolves itself thus into the study of a pair (ideally more than a pair) of stimulus-detection situations and their mutual interactions. The interpretation of changes in detection that are not stimulus induced (depending, say, on endogenous rhythms) likewise, as we have seen, requires a minimum of two stimulus-detection situations. Measures of detection in a single situation cannot discriminate between changes in gain and in selectivity. It is to be hoped that physiological measures will someday enable us to take effective short cuts in this complex process of analysis, as they are starting to do with the orienting reflex; but until these measures themselves are based on a behaviorally sound analysis, we will never be certain that we are pulling on the appropriate bootstrap, despite the feeling of elevation.

Selectivity

Whenever we have a response clearly under the control of a particular stimulus, it is in principle a simple matter to determine the degree to which the other stimuli will control the same response, by the well-known methods of stimulus generalization (Guttman and Kalish,

1956) and of equivalence of stimuli (Klüver, 1933). Similarly, if we have the clear absence of a response to a stimulus, as when there has been habituation or extinction, one can determine the range of stimuli that will fail to elicit the response and those that will elicit the response that has shown habituation. It is important to stress again that simply to show a change in strength of response to a single stimulus is in itself inadequate for demonstrating a change in selectivity. For example, we have seen that "pseudoconditioning" controls often demonstrate that an apparently selective response to a particular stimulus is really unselective in the sense that the organism is likely to respond to any new stimulus after a bout of unconditioned stimuli. Similarly, in case of habituation of the orienting reflex, we have seen that habituation may reduce the sensitivity of orienting reflex to other stimuli. We need only consider the instance of where an organism eventually falls to sleep in the face of a repetitive neutral stimulus. But genuinely selective conditioning and habituation do occur, as we are all aware. One might use the facts of selective changes to infer that, with repetition of stimuli, "models" of the stimuli are established in the nervous system. In the case of conditioning, any new stimulus that "matches" the model produces the conditioned response, whereas a mismatch does not produce it. In the case of habituation, any mismatch produces the orienting reflex, and any match produces absence of response. Sokolov (1960) has discussed these ideas and has shown clear evidence for selective features of habituation of the orienting reflex. Whether habituation *need* imply neuronal models is a moot point (see Chapter 8). At any rate, transfer tests are a *sine qua non* for demonstrations of selectivity of stimulus detection. From the present point of view, we need not be concerned with whether the tests are used to demonstrate the range of stimuli to which the organism is *potentially* sensitive (as in generalization tests) or the delineation of subparts of a stimulus complex that are effective from those that are irrelevant. In practice, many problems arise—the programming of the transfer trials, the use of reward or nonreward on transfer trials, etc. Sutherland (1961) has treated some of the problems briefly but penetratingly in a recent monograph, and the reader will find treatments by many authors (see also Chapter 9). Accordingly, we will not review these problems here, nor will we belabor any further the importance of the testing of a range of stimuli. Instead, we will turn to certain other aspects of stimulus selectivity that have not been much discussed in the literature. In keeping with our original aim, we shall be seeking situations that do not require elaborate "shaping up" procedures.

Multiple Stimulus Sampling

Most of the situations we have been concerned with thus far have involved the simultaneous presentation by the experimenter of a relatively few stimuli, generally just one, against a more-or-less constant background environment. But suppose we put an animal or child in a room full of interesting objects. Its behavior will tell us a lot about the rate and order of stimulus sampling and will tell us the relative preference for the various stimuli. The behavior itself will be complex, and, to quantify it, one must arbitrarily select some specific responses. Eye movements and fixations have been used as responses in a somewhat restricted but highly informative way, with a small stimulus array by

Fantz, Ordy, and Udelf (1962) and others (e.g., Hershenson, 1964) to study the stimulus preferences of young babies. The pattern of eye fixations has also been used to determine which parts of drawings are most frequently selected—with male subjects looking at drawings of females, one obtains more or less the pattern one might expect (Fender, 1964). But eye-movement recordings are technically cumbersome to carry out and generally require immobility of the head, although not always (Cowey, 1963).

Another obvious measure can be obtained simply by recording the stimulus objects actually touched or manipulated. This was the method used recently, for example, to rate the relative attractiveness for children of members of an array of toys (Beyfus, 1964). A somewhat similar procedure has been used by Weiskrantz and Mingay (1967) to study stimulus sampling properties by monkeys, although in this instance it was found necessary to have each stimulus object cover a food reward in order for the behavior to be sustained for more than a few minutes. In this study, we were less interested in stimulus preferences than in the rate and order of sampling. It was found that frontal-lobe lesions significantly affected the order with which objects were selected—the frontal animal showing more randomness than the controls. Control animals tended to select adjacent objects much more predictably than frontals. Frontals also sampled at slower rates and tended to bunch their sampling responses into "bouts," with breaks in between. All kinds of variations are possible that have been scarcely explored: the rate of habituation when food reward is not used; stimulus selection as habituation proceeds; the effects of different positionings of stimuli; the introduction of novel stimuli; variations in the type of stimuli used, including those in tactile and olfactory modalities as well as in visual modalities. This general type of situation is so rich in possibilities, particularly for studying treatment effects, that it is surprising that it has been so little exploited.

On reflection, it will be seen that such a situation—one in which several stimuli are simultaneously presented—is formally similar to one in which signals are deliberately fed into more than one sensory receptor system, as in experiments involving dichotic listening (Cherry, 1953; Broadbent, 1958). Such experiments have been instructive in revealing properties of stimulus sampling, as in showing, for example, that inputs tend to be sampled in clusters appropriate to each ear, although the nature of the stimulus material is important. Inferences have also been possible of the time required to switch from one set of inputs to another (cf. Treisman, 1964, for review). In general, from such experiments one concludes that only a limited amount of information can be sampled per unit time, a conclusion that had been reached already in Biblical times, although the precise specification of this amount is difficult to arrive at (Miller, 1956; Crossman, 1964). Dichotic listening experiments have proved promisingly sensitive to the effects of brain damage in human subjects. It has been reported that unilateral temporal lobectomy affects perception of spoken digits (presented simultaneously to both ears) arriving at the contralateral ear more than at the ipsilateral ear. Furthermore, stimuli arriving at the ear contralateral to the hemisphere dominant for speech (as determined by unilateral amytal injections into the internal carotid artery) were more efficiently recognized than stimuli arriving at the ipsilateral ear (Kimura, 1961a; 1961b).

Another approach to the problem of selection in multiple-stimulus situations is that of Sutherland and MacIntosh (1964), who have taught rats visual discriminations that could be solved according to more than one set of cues, e.g., black vertical bar versus white horizontal bar. Transfer trials were given to each set of cues separately. The researchers conclude that animals tend to select only one set of cues in solving the problem. The stronger the transfer to one set of cues, the weaker the transfer to the alternative set. Thus, as in the dichotic listening experiments, only a particular set of inputs are selected at the expense of the other possible sets. These ideas obviously have a resemblance to earlier ones of Krechevsky (1932), for example, on hypothesis formation, but not all experiments show failure of "additivity of cues" (see Chapter 9; also, Bruner, Matter, and Papanek, 1955 for related experiments). Similar issues arise in the question of "irrelevant incentive learning"—whether or not an animal detects the location, say, of water located in a maze that it is negotiating for food reward. The animal is subsequently tested *thirsty* in the same maze. The result here appears to depend on the state of hunger of the animal —the less hungry he is, the more likely is detection of the irrelevant signals (Thistlethwaite, 1951)—as well as on its positioning in the maze.

The essential property of most of these situations is the simultaneous presentation by the experimenter of a variety of signals all of which have the same formal contingency with respect to reinforcement. It is a property that can be seen as fundamental, not only for providing an operational definition of stimulus selection that conforms closely to everyday usage, but also in allowing us to assess selection by the organism with a minimum of constraints placed upon it.

Investigatory Operants

We have just been referring to the virtues of situations in which population of stimuli are presented simultaneously to the subject and to various features of sampling assessed. The sampling itself, of course, will be primarily successive rather than simultaneous, and, therefore, a situation in which the stimuli are themselves presented successively, under the subject's own control, is very close to ones we have been considering. Many situations used for the study of "exploratory behavior" (see Chapter 6) are precisely of this type. When the instrumental response for production of the stimulus is itself "looking" or some other response on which "looking" is dependent, we come very close indeed to the type of situation described under "multiple stimulus sampling."

Such an arrangement has been used extensively by Butler (1960), with monkeys. The animal is placed inside an opaque cage but is provided with visual access to the environment outside the box when it performs the appropriate response. The response can be pushing open a window, operating a level that opens the window, or simply putting its head within a certain small distance of the window. Butler has used such a situation to determine the types of stimuli that are most effective in sustaining the instrumental responses, and he reports that moving stimuli are preferred to stationary stimuli, colored to uncolored, focussed to blurred, and upright to disoriented (Butler and Woolpy, 1963).

If only a single window is available, as in an early Butler study (1954), then the order in which the stimuli are sampled is entirely under the experimenter's control, and, therefore, the study of selective changes in sampling can be made only by comparing response tendencies considerably separated in time; changes in the ordering of sampling are not amenable to study. As more stimulus alternatives become simultaneously available, so the situation approaches more closely that outlined previously under "Multiple Stimulus Sampling." It might be said that, with the multiple-stimulus Butler situation, one assumes that the animal must remember which stimulus is produced by which response, but similar considerations apply to any multiple stimulus situation in which the stimuli are spread out over a large visual angle. The Butler box, with multiple stimulus response alternatives, at least enables one to define unequivocally the sampling at any point in time. On the other hand, it is not easily adapted to allow the animal to scan a large number of alternatives in rapid sequence.

The largest number of stimulus-response alternatives used by Butler has been two (Butler and Woolpy, 1963), so the situation has not been exploited as it might be, and, moreover, no analysis of the sequential patterning of sampling as yet has been presented for two alternatives. But Butler and Woolpy have shown that the duration of the individual viewing responses contribute more to total viewing than does the number of viewing responses (with a single stimulus alternative). This is interesting in view of Lindsley, Weiskrantz, and Mingay's (1964) finding that frontal lesions shorten the mean duration of viewing responses without altering the number of responses. In addition, inferotemporal lesions have been shown to depress total viewing time (Symmes, 1963) by reducing both the mean duration and the number of responses (Lindsley, Weiskrantz, and Mingay, 1964). But these effects of treatments were relatively nonspecific for the range of stimuli used.

Visual Search Situations

In the paradigm just discussed, no specific reward contingency exists for any particular stimulus choice. There is no "correct" stimulus, and the subject is free to do what it wishes. As soon as one rewards a particular stimulus selectively, the sampling obviously is likely to come under the control of that contingency. However, there are discrimination learning and stimulus matching situations that, although they suffer from this limitation in the present context, nevertheless seem to be sensitive to stimulus numerosity and quality in a way that allows one indirectly to infer something about the nature of stimulus sampling. Moreover, the situations have been sensitive to treatments such as frontal-lobe lesions.

Teuber (1964), for example, has reported an experiment in which human brain-injured subjects were presented with a large array of 48 two-dimensional patterns distributed irregularly over a screen. In the center of the array there was a duplicate of any of the 48 patterns. The subjects' task was to locate the pattern in the array that matched the one in the center. The measure was speed of correct identification (by pointing). It was found that frontal lesions were associated with a reduction in the speed of search and, with unilateral cases, an asymmetry of searching time, patterns opposite to the side of the lesion requiring a longer time for identification.

A formally similar situation was used by Buffery (1964) to study the effects of cortical lesions in monkeys. It also involved a simultaneous matching of a central stimulus with one of a set of stimuli surrounding it. Buffery found the bilateral frontal lesions produced an increasing deficit in performance as the number of surrounding stimuli was increased from two to four.

Buffery also used a visual discrimination learning situation in which he varied the quality of unrewarded and rewarded objects and also varied the number of unrewarded objects. He found very striking evidence that frontal monkeys were impaired as the number of stimuli was increased above four (but no impairment below four), provided the unrewarded stimuli were novel. This experiment fits in line with the previous evidence and also with other experiments (e.g., Mishkin, Prockop, and Rosvold, 1962; Gross, 1963) suggesting that frontal monkeys tend to overreact to novel stimuli.

There are experiments in which there are no differentially distinctive cues. The animal has a number of response panels, only one of which produces reward on any given exposure. The animal's strategy in distributing his responses allows one to infer something of his sampling of positional information. Meyer and Settlage (1958), for example, using four response positions, found that frontal monkeys were more random in the ordering of their response sequences; broadly similar results have been reported by Harlow, Akert, and Schiltz (1964). But Harlow, Akert, and Schiltz also reported significantly more repetitive errors (returning to the same position more than once per exposure), which makes the result difficult to dissociate from a memory disorder.

Selective Probability of Detection

Any classical psychophysical function can be thought of as a function relating probability of detection to some physical variable. We have already seen the use of the tachistoscope to study changes induced by brain-stem stimulation (Fuster, 1958) in the function relating probability of detection to length of exposure. The same method has been used to study *selective* changes in probability of detection and, therefore, is directly relevant to our present concern. For example, numerous studies of "perceptual defense" have been reported purporting to show that certain "emotionally charged" words or patterns are less likely to be reported by human subjects than are "neutral" stimuli at brief exposures. The literature in the area of research is extensive, and there are many problems of interpretation in the results, e.g., whether the change is genuinely perceptual, as opposed to the possibility that the stimuli are genuinely seen but not reported because of embarrassment. There would be no virtue in our trying to pass judgment on the results; the material and issues are reviewed by Brown (1961). Our purpose is simply to point out the very direct relevance of the method to the study of changes in "tuning."

The tachistoscopic method has been used very effectively by Grindley (1931) to study the effect of direction of voluntary attention to a given part of the visual field on the detection of signals. Subjects were required to fixate the center of a display. They could report the orientation of a test figure in a given part of the visual field more accurately if they knew in advance in which part of the field the test figure was to be flashed briefly. This was especially the case when other irrelevant forms were exposed in other parts of the field. Grindley has taken extreme care, by monitoring eye movements, to ensure that changes in fixation could not account for his results. But such an explanation is entirely ruled out in the more recent study of Sperling (1960), who reported very convincing effects even when subjects were not instructed to which part of the stimulus display to attend until after the display had been presented tachistoscopically.

A powerful use of tachistoscopic thresholds has been made by Kinsbourne and Warrington (1962a; 1962b; 1963) in their evaluation of certain types of disorder caused by brain injury in man. For example, they have shown that certain cases (probably associated with left posterior cerebral damage) have difficulty in identifying more than a single letter or form when presented tachistoscopically, although their threshold for single stimuli is within normal limits (1962a, 1963). Interestingly, even when single stimuli are presented successively, perception of the second stimulus is very impaired unless a long interval is allowed to elapse between the first and second. In terms of our distinction between gain and tuning, these results do not neatly fall into either category, but, insofar as they suggest a nonspecific change in the rate at which multiple signals can be detected, they are more closely relevant to the former. A clearer instance of an alteration in tuning is found in the same authors' analysis of cases with right-hemisphere disease. When groups of letters or visual forms were presented tachistoscopically, the patients tended to make errors in reporting those components located to the left of the array (even though the authors state that the entire array was presented in intact regions of the visual fields). It is concluded that the patients suffer from an "abnormal distribution of visual attention."

Summary

Although this treatment has been somewhat sketchy, we have touched on a wide range of issues, and it is time to draw the threads together. We have considered signal detection by the organism as being subject to two types of control: gain and tuning. The emphasis in this chapter has been not so much on how these controls are altered, because that question largely reduces to the issues discussed in Chapters 6, 7, and 9, but on the question of how the particular settings of these controls can be assessed. *Gain* can be studied by using situations that are themselves relatively ineffective in altering sensitivity, as in certain probability of detection experiments. But many stimuli used to gauge the level of gain themselves alter the level, and certain experimental situations can be contrived to study both the initial level and the induced change in the level. We can distinguish two types of these "reactive sensitivity" situations: ones in which the stimuli eventually habituate and ones in which they do not. The former has been very usefully exploited for the analysis of various properties of the so-called orienting reflex. The latter uses stable rewards and punishments. With all of these situations many attempts have been made to discover physiological correlates with which to assess the level of gain. These on occasion have been very promising, but a plea is made for the necessity of behavioral validation, and certain suggestions are made about the properties that these validating behavioral situations must possess. One of the points that emerges is that measures of detection using a single class of stimuli cannot logically discriminate between changes in gain and in tuning.

Assessment of changes in *tuning* involves the same type of operations as those just mentioned, because the question is merely whether the changes are specific or general. Thus, probability-of-detection situations have been used to study specific changes in detectability, as in a variety of tachistoscopic experiments. Investigatory operants also provide a useful handle on the problem of tuning. As the number of simultaneously available stimulus alternatives in an investigatory operant situation increases, so it approaches a class of situations that have special merit for the study of tuning. The essential property of this class is the simultaneous presentation of signals, all of which have the same formal contingency with respect to reinforcement. It is a property that not only provides an operational definition of stimulus selection that conforms closely to what is often meant by the term *selective attention* in everyday usage but also allows us to assess selection by the organism with a minimum of constraints placed upon it.

REFERENCES

BEYFUS, DRUSILLA. 1964. What sort of toys do children like? London Sunday Times Magazine, December 6.

BILLS, A. G. 1931. Blocking: A new principle of mental fatigue. *Am. J. Psychol.*, 43, 230.

BRIDGER, W. H. 1960. In Brazier, M. (Ed.), *The central nervous system and behavior.* New York: Josiah Macy, Jr. Foundation.

BROADBENT, D. E. 1958. *Perception and communication.* New York: Pergamon Press.

BROWN, W. P. 1961. Conceptions of perceptual defence. *Brit. J. Psychol. Monogr. Suppl.*, 35, 1–107.

BRUCE, R. H. 1938. The effect of lessening the drive upon performance by white rats in a maze. *J. comp. Psychol.*, 25, 225–248.

BRUNER, J. S., MATTER, J., & PAPANEK, M. L. 1955. Breadth of learning as a function of drive level and mechanization. *Psychol. Rev.*, 62, 1–10.

BUFFERY, A. W. H. 1964. *The effects of frontal and temporal lobe lesions upon the behaviour of baboons.* Unpublished doctoral dissertation, Cambridge University.

BUTLER, R. A. 1954. Incentive conditions that influence visual exploration. *J. exp. Psychol.*, 48, 19–23.

BUTLER, R. A. 1960. Acquired drives and the curiosity-investigative motives. In Waters, R. H., Rethlingshafer, D. A., & Caldwell, W. E. (Eds.), *Principles of comparative psychology.* New York: McGraw-Hill.

BUTLER, R. A., & WOOLPY, J. H. 1963. Visual attention in the rhesus monkey. *J. comp. physiol. Psychol.*, 56, 324–328.

CHERRY, E. C. 1953. Some experiments on the recognition of speech, with one and two ears. *J. acoust. Soc. Amer.*, 25, 975–979.

CHOW, K. L., & ORBACH, J. 1957. Performance of visual discriminations presented tachistoscopically in monkeys with temporal neocortical ablations. *J. comp. physiol. Psychol.*, 50, 636–640.

COWEY, A. 1963. The basis of a method of perimetry with monkeys. *Quart. J. exp. Psychol.*, 15, 81–90.

CROSSMAN, E. R. F. W. 1964. Information processes in human skill. *Brit. med. Bull.*, 20, 32–37.

DEMENT, W. C., & KLEITMAN, N. 1957. The relation of eye movements during sleep to dream activity: An objective method for the study of dreaming. *J. exp. Psychol.*, 53, 339–346.

DEUTSCH, J. A., & HOWARTH, C. I. 1963. Some tests of a theory of intracranial self-stimulation. *Psychol. Rev.*, 70, 444–460.

DUFFY, E. 1932. The measurement of muscular tension as a technique for the study of emotional tendencies. *Amer. J. Psychol.*, 44, 146–162.

DUFFY, E. 1957. The psychological significance of the concept of "arousal" or "activation." *Psychol. Rev.*, 64, 265–275.

FANTZ, R. L., ORDY, J. M., & UDELF, M. S. 1962. Maturation of pattern vision in infants during the first six months. *J. comp. physiol. Psychol.*, 55, 907–917.

FENDER, D. H. 1964. Control mechanisms of the eye. *Scient. Amer.*, 211, No. 1, 24–33.

FREEMAN, G. L. 1940. The relationship between performance level and bodily activity level. *J. exp. Psychol.*, 26, 602–608.

FREEMAN, G. L. 1948. *The energetics of human behavior.* Ithaca, N. Y.: Cornell University Press.

FRICK, F. C., & MILLER, G. A. 1951. A statistical description of operant conditioning. *Amer. J. Psychol.*, 44, 20–36.

FUSTER, J. M. 1958. Effects of stimulation of brain stem on tachistoscopic perception. *Science*, 127, 150.

FUSTER, J. M., & UYEDA, A. A. 1962. Facilitation of tachistoscopic performance by stimulation of midbrain tegmental points in the monkey. *Exp. Neurol.*, 6, 384–406.

GALAMBOS, R., SHEATZ, G., & VERNIER, V. G. 1956. Electrophysiological correlates of a conditioned response in cats. *Science*, 123, 376–377.

GERKEN, G. M., & NEFF, W. D. 1963. Experimental procedures affecting evoked responses from auditory cortex. *EEG clin. Neurophysiol.*, 15, 947–957.

GRINDLEY, G. C. 1931. Psychological factors in peripheral vision. Medical Research Council (Gt. Britain), Special Report Series No. 163.

GROSS, C. G. 1963. Locomotor activity following lateral frontal lesions in rhesus monkeys. *J. comp. physiol. Psychol.*, 56, 232–236.

GUTTMAN, N., & KALISH, H. I. 1956. Discriminability and stimulus generalization. *J. exp. Psychol.*, 51, 79–88.

HARLOW, H. F., AKERT, K., & SCHILTZ, K. A. 1964. The effects of bilateral prefrontal lesions on learned behavior of neonatal, infant, and preadolescent monkeys. In Warren, J. M., & Akert, K. (Eds.), *The frontal granular cortex and behavior.* New York: McGraw-Hill.

HARLOW, H. F., & JOHNSON, T. 1943. Problem solution by monkeys following bilateral removal of the prefrontal areas: III. Test of initiation of behavior. *J. exp. Psychol.*, 32, 495–500.

HEARST, E., BEER, B., SHEATZ, G., & GALAMBOS, R. 1960. Some electrophysiological correlates of conditioning in the monkey. *EEG clin. Neurophysiol.*, 12, 137–152.

HEBB, D. O. 1955. Drives and the C.N.S. (Conceptual Nervous System). *Psychol. Rev.*, 62, 243–254.

HERNÁNDEZ-PEÓN, R., GUZMAN-FLORES, C., ALCARAZ, M., & FERNANDEZ-GUARDIOLA, A. 1957. Sensory transmission in visual pathway during "attention" in unanesthetized cats. *Acta neurol. Lat.-Amer.*, 3, 1–8.

HERNANDEZ-PEÓN, R., JOUVET, M., & SCHERRER, H. 1957. Auditory potentials at cochlear nucleus during acoustic habituation. *Acta neurol. Lat.-Amer.* 3, 144–156.

HERNANDEZ-PEON, R., SCHERRER, H., & JOUVET, M. 1956. Modification of electrical activity in cochlear nucleus during "attention" in unanesthetized cats. *Science*, 123, 331–332.

HERSHENSON, M. 1964. Visual discrimination in the human newborn. *J. comp. physiol. Psychol.*, 58, 270–276.

HINDE, R. A. 1960. In Brazier, M. (Ed.), *The central nervous system and behavior.* New York: Josiah Macy, Jr. Foundation.

HORN, G. 1960. Electrical activity of the cerebral cortex of the unanaesthetized cat during attentive behavior. *Brain*, 83, 57–76.

HORN, G. 1965. Physiological and psychological aspects of selective perception. In Lehrman, D. S., Hinde, R. A., & Shaw, E. (Eds.), *Advances in the study of behavior*. Vol. 1. New York: Academic Press. Pp. 155–215.

HOWARTH, C. I., & BULMER, M. G. 1956. Non-random sequences in visual threshold experiments. *Quart. J. exp. Psychol.*, 8, 163–171.

JOHN, E. R., & KILLAM, K. F. 1959. Electrophysiological correlates of avoidance conditioning in the cat. *J. Pharmacol. exp. Ther.*, 125, 252–274.

JOUVET, M. 1961. Telencephalic and rhombencephalic sleep in the cat. In Wolstenholme, G. E. W., & O'Connor, M. (Eds.), *The nature of sleep*. London: Churchill. Pp. 188–206.

KIMURA, D. 1961a. Cerebral dominance and the perception of auditory stimuli. *Canad. J. Psychol.*, 15, 166–171.

KIMURA, D. 1961b. Some effects of temporal-lobe damage on auditory perception. *Canad. J. Psychol.*, 15, 156–165.

KINSBOURNE, M., & WARRINGTON, E. K. 1962a. A disorder of simultaneous form perception. *Brain*, 85, 461–486.

KINSBOURNE, M., & WARRINGTON. E. K. 1962b. A variety of reading disability associated with right hemisphere lesions. *J. Neurol. Neurosurg. Psychiat.*, 25, 339–344.

KINSBOURNE, M., & WARRINGTON, E. K. 1963. The localizing significance of limited simultaneous visual form perception. *Brain*, 86, 697–702.

KLEITMAN, N. 1963. Sleep and wakefulness. Chicago: University of Chicago Press.

KLÜVER, H. 1933. *Behavior mechanisms in monkeys*. Chicago: University of Chicago Press.

KRECHEVSKY, I. 1932. "Hypotheses" in rats. *Psychol. Rev.*, 39, 516–532.

LANSING, R. W., SCHWARTZ, E., & LINDSLEY, D. B. 1959. Reaction time and EEG activation under alerted and nonalerted conditions. *J. exp. Psychol.*, 58, 1–7.

LINDSLEY, D. B. 1951. Emotion. In Stevens, S. S. (Ed.), *Handbook of experimental psychology*, Ch. 14. New York: Wiley.

LINDSLEY, D. B. 1960. Attention, consciousness, sleep and wakefulness. In Field, J. (Ed.), *Handbook of physiology*. Ch. 64. Washington, D.C.: American Physiological Society.

LINDSLEY, D. F., WEISKRANTZ, L., & MINGAY, R. 1964. Differentiation of frontal, inferotemporal, and normal monkeys in a visual exploratory situation. *Anim. Behav.*, 12, 525–530.

MALMO, R. B. 1959. Activation: A neuropsychological dimension. *Psychol. Rev.*, 66, 367–386.

MEYER, D. R., & SETTLAGE, P. H. 1958. Analysis of simple searching behavior in the frontal monkey. *J. comp. physiol. Psychol.*, 51, 408–410.

MILLER, G. A. 1956. The magical number seven, plus or minus two: Some limits on our capacity for processing information. *Psychol. Rev.*, 63, 81–97.

MISHKIN, M., PROCKOP, E. S., & ROSVOLD, H. E. 1962. One-trial object-discrimination learning in monkeys with frontal lesions. *J. comp. physiol. Psychol.*, 55, 178–181.

RINALDI, F., & HIMWICH, H. E. 1955. A comparison of effects of reserpine and some barbiturates on the electrical activity of cortical and subcortical structures of the brain of rabbits. In Miner, R. (Ed.), *Reserpine in the treatment of neuropsychiatric, neurological and related clinical problems*. Ann. N.Y. Acad. Sci.

SHARPLESS, S. K., & JASPER, H. 1956. Habituation of the arousal reaction. *Brain*, 79, 655–680.

SOKOLOV, E. N. 1960. In Brazier, M. (Ed.), *The central nervous system and behavior*. New York: Josiah Macy, Jr. Foundation.

SPERLING, G. 1960. The information available in brief visual presentations. *Psychol. Monogr.*, 74, No. 11, 1–29.

STENNET, R. G. 1957. The relationship of alpha amplitude to the level of palmar conductance. *EEG clin. Neurophysiol.*, 9, 131–138.

SURWILLO, W. W. 1963. The relation of simple response time to brain-wave frequency and the effects of age. *EEG clin. Neurophysiol.*, 15, 105–114.

SURWILLO, W. W. 1964. The relation of decision time to brain-wave frequency and age. *EEG clin. Neurophysiol.*, 16, 510–514.

SUTHERLAND, N. S. 1961. The methods and findings of experiments on the visual discrimination of shape by animals. *Exp. Psychol. Soc. Monogr.*, 1, 1–68.

SUTHERLAND, N. S., & MACKINTOSH, J. 1964. Discrimination learning: Non-additivity of cues. *Nature*, 201, 528–530.

SYMMES, D. 1963 Effects of cortical ablations on visual exploration by monkeys. *J. comp. physiol. Psychol.*, 56, 757–763.

TEUBER, H.-L. 1964. The riddle of frontal lobe function in man. In Warren, J. M., & Akert, K. (Eds.), *The frontal granular cortex and behavior.* New York: McGraw-Hill.

THISTLETHWAITE, D. L. 1951. A critical review of latent learning and related experiments. *Psychol. Bull.*, 48, 97–129.

TREISMAN, A. M. 1964. Selective attention in man. *Brit. med. Bull.*, 20, 12–16.

WEISKRANTZ, L. 1957. Reserpine and behavioral non-reactivity. In Garattini, S., & Ghetti, C. (Eds.), *Psychotropic drugs.* Amsterdam: Elsevier.

WEISKRANTZ, L., & MINGAY, R. 1967. Patterns of selections by monkeys with lesions of the cerebral cortex. *Nature*, 213, No. 5076, 573–574.

WIKLER, A. 1952. Pharmacologic dissociation of behavior and EEG "sleep patterns" in dogs: Morphine, N-allylnormorphine, and atropine. *Proc. Soc. exp. biol. Med.*, 79, 261–265.

WILKINSON, R. T. 1960. The effect of lack of sleep on visual watchkeeping. *Quart. J. exp. Psychol.*, 12, 36–40.

WOODWORTH, R. S., & SCHLOSBERG, H. 1955. *Experimental psychology.* New York: Holt, Rinehart and Winston.

WORDEN, F. G., & MARSH, J. T. 1963. Amplitude changes of auditory potentials evoked at cochlear nucleus during acoustic habituation. *EEG clin. Neurophysiol.*, 15, 866–881.

CHAPTER 11

Alteration of Perception and Memory in Man: Reflections on Methods*

B. MILNER AND H.-L. TEUBER

Introduction

THIS chapter differs from others in this volume in two respects: it deals with man, whereas all the other chapters deal with infra-human species, and it is of necessity selective. Attempts at covering the full range of methods available for assessing human behavior would require a volume of greater length than the rest of this book. We have therefore chosen for discussion the topics that are close to our own concerns: changes in perception and memory after brain injury or ablation. Even within these bounds we have singled out certain methods to the neglect of others, either because these methods have already led to reasonably secure results, or because they seem to us particularly promising although they have not yet been used according to their promise.

Despite the fact that nearly all our examples will be drawn from analyses of human behavior after focal brain lesions, the logic of our approach and often the actual techniques may be extended to assessments of changes induced by other means, such as drugs, fatigue, convulsions, or sensory deprivation. Yet, whatever the clinical or experimental condition under study, our aim throughout has been to explore abnormal behavior less for its own sake than for the clues it holds for an understanding of normal function.

Distinctive Features of Studies on Man

There are difficulties peculiar to any analysis of human behavior. Thus, it is obvious that man can rarely be subjected to such radical treatment as is frequently applied in animal experiments. Moreover, circumscribed surgical removals from the human brain are necessarily superimposed on preexisting pathology; in cases of accidental trauma,

* Preparation of this chapter was aided by the Medical Research Council of Canada (through their award of a Medical Research Associateship to Dr. Brenda Milner) and by grants to Dr. H.-L. Teuber from the National Aeronautics and Space Administration, the National Institute of Mental Health, and the Hartford Foundation.

on the other hand, the brain is healthy before the injury, but the precise extent and location of the lesion often remain unknown. Nevertheless, the advantages of studying human behavior in all its diversity seem to us to outweigh these difficulties. Subtle alterations of behavior can be detected in man that even the most refined measures applicable to animals would miss. In addition, man's behavioral repertoire contains activities that are simply not found at lower phylogenetic levels.

So far as is known only man has language in the sense of an individually acquired system governed by phonetic, syntactic, and semantic rules capable of generating a virtually infinite number of sentences that the speaker himself has never heard before. Correlated with the appearance of language is an evident increase in the complexity and versatility of coordinated motor acts, particularly those involving the construction and use of tools and the production of pictorial representations of the environment. There is capacity for long-term planning, including the deferral of an intended action for hours, days, or years.

It is still not clear what evolutionary changes in structure account for these vast advances in function. However, there is one feature that distinguishes the cerebral organization in adult man from that found in even the highest subhuman primates: the differential specialization of the cerebral hemispheres. Lesions in one of them, usually the left, may disrupt certain aspects of language, while leaving performance on certain nonverbal tasks essentially unimpaired; lesions in the other hemisphere may produce the converse picture. This reciprocal specialization makes it imperative that the role of language in our test procedures be considered with some care.

Verbal and Nonverbal Tasks

Since language is so vulnerable to lesions of the left hemisphere, we cannot rely as much as we might wish on a patient's verbal reports; nor can we limit ourselves to tasks that require comprehension of verbal instructions, particularly if we want to compare the performance of dysphasic and nondysphasic patients with respect to the nonverbal dimensions of behavior. At the same time, considerable efforts have to be made to tap language as such, by including tasks sensitive to even minimal disorders in that sphere. Lastly, we have to attempt to develop some tasks that are genuinely language-free, in the sense that they do not permit solution by explicit or implicit verbalization on the patient's part.

Thus, the use of language can obscure as well as illuminate. A patient may tell us freely what no amount of formal testing could have elicited from a monkey. On the other hand, his use of language may mask a genuine trouble that could have been brought out by language-free tasks. Hence, complementary investigations by verbal and nonverbal methods are needed whether one is analyzing perception, memory or thought.

Give-and-Take Between Work on Animals and Work on Man

Our emphasis on differences between animal and man should not detract from the gains that can be made in the study of man if one introduces methods that originated in the animal laboratory, just as clinical observations have often been the source of new animal experiments. Observations on visual-field defects in man guided the early animal studies involving selective ablation from the higher visual pathways, and the subsequent mapping of retinocortical projections by macro- and microelectrode techniques. Conversely, Loeb's experiment in the 1880s, which involved double simultaneous stimulation in the dog (Loeb, 1884), found its way soon afterwards into the clinic. Loeb tested dogs with unilateral frontal or unilateral occipital-lobe lesions by presenting two lures, one to each side of the animal, and an analogous method is still a powerful tool for demonstrating sensory defects in man.

In other cases, seemingly identical tasks presented to animal and man may be far from equivalent. An example is the well-known delayed-response test (Carr, 1913; Hunter, 1913), which is exquisitely sensitive to bilateral frontal-lobe lesions in subhuman primates (Jacobsen, 1935) but often unrevealing if given in identical form to a patient with frontal-lobe damage (Chorover and Cole, 1966). On this task the subject has to recall from trial to trial which of two identical-appearing containers conceals a lure. The lure is placed in the container for each trial, in the subject's full view, at the beginning of a delay period of, say, 5, 10, or 20 seconds before permitting a choice. A monkey with bifrontal lesions will fail in this task, but a human subject may recode the situation by telling himself (not necessarily aloud), "It's under the cup on the left," and thus solve the task by processes unavailable to the monkey.

The converse has also been proposed, namely, that certain superficially dissimilar tasks presented to man and monkey may turn out to tap analogous processes in the two species. For some time, one of us (H.-L. Teuber) has argued that the proper equivalent for delayed-response tasks, as applied to the monkey, might be found for man in certain perceptual and perceptual-motor tasks of the type first introduced by Aubert over a century ago (Aubert, 1861), tasks in which the subject has to adjust a luminous line in a dark room to the apparent vertical, while his head and body are tilted (Teuber and Mishkin, 1954; Teuber, 1966a). Under these conditions, patients with lesions of the frontal lobes or basal ganglia make large errors. Their impairment has been interpreted as a specific difficulty in coordination between perception and posture, as if the patients could not properly take their posture into account, and this interpretation has been extended to the delayed-response deficit in the monkey. Whether correct or not, such presumed functional equivalence of superficially dissimilar tasks points the way towards further analysis; for instance, the human perceptual-motor task should now be adapted for use with monkeys.

An extreme instance of discrepancy between the outcomes of similarly placed lesions in man and monkey can be found in the effects of bilateral removals from the hippocampal zone. In man, these ablations are followed by devastating amnesias (Milner, 1958, 1966; Scoville and Milner, 1957) that have no parallel in the monkey. This lack of congruence may mean that we have thus far been unable to put the experimental question to the two species in a comparable manner or that bilateral mesial temporal-lobe excisions in man interfere with processes that are restricted to our species.

Main Sources of Data

Even the most careful consideration of methods derived from work with animals cannot take the place of direct approaches to the study of man. Here one relies on the interplay between two principal sources of data: (1) informal observations of a patient's everyday behavior, guiding the observer to make conjectures about the essential change, and (2) the more rigorous testing of such conjectures by means of formal tasks that are necessarily and deliberately focused on a limited aspect of behavior. The use of such formal tasks, ordinarily applied to larger groups of cases and to control subjects, does not exclude but rather requires that we learn whatever we can from the patient's own comments and from intensive study of the individual case.

INFORMAL OBSERVATIONS. Particular testing procedures are often derived from casual descriptions of a patient's difficulties. It is well known that acute parietal-lobe lesions in man tend to be associated with marked trouble in route finding. Occasionally, it has been noted that this trouble is exacerbated in the dark. Accordingly, a test of route finding was constructed, employing visual and tactual presentation of maps (Semmes *et al.,* 1955). The test not only confirmed the dependence of the impairment on parietal-lobe injury but also the fact that the deficit was not modality-specific. The test thus corroborated one's clinical impressions and refined them, by detecting a disturbance of spatial orientation in cases tested years after the acute phase, when the disorder had become minimal and when many of the patients were themselves unaware of its existence.

What a patient and his close associates have to say can be most revealing, whether or not it generates further tests. Those of us who deal with ictal disorders have learned to listen to a patient's own description of his experiences, which may involve feelings of familiarity or strangeness, sudden fear, forced thinking, or distortions and hallucinations in any of the sense modalities. Similar phenomena may be encountered under the influence of certain drugs, and here, too, the subject's own descriptions are of necessity a primary source. Two points need to be made, however. It is most desirable to correlate subjective reports, say of a mescaline or LSD state, with concomitant objective measures of such things as averaged evoked responses to sensory stimulation or such psychophysical measures of absolute or differential thresholds as might be obtainable. Furthermore, a subject's introspective report is inevitably contaminated by the interpretations he imposes upon his own experience. When Sir Humphry Davy took laughing gas for the first time and exclaimed, "Nothing exists but thought," it was not immediately clear whether his remark was the sole effect of the nitrous oxide or of nitrous oxide in conjunction with a prior reading of Bishop Berkeley.

Not infrequently, a patient's remark may seem misleading at first but may later take on a different meaning with additional information. A patient with massive frontal lesions baffled one of us by insisting that his main trouble was his memory. A simple memory loss seemed to make little sense; neither this patient nor others with frontal-lobe lesions in the group under study had shown any striking evidence of memory impairment (Teuber, 1964). On further questioning, the patient explained, "the trouble with my memory is that I cannot forget; I cannot forget those things that I should."

INTENSIVE STUDY OF THE INDIVIDUAL CASE. Most of the early work on alterations of behavior after brain lesions in man was based on intensive and prolonged studies of single cases, and the investigation of drug effects was similarly oriented toward detailed descriptions of one case or a few. There still is a place for this approach, particularly where the patient's syndrome appears to be itself unique, or in those cases of brain injury or ablation where the lesion is known to be rare. A particularly telling example is the global amnesia found after bilateral mesial temporal-lobe resection for epilepsy in man (Scoville and Milner, 1957). In this instance, a heretofore untried surgical procedure was followed by unexpected and undesirable effects of such severity that the procedure is unlikely to be repeated, and the resulting syndrome, an amnesia uncontaminated by other changes, not likely to be found elsewhere. Hence, it becomes imperative that such a singular condition should be studied as thoroughly as possible. An equally strong case can be made for the intensive and prolonged follow-up studies of patients with surgical transection of the corpus callosum and of other interhemispheric commissures (Sperry, 1961, 1964, 1966; Gazzaniga and Sperry, 1967). These cases are still rare, and the peculiar surgical state makes it possible to investigate separately, in one and the same patient, the various ways in which sensory inputs are processed differentially in the right and the left cerebral hemispheres.

Although the continued importance of individual case studies thus cannot be gainsaid, there are certain dangers. Exclusive reliance on the single case has at times misled investigators who inadvertently trained their patients over many testing sessions so that the patients' behavior conformed increasingly to what the investigators expected of them; the famous case Schnei of Goldstein illustrates this hazard (Teuber, 1966b). Moreover, when the value of a single case depended crucially on the nature of the lesion, autopsy data have at times led to bitter disappointment. An extreme example is provided by Brickner's patient, Joe A., who was studied for many years as an instance of frontal-lobe symptomatology (Brickner, 1936). On autopsy, he was found to harbor multiple lesions scattered throughout the brain, including the occipital lobes (Brickner, 1952).

GROUPS OF CASES. The pitfalls of such intensive work on single cases can be avoided by studying larger groups, yet studies of groups have difficulties of their own. The larger the number of cases, the greater the limitations on what can be done with the individual patient, often to the detriment of a deeper understanding of mechanisms underlying his behavior. Selection of cases can also be a problem, even with large numbers of patients. In most clinical situations, patients come to the investigator's attention because they have special trouble or think they do, so that selection of cases is necessarily biased. Such a bias becomes serious if one wishes to compare contrasting groups. Thus, many of the early statements about effects of frontal lesions in man are suspect because the very numerous negative cases (i.e., patients with frontal lesions but without serious symptoms) were missed.

Sometimes another bias creeps in by way of ill-chosen contrasting groups. In one of the most critical earlier studies of frontal as compared with nonfrontal brain lesions in man (Rylander, 1939, 1943), the selection of groups with contrasting lesions (parietal, temporal, occipital) was constrained by systematic exclusion of all cases with aphasia or other complex disturbances, so that the conclusion offered (that the frontal-lobe syndrome was intellectually more disabling than symptoms due to lesions elsewhere in the brain) was both inevitable and false.

Ideally, one should be able to study cases of cerebral lesions irrespective of clinical need and to identify cases for study because they have a lesion and not because of any presenting symptoms, but this condition is rarely realized.

Patterns of Symptoms

The greatest advantage gained by studying larger groups of cases lies in the opportunity for searching in this way for patterns of symptoms, their association and dissociation (Teuber, 1950, 1955). As the example just given indicates, cases for this purpose should be classified, separately and independently, (1) according to the known or presumed site of their lesions; e.g., frontal *vs.* all others, right *vs.* left; and (2) according to presence or absence of objective signs of behavioral change; e.g., change in two-point threshold on the left hand, or presence of visual-field defect (quantitatively assessed) in the right homonymous half-fields. By searching for correlation of symptoms with particular loci of lesions, one can utilize results derived from groups of cases with variously localized cerebral lesions as a biological alternative to factorial analysis: separate vulnerability with differently placed lesions, implying, in principle, separable mechanisms.

Yet, for an understanding of mechanism—the change in function underlying the symptom—more is needed than localization of lesion effects, no matter how systematic the survey of unbiased lesion groups. What is needed beyond this is the use of multiple tasks designed to delineate the suspected alteration, not only by showing what is amiss in the patient's performance but also by identifying equally clearly whatever has remained intact.

In fact, study of patterns of symptoms, by means of multiple, convergent, or complementary tasks, can be carried out in relative independence from questions about the exact location of the cerebral lesions; in the case of drug effects, behavioral changes can be analyzed without a full comprehension of their neurochemical bases. Symptoms can be associated or dissociated, and their dissociation can take different forms.

SYMPTOM ASSOCIATION. Association of symptoms can be particularly revealing if an association is both definite and unexpected. Thus, what might have seemed an isolated breakdown in pattern perception through the sense of touch takes on a rather different aspect, if it turns out that the same patients who show this failure of tactile perception also have severe difficulties in the route-finding tasks, visual and tactual, that have already been described (Semmes, 1965).

SYMPTOM DISSOCIATION. Dissociation of symptoms can be similarly revealing of underlying changes in function. (See also Chapter

15.) Such symptom dissociation takes either of two forms: (1) hierarchical ordering or (2) double (or multiple) dissociation. In the first instance, a given symptom may be found in the absence of some other symptom, but never conversely. In cases of double dissociation, one symptom is found with one particular lesion but not with a contrasting lesion, and conversely, thereby suggesting separable mechanisms.

Thus, visual-field defects tend to be associated with impaired performance on the tachistoscope: the patient with defective fields requiring much longer exposure times than normals to recognize pictures shown in a flash. On the other hand, poor performance on tachistoscopic tasks may also be seen in the presence of cerebral lesions that do not produce visual-field defects, illustrating what we designate as "single dissociation."

In contrast, "double dissociation" can be seen in the test of setting a luminous line to the visual vertical, where it turned out that lesions of anterior brain regions produced difficulties in setting the line when the patient's head and body were tilted; those with parietooccipital lesions had much less difficulty in this respect. Conversely, patients with such parietooccipital penetrations performed much more poorly than those with frontal ones on a somewhat different task: that of setting a line to the vertical while their own body was upright, but the line had to be adjusted against an interfering (obliquely striped) background (Teuber and Mishkin, 1954). By searching for such patterns of symptoms and by systematically varying the tasks employed, we can hope to get at root changes in perception or in other aspects of behavior, as will be illustrated on the pages that follow.

Perception

H.-L. Teuber

Alterations in perception in any sensory modality pose a peculiar task for the investigator. To the patient, these alterations are often quite obvious, whether they are the outright and persistent distortions of contours after acute involvement of higher visual pathways or the fleeting but frightening distortions of things seen or felt in certain ictal disorders. But we have noted how easily a patient may mislabel or misinterpret his own condition; and there are, of course, a great many instances where he either cannot or will not tell what he sees or hears or feels, or how the appearance of the world has changed for him.

It is for these reasons that many neurologists prefer studies of alterations in motor function to those in perception; manifestations of motor disorders are independent of the patient's introspection and report. By the same token, however, any investigation of motor performance requires more than mere description of what the examiner himself can perceive, because proper investigation of motor disorders, particularly on the level of routine neurologic examination (e.g., assessment of strength, tone, or reflex status), involves systematic manipulation of the stimulus. The best description of altered motor function is accordingly to be sought in defining those stimuli that are adequate for eliciting certain movements.

Paralysis is not merely characterized by apparent absence of certain complex motor sequences, but often by changes in the stimuli adequate to provoke a movement. Whether we study altered motor performance or perception, our problem is not properly characterized by saying that we are searching directly for changes in response; what is needed is discovery of the stimulus. Description of responses, by the patient or the examiner, must be supplemented by the experimental variations in the stimulus situation that permit one, ultimately, to specify the nature of the stimuli that have become adequate for certain responses.

Accordingly, we shall survey what we consider as a proper experimental approach to altered perception in three major sensory modalities: vision, somesthesis, and audition. We shall also include brief descriptions of special techniques that can be employed in the search for adequate stimuli, irrespective of any particular sensory modality.

It will be apparent that vision receives a greater share of our attention than the other modalities. Here, again, the reason is that more has been done to elucidate changes in that sensory sphere than in the others, so that it becomes possible to illustrate some of the principles that underlie the study of perceptual alteration by concentrating on the sense of sight.

I. Vision

Alteration in vision can range from seemingly elementary losses (e.g., scotomata, or areas of acquired blindness in the visual field) to subtle or severe disturbances of discrimination or object recognition. The observer's task is not only to detect such changes, whether fleeting or permanent, but also to analyze them so that we can answer questions such as these: How blind is a seemingly blind area of the field? What is the nature of residual function? What changes, if any, can be detected in the parts of the field where vision seems to be preserved? And are there changes in complex visual functions (e.g., discrimination, object recognition) that can appear in dissociation from any of the more elementary visual changes, so that the latter could not be invoked to account for the failures of recognition? Here, as elsewhere, the search for patterns of symptoms is the first step toward an analysis of the changes in perception in terms of underlying function.

A. ELEMENTARY CHANGES. We shall begin with an apparently simple situation: A patient is found to have a scotoma, an island of acquired blindness in each of the monocular visual fields, as indicated in Fig. 11-1. Such a gross disturbance of vision, following a through-and-through wound of the occipital pole, by a small projectile, at once sets several tasks:

a. We must marshal methods for delineating the scotoma, selecting the particular psychophysical techniques that are appropriate for its demonstration.

b. We must consider the ways in which the patient himself describes the change in his vision.

c. We must test, with various simple devices, the status of residual vision, so that we may be able to say how perception can proceed in the presence of such a conspicuous gap in the visual field.

1. *Demonstrating the Scotoma.* The well-defined area of "blindness," shown in Fig. 11-1, is the result of a definite procedure: A white paper

disc, one degree of arc in diameter, is presented at various points in a perimeter arc, under 7 foot-candles of illumination, either moving or stationary, at a 33 centimeter distance from the patient's eye. The area given in black on the resulting chart (Fig. 11-1) represents the region in which the patient cannot discriminate presence from absence of the stationary white disc presented under the conditions just specified. A different illumination or a larger or smaller target, or one with different spectral character or different reflectance, or a moving rather than a stationary one, might have given us a scotoma of different size and contour than the one shown in Fig. 11-1.

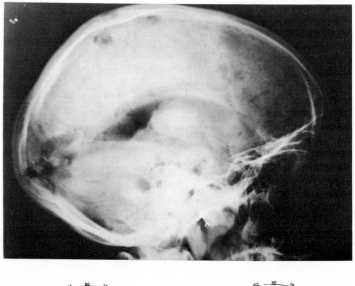

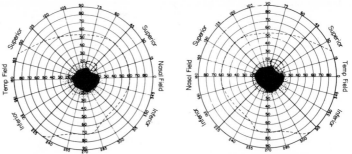

Fɪɢ. 11-1. Dense central scotoma (see visual fields, below), caused by a penetrating missile wound of the occipital pole (see pneumoencephalogram, above).

It is for this reason that Harms (1960, 1965) introduced a perimeter that permits continuous variation of target intensity and target size, as well as separate and continuous variation of background illumination within a half-sphere, into which the targets are projected. This apparatus permits one to bring in targets from below threshold by gradually increasing their intensity and to make them disappear again by gradual reduction of intensity, so that the examiner can employ the classical psychophysical method of ascending and descending series of trials, at any point of the visual field. In addition, the Harms perimeter permits one to use selected spectral values for the targets, so that one can obtain *color fields* in a systematic fashion. The apparatus can also function as a *flicker perimeter* because rotating shutters within the optical system provide for intermittent exposure of the target at continuously variable rates. As in our earlier studies (Teuber, 1950), special fields can thus be obtained in which the deciding factors are not the patients' reports of absence or presence of a stationary target but the fusion thresholds for a flickering light. This technique can reveal alterations (in terms of abnormally low fusion-thresholds) in some areas that may seem normal on routine perimetric testing with stationary targets (Battersby, 1951; Teuber, 1950; Teuber and Bender, 1948).

The precise extent of a scotoma is, therefore, a function of the defining stimulus conditions: some scotomata exist only for very small or very dim targets or appear only as so-called relative scotomata on prolonged inspection of small stationary targets or on flicker perimetry, as regional reductions in fusion thresholds for a flickering light. As it happened, the scotoma shown in Fig. 11-1 was dense or absolute in the sense that no change in target size, illumination, spectral value, or target motion led the patient to report the target as long as it was by more than two degrees within the boundaries of the scotoma sketched in Fig. 11-1. Nevertheless, the boundaries varied by several degrees in all meridians when the parameters of stimulation were changed, an observation that would have yielded gently sloping, rather than abrupt, boundaries for the scotoma if it had been plotted on a Harms perimeter.

Two modifications of these methods add to their precision: a variable-speed motor may be introduced to drive the target with various angular velocities along any given meridian, thus allowing one to plot fields for movement as a function of speed and direction of target motions. Second, one can employ a procedure for control of fixation by the patient himself through a simple device that has been in use with our cases of gunshot wounds of the brain since World War II (Teuber, Battersby, & Bender, 1960): a narrow patch of luminous paint, or a small circular light, is placed well within the region on the perimeter surface that corresponds to the patient's normal blind spot (in those patients where this blind spot is not itself involved in the acquired scotoma). Whenever the patient sees this light, one has prima-facie evidence that he has either shifted his gaze, so that he is not using his regular fovea, or that his eye has undergone some considerable cyclotorsion. In the cases where a patient uses a vicarious fixation mechanism (pseudofovea), the method enables one to define the location of this false fovea (Teuber, Battersby, and Bender, 1960).

Ideally, a system should be developed that would obviate voluntary fixation on the patient's part, so that perimetry could proceed while he moves his eyes. The prototype for such a system is the method devised by Cowey and Weiskrantz (1963; Cowey, 1963) for taking visual fields in the experimental monkey: the animal looks onto a surface where there is an array of small signal lamps; he signals a change in this array by pressing a lever (for a reward), and his success or failure in detecting a change is correlated, afterwards, with the momentary positions of his eye that have been continuously recorded by cinematography. Although laborious, the method has sufficient precision to detect the normal blindspot, as well as any pseudofoveae; it has been applied with great success to the monkey in comparing scotomata after retinal and after occipital lesions (Cowey, 1967; Weiskrantz and Cowey, 1967). The method can obviously be applied to man, permitting one to obtain visual fields in relatively uncooperative adults or in small children; alternatively, it may be possible to take the technique one step further, by monitoring eye positions and simultaneously projecting the targets in such a way that they appear in prearranged relation to the momentary ocular positions; such a system for automatic perimetry is currently under construction (Sheena, Ph.D. dissertation in progress, Massachusetts Institute of Technology). If successful, the method would make it possible to measure scotomata while the eyes are in normal motion, but it would still be necessary to obtain some verbal report from the patient as to whether he sees a target in the crucial portions of his field or not.

Harms suggested some time ago (1937) that objective nonverbal indices might be obtained by monitoring pupillary reactions to light, on the premise that pupillary constriction to a test light should be absent or diminished if the light is directed at an area of absolute or relative scotoma. The claim is paradoxical because pupillary reactivity is said to be essentially normal, in man and monkey, after complete destruction of primary visual cortex (and abnormal in strabismus, or during retinal rivalry; see Bárány and Halldén, 1948; Bielschowsky, 1931; Harms, 1937; Richards, 1966). Definitive tests of pupillary reactivity upon stimulation of areas involved in a scotoma are needed, although presence or absence of pupillomotor effects evoked by light have little bearing on the question of whether a subject can or cannot *report* a photic stimulus, just as little as optokinetic nystagmus (the reflex eye movements evoked by moving stripes) can be taken to represent evidence for "perception of movement."

There are further paradoxes. It is usually assumed that such a gross symptom of visual-field defect as an absolute scotoma, if found homonymously in each of the two monocular fields, reflects a corresponding lesion in the higher visual pathways; yet the converse need not be assumed: a small lesion of the higher visual pathways need not be accompanied by a scotoma (Weiskrantz, 1961). Each retinal ganglion cell has a receptor field that subtends a considerable subset of points in the total visual field, and neurons in the primary visual cortex, in turn, receive the converging output of a number of these retinal ganglion cells, often arranged in a line (vertical, horizontal, or oblique), so that the resulting cortical receptor fields may subtend an even more extensive, oblong stretch within the total field of vision (Hubel, 1958; Hubel and Wiesel, 1960). If one further assumes that adjacent cells in retina, and in cortex, have adjacent but overlapping receptor fields, then the degree of overlap obviously increases as one goes from retinal to cortical levels. As a result of these arrangements, small cortical lesions in the visual area may escape detection, because they could be below the critical size necessary for producing scotomata, and larger lesions at cortical levels might produce scotomata that seem smaller than one would expect from the effect of corresponding retinal lesions or from the electrophysiologic data on retinotopic principles of cortical organization (Cowey, 1967; Weiskrantz and Cowey, 1967).

A puzzle remains, nevertheless, if one considers the problem of absolute scotomata following circumscribed cortical lesions sufficient for producing them: radical removal of visual cortex in the monkey has been found not to produce total blindness; instead, Klüver's classical studies (1942b) have demonstrated a residual capacity for discrimination of total luminous flux (in the absence of discrimination for patterns) and, more recently, Weiskrantz (1963) has shown an additional capacity for discrimination of "speckled" fields from any shade of gray, as if there were some dimension of "interruptedness," or total length of contour, available to the monkey after extensive occipital lobectomy.

The situation for man (after total destruction of area 17) is much less clear: either autopsy data are lacking or behavioral tests have been inadequate to define what residual vision was present before death. Nevertheless, the few available cases (including the one described by Teuber, Battersby, and Bender, 1960) strongly suggest that the condition in man, after bilateral loss of primary visual cortex, is not too dissimilar from that found for the monkey. This fact makes it all the more suprising that partial destruction of optic radiation or cortex should lead, at times at least, to the absolute scotomata of the kind described. More work on residual vision within such seemingly absolute scotomata is needed. If no residual vision is found in some, at least, one may be forced to conclude that one is dealing with a situation where partial lesions of a particular system are more damaging than total removal of that system.

2. *Assessing Completion.* There are still further phenomena that are unexplained: if a patient with a scotoma such as the one shown in Fig. 11-1 presents himself to us, he is not likely to complain of having a large blind spot in the center of his visual field. Instead, he will say that his acuity is diminished, that he has difficulties with detail vision. But his experienced visual field has its subjective middle, its right and left, its above and below, just like anybody else's field of vision (Teuber, 1966b). Such "completion" of the subjective field must not be confused

Fig. 11-2. Redundant pattern (after MacKay, 1957), useful in studying certain forms of "completion" in defective visual fields.

with denial of (cortical) blindness which we believe occurs only when general confusion is superimposed on a massive disturbance in the higher visual pathways (see Teuber, Battersby, and Bender, 1960). The patient whose fields appear in Fig. 11-1, just like many others in that group, admits that he has trouble with his sight: he simply does not experience the boundaries of his scotoma under ordinary circumstances of stimulation. The scotoma is a product of the special tasks set by perimetry; the resulting area of blindness defines, in the terminology of the earlier observers, a "vision nulle" rather than a "vision noire."

If the patient insists that he sees no obvious gaps in any given scene, the next step would be to present him with a horizontal line crossing the area of blindness and extending beyond it at either end and to question him whether that line is uninterrupted. If he says again that there is no discontinuity in the line, the next step is to introduce a gap into the line and to keep the gap well within the area of blindness. If the gap is not perceived, we have evidence for an unusual kind of stimulus equivalence (interrupted and uninterrupted lines) and can proceed to other more complex stimuli in the hope of defining the limits of the tendency toward completion.

If it turns out that completion is maximal for simple lines and direction of lines, and is most readily elicited by redundant line patterns, as those constructed by Professor MacKay (Fig. 11-2; MacKay, 1957), then one can consider the bearing of these findings on recent disclosures in normal visual physiology: the density of cells in the primary visual cortex that act as simple line and direction detectors, i.e., those whose receptor fields have the intrinsic organization that makes them maximally sensitive to lines running in a particular direction in the frontal plane, horizontal, vertical, or oblique.

As Hubel and Wiesel (1960, 1965) have shown, these simple direction-sensitive neurons in the cortex are indifferent to the length of the linear contours to which they are attuned; a line protruding at either end, beyond the boundaries of the receptor field, is as effective as one just fitting inside the field. The further conjecture is close at hand that the spontaneous and illusory overlay of any given scene by subjective linear patterns, during visual fits (see Teuber, Battersby, and Bender, 1960) or certain migraine attacks (Lashley, 1941) or in drug-induced hallucinoses (Beringer, 1927; Klüver, 1928) might represent a free-wheeling or *in-vacuo* discharge of such line-detecting elements in the cerebral visual system.

Completion effects for simple lines and reduplicated linear arrays across gaps in the visual field might thus reflect the survival (in the margin of the lesion) of sufficiently many neuronal elements in the primary visual cortex capable of signaling directions by means of corresponding discharge rates. Distortion of these rates of discharge in the acute stages after occipital lesion could lead to subjective tilts or distortions of the scene; but this is still more of a conjecture than what has been asserted thus far. Nor do we know quite how to account for the recent observation that completion is readily obtained with fields that are filled entirely with "visual noise," such as the randomly moving dots that can be produced by a computer. Is this completion for noise merely a case of the principle suggested by MacKay (1966) that the central nervous system operates on a null-hypothesis, abandoning a particular perception only if there are sufficient (sensory) grounds for disproving it? Or is the completion of randomly moving dots another instance of a residual capacity to apprehend speckled fields, even in the absence of primary visual cortex?

Whatever the answer, we should note that rather special effects can be obtained by superimposing the visual noise upon MacKay's redundant linear patterns, such as the radiating lines (shown in Fig. 11-2) or sets of concentric circles. Combining the noise with the radiating lines, for instance, induces in normal subjects an illusion of regular motion, clockwise, counterclockwise, or both simultaneously: the dots are no longer seen as bouncing about randomly, but seem to move at right angles to the lines (MacKay, 1957).

This normal perceptual effect can at times convert a negative scotoma (i.e., one that is not seen as such by the patient) into a positive scotoma (i.e., one of which he is subjectively aware). This comes about because the patient obtains the normal induction effect (dots moving at right angles to the lines) in those parts of his field that are comparatively normal. However, in the area corresponding to his scotoma he sees the lines (a case of ordinary completion) as well as randomly moving dots between them (MacKay, 1957; Teuber, 1966a,b). It appears as if the "completed" line segments cannot impose the directed motion upon the randomly moving dots, so that the latter are seen, in a sense, in a more veridical manner within the scotoma than outside it. By virtue of this differentiated mode of appearance of the dots, the mere device of superimposing redundant line patterns on visual noise can produce an entoptic visibility for a scotoma that the patient ordinarily would fail to perceive.

A related phenomenon is the entoptic visibility of some scotomata on prolonged inspection of uniformly colored surfaces (Brückner, 1917; Teuber, Battersby, and Bender, 1960). This seems to happen, in particular, when a large scotoma has the characteristic "claws," often seen after penetrating occipital trauma (Fig. 11-3). Such a relatively narrow excrescence, encroaching on a region of the visual field close to the fovea, may become perceptible to the patient, while he

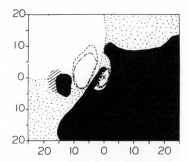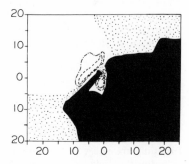

FIG. 11-3. Central visual fields in a case of penetrating missile wound of occipital region. Solid black areas indicate blindness to one-degree white targets; stippled regions, areas of "amblyopia," i.e., abnormally fluctuating thresholds for one-degree white targets. Dashed lines indicate boundary of area in which red, one-half degree targets are discriminated from green, blue, and yellow targets of same size, under same illumination. Dash-and-dot lines mark the corresponding boundaries for one-half degree green. Note displacement of normal blind spot (black oval on left) from its expected position (slanted lines), and "claw-shaped" excrescence of scotoma to left of fixation point.

is staring at a red surface, as a faint greenish line (Teuber, Battersby, and Bender, 1960); in the after-image, this part of his scotoma may appear in red, while the rest of his visual field appears green. Such completion for color, with indication of color contrast, may reflect the way in which receptor fields for color are organized (Wiesel and Hubel, 1966).

We have developed this chain of arguments in order to show how relatively simple observations of altered perceptual function may lead one to a consideration of possible underlying mechanisms, as soon as simple descriptions are checked against equally simple experimental manipulations of the perceptual stimuli.

The task for the investigator becomes slightly different whenever he tries to search for more subtle changes in perception. This task, however, differs only in degree from that posed by such obvious alterations as in gross scotomata; the methods for detecting residual vision within the confines of a scotoma and the methods needed for seeking out minimal changes in superficially intact parts of the visual field are essentially the same.

B. The problem of defining amblyopia. In characterizing intermediate degrees of change in visual function, short of the blindness found within areas of absolute scotoma, the term *amblyopia* is frequently employed. Yet unless the nature of the visual changes is specified, the term amblyopia can be a serious obstacle to one's understanding. Areas of amblyopia are often found near a scotoma, as if the amblyopic region represented an attenuated form of the change that produced the scotoma itself (see the stippled area in Fig. 11-1). In other instances, one encounters a hemiamblyopia where homonymous half-fields show reduction but not loss of visual capacity, in contrast to those forms of outright hemianopia where a homonymous half of the visual field appears to be blind. Yet even in the latter case, we have always found subtle but significant alterations in the seemingly intact half-fields (Teuber, Battersby, and Bender, 1960; Teuber and Bender, 1948, 1949, 1950; Wertheimer, 1912), such as a slight reduction in fusion thresholds for flickering light, changes in dark adaptation and in thresholds for apparent movement.

The same changes, but more pronounced, characterize the regions that are ordinarily called amblyopic, as in the more affected half of a hemiamblyopic field: marked reduction in flicker fusion, obvious change in thresholds for apparent motion, and concomitant changes in two-point resolution and in Vernier acuity. Contrary to earlier claims, those different aspects of vision have not been found to be dissociable, in our own work, so far: a loss of form perception is not found in the presence of normal perception of motion if both aspects of visual function are subjected to equally detailed psychophysical tests.

A limiting case of stimulation by intermittent exposures (flicker) is the use of pairs of exposures succeeding each other with variable interstimulus intervals (ISI). Two kinds of conditions should be distinguished: (1) When the stimulus patterns have adjacent contours (such as the familiar test pattern of a disk and a concentric ring) one may speak of metacontrast (Schiller, 1965). (2) When the two patterns that succeed each other overlap in the visual field, one can speak of masking, or blanking effects (Schiller, 1966). Metacontrast is probably a special form of apparent movement (Schiller, 1966), so that alterations in the optimal ISI in an abnormal region of a visual field would be merely an instance of deranged apparent-motion effects. On the other hand, an abnormal enhancement of blanking (apparent erasing of an initial pattern by one that succeeds it in the same area) can also be observed. Such exaggerated blanking is typical of amblyopic regions of defective visual fields where recovery from an initial stimulus has been shown to be abnormally prolonged (Battersby et al., 1960).

Particularly instructive are cases without any known lesion, such as the amblyopias in strabismus that have been called amblyopias of disuse (ex anopsia). In such instances, there is said to be a virtual loss of form perception while such elementary visual functions as threshold requirements for detection of various spectral lights are supposedly intact (Wald and Burian, 1944). However, careful flicker perimetry in such amblyopic fields (Feinberg, 1956) reveals a reduction of fusion thresholds in the center of the field, the reduction extending over an area of about 20°, indicating that temporal resolution of intermittent input is as definitely affected as is the apprehension of stationary patterns (Fig. 11-4). Spatial summation in such areas of maximal amblyopia is correspondingly disturbed (Flynn, 1967).

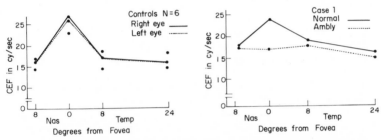

FIG. 11-4. Flicker-fusion contours in six normal controls (left) and in a case of unilateral strabismus and amblyopia ex anopsia (right). Solid lines: results for normal eyes; dotted lines: results for amblyopic eye. Single dots in graph on left indicate range of mean fusion values at each position in the normal visual fields (after Feinberg, 1956).

Positive Symptoms. The changes described so far can all be subsumed under the heading of *reduction* in function, but there is an entire array of symptoms in the visual sphere that could receive Jackson's favorite label of "positive symptoms," because they seem to issue from a visual system that is only imperfectly under stimulus control.

Thus, after acute trauma to the occipital region, one often finds a persistent warping of subjective visual coordinates (Teuber and Bender, 1949), signalized in misreaching for objects and in subjective reports that, say, everything on the patient's left seems abnormally small and too far away or that contours in certain directions appear to be doubled or further multiplied. Such distortions of things seen, in the form of micropsia or teleopsia, dysmorphopsia, or monocular diplopia and polyopia, are associated with abnormalities of motion perception, so that objects in an area of micropsia may seem to move abnormally fast, or that movements seem dissected into series of simultaneously presented frames (Critchley, 1951; Teuber and Bender, 1949).

Most of these subjective distortions recede after days, weeks, or months following an acute cerebral injury, but they can return in the course of an ictus, so that a patient many years after an occipital or temporal-lobe penetration may experience momentary distortions of things seen, or bouts of polyopia, lasting seconds or minutes (Teuber, Battersby, and Bender, 1960). In some instances, there can be outright disarticulation of visual space so that things seen in, say, the left lower quadrant of the field appear transiently upside down in the right upper quadrant. Such cases of optical allesthesia indicate that during the attack there can be a severe perversion of visual local signs without any loss of object recognition. Ictal perceptual disorders tend to appear after right-hemisphere lesions, in the occipital and occipito-temporal zones, with somewhat greater frequency than after similar lesions on the left (Teuber, Battersby, and Bender, 1960).

Such claims for a right-left asymmetry in perception can be challenged by pointing out that the differential association between aphasia and left-hemisphere lesions might account for the apparent preponderance of episodic disturbances of perception following lesions on the right: visual fits might arise equally often from right and left lesions, but patients with more massive lesions of the left hemisphere might merely fail to report them because of their difficulties with language. This argument is probably invalid, because the cases of penetrating missile wounds for which the asymmetry was found included only a very small number of persistent and severe aphasias. Furthermore, there are similar observations on effects of cortical stimulation, of the exposed cerebral hemispheres in conscious man (Mullan and Penfield, 1959), indicating that right-temporal stimulation produced perceptual illusions and distortions much more often than corresponding stimulation on the left. Neglect of one lateral half of visual space, or lateralized distortions, or lateralized difficulties in visual guidance of skilled acts are likewise more frequently observed after right hemisphere lesions (Brain, 1941; Dide, 1938; Hebb, 1939; Hécaen, Ajuriaguerra, and David, 1952; Hécaen and Garcia-Badaracco, 1956; Hécaen, *et al.*, 1956; Milner, 1954, 1958, 1960; Paterson and Zangwill, 1944).

Similar phenomena are often seen in toxic states, particularly if induced by drugs. It is not always appreciated how easily positive symptoms of this sort can give way to negative symptoms, i.e., to outright loss in function. In a typical episode, a volunteer subject under mescaline asked, "what are you doing to the floor?" and then explained that the room in which he sat had appeared suddenly distorted, so that the left half seemed to slope steeply downward and away from him. Two minutes later, this man had a definite left homonymous hemianopia (demonstrable on confrontation) lasting for several minutes. Such disconcerting transitions, from abnormal activation to inactivation of parts of the visual system, are common.

C. COMPLEX ALTERATIONS OF VISUAL PERCEPTION: DISORDERS OF OBJECT RECOGNITION. Every disorder reviewed so far can be considered as compatible with a principle of perceptual integration that one of us (Teuber, 1965a, b, 1966c) has recently called *cascade specification of input*. From this view, successive stages in the ceptor fields in the retina, with their preponderant organization into excitatory (or inhibitory) center and inhibitory (or excitatory) surrounds can function as contrast enhancers or "spot detectors." Cortical receptor fields are based on the confluence (by convergent connections) of several of these retinal receptor fields that overlap forming vertical, oblique, or horizontal oblongs, and thus are functioning as line and direction detectors, because they are elongated, have preferred orientations, and possess excitatory (or inhibitory) ridges and inhibitory (or excitatory) flanks. At successively higher steps based again on convergent discharges, these line- and direction-extracting elements can be combined into corner or protuberance detectors with particular orientations, or pattern-analyzers that function irrespective of exact location of the features to be analyzed (Hubel and Wiesel, 1965). Receptor fields for color have similarly complex organization, with preferential tuning to one spectral value in the central portion of the receptor field, and to another spectral value in its peripheral portions (Wiesel and Hubel, 1966).

The primary stages of this feature-extracting system are undoubtedly innate (Wiesel and Hubel, 1963), but it is unknown at what stage this cascade specification breaks off, so that it has to be supplemented by some other mechanisms, possibly involving learning. Does the cascade-specification principle extend far enough to permit us to recognize a face as that particular face among a thousand faces?

There are at least three aspects of perception that must involve more than this hypothetical feature-extracting process. These additional aspects clearly depend on the exposure-history of the organism.

First, there is the way in which the perceiver has to acquire and maintain the capacity for taking his own movements into account when he regards a scene. Verticals have to remain subjectively vertical when he tilts his head; the scene must remain relatively stable when he moves his eyes. Second, there is the capacity to name what one sees and to comprehend conventional symbols, such as numerals and letters, not only as patterns but also as denoting some verbal symbol. Third, there is the general capacity to identify and recognize objects seen, a prerequisite for naming them, but quite separable because one can indicate one's comprehension in nonverbal ways, as by appropriate manual use of an object (provided there is no selective loss of manipulation). Each of these three aspects or levels of performance can be disturbed separately by lesions, and there are probably still other ways in which the more complex achievements of perception and recognition can go awry. It is for that very reason that we object as strenuously to the term *agnosia* as we do to the term *amblyopia*. These clinical shorthand expressions conceal the diversity of mechanisms that can be disturbed and blunt one's efforts at delineating the nature of the fundamental changes.

Undoubtedly, much that has been described as agnosia in the clinical literature (Pötzl, 1928) may reflect a premature termination, so to speak, of the hierarchical feature-extracting process just discussed, so that the perceptual patterns are underspecified. Many of the disorders described in the preceding section, where we dealt with reduction in the resolution of spatially and temporally separated inputs, may look like a selective breakdown in so-called higher perceptual functions. That is, it may seem as if the recognition of objects had been disturbed in isolation, yet these seeming higher-order disturbances would be mere consequences of inadequate input processing. Bay (1950, 1953) among others, has forcefully argued that *all* disturbances of visual object recognition may be reduced to special forms of visual-field change, involving abnormal instability of thresholds and, particularly, abnormally rapid fading of contours on prolonged exposure (Funktionswandel, von Weizsäcker, 1923). What has been called Simultanagnosia (Wolpert, 1924; Kinsbourne and Warrington, 1962, 1963; Luria, Pravdina-Vinarskaya, and Yarbus, 1963) may be of this sort, where a patient is unable to keep a complex scene in view, so that he describes parts of the scene without any relation to other parts.

A more pronounced manifestation of the same disorder might be Balint's syndrome (1909), where the patient seems literally incapable of seeing more than one object at a time, regardless of its size; these patients usually have bilateral occipital as well as bilateral frontal lesions. In such cases, there is severe optic ataxia: the patient cannot shift his gaze from one object to another. In milder forms of this disorder, the patient develops trick movements of the head, permitting him to shake his eyes loose by means of self-produced vestibular stimulation.

Such changes at the level of the visual field and of oculomotor control can certainly suffice to produce a semblance of agnosia. The question remains, however, whether such field alterations are always necessary, as Bay asserts. We believe that there are other syndromes involving complex changes in perception that, by their disproportionate severity, over and beyond the visual field changes, compel us to admit the existence of separable mechanisms.

1. *Role of Motor-to-Sensory Discharges (Corollary Discharge Mechanisms)*. Experimental analysis of these hypothetical syndromes is incomplete, but some tentative descriptions can be offered. It is evident that vision entails more than passive reception and progressive hierarchical extraction of spatiotemporal features of the input. As we have pointed out, active movement of the eyes leaves the perceived world stable, but passive movement (as that produced by pushing against one's eyeball) makes the scene jump. Analogously, acutely induced nystagmus (as by injection of barbiturates) makes the subject complain of oscillopsia, a subjective to-and-fro motion of the scene. (In contrast, so-called congenital nystagmus, even though long-standing, is not accompanied by oscillopsia.) Recently acquired paralysis of extrinsic ocular muscles is experienced by the patient, not as an inability to move his eyes, but as a subjective jumping of the scene every time he intends to move his eyes and is unsuccessful in doing so.

Such phenomena have been interpreted (Teuber, 1960, 1961; von Holst, 1957; von Holst and Mittelstaedt, 1950) as indicating a mechanism whereby a self-produced movement is initiated not only by the classical efferent discharges to the musculature but also by a concomitant (corollary) discharge, directly and centrally, from cerebral motor to cerebral sensory systems. This corollary discharge is assumed to be present in all voluntary movements but absent in purely passive ones; it presets the sensory systems for the changes in the input (e.g., spatial transformations) that are the anticipated consequences of the willed movement. Illusions result when the sensory surface is passively displaced (because the ensuing object-displacement of the scene goes unchecked by any central corollary discharge) or when an active movement is intended but not executed, producing a mismatch between outcome and expectation. In the latter case, the mechanism for constancy (the corollary discharge) impinges upon the sensory system, unchecked by any objective displacement of the scene: the "constancy" turns into an illusion (Tausch, 1954; Teuber, 1960).

It is tempting to consider, in this context, the ictal or persistent distortions of size and distance, already mentioned, that tend to appear after lesions to the posterior third of the brain, or under the influence of hallucinogenic drugs with their presumed affinity for mesial temporal and for "limbic" regions of the forebrain. Normal "constancy of size" can be thought of as a compensatory increase in apparent dimensions as objects recede, counteracting the shrinking in their projected size. The converse would be assumed to happen as objects approach the eye: their increase in projected size would be counteracted by a centrally triggered reduction in all dimensions.

Such a rescaling (Richards, 1967a, b) is probably coupled with certain oculomotor activities, because it is known that size-constancy effects are strong over the distances over which accommodation and convergence operate. At greater distances, the effect rapidly diminishes. Small scotomata lying near the fixation point might possibly serve as a probe in exploring this hypothetical mechanism, because their projected sizes, plotted at different distances on a tangent screen, may differ somewhat from the sizes expected on the basis of the law of the visual angle. Stronger evidence can be obtained by using peripherally acting drugs: if one infiltrates the eye of a normal subject with homatropine, thus paralyzing accommodation, the lens is set for distance, and near objects are blurred. Any deliberate effort at accommodating for near objects then leads to a marked subjective shrinkage in the dimensions of all objects, a micropsia, as if the compensatory process that normally guarantees constancy (by decreasing the size of near objects) were running off *in vacuo*.

Conversely, if one produces a spasm of accommodation (as by instilling physostigmine into the eye), the lens is maximally accommodated for nearby objects, while objects seen at greater distances appear blurred. Any effort at relaxing accommodation so as to overcome the blur of distant objects produces a macropsia, i.e., a subjective enlargement of things seen. It is conceivable, but not proven, that temporal-lobe attacks might involve a free-wheeling of this mechanism.

The drastic, if transitory, effects of certain forms of restricted rearing on normal shape and depth perception may be intelligible in the same terms. Prolonged rearing in darkness or in diffuse light, at least in cats and monkeys, and probably in man, produces an atrophy of the central form-extracting apparatus: the cortical receptor fields, with their direction sensitivity and form sensitivity, disappear after some months, to give way to what is probably similar to the state of an adult primate after visual-cortex ablation (although a direct experimental comparison of the two conditions is still lacking). In contrast, normal receptor fields at the cortical level appear to be preserved when the animals (cat or monkey) are kept in patterned light, but their perceptual capacity can be severely reduced if the exposure to patterned light is combined with purely passive movement.

The prototype for these experiments on restricted rearing (with motor rather than sensory deprivation) were the experiments in which a normal adult was fitted with distorting (prismatic) spectacles. The prisms impose tilts and curvatures upon contours and displace whatever is seen (Wundt, 1898). As Held and his coworkers have shown, far-reaching adaptation to the optically induced distortions and displacements is achieved as long as the spectacle wearer moves actively about while inspecting his visual environment through the distorting prisms (Held, 1955; Held & Freedman, 1963). Conversely, passive exposure (e.g., being moved about in a wheelchair while wearing the distorting spectacles) fails to produce any adaptation. It thus seems evident that self-produced movement (i.e., movements associated with corollary discharges) are necessary for perceptual adaptation under these conditions of rearranged input.

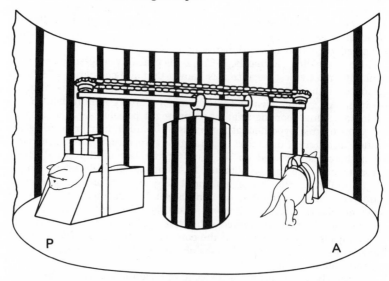

Fig. 11-5. Kittens in apparatus used by Held and Hein (1963) to demonstrate role of active movement in the acquisition of visuomotor coordination. The kitten on the right (Kitten A) walks actively about, while transmitting its movements to a litter mate on the left (Kitten P), who is being moved passively in the gondola. For further explanations, see text.

In view of the pervasive role of voluntary (self-produced) movement in readaptation to altered sensory input in the adult, Held and Hein (1963) have further suggested that movement must play a similar role in the initial acquisition of sensorimotor coordination during early development. The results of a series of animal experiments have been in accord with this expectation. Thus, a kitten whose visual exposure is limited from birth to the inside of the drum shown in Fig. 11-5 will exhibit essentially normal form and depth perception when tested after several months of the restricted exposure provided he moves himself actively about (A in Fig. 11-5). On the other hand, the same exposure under passive conditions, e.g., within a gondola (P in Fig. 11-5), in which a "passive" kitten is carried about by an "active" littermate, precludes the normal development of visuomotor coordination. Such a passively moved kitten evidently lacks opportunity for correlating its self-produced motor output with the corresponding changes of visual input: on release from the apparatus, several days of active locomotion in a patterned and illuminated environment are needed to establish normal form and depth perception (Held and Hein, 1963).

If instead, one eye of a kitten is given active exposure and the other eye passive exposure, under the conditions just described, then the "im-perception" is limited to the passive eye, in a manner reminiscent of the so-called suppression of (pattern) vision in the strabismic eye of pa-tients with amblyopia ex anopsia. So far, at least, available electro-physiologic evidence points to normal receptor-field organization in the visual cortex of these animals regardless of whether the striate cor-tex is driven through the active or the passive eye. The root of the per-ceptual disorder must lie elsewhere.

In fact, we have postulated that profound and lasting disorders of the corollary discharge mechanism can be produced in man as well as in lower forms by lesions of the frontal lobe or basal ganglia (Teuber, 1964, 1966a; Teuber and Proctor, 1964). The evidence on this point, up to now, is actually somewhat better for the monkey than for man, because Bossom (1965) has shown severe losses in capacity for adap-tation to distorting prisms in monkeys with bifrontal lobectomies or bilateral lesions in the head of the caudate nucleus. For men with frontal lesions the data are so far restricted to observations of failure on the visuopostural task already described (the setting of the visual vertical with head and body tilted), together with a possibly more tran-sient disturbance of performance on tasks involving searching for visual objects in a large array (Teuber, 1964, 1966a).

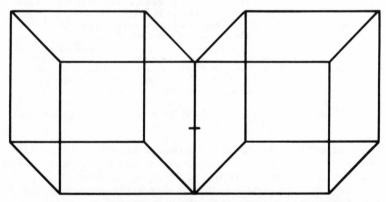

FIG. 11-6. Double Necker-cube, arranged to induce fluctuations in per-spective to either side of the fixation mark (small horizontal bar placed across central vertical line), or on both sides together (see Cohen, 1959b; Teuber, 1960).

Patients with frontal lesions also act in a peculiar way when con-fronted with figures drawn in reversible perspective (Harrower, 1939; Rubin, 1915), such as the familiar Necker cube or variations of that figure involving two cubes drawn side by side in ambiguous linear perspective (see Fig. 11-6). On prolonged inspection of this double cube, men with unilateral frontal penetration by a shell fragment obtained much less reversal than normal control subjects or than men with lesions elsewhere in the brain (Cohen, 1959a, b; Teuber, 1960). In con-trast, men with bifrontal lesions differed from all other groups by reporting an excessive number of reversals (see Fig. 11-7).

It is likely, however, that these bifrontal lesions differed significantly in extent and localization from the unilateral frontal lesions, because the patients with bifrontal damage had sustained injuries to the frontal poles or dorsal convexity, while the unilateral frontal lesions tended to

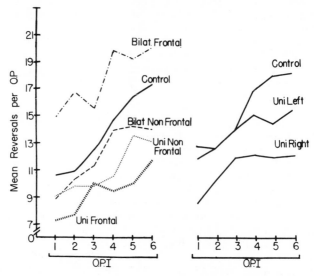

Fig. 11-7. Reversals of the Necker-cube shown in Figure 11-6 as a function of brain injury. Average number of reversals (ordinate) is plotted for each of six successive 15-sec. observation periods (abscissae). Normal adults (controls) show reversal rates which increase up to the middle of the total 1 1/2 min.-period and then level off. Patients with unilateral frontal lesions show fewer reversals than those with lesions elsewhere in the brain (unilateral or bilateral nonfrontal brain lesions). Patients with unilateral lesions of the right hemisphere show fewer reversals than those with unilateral lesions of the left hemisphere. Patients with bilateral frontal lesions (upper left), however, show significantly higher reversal rates than controls and all other groups with brain injury (from Cohen, 1959b.)

be deeper and more lateral. But even though the unilateral and bilateral lesions may not have been altogether comparable, it is worth noting that the anomaly in perspective reversals, in the frontal group, was signalized in either direction, that of abnormally low and abnormally high frequency of spontaneous shifts in perspective.

It remains to be seen whether all of these somewhat disparate symptoms can be considered a basic disturbance of corollary discharge, as one of us has suggested (Teuber, 1964). To test this notion, one should obtain systematic data on perceptual-motor adaptation to prisms in patients with lesions of the frontal lobe or of the basal ganglia. An isolated but promising observation in this connection has just been made by M. Potegal (unpublished) on a patient of W. B. Scoville's when a small clot had been removed from the head of the right caudate nucleus. This patient adapted to a prism at essentially normal rates when the base of the prism pointed away from his lesion, but not at all when it pointed towards it.

Whatever the outcome of further studies, so much is clear: one can delineate with fairly simple methods an entire array of visual-perceptual and perceptual-motor disorders in man, which appear in the absence of any direct involvement of primary visual pathways. In many of these disorders a specific breakdown of sensorimotor coordination seems to play a role. Yet there is no question that other forms of complex disorder of perception exist that are difficult to reduce to disturbances in the hypothetical processes that relate motor to sensory mechanisms.

2. *Specific Trouble with Naming.* Common among the disorders that transcend perception is the acquired difficulty of finding names for objects seen. General difficulty with object naming is one of many manifestations of aphasia, but there have been recurrent claims that difficulty in naming may be disproportionately greater for visually presented objects than, say, for palpated ones. This is as if the perceptual process in a particular modality could not find access to the language mechanism, although the perceptual processing as such is not at fault. Whether such modality-specific dysphasias really exist is difficult to tell, but there are certain syndromes that have been interpreted in these terms, such as the acquired tendency (often seen after left posterior-lobe lesions in the elderly patient) for confusion of color names. Some of these patients are perfectly capable (as Gelb and Goldstein already stressed, 1924) of asserting that "the grass is green" or that "the sky is blue," but they will give random names to colored chips or to colored wools put before them, as long as there is no readily learned verbal or otherwise familiar context to assist them in choosing the name. The trouble in color naming can at times be dissociated from any difficulty in discriminating hues, because nonverbal tests of discrimination can show in some instances that the capacity for discriminaton and for matching of colors is intact (De Renzi and Spinnler, 1967; Geschwind and Fusillo, 1966).

Unfortunately, much less is known about the presence or absence of other symptoms in the same patients, such as difficulty with reading. Such forms of dyslexia are often claimed to appear in conjunction with the color-naming difficulty, but it is not known whether the associations are obligatory or merely optional, occurring when they do occur as a result of the proximity of (potentially separable) foci in the brain.

Dyslexia itself is likewise a designation that reflects a conglomerate of possibly distinct types of disturbances in reading. It is the net result, the breakdown in the recognition of letters or words, that is so salient as to evoke the clinical label *dyslexia,* but the ways in which reading breaks down in the presence of certain lesions (usually on the left, in the areas of confluence of posterior parietal, posterior temporal, and occipital lobes) strongly suggests a multiplicity of underlying disorders. Comparatively few of these (not uncommon) cases have been fully investigated (Stengel, 1948); but it is clear that some of these dyslexias are perceptual (Critchley, 1964), while others fall, rather, into the troublesome category of acquired and selective difficulties of naming.

Consider the form of dyslexia in which the patient fails to distinguish capital letters such as P and R, or lower-case letters such as p and q. Here the root of the difficulty appears to involve discrimination of patterns that differ only in some small detail (P and R) or of patterns that are identical except for being mirror images of each other (p and q). The feature-extracting process seems to break off in such cases at some suboptimal level, or there may be specific difficulties with spatial organization (as signalized in the confusion of mirror images). Yet not enough evidence has been assembled to show whether or not these perceptual forms of dyslexia are modality-specific. Are the same troubles found on palpation of block letters by the blindfolded patient? Also, there is no clear picture of the relative frequency with which these difficulties in "reading" individual symbols are associated with difficulties in their arrangement into words and sentences. Here certain characteristic difficulties with serial order may come into play (Lecours, 1966), because misreadings and misspellings seem to follow a regular pattern in which repeated letters play a special role (MacKay, in preparation).

It is generally true that perceptual forms of dyslexia, although probably modality-specific (i.e., visual), are unlikely to be material-specific; i.e., similar difficulties of discrimination often can be demonstrated for nonverbal material as well as for letters or words. Again far too few of the reported cases have been properly tested, but some that have show conspicuous difficulties in distinguishing obliques running in opposite directions ($\diagdown$ vs. $\diagup$, or $\diagup$ vs. $\diagdown$), even though they can readily distinguish horizontals from verticals (—vs. |) just as has been shown for normal children below the age of four (Rudel and Teuber, 1963, 1967), and for the octopus at any age (Sutherland, 1957; Young, 1960, 1961).

There is, however, a kind of dyslexia that stands in contrast to the more obviously perceptual forms: a patient may be able to discriminate letters without fail, yet it may be difficult for him to name them or to combine them into words. In these cases, one gets the impression that the root of the difficulty is not in the discrimination of the visual patterns. Instead, there seems to be a specific failure of the patterns to evoke their names: the names of individual letters, or the words that go with their combinations into appropriate strings (cf. Marshall and Newcombe, 1966). The disorder thus seems material-specific; it may not be modality-specific; i.e., if the letters and words are presented to the sense of touch, a relief or a series of wooden block letters, the disorder may be present as well, although here again, the data are scarce and incomplete. One of our own patients, with massive trauma (by a blunt instrument) to the left occipitoparietal region resulting in an incomplete right hemianopia, typically read fairly long, low-frequency words (e.g., *hippopotamus*) without trouble but continued to have trouble with the "little words," especially high-frequency prepositions, such as *of, to, on.* Thus, he kept looking at the word *to* in a sample text, guessing at what he should call it: "It's a short word—probably a preposition—maybe it's *om,* but, no, there is no such preposition in English." Yet he could sort cards with single letters, various two-letter combinations, or longer words without any difficulty. When given a card bearing the word *to,* he distinguished it by sorting from other cards with various other letter combinations and matched it correctly to the only card in the array that bore the letter combination *to.*

Such syndromes have often been interpreted as "conduction defects" (Geschwind, 1965), or "disconnection syndromes," thereby giving an anatomical basis, as first proposed by Liepmann (1900), to the observed failure of the perceptual process to evoke the appropriate verbal responses, even though the latter are present in spontaneous speech. Such an interpretation remains conjectural in most instances, but there are recurrent reports (since Dejerine's time; see Dejerine, 1892) associating this type of dyslexia with destruction of the posterior part of the corpus callosum (Geschwind, 1962).

The potential significance of these large interhemispheric commissures in man has been underscored by the recent series of case descriptions from Sperry's laboratory (Sperry, 1964, 1966), where patients with extensive surgical interruption of interhemispheric connections have been studied in some detail. In such patients the right half-field, and the right hand, are primarily connected to the left hemisphere; thus, objects shown to the right of the fixation point, or palpated with the right hand, are promptly recognized and given their appropriate names. In contrast, the left half of the visual field, and the left hand, are disconnected from the left hemisphere above the midbrain level so that their input is directed primarily to the right hemisphere, which in the majority of patients has much less capacity for language than the left. Accordingly, objects shown to the left of the fixation point, or placed into the left hand, are mislabeled, the patient reacting to the sensory input with almost randomly chosen words. However, their mis-naming is not a sign of failure of discrimination, or even recognition: they can touch an object, with their left hand, can select it from an array of other objects, and can use it appropriately. In these cases, there is little question that the explanation for the inability to name any input processed primarily in the right (or aphasic) hemisphere should not be sought in the nature of the perceptual mechanism but should be sought in its separation from those regions in the left hemisphere that are primarily concerned with speech.

A somewhat similar picture had been observed, simultaneously and independently, by Geschwind and Kaplan (1962) in a case of extensive tumor of the corpus callosum in its anterior portions; in that case, the trouble with naming was maximal for objects palpated by the left hand, strongly suggesting the possibility of modality-specific difficulties with naming, in keeping with the known segregation of modalities in the callosum, where the posterior, splenial portion, at least in the monkey, is more intimately related to vision, and the more anterior portions, to touch.

More recent follow-up studies in Sperry's series have shown, inci-dentally, that the aphasia of the right hemisphere in such cases need not be absolute; apparently, some of these patients acquire the capacity to select a particular object with their left hand, upon oral or written command (Sperry and Gazzaniga, 1967). Such observations are com-patible with the view that some language comprehension is mediated by the right hemisphere, even in cases where the right hemisphere re-mains inadequate for the mediation of emissive speech.

3. *Disorders of Recognition.* So far we have avoided confrontation with one of the oldest and most baffling claims for complex disorders of perception: the existence of a failure of recognition that is referable neither to subtle changes in the sensory processing of the input nor to disorders of naming. The two limiting sets of conditions: failure of processing and failure of naming, thus bracket, so to speak, the alleged disorder of recognition per se, which would appear in its purest form as a normal percept that has somehow been stripped of its meaning.

Object agnosia, in that strong sense of the term, would then not be reducible to visuospatial difficulties, nor to rapid fading of parts of a scene; instead, the patient can discriminate what he sees and can select an identical or similar object from sample; he may even be able to draw what he sees, but he cannot name it, not because he cannot find the right word (as in the cases of callosal section) but because he does not comprehend what he sees.

It is indicative of the primitive state of our field that there is no agree-ment on whether such object agnosias, specific to a given modality (visual, tactual, auditory), really do exist, and, if they do, on how they should be interpreted. It is certainly true that the number of such cases in the neurologic and neuropsychologic literature has declined as rapidly as more refined methods for assessing basic sensory function have become available. It would certainly be more parsimonious if all of the alleged instances of visual object agnosia could be safely reduced to some sensory change, but there can be no assurance that there might not be a few convincing cases where the sensory changes, although fully explored, might turn out to be insufficient to account for the loss of object meaning. Unfortunately, the sensory status in patients who seem to present selective losses of object recognition is hard to ascertain, because their condition is usually complicated by dysphasia or by disorders of skilled movement (Lange, 1936). Moreover, these patients tend to be too ill to tolerate the extended examinations one would wish to perform, beginning with determinations of the state of their visual fields and with determinations of the patients' capacity for spatial and temporal resolution of visually presented patterns (Ettlinger and Wyke, 1961). Yet, without such information, the postulated selectivity of the defect of recognition may remain impossible to demonstrate.

It is for this reason that one might wish to search instead for attenuated forms of disorder by deliberately reducing the adequacy of the visual stimulus. One of these methods is tachistoscopy, the artificial reduction in exposure time (Poppelreuter, 1917). Another is serial presentation of contours at varying rates, as can be done by drawing an object with a luminous point source on a translucent screen or by exposing it sequentially behind a slit. Still other methods involve the introduction of an interfering background or of overlapping and embedding patterns by which the figure to be detected is effectively concealed (see Fig. 11-8; Gelb and Goldstein, 1920; Gottschaldt, 1926, 1929; Poppelreuter, 1917; Russo and Vignolo, 1967; Teuber and Weinstein, 1956; Vignolo, 1967). Further, one can employ deliberately fragmented, incomplete or dissected patterns (De Renzi and Spinnler, 1966b; Mooney, 1956, 1957; Street, 1931), particularly in the form in which a very sketchy outline is completed in a stepwise fashion on successive exposures (Gollin, 1960; Heilbronner, 1905; Warrington and James, 1967; see Fig. 11-9). Tachistoscopy has always been used in this fashion to elicit early stages in recognition: the guesses or provisional hypotheses of what it is that is contained in a test pattern when the exposure is too short to permit full recognition. The method gains in precision if each exposure is followed by a blanking flash, preventing postexposure readout of information from any after-images that might persist (see Averbach and Sperling, 1961) and permitting manipulation of intervals between exposure and blanking flash.

As employed with cases of cerebral lesions, or in other abnormal states, one ordinarily exposes the test pattern by beginning with very short exposures and then increases the exposure time until some criterion of reasonably complete recognition is attained. If recognition of a picture is indicated by naming, as is usual on such tests, care must be taken to distinguish the time needed for recognition from that needed for finding the word, a precaution suggested by Oldfield (1966; Oldfield and Wingfield, 1965; Newcombe, Oldfield and Wingfield, 1965). For recognition of tachistoscopically exposed letters and words, their frequency of occurrence in ordinary text needs to be taken into account as well (Solomon and Howes, 1951; Thorndike and Lorge, 1944).

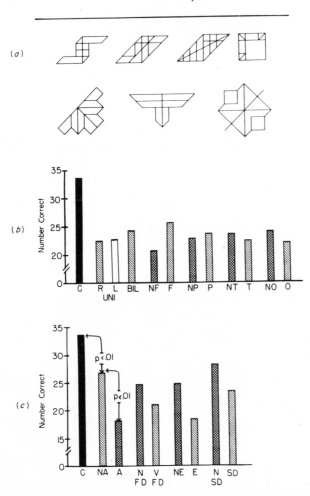

FIG. 11-8(*a*). Sample of hidden-figure test (based on Gottschaldt, 1926, 1929); the figure in the upper right-hand corner has to be detected and traced in each of the figures below. (*b*). Results (number of figures correctly traced, out of a possible total of 48) for normal control subjects (solid black bar, C) and for patients with various penetrating brain wounds, *viz.*, BIL, R, and L: those with bilateral, or right or left unilateral lesions, respectively. F and NF: patients with known frontal lesions (F) *vs.* all those with brain injuries elsewhere (NF); and correspondingly for P (parietal), T (temporal), and O (occipital). Note that all patient groups fall below the performance level of the control subjects, irrespective of presumed site of lesion (from Teuber and Weinstein, 1956). (*c*). Results analyzed according to associated symptoms, i.e., presence of sensory deficit (quantitatively defined), (SD) *vs.* absence of such deficit (NSD); presence of posttraumatic epilepsy (E) *vs.* absence (NE); presence of visual field defect (VFD) *vs.* absence (NFD); and presence of aphasia (A) *vs.* absence (NA). Note that only the aphasics fall significantly below the level of all of the other brain-injured patients, without such symptoms; all other symptom groupings fail to indicate such differential effects.

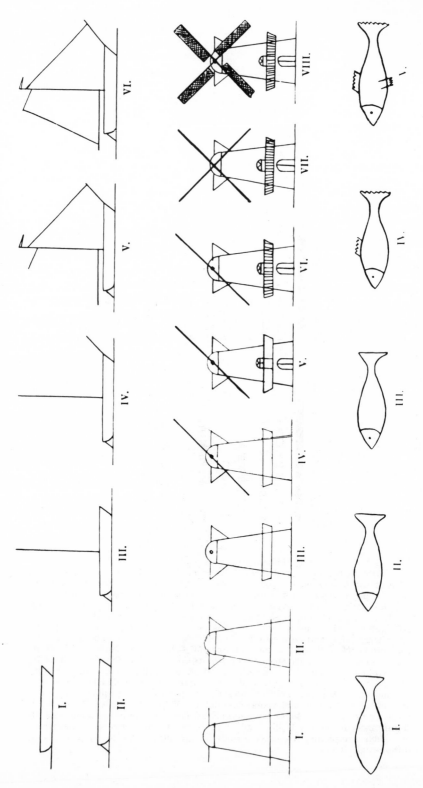

Fig. 11-9. Samples of Heilbronner's figures (1905), the prototype of many similar tests. Each figure in any given series is shown to the patient individually in the orientation

Despite its venerable age, tachistoscopy remains insufficiently explored. We still do not know why normal children take so much longer than adults before recognizing patterns in tachistoscopic exposures, nor do we have adequate parametric studies in which the angular size of a tachistoscopic display is varied concomitantly with exposure times. It is likely, but not proven, that children may require disproportionately longer exposures than adults as the size of a display is increased, and the same may be true of patients who harbor cerebral lesions at certain critical sites.

More is known, however, about those methods whereby patterns are rendered deliberately ambiguous, such as the use of overlapping or embedded designs (Gelb and Goldstein, 1920; Gottschaldt, 1926, 1929; Poppelreuter, 1917). Groups of patients with penetrating trauma in any lobe within the cerebral convexity can exhibit difficulties of optical analysis on embedded-figure tests. These remarkably nonspecific results that had been obtained in our cases with missile wounds of the brain (Teuber and Weinstein, 1956) in analogy to the equally nonspecific starting-position effects on the Aubert task (cf. Teuber and Liebert, 1958) have recently been extended by Russo and Vignolo (1967) to other types of intracranial pathology, such as cerebrovascular accident or neoplastic disease. A search for associated symptoms in the study of trauma cases had shown that patients with and without visual-field defect and those with and without sensory deficits did equally poorly on the hidden-figure task; only those with aphasia showed significantly greater impairmant on this task than all other brain-injured groups combined, and these, in turn, performed more poorly than the controls (Teuber and Weinstein, 1956). Again, the same selective association between aphasia and maximal impairment on the hidden-figure task was found in the more recent study by Russo and Vignolo (1967; Vignolo, 1967) in spite of the different etiology of cerebral lesions in their study.

In view of this remarkable vulnerability of performance on hidden-figure tasks to convexity lesions in adults, efforts have been made to devise analogous tasks for children (Cobrinik, 1959; Ghent, 1956). There is a special difficulty here because normal children are notoriously bad at solving these perceptual tasks (Ghent, 1956; Witkin, 1950). Yet easier versions have been designed (e.g., Cobrinik, 1959) that can be used to bring out deficits in children with various early brain injuries, the deficit being in some proportion to rated severity of neurologic impairment (as assessed, for instance, by the number of limbs involved in reflex changes). On the other hand, the correlation between results on Cobrinik's version of the hidden-figure task and ordinary intelligence-test scores (whether expressed as mental ages or intelligence quotients) is quite low.

What is needed is further variation of the material employed in these tasks. A tactual version of the hidden-figure test has been introduced by Axelrod and Cohen (1961) but has so far been used almost exclusively with elderly patients without known focal pathology, so that one cannot say, as yet, whether the generalized difficulty with hidden-figures after brain injury is specifically visual or goes beyond the visual modality, as seems more likely.

Furthermore, the relevance of experiments on hidden figures to general problems of visual recognition depends on how one evaluates the role of familiarity of the patterns employed. The relative familiarity of the objects depicted in the mixed-figure tests, illustrated in Fig. 11-10 (a test we have used with children; Teuber, 1960) definitely enters into the ease or difficulty of detection, but similar statements are much harder to make with regard to the geometric patterns contained in the hidden figures devised by Gottschaldt (1926, 1929).

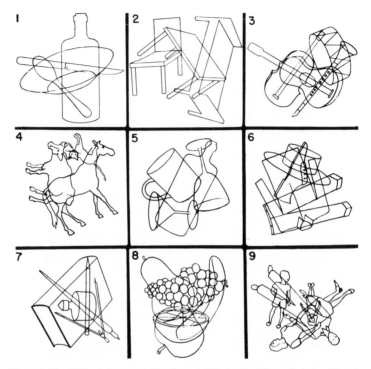

Fig. 11-10. "Mixed figures" (Teuber, 1950, 1960; illustrated by Ghent, 1956) used in testing normal children and children with brain injuries. Each of the nine composite drawings was presented individually, on cards, in the orientation indicated but without the numbers shown. Response consisted of naming and tracing the component figures, but multiple-choice versions, obviating tracing and explicit verbal responses, are readily constructed. These tests have their prototype in a composite drawing used by Poppelreuter (1917).

It is for this reason that a computer display has been developed (Green, Wolf, and White, 1959) and recently presented to children with various cerebral lesions (Reed and Pollack, 1963), which requires the detection of horizontal or vertical regularities in a welter of dots. From frame to frame the statistical likelihood of horizontal or vertical sequences is systematically varied. The elementary nature of the pattern (horizontal or vertical striations) makes the task quite dissimilar, on the surface, from the picture recognition under conditions of concealment by overlapping or embedded contours; but it is conceivable that patients with maximal difficulties on one of these tasks may also have considerable difficulties on the others. One should further ask whether the same patients also have difficulties on tachistoscopic presentation of highly familiar patterns.

Such a search for groupings of symptoms is likely to yield some insights into the nature of disturbances of recognition. If a patient performed quite well on the detection task set by the computer display but did poorly with familiar objects and their pictorial representations, one would be more inclined to accept the old view that there can be a loss of long-standing traces. However, if patients perform equally poorly on the computer task and on tasks involving familiar objects, we must assume that their difficulty lies in the extracting of features, so that the (hypothetical) traces or established schemata might be intact, but the sensory input inadequately processed so that it cannot be properly matched against the existing schemata (Oldfield and Zangwill, 1942a, b). The further possibility must be kept in mind that breakdown of recognition might reflect either of the two forms of disturbance, with some patients showing one and others the other, in line with the old conjectures about two types of agnosia, called, respectively, associative (supposed loss of traces) and apperceptive (supposed failure in the processing of input).

4. *Recognition of Faces.* An even more puzzling series of issues is raised by those claims that involve the existence of material-specific agnosias, such as agnosia for faces (prosopagnosia; Bodamer, 1947). In the extreme case, the patient may still call a face a face and will be able to discriminate, identify, and name all sorts of ordinary objects; yet he does not recognize a particular face as that of his wife; he fails to distinguish his physicians (until he hears their distinctive voices); and he complains that he cannot tell faces apart except by such crude external criteria as whether or not the particular persons are wearing glasses or as whether or not they are bald (Hoff and Pötzl, 1937).

It is hard to believe that such a difficulty should be as specific for faces, as has been claimed, although a mild difficulty with facial recognition can be demonstrated for patients with right rather than left hemisphere lesions (see De Renzi and Spinnler, 1966a), and recall of faces (shown on photographs) is definitely impaired by lesions of right temporal cortex (Milner, 1960). Faces are highly idiosyncratic, and normal people differ widely in their capacity to distinguish (and remember) them. On the other hand, too few tests of other complex visual discriminations have been performed to rule out the possibility that some subtle perceptual difficulty of a nonspecific kind is involved (see Hécaen *et al.*, 1957).

It is clear what methods would be required: first, one needs the techniques that could yield a systematic comparison of recognition for faces as opposed to recognition of other materials; for the milder forms of supposed prosopagnosia this could be done on the tachistoscope; prolonged exposures would be needed for cases where the disorders of recognition seem severe. Beyond checking on the selectivity of the trouble with faces, one would want to analyze the specific difficulty, if it does exist (Gloning *et al.*, 1966). Thus, Gloning and Quatember (1966) have employed fragmented faces by omitting upper, lower, or lateral portions of snapshots or drawings. They reported a curious difficulty on the part of two patients, who failed to recognize the upper portions of faces that include the eyes. Others before them have used the series of sketchy faces employed by Mooney (1956, 1957) with the result that right rather than left hemisphere lesions turned out to be most directly associated with impairment on this task (Lansdell, 1968; Milner, 1967; Newcombe, 1968), although certain graphic material other than faces, such as fragmented drawings, seemed to present similar difficulties to patients with right temporal lobe lesions (Meier and French, 1965; Milner, 1954).

In a sense, all of these techniques are variants of Klüver's method of equivalent-nonequivalent stimuli (Klüver, 1933; Lashley, 1938); this method has been used much more with animals than with man, but, it remains a potential resource for exploring perception and its anomalies in children and adults. In dealing with faces in particular, one might employ the Brunswik-Reiter technique of systematically varying crucial features in a series of highly schematized drawings of faces (Brunswik, 1934; Brunswik and Reiter, 1937; see Fig. 11-11), a technique which illustrates the essential identity of Klüver's method of equivalent-nonequivalent stimuli with the schematic or dummy stimuli of the ethologists (Hinde, 1966; Tinbergen, 1951).

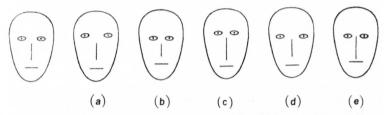

(a)   (b)   (c)   (d)   (e)

FIG. 11-11. Sample of six schematized faces from the series of 189 schemas developed by Brunswik and Reiter (1937). On left, basic schema from which all others are derived by systematic variation of some or all of five parameters, viz., (a) horizontal distance between eyes; (b) vertical position of eyes; (c) vertical position of nose; (d) length of nose; and (e) vertical position of mouth. In the original study by Brunswik and Reiter (1937), judgments were obtained from normal subjects regarding the presumed intelligence of the person "portrayed" by these schematic faces, their character, mood, age, and occupation. No cross-cultural use of this technique has come to our attention.

Should it turn out, in fact, that a selective agnosia for faces can occur in man, we would have to consider its possible bases with some care. It could, in fact, imply a selective loss of certain remote visual memories, just as the agnosias, as such, have been interpreted as losses of old traces, in direct contrast to the more typical forms of anterograde amnesias (described later in this chapter). Patients with anterograde amnesia have their greatest difficulty in proceeding from short-term to long-term memory but find it relatively easy to retrieve old material, and the patients show nothing like a perceptual, let alone "gnostic," disorder (Milner, 1966).

As we have seen, the alternative to interpretation in terms of destruction of specific traces is interpretation in terms of process: normal discriminability of faces is the result of a fairly prolonged exposure to a variety of faces; it involves, presumably, some subtle and non-verbalized learning of certain idiosyncratic features ("critical details") or of certain perceptual dimensions (Gibson and Gibson, 1955) that permit one to classify various faces in terms of such variables as, say, interpupillary distance, height of forehead, and width of cheekbones. There is the familiar example of perceptual learning, on the part of a white visitor to China (or conversely, a Chinese visiting America). At first, most of the Chinese faces are indiscriminable, but, once one is fairly familiar with a few individual faces, something seems to have been learned that generalizes to all Chinese faces: "Knowing" a few makes all the others more distinguishable.

Conceivably, an agnosia for faces could be due to a loss of such an acquired system of rules for classifying facial differences. Alternatively, and even more speculatively, we could assume that the initial basis for discrimination and identification of faces and of facial expressions involves some innate schemata onto which the subsequent, perceptual differentiations are merely superimposed (Ahrens, 1954; Kaila, 1932; Spitz and Wolf, 1946). This strong but as yet unprovable assumption would make a selective loss of capacity for identifying faces, following certain focal lesions in man, somewhat less paradoxical than it now appears to be.

II. *Somesthesis*

Alterations in somatic sensation and its various submodalities, such as touch-pressure, appreciation of limb position and limb motion, and sensitivity to temperature and to pain, are powerful indices of altered brain function whether the changes are induced by lesions, by drugs, or by extreme environments, such as prolonged sensory deprivation. Detection and analysis of these changes call for methods directly analogous to those described for the study of alterations in vision. Thus, traditionally at least, one tends to look upon the various psychophysical techniques for measuring threshold changes as disclosing somewhat more "elementary" aspects of somesthesis, presumably dependent on the integrity of peripheral sensory pathways and primary central projection systems. In contrast, more subtle aspects of somatosensory function are assumed to be involved in tasks of discrimination of haptic qualities of objects, their texture, size, and shape, or in tests that require the tactile apprehension of linear configurations drawn or impressed upon the skin. Lastly, there is the unsolved question of whether or not there could be a selective failure of object recognition through the sense of touch, in the absence of general dementia and in the absence of more elementary tactual or kinesthetic deficits sufficient to account for the failure of tactual recognition.

Yet, serious problems are involved in such a threefold subdivision of somatosensory functions, analogous to the difficulties in the study of vision. The so-called elementary aspects of somesthesis, as defined by various threshold tests, may be much less elementary than they appear. If one requires a patient to report the perceived temperature of a cold probe or the presence or absence of a punctiform pressure stimulus, one demands of him inevitably that he exclude all kinds of "extraneous" sensory impressions, and one forces him to concentrate on a particular physical dimension such as temperature or pressure per se. His natural impulse might be, instead, to report the stimulus object rather than some abstract dimension; he responds by announcing that he felt a round, hard, cold, metallic sphere (in the case of the thermal probe) or a soft contact with a nylon filament (in the case of the pressure stimulus). Such natural tendencies to report in terms of the object evoking the sensation rather than in terms of the sensations evoked were castigated early in this century as involving the "stimulus error" (Titchener, 1910; Boring, 1957), and well-trained subjects for sensory experiments had been indoctrinated to avoid this error. Yet, it is evident that the stimulus error is, in fact, the normal response; in contrast, the focusing on one's own sensory process as such is artificial and difficult.

The classical psychophysical procedures are thus doubly taxing, first by demanding a special attitude of the observer, and, secondly, by confronting the observer with what are relatively inadequate stimuli. Just as the visual system of higher vertebrates is primarily responsive to patterns rather than to isolated dots of light or to the total flux filling the field of vision, so the somatosensory systems are unlikely to have evolved any natural affinity for punctate temperature stimuli or for similar inputs with a low probability of occurrence in the natural environment of the organism; the apprehension of such stimuli is clearly of little value for survival.

Perhaps it is this very fact of artificiality and relative inadequacy of the stimuli employed that makes those supposedly elementary methods so sensitive to lesions or other changes in the nervous substrate. By the same token, one could understand why a supposedly higher-order breakdown in object recognition is disproportionately rare as compared with the frequent disturbances of "elementary threshold function" (Goldstein, 1916; Goldstein and Reichmann, 1920).

At the same time, difficulties with tactual discrimination of objects and with their recognition through the sense of touch remain uninterpretable until we have sufficient information on the status of the seemingly elementary aspects of somatosensory function.

A. ELEMENTARY THRESHOLD FUNCTIONS. In recent work, several aspects of somatic sensitivity have been intensively investigated: touch-pressure, two-point discrimination, point localization, and sense of passive movement at a joint. Most of this work has concentrated on analyzing sensory functions of the hand, but the methods are applicable to other body parts.

1. *Punctate Pressure.* Assessing thresholds for detecting graduated pressure stimuli applied to different parts of the body surface (von Frey and Kiesow, 1899; von Skramlik, 1937) is the direct analogue, in somesthesis, to the plotting of visual fields. However, instead of using the arbitrary definition of abnormality of function employed in the taking of visual fields, the determination of altered touch thresholds for a given part of the body is made by comparing a subject's performance with that of a sufficient number of control subjects (Semmes *et al.*, 1960). The statistical procedure has permitted us, for instance, to define altered touch thresholds after penetrating brain wounds in an earlier study (Semmes *et al.*, 1960) as "slightly abnormal," if the value obtained for a given patient differed from the corresponding control-group mean at the 1 percent level, implying that such an anomaly would have occurred through chance fluctuations about once in a hundred cases. Analogously, the definition of a "severe defect" requires a threshold value that differs from the control group mean at the .1 percent level, so that it would occur only once in a thousand consecutive normal subjects by chance alone.

In our current procedure, calibrated nylon filaments of different diameters are employed, rated for tensile strength (in tenths of milligrams) upon bending against one cup of a chemical balance. These filaments are applied to the selected spot on the skin (marked in advance with a marking pen), beginning with very fine filaments clearly below threshold and proceeding in ascending order of strengths until the subject first reports a contact. As soon as a report is obtained, a filament three steps above the one just reported is applied, followed by serial presentation of filaments in decreasing order of strengths until the subject stops reporting the contact. In this fashion, the first stimulus reported in an ascending series is recorded, as is the last one in a descending series, the procedure being repeated for any given point on the skin for six complete series of trials, alternatingly presented in ascending and descending orders.

The method is admittedly laborious compared with the familiar clinical assessment of sensation by cotton wisp and pin. In acutely ill or toxic patients, such elaborate psychophysical procedures have no place; but, in searching for stable effects of lesions in the peripheral or central sensory pathways, the quantitative precision and objectivity of the method makes it a procedure of choice. Not unlike other psychophysical procedures, the method tends to identify hysterical patients by virtue of their bizarre responses, and it can unmask malingerers, who cannot gauge how to respond to the stimuli unless they elect not to respond at all. A further advantage of the method of serial testing with alternately ascending and descending orders of stimulation is the obvious one that the six values obtained can be employed not only to compute a mean but also to estimate variability and to gain a quantitative measure of trends in thresholds from earlier to later trials.

In this way, these techniques are suitable for testing the claims for the allegedly characteristic change in mode of sensory functioning, the so-called Funktionswandel first proposed by von Weizsäcker (1923) and by his students (e.g., Stein, 1923) and more recently utilized by Eberhard Bay (1950) in his attack on the notion of agnosia. The claims for Funktionswandel in the tactile sphere are analogous to those for vision. They imply that thresholds in an area where sensation is actually defective may at first appear to be normal but become increasingly elevated (i.e., sensitivity declines) as testing progresses within a session. Bay has suggested that the alleged integrity of basic sensation, in certain forms of defective object recognition by touch ("pure" astereognosias) may be more apparent than real: prolonged testing would reveal in such cases a progressive deterioration in elementary tactile sensitivity as a direct function of repeated trials.

In our own experience, this shift in thresholds over time, during testing, is rare and not necessarily diagnostic of a particular location of lesion. At least, there are no adequate data, so far, to rule out the possibility that these infrequent forms of sensory change might not also appear after certain cord lesions (as claimed long ago by Delay, 1935) and perhaps even after incomplete lesions of peripheral nerves.

2. *Two-Point Discrimination.* Instead of varying pressure applied at a single point, the classical touch-compass technique for assessing spatial resolution applies two blunt points of an esthesiometer, simultaneously, to the subject's skin at constant supraliminal pressure while varying the distance between the two points (in millimeters) in order to define the minimal distance between the points at which the subject can report them as two distinct impressions. This form of spatial resolution is finest at the tip of the tongue and on the finger tips and becomes progressively less refined as the touch compass is applied to more proximal parts of the body, in line with Sherrington's classical diagram (1900, Fig. 11-12). Precision of result depends, however, on whether testing is done according to a rigorous schedule, in analogy

to that employed for testing cutaneous pressure sensitivity, involving alternating ascending and descending trials, as well as a predetermined number of catch-trials (only one point of the compass applied, instead of two). This procedure leading to six threshold values (three from ascending series of trials and three from descending series of trials) is repeated for transverse and longitudinal placements of the touch compass in a given location on the subject's limbs, e.g., across the palm and along the proximodistal axis of the palm, the transverse placement leading ordinarily to better two-point resolution than the longitudinal, as was already observed by E. H. Weber (1846), the earliest user of the touch compass. In applying the procedure to patients with focal cerebral lesions (Semmes et al., 1960) or cortical removals (Corkin, Milner, and Rasmussen, 1964), statistical criteria of "slight" and "severe" defects are employed, the norms being obtained from control groups in the manner described for tests of punctate tactile thresholds.

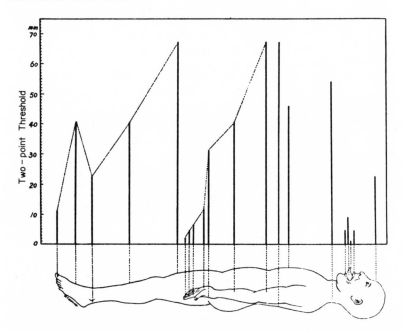

FIG. 11-12. Mean thresholds (in millimeters) for tactile two-point discrimination as a function of body part tested. Data derived from Weber (1846) and plotted by Sherrington (1900) for his chapter on somesthesis in Schaefer's *Textbook of Physiology*.

3. *Point Localization.* "Spot-finding" on the skin is similarly investigated by stamping a grid on the cutaneous area to be tested and by applying a brief supraliminal pressure stimulus at the center of the grid. This center-contact serves as a standard for a given series of trials that consists of successive applications of the same supraliminal stimulus to different locations, in predetermined order, along a particular direction on this grid (Semmes et al., 1960). The subject's task is simply to indicate for each of the comparison stimuli whether it is or is not at the same location as the standard. The method yields a

scatter plot of punctate localizations, capable of revealing not only degrees of accuracy for a given region but also any trends towards systematic displacement, e.g., distal, that might exist. Again, as for tests of punctate-pressure sensitivity and two-point resolution, norms are obtained from control groups, and slight and severe deficits are defined statistically as described.

4. *Sense of Passive Motion and Position.* A fourth technique used extensively in gauging sensory after-effects of cerebral lesions involves tests of "position sense" and "sense of passive movement." In their simplest (clinical) form, these tests consist of moving a patient's joint, e.g., by bending the distal phalanx of one finger upward or downward; the patient, with eyes closed, has to report the occurrence of the motion and its direction. Success or failure depends on the extent, speed, and acceleration of the imparted motion, and these stimulus parameters are difficult to standardize as long as the apparatus employed consists of the examiner's own hand. It is remarkable, nevertheless, that results are rarely equivocal. In the study of gunshot-wound cases (Semmes *et al.*, 1960), decisions about presence or absence of defective "sense of passive movement" were based on the pooled ratings of three independent examiners, who assigned three values, "normal," "moderately impaired," and "severely impaired," to the performance of their subjects. Only occasionally did one of these ratings (out of three) differ from the others, and never by more than one scale-point.

In more recent studies in patients with cortical excisions, in Montreal, a still simpler method has been adopted (Taylor, unpublished). Each of the distal phalanges is tested 12 times resulting in 60 values for each hand. In 40 normal subjects, the resulting score for the hand tested second was 60 (i.e., 60 correct judgments) or, at the least, 59; for the hand tested first, the score fell only once as low as 57 in the 40 consecutive control subjects. As a result of this screening procedure, a score below 54 was considered a severe defect, and one between 54 and 57 as a slight defect in sense of passive movement for that hand.

5. *Patterns of Sensory Change.* The four techniques discussed thus far are necessary for any inclusive survey of sensory status and for comparing patterns of sensory changes after different lesions or treatments. Yet, while necessary, the methods are clearly insufficient; similarly detailed and quantitative techniques are needed for exploring pain and temperature thresholds (Beecher, 1959a, b; Lele, 1954; Lele and Wedell, 1956; McMurray, 1950), the procedures becoming important if one hopes to gauge the validity of Henry Head's view (1920) on the patterns of sensory change that convert an "epicritic" into a "protopathic" mode of functioning, or if one wishes to validate Head's descriptions of the so-called thalamic syndrome, with its hyperreactivity to pain and its intolerance of mild repetitive stimulation (e.g., by repeated touch with von-Frey hairs), together with an apparent elevation of ordinary pain and touch thresholds over the affected side of the body. Such studies are all the more needed because there have been recent attempts to revive Head's original claim for the separate existence of an epicritic and a protopathic sensory system (Mountcastle, 1961; Rose and Mountcastle, 1959).

Although incomplete, the four quantitative sensory tests we described are capable of disclosing minimal residual effects of cerebral lesions. Thus, one may expect to find significant losses on a few fingertips of one hand in patients who initially may have presented a complete hemisensory syndrome. In such cases, the original syndrome can often be reinstated transiently by injection of Sodium Amytal or similar drugs.

The methods also permit detection of the threshold changes that go in an unexpected direction, producing hyperesthesia. Most forms of so-called protopathic change in somatosensory function, whether due to peripheral or central lesions, involve the typical combination of hyperpathia and hypalgesia: sensitivity to painful stimulation is diminished (thresholds are elevated), but there is definite overreactivity to the painful stimuli that can be felt. The same is true for pleasurable stimuli; the patient overreacts as soon as threshold is exceeded.

It was therefore a matter of considerable surprise to us when we encountered a definite reduction in touch thresholds in children with certain forms of congenital brain damage (Rudel, Teuber, and Twitchell, 1966). These abnormally low touch thresholds were found on the hand with maximal reflex changes; the hyperesthesia was not associated with any compensatory impairment in spatial resolution of stimuli, although tactual object recognition by that hand was poor.

Among the few precedents for such abnormally low touch thresholds are findings on the sensory status of amputation stumps (Teuber, Krieger, and Bender, 1949), where two-point thresholds in above-the-knee amputees were found to be much better on the skin of their stump than in corresponding areas of the sound limb. In a subsequent extension of these studies to above-the-elbow amputees, Haber (1955) was able to demonstrate abnormally good thresholds for light touch, two-point discrimination, and point localization, employing the methods we have just described. Moreover, he reported that such paradoxically good thresholds were optimal in the amputees who claimed that their phantom limbs had become telescoped, so that the illusory parts had come subjectively close to, or had become identified with, the tip of their stump (Haber, 1955). A possibly related phenomenon is the paradoxical improvement in somatic sensitivity following sensory deprivation, whether general (Bexton, Heron, and Scott, 1954; Doane et al., 1959; Vernon and McGill, 1961; Zubek, Flye, and Aftanas, 1964a, b) or localized (Aftanas and Zubek, 1964), but the bases for any and all of these hyperesthetic states remain to be discovered (see also Duda and Zubek, 1965).

The methods described have also contributed some unexpected and partly controversial results. In a systematic study of over one hundred cases of penetrating missile wounds of the brain, lasting alterations in sensation were found occasionally on a patient's ipsilateral hand and not only on the hand opposite to his cerebral lesion, where such a change would be expected (Semmes et al., 1960). In a partial replication, similar unorthodox ipsilateral effects were found in the Montreal laboratory (Corkin, Milner, and Rasmussen, 1964). In both laboratories, such ipsilateral effects appeared primarily on tests of point localization and less often on any of the other three tests.

In addition to these results, the earlier study (involving missile wounds of the brain) reported a definite asymmetry of effects: the ipsilateral changes in sensation tended to occur more with wounds of the left hemisphere than with those of the right hemisphere. This sort of asymmetry was not found in the series of cases studied in Montreal where selective cortical removals had been performed for relief of epilepsy (Corkin, Milner, and Rasmussen, 1964).

It is still impossible to say whether this discrepancy is due to the greater depth of the cerebral lesions in the series of gunshot wounds or to some other factors such as (possibly) a differential survival rate after right and left hemisphere trauma. Nor do we know, as yet, how to evaluate a further observation made in cases of missile wounds of the cerebrum. Considering threshold values for right and left hands separately, and disregarding the presumed site of the cerebral lesion, we noted that sensory defects of the right hand tended to be highly correlated. Presence of one type of change, e.g., decreased pressure sensitivity, made it more likely that there would be abnormalities on the other three tests of somatic sensitivity. Conversely, for the left hand, there was no significant correlation between changes in touch-pressure and the other aspects of sensation.

Much more work is needed to confirm and analyze these apparent differences in pattern of threshold changes between the two hands, although the results from the missile-wound cases were considered indicative of an underlying difference in the organization of sensory mechanisms in the two cerebral hemispheres. Briefly put, most of the observations appeared compatible with the following formulation: sensory functions of the right hand seemed to depend on the integrity of a fairly circumscribed region (the sensorimotor strip) in the left hemisphere, but functional representation for the left hand tended to be more widely dispersed over the right and left cerebral hemispheres (see also Foix, 1922). Cross-validation to other types of cases is still needed, because in the Montreal series, where excisions were confined to the cortex, only those encroaching on the postcentral gyrus (right or left) were found to produce any lasting sensory deficits. Severe deficits of the hand were confined to removals from the contralateral cortical hand area (defined by electrical stimulation during surgery); ipsilateral deficits, however, tended to appear in one-third of the cases, on point localization, with excisions involving the postcentral gyrus but not necessarily the primary hand area. These results may point to a role of the second sensory area in producing ipsilateral sensory deficits.

Some hints of the asymmetric effects of deep subcortical lesions on sensitivity were reported by Proctor, Riklan, Cooper, and Teuber (1963), who applied the four somatosensory tests here described to Parkinsonian patients before and after surgical destruction aimed at the ventrolateral nucleus of the thalamus. Before surgery, their patients showed essentially normal sensitivity on all four tests. Following surgery, however, there were some transient sensory changes. This was found for two-point discrimination, which was impaired on the left hand after right thalamic lesions and on both hands after left thalamic lesions (Proctor *et al.*, 1963).

6. *Exploiting Uncertainty of Stimulation.* On ordinary tests of tactual thresholds, the subject knows in advance where to expect the stimulus: quite different results might emerge if one were to compel the subject to attend, simultaneously or successively, to different parts of a sensory surface and if one were to manipulate the degree of uncertainty as to where the next stimulus will fall.

A limited attempt of this sort was made when ordinary tactile thresholds were obtained in normal subjects (by Meyer, Gross, and Teuber, 1963), under conditions where the stimuli impinged in series on one, two, or three predetermined regions of the subject's body, viz., the tip of a finger, the center of the palm on the same side, or the center of the palm on the opposite side. When the thresholds were obtained by stimulating one and only one spot, they were optimal, but they were immediately raised when the subject had to shift his attention, in an irregular series, from fingertip to ipsilateral palm, and they were still further raised, and disproportionately so, when he had to cross the midline and attend to occasional contacts on the opposite palm (Meyer, Gross, and Teuber, 1963). Unfortunately, this study did not deliberately vary the probability structure of this stimulus sequence, e.g., from maximum certainty to maximum uncertainty, so that this dimension still remains to be explored.

In fact, what is currently meant by sensory deficit may well turn out to be restricted to the outcome of classic tests in which the mode and the site of stimulation are expected and unvarying throughout the testing session. Quite a different relation between cerebral substrate and sensory function might emerge as soon as sensory tests employ gradations in the uncertainty of sensory stimulation.

7. *Assets and Liabilities of Detection Theory.* One should also try to assess the possible advantages of discarding classical threshold concepts altogether in dealing with abnormal sensory states and of employing, instead, the more recently developed theory of detection. This approach, fashioned after statistical decision theory and originally applied to electronic detectors, has the merit of separating the sensitivity characteristics of an observer from the criterion of detection he adopts (Green and Swets, 1966). Performance on sensory tests is thus described by an "ROC" curve, which specifies the receiver's operating characteristics and permits one to estimate quantitatively his tendency to miss stimuli when they are present as well as his tendency to report them when they are not ("false-alarm" rate). It remains to be seen whether a detection theory (which dispenses with the concept of a threshold) can be upheld in the face of an actual neurologic defect that is customarily interpreted as an increase in thresholds for particular sensory stimuli.

We should note, in this connection, that the sensory performance parameters of detection theory can be obtained directly from one version of classical (Fechnerian) psychophysics, viz., the method of constant stimuli, as Treisman (1965) has demonstrated. In a similarly critical vein, Carterette (1967) has recently pointed out that the "ideal-observer theory is a normative theory and could have the effect of delaying rather than inducing a search for actual mechanisms" (p. 633).

8. *Scaling: The Assessment of the Subjective Magnitude of Stimuli.* A more conspicuous gap in current work on the perceptual changes that result from brain injury, drugs, or other unusual conditions is the complete neglect of available techniques for sensory scaling. The methods, extensively applied to normal observers, permit one to estimate the rates at which the magnitude of sensation grows as a function of stimulus intensity (Stevens, 1957). Such scaling techniques would seem to be particularly appropriate because diminished sensitivity (i.e., raised sensory thresholds), especially after cerebral lesions, can be associated with an abnormally rapid growth of subjective intensity of sensation. Work still in progress (Teuber, Corkin, and Twitchell, in preparation) strongly suggests that such a phenomenon can be seen in patients with hemisensory syndromes (i.e., with ele-

vated touch thresholds on one side of the body, opposite an injured cerebral hemisphere).

These patients may require considerably greater physical intensity of stimulation on their defective side, as compared with their normal side, before they can detect a tactile stimulus (e.g., a nylon filament of a given tensile strength). However, as intensity of stimulation is increased, the subjective magnitude of the resulting pressure sensation increases more rapidly on the impaired than on the normal side. As a result, a level of physical intensity may be reached where the stimuli are physically as well as subjectively matched, in spite of the fact that the "absolute" threshold on the defective side is grossly elevated. One such patient, while being tested, expressed this situation quite directly by telling us, "I tend to equalize," i.e., equate the stimuli that impinged successively on the impaired and unimpaired sides of his body. The phenomenon may be analogous to the recruiting of loudness, in cases of reduced auditory acuity (cf. Hirsh, 1952; von Békésy, 1965; Dix, Hallpike, and Hood, 1948); similar recruiting effects should be searched for in brightness perception, in the presence of hemiamblyopia.

It is too early to say whether such recruiting is invariably indicative of central (rather than peripheral) lesions in the various sensory systems. Nor is it clear whether the phenomenon, where it does appear, is a reflection of some gradual adaptation to the impairment or an immediate and automatic consequence of reducing the number of available central neurons. If the latter interpretation is correct, it might imply that subjective intensity is not directly correlated with the absolute number of neurons activated by a sensory input but that it reflects, instead, the ratio of active to inactive neurons in a total available pool. But other interpretations of the recruiting effects, in any modality, are possible. One suggestion that has been offered for the auditory case is that there might be an increase in "neural noise" (Gregory and Wallace, 1958) so that a low-intensity signal remains submerged in the noise but emerges from it as the ratio of signal to noise is changed with increasing signal intensity. Alternatively, recruiting effects may be attributed to some supersensitivity of partially isolated central neurons (Drake and Stavraki, 1948), or it could reflect the loss of some specific systems that normally act in an inhibitory or modulating fashion upon the raw sensory input (cf. Fex, 1962). The rare but definite instances of hyperesthesia (better-than-normal sensitivity) after certain cerebral lesions, discussed previously, may be a related problem.

9. *The Use of Multiple Stimuli.* The normal perceiver is ordinarily confronted by an environment in which manifold patterns, in different senses, impinge upon him simultaneously, yet he is able to turn from one complex of stimuli to another. Massively redundant or noisy fields evidently strain this mechanism, which appears to require some intermediate level of stimulus variation. For the same reason, single stimuli persistently applied, as on the threshold tests just described, represent an unnatural and hence stressful mode of stimulation. More revealing, however, are those situations in which a few stimuli, distributed over different parts of the sensory surface, are administered either simultaneously or in rapid succession so that one can tap what earlier generations of psychophysicists have called the "perceptual span" or the "distribution of attention." In the limiting case, two stimuli are applied simultaneously in the tactual, visual, or even

gustatory modality, either to homologous or heterologous body parts. The objective of such double simultaneous stimulation is to uncover situations in which each of the two stimuli would be reported if each were applied alone but in which only one of the two stimuli would be reported if both were applied together.

The resulting failure to report has been variously designated as "extinction" (Bender, 1945; Teuber and Bender, 1949) or as "inattention" (Critchley, 1949). We prefer "extinction" because it is intended to be purely descriptive, to "inattention," with its seeming implication that the mechanism of attention might be known and that one could lose attention, so to speak, for one part of one's body. The tactual form of extinction is analogous to the visual form: on stimulation with a target, in the periphery of the patient's field of vision to the right, and then to the left, as indicated in Fig. 11-13, the patient can describe and localize the target; but when a target to the left is shown while the one on the right is still present, the patient exclaims, "One of them (the one on the right, in this particular patient) fades away— now it's gone" as though extinction were an extreme form of what has been called obscuration (Bender, 1945; Bender and Teuber, 1946). In such cases one obtains the impression of an active process, an abnormally enhanced lateral interaction in the neural substrate, as if two regions got in each other's way (Denny-Brown, Meyer, and Horenstein, 1952; Teuber, 1962a). A particularly instructive example can be found on tests of comparison of lifted weights, when successive tests

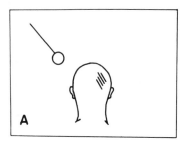
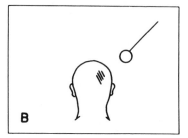

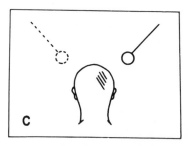

Fig. 11-13. Extinction on double simultaneous stimulation in a case of right posterior parietal shell-fragment wound. (A) The single visual target, exhibited to the patient's left, is properly reported by the patient and localized by pointing. (B) The same is true for the single target on the patient's right. (C) Upon simultaneous presentation of two targets, one right, one left, the one on the left is rendered imperceptible, i.e., the patient reports "it's fading away," and cannot locate it until the target on the right side is removed (from Teuber, Battersby, and Bender, 1960).

with either hand are compared with results of simultaneous bimanual testing (Teuber, 1962a).

In rare instances, extinction of visual or tactual stimuli has been observed in the absence of any other sensory deficits: for instance, the abnormal interaction between simultaneously hefted weights has been noted as a remarkably solitary sign of parietal-lobe disease (Mohacsy, Krueger, and Teuber, 1958). Conversely, however, not all cases of lateralized somatosensory deficit or of hemiamblyopia show extinction. It is simply not known to this day why extinction occurs when it does and why it fails to occur when it does not occur (Krueger, Price, and Teuber, 1954). As has often been pointed out (e.g., Critchley, 1953), right parietal-lobe lesions can be sufficient but are not necessary. Perhaps more than one lesion is required to bring out this symptom in persistent form, but so far no convincing replication of the phenomenon has been achieved by placing experimental lesions in the brains of species below man unless one counts the behavior of Loeb's dogs (Loeb, 1884) as an instance of extinction. Yet modern work strongly suggests that unilateral occipital lesions (as produced by Loeb) result in visual-field defects rather than in extinction. The effects of frontal lesions are conceivably different in character, being more transient (Kennard and Ectors, 1938; Welch and Stuteville, 1958) and possibly more a matter of paralysis of voluntary gaze to the affected side (i.e., contralateral to the frontal lesion; see Silberpfennig, 1941). Similar difficulties of visual search, to the side opposite a lateral frontal lesion in man, have been reported and assessed in some detail with special tests (Teuber, 1964; Teuber and Bender, 1951). One should note, however, that the contralateral transient neglect after unilateral frontal lesions in monkeys has been reported to involve tactual and auditory stimuli as well as visual ones (Welch and Stuteville, 1958).

Although physiologic mechanism and precise localization of extinction remain elusive, the technique of double stimulation affords a rapid and sensitive means of detecting anomalies of perception apparently irrespective of their etiology: for instance, under the influence of drugs, or in the aftermath of general anesthesia, normal adults will show considerable extinction on homologous and heterologous tactual stimulation. After general anesthesia, these anomalies last longer the older the patient, suggesting a rather disquieting slowness in recovery from routine narcosis with advancing age.

Much remains to be done in exploring the role of intensity, place, and timing of the stimuli that tend to produce extinction. Nonhomologous stimulation (e.g., one side of face, and contralateral hand) is often said to reveal "rostral dominance." The patient is more likely to report the contact impinging on his face than that on his hand. Alternatively, he may exhibit rostral displacement by reporting the pair of stimuli (which had been to one side of the face, and to the contralateral hand) erroneously as "both sides of face." However, as Korin and Fink (1957) have shown, systematic variation of stimulus strength can abolish such tendencies toward rostral dominance and rostral displacement, provided that intensity of stimulation of any given body region is adjusted to the tactile threshold for that region.

In many cases, extinction is no longer noted, once strict simultaneity is abandoned, especially if one lets the stimulus to the affected side precede that to the less affected side. In fact, as Birch and co-workers have shown quite recently (Birch, Belmont, and Karp, 1967), one can at times reverse the usual effects of double stimulation by asynchronous stimulation, so that the patient will report the stimulus to the affected side (which is being stimulated first) rather than the one to the less affected side of his body (which is stimulated with a specified temporal delay). These aberrant effects of nonsimultaneous stimulation foreshadow the importance of strict simultaneity of input on the various dichotic tasks (two-channel listening), which will be described in a later section.

B. TACTILE APPREHENSION OF OBJECT QUALITIES. Discrimination of objects through the sense of touch can be disturbed, as one might expect, in the presence of threshold changes: if there is frequent extinction, if tactile sensitivity is poor, if two-point discrimination or point localization is impaired, corresponding difficulties in distinguishing or identifying objects by touch alone are to be expected. Moreover, as soon as tactual discrimination of objects involves active palpation and thus sequential exploration with the moving hand, defective sensibility for joint position and joint movement may be reflected in some failure of object discrimination.

Still, threshold changes may be found in the absence of significant impairment of object discrimination, and the converse can also occur, so that object discrimination seems impaired in the absence of threshold changes. Here as elsewhere, such dissociations of symptoms can take us at least part way from descriptions of behavioral change in terms of *products* (failure of object discrimination, not further analyzed) toward descriptions in terms of *process* (i.e., toward the nature of altered perceptual function).

A series of object-quality discrimination tasks has been devised (by Semmes, Weinstein, Ghent, and Teuber; see Teuber, 1959) to provide relatively objective and quantitative measures of capacity to apprehend tactual object qualities such as roughness, texture, size, bidimensional patterns, and tridimensional shape. Thus, on the task involving discrimination of degrees of roughness, the subject palpates a series of sandpapers with his fingertips. Grain size and density vary across the range of sandpapers from fine to coarse; the papers are hidden behind a black curtain to conceal them from the subject's sight. The subject is permitted to explore the entire series and is then given a duplicate of one of the papers, also behind the curtain. He palpates this duplicate (the standard) and then proceeds to search for the matching paper within the array (Weinstein et al., 1958).

This procedure is repeated in prearranged order for each of the grades of roughness in the array; for any given mismatch, the degree of error can be expressed in terms of the number of steps along the array that intervene between the standard and the comparison stimulus chosen by the subject. One notes that this simple method permits one to assess ability to gauge degrees of roughness separately for each hand (or, if one wishes, separately for each fingertip); the method also lends itself to bimanual testing, so that the subject explores the standard with one hand and then reaches for the comparison stimulus with the other, a procedure which may disclose, in certain cases, a systematic mismatch tendency between the hands, provided there are no disturbances in spatial orientation with respect to the array.

Analogous methods have been employed in testing tactual size discrimination by presenting an array of wooden cubes varying in small steps (2 mm.) along the array (Weinstein, 1962) and also for assessing capacity to discriminate (and match) textures, two-dimensional patterns, and three-dimensional shapes, except that these additional tests lack the simple dimensional structure provided by degrees of roughness or size. Appreciation of texture is tested by presenting a series of common surfaces (such as glass, wood, and coarse cloth) in small windows along a horizontal board, again behind a black curtain to exclude them from the subject's sight. Bidimensional patterns are provided by raised metallic templates, each affixed to a leaden cube, as shown in Fig. 11-14 (Ghent et al., 1955).

Fig. 11-14. Bidimensional forms used in pattern discrimination test (Ghent, 1955). For each trial, one of the patterns is placed for five seconds on the subject's palm, and then placed within the array. The subject then palpates the six patterns, attempting to identify the one which has just been placed on his hand. Vision is excluded by the simple device of screening the patterns with a black cloth. For further details, see text.

These bidimensional patterns had originally been employed by S. I. Franz in studies of transfer of training from one hand to the other (1933); they are placed, one at a time, on the subject's supported palm to afford a deliberately unnatural and difficult mode of presentation. After each exposure of a particular pattern, the subject searches with active hand and finger for the matching pattern in the array. Again, right and left hands can be tested separately, as well as hand-to-hand transfer. On the test for discrimination of solid shapes, shown in Fig. 11-15, active palpation is permitted throughout. This test has now been modified for use with children (Rudel and Teuber, 1964).

In patients with cerebral lesions, difficulties on all these object-quality discrimination tests can be expected if preliminary testing with the threshold tasks described in the previous section has disclosed diminished sensitivity, but this association is not mandatory.

Fig. 11-15. Tridimensional forms used in tests of pattern discrimination. A duplicate of each of the patterns in the array is given to the patient to palpate, one at a time, behind an opaque screen which prevents his seeing the patterns. Following each palpation of a test pattern, the patient attempts to identify, again by palpation, the matching pattern in the array.

Some patients with mild threshold changes may have essentially normal scores on object-quality discrimination tasks. (In future applications, these object-discrimination tests should be standardized in the same fashion as the elementary threshold tasks so that levels of defective performance from mild to severe can be statistically defined.) More intriguing, however, is dissociation of symptoms in the opposite direction: breakdown on some of the object-discrimination tests in the absence of elementary threshold changes. This dissociation takes two forms, one partial, the other complete.

The *partial dissociation* is represented by numerous cases of sensory deficit of one hand (as established on threshold tests). In such patients, if the affected hand shows an associated difficulty with object-quality discrimination (particularly for bidimensional patterns and solid shapes), the probability is high that the other hand would show similar trouble on these same discrimination tasks, even though there are no demonstrable sensory-threshold changes in that hand (Teuber, 1959). This partial dissociation is an approximation to "astereognosis," as usually defined. It represents a failure of object discrimination in the absence of the sensory changes that could account for it. At the same time, the condition does not fully conform to the strict definition of tactual agnosia because there are threshold changes, albeit in the other hand. The condition of the hand with selective discriminatory deficits is reminiscent of those subtle changes in the visual field that were found on the seemingly intact side of the field, opposite a demonstrable scotoma.

Complete dissociation, however, is also found, even though rarely. There are cases of significant deficits in bidimensional and tridimensional-form discrimination, without any elementary threshold changes of either hand. Nevertheless, this type of alteration does not conform to the classical concept of tactual agnosia either. To be sure, there are no threshold changes sufficient to account for the failures of discrimination, nor need there be dementia, but there is invariably a significant deficit of *spatial orientation,* as assessed by route-finding tasks (Semmes et al., 1955), even when the spatial orientation is gauged by means of the visual (and not the tactual-kinesthetic) version of that task (Semmes, 1965; Semmes et al., 1963). We thus have a clear dissociation of tactual discrimination deficits from elementary threshold changes, but we have an association with a supramodal "spatial" deficiency that apparently accounts for the difficulties of our patients with the discrimination of bi- and tridimensional forms.

One final point needs to be made before leaving this matter in its present unsatisfactory state: there are subtle deficits of what might be called perceptual learning, in the tactual sphere, which can be strictly lateralized, although they are independent of tactile threshold changes (Ghent et al., 1955). The discriminanda employed are shown in Fig. 11-14, and Fig. 11-16 gives the results of testing each hand separately, for three trials, with each pattern, in the presence of a unilateral cerebral lesion by penetrating missiles. As it turned out, there was significant improvement of performance on this task, from first to third trials for each pattern, in the less affected hand, i.e., the hand ipsilateral to the injured hemisphere. The hand contralateral to the injured hemisphere failed to show any improvement over the range of trials. This failure to improve was obvious not only in the presence but also in the absence of sensory threshold changes in that hand (see Fig. 11-16). Larger

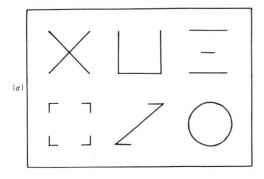

(a)

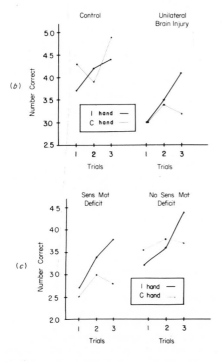

Fig. 11-16. Results obtained on successive trials for tactual discrimination of forms (the two-dimensional forms shown in Fig. 11-14, and again shown schematically, here on top, in (a). Upper graph (b) shows results for control subjects, on left, and for patients with unilateral brain injury, on right. For the patients, the letters I and C designate, respectively, results for the hand contralateral and ipsilateral to their cerebral lesion. For the control subjects, the right hand was arbitrarily designated as ipsilateral, and the left, as contralateral. (c). Results of tactual discrimination test for patients, regrouped according to presence or absence of sensorimotor deficit quantitatively defined (based on Ghent et al., 1955). For details, see text.

groups of cases or more precisely localized lesions might still reveal a localization that could have been missed. It is also clear that longer series of trials, or other discriminanda might have yielded somewhat different results.

3. IS THERE EVER TRUE TACTUAL OBJECT AGNOSIA? One inevitably asks: Is there ever a pure haptic imperception, a selective loss of tactual recognition of objects, beyond the partial or impure forms already described? Just as for visual agnosia, the answer remains unclear. Most of the earlier reports claiming pure tactual agnosia were not conceived in terms of the (presumably altered) perceptual process. One thus has little evidence to counter the arguments of those (like Bay and Critchley) who insist that tactual agnosia does not exist, except in cursory descriptions of complex sensory disorders that remain essentially unanalyzed.

Apparent difficulties with tactual object recognition in disconnection syndromes certainly fail to conform to the notion of pure astereognosis. On the evidence available so far (Sperry, 1961, 1964, 1966; Geschwind and Kaplan, 1962), the trouble appears to be, just as in vision, one of naming and not of apprehension, nor of proper classification (e.g., in terms of use). Thus, a patient with extensive transection of interhemispheric pathways will discriminate sequentially-presented objects through palpation with either hand, yet he can name the objects he palpates only if they are presented to his right hand, i.e., the one with direct access to the (dominant) left hemisphere. Objects presented to the left hand, however, are either not named at all or given random descriptions, even though the patient is able with that speechless hand to match a standard object against its duplicate in an array. The possibility remains that subtle but undetected differences in complex tactual performance of the two hands might exist in these and similar cases, but the picture at this stage is not one of agnosia for touch but an inability to name what is correctly felt.

Any search for astereognosis would have to consider, as Birkmayer (1951) has stressed, the rather special requirements of object recognition through the sense of touch: exposure is ordinarily sequential, and successive impressions need to be matched against an anticipatory schema of what the palpated object might be. Certain critical details need to be singled out, retained in short-term memory, and rechecked before deciding which object is being felt. Rapid fading or abnormal interaction of successive impressions would therefore be especially disruptive for haptic recognition, as would be persistent after-sensations. Patients with focal parietal lesions have in fact been reported to overestimate the second of two weights put successively on their palm (Weinstein, 1955), their overestimation being clearly in excess of that normally found under such conditions of successive stimulation (the "negative time errors" for weight; see Köhler, 1923). This observation should be studied by other methods, and in other sensory modalities (Teuber, 1962b), particularly since the enhanced overestimation is said to occur in either hand, contralateral as well as ipsilateral to a unilateral parietal lesion (Weinstein, 1955).

In contrast, few if any effects of parietal lesions have been disclosed by tests of tactile-kinesthetic after-effects following prolonged palpation of objects (Köhler and Dinnerstein, 1947)—analogous to the figural after-effects in vision (see Köhler and Wallach, 1944). Earlier reports of massive changes in after-effects (in the presence of diffuse brain disease; Klein and Krech, 1952) stand in conflict with negative findings on cases of focal trauma (Jaffe, 1954). In any case, the question of the existence of astereognosis, and of its nature if it does exist, remains.

Possible Physiologic Mechanisms. Despite rapid advances, the neurophysiology of somatic sensation offers relatively little help. For more than a decade, we have known (mostly through the work of Mountcastle, 1961) of the extreme specificity of thalamic and cortical cells in the central somatosensory systems. Individual neurons have clearcut affinity for particular inputs: movements at a particular joint in a particular direction, and light touch in a particular receptor field on the skin. Cells with similar predilections for stimuli in a particular submodality are congregated in cortical columns that represent microorgans at that level. Destructive lesions involving sufficiently many of such columns should then result in specific threshold changes in the corresponding submodalities, and this is apparently the case.

Yet there is hardly any clue as to what might represent, in the somatic-sensory sphere, the feature-detecting systems for analysis of spatial patterns that are so strikingly apparent in the visual cortex, as analyzed by Hubel and Wiesel (1965). Is the basic principle different for somesthesis from that for vision? Or have we yet to apply the adequate stimulus for detecting analogous form-extracting units in the somatosensory sphere? Whatever the answer, it is clear that the problem of tactual agnosia is far from trivial because it involves the question of how form perception in the tactual modality works and of how it breaks down.

III. *Audition*

Changes in auditory perception after cerebral lesions or ablations in man are less clearly delineated than corresponding changes in vision: in cases of injury to the central visual pathways, lesions beyond the chiasm are followed by homonymous visual-field defects, except in the rare instances of a field defect limited to the so-called monocular crescent (Teuber, Battersby, and Bender, 1960). In the auditory system, changes at the level of the middle and inner ear or of the auditory nerve have been thoroughly explored, but changes at higher levels of the neuraxis are relatively little understood, and there is no single sign of "central" auditory impairment, as are homonymous field defects for lesions of retrochiasmal visual pathways.

In the absence of such central signs, the typical approach to assessment of auditory functions after cerebral lesions and ablations in man begins with all the elementary procedures, such as pure-tone and click audiometry, that have their place in the routine assessment of the middle and inner ear function. Tests of more subtle or complex changes assignable to involvement of central portions of the auditory pathways still need to be developed, although there exist reasonably efficient tests of discrimination of nonverbal sound patterns (rhythms, melodies) and of speech samples under experimental conditions that are more comparable to the elaborate tests of visual and tactual object discrimination that have already been described. The most likely candidates for tasks selectively sensitive to central lesions, however, are the methods that involve simultaneous but different input to the two ears (dichotic stimulation; see following), thus forcing the listener to integrate information presented to the separate peripheral channels. These methods range from those involving binaural localization of clicks (Teuber, 1962), to those presenting different frequency bands of the same auditory message, simultaneously to the two ears (Bocca, 1958; Bocca *et al.*, 1955; Matzker, 1958), and to those that are the manifold applications of Broadbent's technique in which quite different messages enter the two ears at the same time (Broadbent, 1954; Broadbent and Gregory, 1964).

A. ELEMENTARY AUDITORY TASKS. Assessment of auditory thresholds traditionally employs the stimuli that could be considered simple or elementary in terms of physics: pure tones or bursts of noise ("clicks"). One could argue, again, that the elementary nature of the stimuli is only apparent, because the auditory systems of most animals and of man are unlikely to have evolved to receive such "pure" but unnatural stimuli, instead of those of biologic significance (such as species-specific calls in lower forms and speech sounds in man).

If one does employ pure tones for measuring the acuity in either ear, the method of choice has been the Békésy audiometer (von Békésy, 1947), in which tones are brought automatically from below threshold, at any given frequency, and down again, permitting repeated runs across the audible spectrum, in alternating ascending and descending presentations of the test tones. In method this corresponds closely to the technique of taking visual fields on a Harms perimeter or to that of taking tactile thresholds by our modified von-Frey techniques.

Differential limens for frequency or intensity can be similarly determined, although this has rarely been done. Both absolute and differential thresholds can be obtained in the presence of a masking noise applied to the same or opposite ear, thereby permitting one to establish signal-to-noise ratios. It is likely but not proven that these ratios might be abnormal in the presence of certain cerebral lesions, even where ordinary thresholds (absolute or differential limens) could be unaffected.

Another important lead is contained in the work of Gersuni (1965) and his collaborators (Baru, Gersuni, and Tonkonogii, 1964). Gersuni points out that the acoustic signals employed in testing auditory sensitivity after cortical lesions or ablations may be inappropriate by virtue of their relatively long duration. If one tests auditory acuity, instead, with very short bursts of noise (from 10 to 20 milliseconds), a marked reduction in acuity for the ear contralateral to auditory cortex lesions can be detected; this difference, however, vanishes if the duration of the test signal is sufficiently prolonged (Gersuni, 1965). The findings suggest that the auditory cortex may be important for the detection and discrimination of brief transient events but relatively less important for reactions to steady states. Ordinary audiometric procedures, presenting tones for up to a second or more, would therefore be more suitable for detecting peripheral than central lesions in the auditory nervous system.

At the same time, one should be alert to the possibility that certain auditory thresholds, after lesions of the central nervous system, may be abnormally low, just as the somatosensory thresholds in cases of tactile hyperesthesia described above. A first instance of such abnormally enhanced auditory acuity was recently obtained on tests of differential limens for intensity of a 2000-cycle tone (Swisher, 1967). These tests were applied to patients in Montreal before and after unilateral cortical excision from the temporal lobes. The heightened sensitivity to intensity differences was found in those patients who had undergone left temporal removals including the gyri of Heschl, but not in those with corresponding removals from the right temporal lobe, nor in those with the left temporal removals that spared the gyri of Heschl (Swisher, *loc. cit.*). Similar tests of differential sensitivity to frequency change are now in progress.

These studies are of considerable interest since they underscore that differential limens (incremental thresholds) can be changed, although absolute thresholds for tones may be normal. The observation that temporal-lobe excision including the left gyri of Heschl but not the right, are effective in producing the baffling form of hypersensitivity in man fits other data on asymmetric organization of the human temporal lobes (Milner, 1954, 1962, 1967) and underscores the important difference between man and subhuman forms in this respect. The physiologic basis of the hypersensitivity produced by cortical excisions on the left nevertheless remains obscure. Swisher (1967) suggests that the removal of a normally acting efferent control system might play a role in this and other forms of hypersensitivity, but this remains a matter for conjecture.

1. *Binaural Localization of Sounds.* An approach to an intermediate level of task-complexity is represented by tests of binaural localization of sounds. Much explored in normal subjects, both for ambient sounds and for sounds presented separately to each ear by earphones, possible changes in binaural localization have been only inadequately investigated in patients with cerebral lesions. Systematic mislocalization of ambient sounds may appear at least transiently after parietal lesions but it is not clear to what extent such mislocalizations are specific to auditory tasks, or perhaps equally demonstrable for visual or tactual stimuli (Sanchez-Longo and Forster, 1958; Shankweiler, 1961).

Analysis of altered binaural function is more readily accomplished by using two-channel listening (i.e., dichotic) tasks (Teuber, 1962a; Teuber and Diamond, 1956). Here, click audiograms are first obtained, separately for each ear, and a particular intensity level selected (say 30 db relative to the threshold for each ear). Such intensity-balanced clicks, if presented simultaneously to the two ears, are usually perceived as a single (fused) click, in or near the center of the subject's head. Varying the intensity or the time of arrival at one ear, against the other, produces apparent shifts of the fused click away from the subjective midline, toward the ear receiving the earlier, or the more intense sound. For normal listeners, a time difference of one millisecond between loudness-balanced clicks usually produces the impression that the subjectively fused click has shifted nearly all the way toward the leading ear.

A difference in arrival time between the clicks that exceeds zero by something like a millisecond and a half usually suffices for normal listeners to detect some "roughness" in the subjectively fused click, and with slightly longer time intervals they become convinced that there are two clicks, a strong one in one ear (the "leading" ear) and a faint one in the other (the objectively lagging ear).

Accordingly, one can explore these binaural phenomena in four stages (Teuber and Diamond, 1956): First, one varies the time of arrival of one click relative to the other continuously from zero time difference between ears to several milliseconds difference, and back to zero again. Secondly, one varies the relative intensity of the clicks, over a range of 10 to 20 db, with zero-time difference. Thirdly, one can pit intensity variations against opposing time differences, to determine, e.g., how many decibels are needed at the lagging ear to counterbalance a one-millisecond time lead at the opposite ear. Fourth and last, one can pull loudness-balanced dichotic clicks further and further apart in time so that the listener just begins to report two clicks rather than one, and then approximates the clicks again, in time, so that the impression of duality gives way to one of fusion.

This last phase of the procedure is similar to a tactual two-point discrimination task, and it is therefore of considerable interest that preliminary work suggests a parietal localization for acquired deficiencies in these duality-judgments for dichotically-presented clicks. The discrimination of dichotic clicks also seems extremely vulnerable in normal adults who are under the influence of certain drugs (such as LSD, where the threshold in milliseconds of time separation for perceived duality may be 5 to 10 times that of normal).

A provisional result of these binaural tests is the impression that auditory localizations based on intensity differences and those based on time differences may be separately vulnerable to cerebral lesions, so that some patients have greater difficulty in utilizing intensity cues and others, time cues (Teuber, 1962). If such dissociations can be extended and confirmed, we would have to conclude that at some neural level, separate mechanisms underlie the two forms of binaural localization of sounds.

2. *Use of Objective Indices.* Much recent effort has gone into defining objective (nonverbal and involuntary) indicators for monaural and binaural responses, such as galvanic skin reflexes in children during audiometry (Hirsh, 1952) or computer-averaged cerebral potentials evoked by repeated clicks or tones (although the early reports of auditory evoked potentials in man, by Kiang and others, see Goldstein, 1963, turned out to be due to peripheral muscle potentials rather than to cerebral events). These methods are of interest primarily because they permit experimentation on attention and arousal as factors in determining latency and amplitude of evoked responses. Inexplicably, there have been virtually no attempts to apply those techniques to binaural localization (and two-click discrimination tasks), nor have there been sufficiently systematic attempts to correlate either latencies or amplitudes of auditory evoked potentials to the phenomenon of "recruiting" where the loudness function grows, with abnormal rapidity, in the presence of an abnormally high auditory threshold, as stimulus intensity is increased beyond threshold levels (von Békésy, 1965; Hirsh, 1952).

In vision, there is at least presumptive evidence for a close correspondence between the growth of subjective brightness, as an exponential function of stimulus luminance (Stevens, 1957) and progressively shorter latencies of the averaged evoked cerebral potential (Vaughan, 1966; Vaughan and Hull, 1965; Teuber, 1966b, 1967). In point of fact, both the (subjective) brightness function and the reciprocal of the latency of the evoked potential grow as an exponential function with roughly the same exponent (0.3), and it is quite likely that abnormally "rapid" growth, as in recruiting, could be determined by such latency measures for evoked potentials in vision, somesthesis and audition.

On the other hand, we should stress that earlier hopes of a direct correspondence between the presence of evoked potentials and report-ability of a stimulus were quite unrealistic. It is not at all unlikely that an auditory stimulus, or, for that matter, a visual or a tactual stimulus (Goff, Rosner, and Allison, 1962), would evoke a recordable cerebral response while remaining unperceived (in the sense that it would go unreported by the subject). Only much further work can determine whether or not some characteristic cerebral after-potential would be invariably associated with "reportability." Until then, electro-graphic methods, whether employing GSR or EEG techniques, cannot substitute for the subject's explicit report.

B. PROBLEM OF CHANGES IN PERCEPTION OF AUDITORY PAT-TERNS. Directly analogous to the problems of object-quality dis-crimination in vision and touch is the question of whether cerebral lesions, centrally acting drugs, or other special conditions might selec-tively affect some auditory levels intermediate between threshold functions and such complex achievements as the comprehension of speech. Such an intermediate level might be represented by sound patterns, such as rhythms or melodies.

In the experimental animal, the by-now classical studies of Diamond and Neff (1957) have strongly suggested that bilateral cortical re-movals of temporal neocortex in the monkey and of corresponding regions in the cat can produce lasting deficits in the discrimination of tonal patterns, in the absence of any obvious changes in frequency discrimination or intensity discrimination (at least for tones of long duration). Corresponding disturbances exist in man after right anterior temporal lobectomy. These excisions need not involve the gyri of Heschl, as has been demonstrated in the Montreal laboratories (Milner, 1962, 1967) and confirmed more recently at Johns Hopkins (Chase, 1967). No such deficits are found with comparable excisions in the (dominant) left hemisphere even in the presence of postoperative dysphasia.

A major difficulty in the application of standard tests in this area is the wide range of musical abilities in the normal population, so that ordinary tests of discrimination of melodies or rhythms applied to patients after brain injury inevitably raise questions about their pre-morbid status in this respect. Furthermore, tasks of the sort involved in Neff's and Diamond's successive comparisons of tonal patterns or in Seashore's well-known tests for musical ability (Saetveit, Lewis, and Seashore, 1940) of necessity involve some short-term memory, as will be discussed in a subsequent section. In spite of all these strictures, tests of tonal and rhythmic patterns should be applied in addition to auditory threshold tests with very brief signals and in addition to tests for duration and intermittence of sounds. Difficulties with per-ception of auditory flutter (in analogy to visual flicker) have been reported after mild, nonfocal brain damage and in cases of severe fatigue (Symmes, Chapman, and Halstead, 1955). Whether perform-ance on such tasks is intact or impaired is an important consideration in defining the nature of receptive aphasias.

C. AUDITORY IMPERCEPTION: RECEPTIVE APHASIA. The nature of auditory imperceptions remains as elusive as that of the visual and tactual forms of an allegedly massive yet modality-specific failure of recognition. In one respect at least, the situation with regard to severe auditory imperception is worse: most patients with such a condition not only fail to comprehend instructions but tend to have a severe expressive disorder as well. They tend to speak in "jargon," with a rush of speechlike but incomprehensible sounds, often without apparent awareness of their own disability. It may, of course, be no accident that receptive disorders of language should tend to be associated with expressive ones, while expressive disorders can appear in relative isolation.

The crucial question remains: How does the world sound to such patients? Are we dealing with a unitary disorder of auditory perception which involves language as well as other complex acoustic patterns, or are there different forms, one being an imperception quite specific to language? With the notable exception of Luria's work (1966), few systematic attempts have been made to demonstrate that patients with imperception for speech might have intact capacity to discriminate and identify other complex tonal patterns (but see Dorgeuille, 1966; Spinnler and Vignolo, 1966).

1. *Possible Physiologic Mechanisms.* Recent neurophysiologic studies of single cells in the central auditory pathways (Whitfield, 1967; Whitfield and Evans, 1965) suggest that there are feature detectors in the auditory system analogous to the Hubel-Wiesel cells in the visual system. There are auditory neurons in the cat that are preferentially "attuned" to glissando sounds in upward or downward directions or to other patterns rather than to the unphysiologic stimuli represented by pure tones or clicks. One could argue that the most effective stimuli for entire assemblies of auditory neurons in the cat would be typical cat sounds; a similar specificity (selective "tuning" for the frog's croak) has been demonstrated for the frog's auditory system (Frishkopf and Goldstein, 1963).

It is quite conceivable that higher-order feature-extracting neurons exist in man's auditory nervous system and that auditory imperception would result from a loss of these neurons or from a derangement of their proper interaction. It is also possible, although entirely unproven, that man's auditory nervous system differs from that of other species by virtue of a built-in apparatus for detecting the distinctive features that make the phonemic structure of language possible (Jakobson and Halle, 1956; Kozhevnikov and Chistovich, 1965; Lenneberg, 1967; Liberman et al., 1966; Teuber, 1967; Wickelgren, 1966). This assumption does not mean that language as such is innate because it is evident that each child learns the particular language he hears. Yet the ease with which any language is learned by a normal child does suggest the existence of some innate, central apparatus ready to receive linguistic input and to analyze it in certain ways quite independently of the particular language that is being heard.

Similar unlearned predispositions have been invoked to account for the otherwise inexplicable speed and ease with which children acquire the syntactic structure of their language (Chomsky, 1957; Teuber, 1967). Even the semantic level of language has been approached in analogous terms (Katz and Fodor, 1963), thereby making the parallelism between current linguistic theory and Plato's innate ideas all but complete.

Regardless of the merits of these approaches to certain universals of language, methods for analyzing language disturbances should probe for changes on phonemic and syntactic levels. Roman Jakobson's predictions regarding the most frequent confusions among phonemes in auditory aphasia (1942) are quite specific and testable, even though hardly any systematic tests have been made (but again, see Luria, 1966). Corresponding tests of comprehension of syntactic structure are likewise available but still virtually unexploited (Teuber, 1967). In mild forms of receptive aphasia, simple tests of sentence repetition have been used, often derived from those originally developed for normal children (Brown and Berko, 1960; Dubois et al., 1964; Irigaray, 1967; Marshall and Newcombe, 1966). Alternatively, one can introduce tests involving sentence completion or involving recognition and resolution of ambiguity in ambiguous sentences (MacKay, 1966; MacKay and Bever, 1967) in which the sentences are carefully constructed to contain different types of ambiguity, ranging from so-called surface-structure ambiguity to deep-structure ambiguity (Chomsky, 1957, 1965).

Such approaches encourage the view that the gravest forms of aphasia, when incomprehension of speech is combined with profound expressive difficulties, may reflect a loss of the deep structure of sentences, or, equivalently, a loss of what have been called the projection rules that enable a normal speaker to go from deep to surface structures in producing or receiving a spoken or written sentence.

2. *Further Considerations: Hemisphere Differences in Audition.* If the conjectures just offered are correct, then one would expect that speech and nonspeech patterns would be processed in different ways in the auditory nervous system; speech would somehow engage some specialized feature-extracting mechanisms. This view is strengthened by the steadily increasing evidence for a regional dissociation of the processes underlying the mediation of speech patterns and other sounds; much of this evidence derives from variations and extensions of a method first employed by Broadbent (1954; Broadbent and Gregory, 1964).

In the original version of Broadbent's task, a normal listener receives two strings of signals, e.g., the digits 351 and 827, through earphones, separately for each ear, so that the left ear might receive 827 and the right ear 351. Typically, the digits will be reproduced as 351, 827, or conversely, 827, 351. Thus, the listener deals, first with the input to one ear, holding the other ear's input in some short-term store, and then proceeds to reproduce the other group of digits; interleaving of the digits on recall (e.g., 8 3 2 5 7 1) is extremely rare.

One could argue that this dichotic task taps recall rather than auditory perception, but the distinction becomes somewhat academic if one applies the test as Kimura (1961a, b, 1967) and others have done, in such a way that the digits are presented in strict synchrony, right and left, to the two ears. It is particularly under this condition that an asymmetry between the two channels can be demonstrated: The right ear does better in listeners whose speech appears to be primarily mediated by the left hemisphere (Milner, 1962, 1967). This right-ear superiority in normal right-handed adults was also shown by Bryden (1963), even after order of recall for the two ears had been controlled.

Kimura (1963) has shown such a superior performance for the right ear, on strictly simultaneous (dichotic) testing, in fairly young children (down to the youngest age tested, viz., 4 years), suggesting that the normal asymmetry is established quite early in life. This normal right-ear superiority, however, is reversed in the patients in whom speech is mediated by the right hemisphere. Such abnormal localization of speech mechanisms can be established by the Wada-technique, in which one transiently puts a cerebral hemisphere out of commission by injecting a barbiturate into the common carotid artery of one side (Wada, 1949). In a series of adults for whom such right-hemisphere localization of speech had been established by the Wada technique (Milner, Branch, and Rasmussen, 1964), Kimura (1961a, b) showed that the left ear, rather than the right, exhibited a superiority in simultaneous apprehension of digits on dichotic presentation.

The normal asymmetry between channels (right-ear superiority) is not restricted to digits: other verbal material such as phonetically-balanced words, dichotically presented, is also better perceived through the right ear by normal listeners (Dirks, 1964), and the same can be proven for consonants but not for steady-state vowels, for which the two ears are equally efficient (see Shankweiler and Studdert-Kennedy, 1967).

A right-left difference in the opposite direction is obtained if one presents snatches of melodies dichotically, so that the subject hears one melody in one ear and the other melody simultaneously in the other ear (Kimura, 1964). For this type of nonverbal material, the left ear is superior. This finding cannot be attributed to the fact that Kimura used a recognition task for melodies and a recall task for digits (Kimura, 1961a), because Broadbent and Gregory (1964) had already demonstrated that the right-ear superiority for digits was obtained under either condition of testing, recognition or recall.

Effects of cerebral injuries or ablations, on performance of these dichotic tasks, are in line with what one would predict from observations in normal listeners. Thus, the dichotic test for digits yields below-normal scores, for both ears, in patients with long-standing left temporal-lobe lesions. In contrast, patients with long-standing lesions of the right temporal lobe do not differ significantly from normal control subjects (Kimura, 1961b; Milner, 1962, 1967). Surgical excisions of right temporal-lobe tissue, including the gyri of Heschl, tend to accentuate the right-ear superiority on the dichotic-digits test (Kimura, 1961b); similar excisions on the left diminish the ear-difference, as expected. The situation is quite different for dichotic presentation of melodies: on that task, the right-temporal lobe excisions produce a deficit, again consistent with the ear-difference in normals (Shankweiler, 1966).

It would be of obvious interest if these lateral asymmetries could also be found for another sensory modality such as vision. There are indeed suggestions to the effect that in normals the right half of the visual field might be more proficient for certain verbal tasks and the left half for nonverbal ones (e.g., Kimura, 1966), but the situation is greatly complicated by such factors as reading habits, ocular dominance, and general differences in visual efficiency between nasal and temporal halves in each monocular field. All these factors tend to inter-act, sometimes accentuating and sometimes diminishing a basic right-left difference that may well be there (Bryden, 1960). In any case, Kimura (1966) has reported that capital letters are better recognized on the tachistoscope when they fall into the right half-field of normal observers; the same normal subjects are better at apprehending small clusters of dots if these are presented to the left half of their field (Kimura, 1966). These observations need further confirmation by other techniques; the data were obtained on successive presentation, first to one half of the field, then to the other, so that, in this respect, they are not directly analogous to the two-channel listening tasks where results depend crucially on simultaneity of presentation.

One further refinement of the dichotic techniques should be men-tioned because it involves presenting one type of material (a syntacti-cally complex sentence) concomitantly with another (a simple noise burst, i.e., a "click"). On this test, a sentence is presented to one ear, e.g., "In her hope of marrying Jane was optimistic," and a 10 millisec-ond click is given through the other channel, halfway through the acoustic wave-form represented by the word *Jane*. A majority of normal listeners will mislocalize the click by insisting that it came before *Jane*. It is as if the click had been pulled toward the nearest syntactic junc-tion, thus illustrating a perceptual consequence of linguistic segmenta-tion (Fodor and Bever, 1965; Garrett, Bever, and Fodor, 1966; Teuber, 1967).

This effect cannot be explained as a mere consequence of intonations or pauses that tend to mark a syntactic junction, for the effect persists after those factors have been controlled. For instance, one can change the carrier sentence "In her hope of marrying Jane was optimistic" by replacing the first two words with "But his," leaving the acoustic pattern that follows unchanged. The sentence now reads: "But his hope of marrying Jane was optimistic." With the click placed objectively, as before, under *Jane,* the listeners nevertheless insist that it now appears after *Jane,* in accord with the altered syntactic structure. In addition to these syntactic effects, there is also an "ear-effect;" the click is sub-jectively delayed, irrespective of the sentence structure, if the click is presented to the right ear, in most of the normal observers; the same relative inferiority of the right ear has been noted recently for sonar signals (Chaney and Webster, 1965).

Applications of this technique to children or to cases of brain injury or disease are yet to come, but it is evident that the click within the sentence can be used as a probe for the ways in which the subject has structured the linguistic patterns presented to him. Needless to say, the click-displacement effects disappear if the sentences are given in a language that the listener does not know.

IV. Residual Issues: Methods Applicable to More than One Sensory Modality; Cross-modal Effects

All the preceding sections reflected our conviction that perceptual alterations after brain injury or after other extreme conditions are best defined by systematic variations of stimuli, including those variations that would make the stimuli less effective or deliberately inadequate. At the same time, we attempted to discover the stimulus configurations that were still adequate to engage the perceptual mechanisms, so that one might be able to detect not only what was lost but also what was preserved. This was done separately for each of the three modalities: vision, somesthesis, and audition. We need to survey in more summary form the specialized techniques that must be considered without reference to any single sense modality.

From time to time, selective failure on cross-modal tasks has been considered to be a possible consequence of parietal-lobe disease in adults (Semmes *et al.*, 1954) or of various cerebral lesions sustained in early childhood. However, before one can speak of a specific breakdown of intermodal transfer, one has to be able to show that performance on the component perceptual tasks that are intramodal is intact or at least significantly less impaired. Thus, on tasks involving visual-tactual and tactual-visual transfer for simple pattern-discrimination learning (employing the patterns in Fig. 11-17), one has to show that the

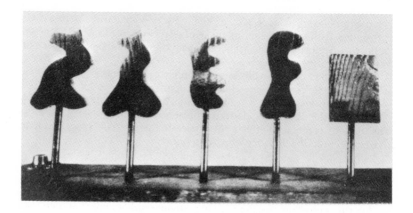

FIG. 11-17. Simple shapes (above) and difficult shapes (below) used in tests of tactual shape discrimination and crossmodal transfer (visual-tactual and tactual-visual) in normal and brain-injured children (from Rudel and Teuber, 1964).

capacity to transfer across modalities is clearly inferior to the capacity to transfer within modalities, i.e., from one series of visual presentations to another visual series or from one tactual series of patterns to another tactual series.

Normal children, 3 and 4 years of age, show excellent visual-to-visual transfer but very poor tactual-to-tactual transfer (Rudel and Teuber, 1963). Their combined (cross-modal) performance, visual-tactual and tactual-visual, falls halfway between that on the purely visual and the purely tactual tasks. As a result of this situation in normal subjects, it is rather unlikely that there would be a selective failure on cross-modal tasks in children with various early brain injuries. In fact, they do particularly poorly on visual-to-visual tasks and nearly as well as normal children on tactual-to-tactual. Thus, effects of early cerebral damage may appear as a leveling of performance on such tasks, the cross-modal now being about as difficult as each of the unimodal tasks (Rudel, 1967).

Intra- and intermodal presentations have likewise been used in adults with various cerebral lesions (Semmes et al., 1954), but the tests were essentially those of problem solving (e.g., conditional reactions), with the discriminanda presented first through one and then through the other sensory channel (tactual-to-visual and conversely). The tasks employed were thus much more difficult than the simple pattern discriminations required in the experiment with children. Adult patients with parietal lesions did more poorly on the crossmodal portions of the tests than did adult control subjects or patients with lesions in other cerebral lobes, but the principles of solution might have been verbalized, and failure of transfer across modalities might have reflected, at least in part, a failure of adequate formulation of these principles of solution, as the authors themselves pointed out.

A similar paradigm was employed by Axelrod (1959) in studies of intramodal versus cross-modal problem solving (auditory and tactual) by three groups of children: sighted children, congenitally blind children, and children who became blind later in life. The congenitally blind showed a definite handicap on the cross-modal portion of the task while those who had become blind were closer in their performance to the sighted control subjects (see also Drever, 1955).

It is clear that much of this work should be repeated and extended with tasks that are less likely to be solved by verbal means (Ettlinger, 1967). A beginning has been made by Krauthamer (1959), who has presented simple visual and haptic outlines under conditions of simultaneous and successive exposure of each pattern, e.g., by simultaneous impression on the skin of tactile patterns, or by flash-exposure of the visual patterns, versus tracing of the same patterns with a stylus on the skin or with a small light source on a translucent screen. As one might expect, different modes of presentation (tracing versus simultaneous exposure) differ in their relative adequacy for a given sense modality; tracing is more natural for tactual and unnatural for visual presentations. These interactions of sense modality and mode of presentation should likewise be considered before proceeding to further explorations of the elusive claims for cross-modal deficits.

Clearly, all tests of perception and its changes, whether within a given sensory modality or across modalities, engage some short-term memory mechanisms during exposure of stimuli; in turn, access to older traces is required for the apprehension of what is seen, felt, or heard. Yet it remains true that disorders of perception can be distinguished from those of memory, because the amnesic syndrome can take a form in which perception is intact.

Memory

B. Milner

The topic of human memory and its disorders appears to warrant detailed consideration, because certain circumscribed brain lesions produce selective effects on memory, the pattern of breakdown not being predictable solely on the basis of experiments with normal subjects. In such cases, a careful analysis of the behavioral change can shed light on normal function.

I. *Criteria of Memory Disorder*

In what follows, the term memory will be used very broadly, to refer to the effects of earlier perceptual experience upon present behavior. Nevertheless, the term is not all-inclusive, and to find out whether or not a particular treatment has affected memory (and affected it *selectively*) requires some preliminary screening, because other changes may easily be misinterpreted as memory defects by a casual observer, and sometimes even by the subject himself. For example, it is important to distinguish between memory loss and an impairment of attention (or vigilance), which, by interfering with initial registration, effectively prevents later recall; an inattentive person may well appear to be forgetful. Secondly, care must be taken to sample behavior widely enough not to mistake general dementia for a selective impairment of memory. Any generalized intellectual decline will include some deterioration in memory, but the symptom is of little significance in the context of so much else that is wrong. Thirdly, it must be kept in mind that certain highly specific perceptual and memory disorders may occur together, in which case it is necessary to show that the memory defect is disproportionate to the perceptual one before it can be said that the change involves memory primarily. These three points will be taken up in more detail below, before attempting any analysis of memory impairment as such.

A. DISORDERS OF VIGILANCE. Sudden fluctuations of attention, occurring regardless of the nature of the task, may have many causes. They may be the behavioral correlates of electrographic epileptiform discharges, as in the brief *absence* of classical petit mal epilepsy; or they may be manifestations of excessive anxiety, or of preoccupation with events outside the immediate test situation. They vary in degree, from the overt lapse which interrupts whatever the subject is doing at the time to the brief moment-to-moment shift in level of alertness which is most easily demonstrated by the use of paced tasks, such as the Continuous Performance Test (Mirsky and Rosvold, 1960) and its variants. Impaired concentration is also revealed by an abnormal unevenness of test performance, the subject often failing an easy item, only to succeed a moment later with a more difficult one. Tests of immediate digit span are sensitive to such fluctuations, since they require perfect reproduction of sequences presented only once. Although such impaired concentration may lead to a patchy performance on recall tasks, it is noteworthy that the most severe amnesic disorders are compatible with normal performance on tasks requiring sustained attention.

B. GENERAL INTELLECTUAL IMPAIRMENT. It is important to sample other intellectual functions before concluding that a particular treatment has affected memory selectively. Thus, Robson, Burns, and Welt (1960) noted that light doses of nitrous oxide seemed to interfere with memory for ongoing events in subjects who were still able to converse "intelligently." Yet, when one such subject, a university graduate, was tested more extensively, it was soon discovered that under nitrous oxide he could neither copy simple designs with blocks, nor do mental arithmetic, nor shift from one mode of solution to another on a sorting test. He had performed all these tasks without the slightest difficulty when breathing air. The effect of inhaling the gas was thus revealed to be a general dementia, in which memory impairment was only one of many deficits, and not the most severe. Similarly, Steinberg and Summerfield (1957) found that subjects were impaired on a verbal rote-learning task during inhalation of nitrous oxide but further experiments showed that the drug also produced defects on a variety of other cognitive tasks (Summerfield, 1964). Instances such as this one point to the need for including a wide range of behavioral measures when assessing the effects of a new treatment.

C. DISORDERS OF PERCEPTION. In seeking to uncover memory deficits specific to one kind of material, it is often difficult to be sure that the seeming impairment of memory is not secondary to a perceptual disturbance. Clearly, where there is severe sensory loss, it will not even be possible to test memory for new material presented in the impaired modality; indeed, any marked perceptual disability will make deterioration in performance after a delay difficult to interpret, and few would be foolhardy enough to try. Where the real problem arises is when subtle perceptual changes, requiring special techniques to elicit, accompany marked memory defects for material which appears to have been perceived normally. For example, right, non-dominant temporal lobectomy is followed by a mild impairment in the tachistoscopic perception of irregular, overlapping nonsense forms (Kimura, 1963) and in the organization of fragmented contours into meaningful percepts (Lansdell, 1968; Milner, 1958, 1968), but it produces a far more striking and consistent defect on a variety of memory tasks involving visual patterns, although such patterns can be discriminated from one another when there is no delay (Kimura, 1963; Prisko, 1963). Here, the disproportion between the impairment after delay and the seemingly mild perceptual disorder leads one to emphasize the effect on memory of a right temporal lobectomy.

This line of reasoning is not, however, completely sound, although the argument would be strengthened if it could be shown that a different treatment caused the same degree and kind of perceptual disturbance as a right temporal-lobe lesion, but without impairing retention of what has been perceived. A more direct approach to the problem is to use a tachistoscopic procedure (first establishing the exposure threshold for perception of the stimulus material, and then testing recognition after a delay) for material which has been presented just above each subject's threshold. In this way, the perceptual difficulty of the task is equated across groups, so that any differential effect in performance after a delay can be taken as evidence of a memory defect. Buffery is now using such a technique to study the effects of unilateral temporal lobectomy on visual memory in man.

II. Memory Defects: Specific and General

Implicit in the foregoing discussion of screening procedures has been the notion that not all memory disorders are alike. The most important distinction to be drawn is that between a disorder which is specific to one kind of material or to one sensory mode and a more general memory loss, or global amnesia. Only the latter will prevent the recall of all aspects of an event, since only the latter is independent both of sensory modality and of the verbal or nonverbal character of the material to be remembered. Moreover, a global amnesia need not be accompanied by any demonstrable perceptual disturbance, whereas we have seen that specific memory defects are very apt to be associated with some perceptual change. Despite these clearcut differences, a marked degree of verbal memory impairment is frequently mis-diagnosed as a generalized impairment of memory, simply because the nonverbal aspects of memory are not adequately examined. In such cases, the patient himself may add to the confusion by complaining of his "poor memory," because he is very conscious of not being able to remember other people's names, or what he reads in the newspaper. Yet the expression is misleading, because the same patient may have completely normal recall of pictures, faces, scenes, or melodies, his defect being specifically verbal.

The evidence for these different kinds of memory disturbance is that, if patients with different brain lesions are tested with a wide variety of recall and recognition tasks (using verbal and nonverbal material and different sensory modes), certain lesions are associated with specific losses which are related to the nature of the material, whereas other lesions produce more generalized defects. For example, if one compares the effects on memory of right and left temporal lobectomies in man, one finds that the significant variable is the verbal or nonverbal character of the material to be memorized. Thus, left anterior temporal lobectomy in the dominant hemisphere for speech causes a lasting impairment in memory for verbal material (Meyer and Yates, 1955; Milner, 1958), regardless of whether auditory or visual presentation is used and regardless of the precise testing technique (Milner and Kimura, 1964; Milner, 1967). Conversely, right temporal lobectomy has been found to impair memory for both visual and auditory patterned stimuli to which a verbal label could not readily be assigned (Milner, 1962a). In contrast to such specific losses, bilateral lesions invading the mesial structures of both temporal lobes (but sparing the lateral neocortex) produce a generalized memory impairment which cuts across the distinction between verbal and nonverbal material or between one sense modality and another, so that the problem is to demonstrate what can be remembered rather than what is forgotten (Scoville and Milner, 1957; Milner, 1966).

Frontal lobectomy can also impair performance on certain tasks which are supposedly testing memory, but in this case the impairment seems to be contingent upon particular conditions of testing rather than upon the nature of the test material, and it may be questioned whether the impaired performance is not a manifestation of something other than a memory disorder. Thus, frontal-lobe lesions are known to be compatible with normal performance on many different kinds of memory test involving a wide range of material (Ghent, Mishkin, and Teuber, 1962; Milner, 1964, 1967); yet patients with such lesions may perform very poorly under conditions of testing in which the subject has to suppress the memory of previous trials and concentrate upon remembering what is immediately present (Prisko, 1963; Milner, 1964). Such proactive interference has also been noted on the Wisconsin Card Sorting test after frontal lobectomy, although this task is not normally regarded as a memory test and can be efficiently performed by patients with severe generalized amnesic disorders (Milner, 1966). Moreover, on sorting tasks as on memory tasks, whether or not a defect is seen after frontal lobectomy seems to depend on the precise conditions of testing (Teuber, Battersby, and Bender, 1951). These observations taken as a whole make it appear unlikely that patients with frontal-lobe lesions have a selective impairment of memory.

III. *Temporal Factors in Memory*

We turn now from an analysis of memory defect in terms of the generality or specificity of what is forgotten to a consideration of temporal relationships in memory, and to such questions as whether recent or remote, short-term or long-term memory has been selectively disturbed by a brain lesion. Here we immediately run into pitfalls of terminology, which come from inconsistency in the use of terms. Thus, it is not always clear whether the expressions *short-term* and *long-term* are being used to refer to a particular experimental design, or to hypothetical underlying processes by which information is stored. Since such distinctions are fundamental to any understanding of memory disorders, some clarification of terms is essential before we can evaluate the contribution of particular experimental methods to the assessment of memory change.

A. RECENT AND REMOTE MEMORY. The generalized amnesias produced by certain circumscribed brain lesions typically have both retrograde and anterograde components. The anterograde amnesia may persist indefinitely with only slight improvement over many years; it means that the patient is able to remember little or nothing of the events of his life since the operation. The retrograde amnesia is more variable and is apt to shrink with time, although it is probably never completely reversible. Thus, the patient will also have difficulty in recalling events covered by a variable period before the operation. In contrast, memory for events earlier in life appears to be entirely normal. It is not at all surprising that both the patient and his family will describe the defect as a *loss of recent memory*, meaning that recent happenings are forgotten, whereas preoperative events remote in time are well recalled. This distinction is clear and useful, provided it is realized that the terms *recent* and *remote* merely refer to the time-scale of the patient's life and contain no assumptions about the underlying mechanism of the disorder. In particular, the term *recent* must not be equated with a short-term memory process.

B. SHORT-TERM AND LONG-TERM MEMORY. These expressions are better used to designate hypothetical processes mediating retention, rather than categories of behavior. Although it can still be argued that the data of normal human forgetting may be explained in terms of a single underlying process (Melton, 1963), the selective memory defects produced by focal brain lesions are hard to reconcile with such a view. Instead, we must distinguish between the primary, or short-term, trace which decays in a matter of seconds when rehearsal is prevented, and the secondary, or long-term, structural change (Waugh and Norman, 1965). These processes must overlap in time, and behavior may be jointly determined by them. A task in which retention is measured a few minutes after presentation of the item to be remembered may well be heterogeneous with respect to the underlying processes, and therefore should not be arbitrarily labelled a short-term memory test. The short-term trace is believed to decay very rapidly with intervening activity (and especially with many shifts of attention), but it is probably also subject to some attrition with time (Brown, 1958; Wickelgren and Norman, 1966). However, Hebb (1961) has shown (and Melton, 1963, has confirmed) that, in normal subjects, cumulative learning of strings of digits can take place, despite the subject's hearing and repeating other series of digits between successive tests, a finding which indicates the early initiation of some structural change.

Such newly acquired traces are, however, likely to be unstable. There is by now much experimental support for the consolidation hypothesis of Müller and Pilzecker (1900), according to which new experience is peculiarly vulnerable to interference and it takes some time for the permanent storage of information to take place. In cases of global amnesia produced by bilateral lesions in the hippocampal zone, this consolidation process appears to have been selectively disturbed. When we analyze the performance of such amnesic patients by the methods to be described below, we find that, with the exception of certain motor tasks, cumulative learning does not take place. Short-term memory for new information is seemingly intact; so also are previously established skills, and the patients are able to recall events from the remote past at least as well as normal subjects. Thus, long-term memory also appears to be unimpaired. Such findings imply that the lesion has disrupted an essential transition process from short-term to long-term memory.

C. IMMEDIATE MEMORY. This somewhat paradoxical term is defined behaviorally, and denotes the amount of material which can be reproduced immediately after presentation. When an observer looks briefly at a complex visual display and then attempts to reproduce all or part of it, he is demonstrating immediate memory. Experiments on partial recall show that the pre-perceptual trace from which this read-out is accomplished contains far more information than the immediate memory store can handle (Averbach and Sperling, 1961; Sperling, 1960), so that the subject's report already reflects some preliminary coding and selection of the sensory input. This earlier phase is usually excluded from any discussion of memory and its disorders.

Immediate memory is most commonly sampled by span tests, which are capacity measures indicating the maximum number of disconnected items that can be reproduced without error immediately after presentation (Jacobs, 1887). The length of the span is limited by how much material the subject is able to rehearse while at the same time attending the new items. In normal subjects, span is relatively invariant for changing items (although it can be increased by practice in regrouping the items). High positive correlations have been found between span for letters, numbers and words, and also between visual and auditory modes of presentation (Kelly, 1954). Most studies have dealt exclusively with span for alphabetical or numerical material; such material is quite uniform, being verbal, highly practiced, and normally used in sequences. An equivalent set of nonverbal measures has still to be developed and may prove hard to achieve. Warrington, Kinsbourne, and Merle (1966) found that normal adult subjects have a lower span for rows of simple curved or oblique lines exposed tachistoscopically than for similarly presented digits or letters. In this case, the items, though simple, were relatively unfamiliar and the subjects appeared to restort to verbal coding in order to retain the sequences. In his clinical investigations of immediate memory, Luria (1966) has sampled a wider range of tasks, including the reproduction of serial hand positions and sequences of geometric patterns. The problem is to devise a constant procedure which will be applicable in different sensory modes and with different kinds of test item. Only with such measures will it be possible to determine (for normal subjects and for patients with different focal brain lesions) how far the capacity of immediate memory depends upon the particular stimuli used.

The issue is not a trivial one: highly specific defects in the immediate reproduction of short sequences have been described in individual cases of severe but focal brain lesion, the defects sometimes appearing to be restricted to one sense modality, and even to one kind of material within that modality. Thus *acoustic-verbal* short-term memory defects (as revealed by the inability to repeat short series of phonemes or disconnected words) have been found to be doubly dissociated, at least in individual patients, from *visual-verbal* defects, and each in turn to be dissociated from defects in the reproduction of short tonal sequences or in the ordering of geometric figures (Luria, Sokolov, and Klinkowski, 1967; Tonkonogii and Tsukkerman, 1965, 1966). Such selective defects are hard to evaluate unless formally similar tasks are used throughout and any differences in task difficulty are taken into account. If modality-specific defects of immediate memory can then be demonstrated, the question of how far they result from subtle perceptual changes affecting that modality will remain to be settled (Aaronson, 1967).

Tests of immediate memory which are not, strictly speaking, measures of span have been used to demonstrate material-specific defects within the auditory modality following different brain lesions. One example of such an immediate-memory test is the dichotic listening technique devised by Broadbent (1954) and subsequently adapted by Kimura (1961) to the study of patients with focal brain lesions. In Kimura's procedure, already mentioned under Audition (p. 322), different digits are presented simultaneously to the two ears by means of stereophonic earphones, six digits in all being presented on any given trial, and the subject is merely required to report all the digits he heard, in any order. Kimura (1962) has argued that such tasks should be regarded as measuring perception not memory, since they do not demand the setting-up of long-term traces and are akin to span tests in their insensitivity to global amnesic disorders. Our own inclusion of the dichotic techniques under the heading of perception reflects the same bias. Nevertheless, the successful performance of these tasks implies a short-term memory process, as does any sequential activity. Kimura found mild deficits in total score on a dichotic-digits task in patients with lesions of the left temporal lobe anterior to the speech zone, but no impairment after right temporal-lobe lesions of comparable locus and extent. Within the left temporal-lobe group, the deficits on this short-term verbal memory task were dissociable in individual cases from the impairment involving long-term verbal memory (visual and auditory) which will be described later in this chapter (Milner, 1967a).

Just as the dichotic-digits task requires the short-term storage of a verbal sequence, so the Seashore Tonal Memory test (Saetveit, Lewis, and Seashore, 1940) requires short-term retention of a brief sequence of nonverbal auditory signals. The storage aspect of this task cannot be regarded as an irrelevant factor in bringing about the defect found after right temporal lobectomy. Patients with right temporal-lobe lesions show normal pitch discrimination for single pairs of notes, but when, as on the Tonal Memory test, they are asked to indicate which note has changed in pitch at the second playing of a simple melody, they fail (Milner, 1962a). Yet the pitch discrimination required is well above their differential threshold. In this case one has to suppose that there is an impairment in the holding, or short-term, memory process, such that the trace of the first sequence of notes decays before the second can be compared with it. This task, like the dichotic-listening task, can be performed normally by patients with global amnesia.

IV. Principal Methods of Investigation

The main techniques which have been used to elucidate memory disorders in man have provided measures of retention after a delay, and not merely of immediate memory. Some of the more important of these methods will be described below. For convenience of exposition they have been grouped under the three headings of *free recall, recognition,* and *learning,* although some techniques do not fit neatly into any of these categories.

Since we believe in the need for sampling a wide range of behavior, we shall not restrict ourselves to the matching techniques justly emphasized by Weiskrantz in the study of experimentally induced amnesia in lower animals. It is true that matching (or recognition) tasks have an important place, especially in studying reversible treatment effects, but failure on a one-trial matching task does not rule out the possibility of demonstrating some retention of new information with intensive practice (that is to say, on a learning task). The objection that learning involves more than memory need not worry us unduly; with the variety of tasks available for studying human behavior, it will be possible to distinguish between failure due to forgetfulness and failure for some quite other reason. Moreover, success on a learning task is proof that some storage of new information is possible, and this very fact is in doubt in some cases of global amnesia.

A special problem arises in trying to test memory under a brief reversible condition, such as that produced by the intra-carotid injection of Sodium Amytal, where one hemisphere is partially inactivated for five to ten minutes by the drug, and the time available for testing memory is shorter still. Under such conditions, testing is hampered not only by shortage of time, but also by the fact that the patient may be anxious and confused as a result of the unfamiliar and unavoidably stressful circumstances in which the memory appraisal is being carried out. Assessment of possible memory change during a brain operation (occurring, say, as a result of electrical stimulation) is open to even more severe limitations. In such cases, the tests have to be extremely simple and the subject has to be thoroughly drilled beforehand in the kind of procedure to be followed, although the particular items to be remembered will be new. When these conditions are respected, it is possible to obtain orderly and meaningful data. These problems will be further illustrated in the context of specific methods.

A. FREE RECALL. In man the most straightforward way of testing memory is to ask the subject to reproduce as much of the original material as he can. In the case of immediate memory span, perfect reproduction is required; for material in excess of the span, the total number of units correctly reproduced is the measure of recall. This method lends itself well to the study of verbal memory, but only if care is taken to ensure that the subject is not unduly anxious when the material is first presented. For this reason, no experimental session with a patient should begin with a free recall test, but with some buffer task which is less threatening.

Any marked disturbance of verbal memory can be expected to affect even the immediate recall of quite short passages of connected prose, although an individual sentence may be correctly repeated immediately upon hearing it. This degree of verbal memory impairment is found in some patients tested in follow-up study after left temporal lobectomy (Milner, 1958, 1967). In such cases, continued attention to new information, whether by paced reading or by listening, will prevent rehearsal of the earlier input, and much information will be lost within a very short time. Slight defects, on the other hand, may only be brought out by further testing of recall after a longer period filled with other activities. By this approach, it has been possible to demonstrate a verbal memory defect preoperatively in patients with longstanding epileptogenic lesions of the left (or dominant) temporal lobe (Milner, 1958). Such patients have trouble recalling the content of short prose passages one hour after hearing them, although their initial reproduction of this material is not significantly inferior to that of other patient groups or of normal control subjects.

The importance of sampling both immediate and delayed recall in trying to uncover mild specific defects can also be illustrated from the free recall of geometric designs after right temporal lobectomy. Such regular, easily reproducible, designs are widely used in the clinic for testing "visual memory" (Benton, 1943; Wechsler, 1945), but this kind of material invites verbal recoding during the preliminary inspection period. In this situation some patients with right temporal-lobe lesions explicitly resort to verbal classification as an aid to memory. In such cases, the immediate reproduction (when the designs are still fresh in the mind, so to speak) may be reasonably accurate, but on further testing, after a delay of an hour or more, the hastily improvised verbal labels do not suffice to reinstate the original pattern, and may even be misleading. If an abstract design is labelled "an envelope," or "a wineglass," the subsequent reproduction without visual representation as a guide may be distorted to resemble the hypothetical object more closely than did the original design. The distorting influence of verbal labels has long been recognized as a powerful factor in normal memory (Bartlett, 1932; Carmichael, Hogan, and Walter, 1932); its role is enhanced in the presence of a lesion which appears to interfere with the more direct storage of visual information. Here, the use of delayed recall enables one to demonstrate a selective defect in visual reproduction after right temporal lobectomy, a defect which is doubly dissociable from the impairment of verbal recall produced by corresponding lesions of the opposite, left hemisphere.

Although free recall methods have been shown to be of value in assessing memory for verbal material or for regular geometric forms, a problem arises when they are used to study retention of material which is difficult to reproduce even with a model to copy. Individual differences in drawing or singing ability will inevitably contaminate the recall of complex irregular patterns or musical phrases, and, in addition, it may be difficult to achieve an objective method of scoring. Moreover, verbal material itself poses similar problems when free recall is used to study memory in patients who are so severely dysphasic that they cannot repeat words or phrases, either in speech or writing, which they may still be able to recognize. For these reasons it can be argued that the free recall method loses its validity as a means of testing memory as soon as the material to be remembered ceases to be made up of well-practiced responses still in the subject's repertoire, and that in these cases we should only use recognition methods.

There is, however, a risk of losing much valuable information if recall is thus summarily abandoned. Precisely because difficulties of execution are not necessarily hierarchically linked to memory disorders, a dissociation between the two can sometimes be most tellingly demonstrated by a recall method used in conjunction with copying from a model. For example, the subject may first be instructed to make as detailed a copy as possible of the well-known Rey-Osterrieth figure (Rey, 1942; Osterrieth, 1944); then some time later he can be asked to reproduce the entire complex pattern from memory. The initial score reflects drawing disability and disorders of space perception; the recall score reflects, in addition, any visual memory impairment. Preliminary experiments at the Montreal Neurological Institute by L. B. Taylor suggest that patients with right temporal-lobe lesions have a selective impairment of recall, whereas the few patients with parietal-lobe lesions whom he has tested showed relatively stable retention, despite having difficulty in copying the figure without distorting it.

Taylor is studying patients by this method before and after different unilateral cortical excisions. He uses the original Rey figure preoperatively and has devised the alternative form shown in Fig. 11-18 for postoperative testing. His results for two patients with differing lesions of the right posterior cortex are shown in Fig. 11-19. The upper figures are the copies; the lower figures represent delayed free recall. On the left are the reproductions of a young man, J. A. D., who had undergone a radical right temporal lobectomy two weeks before. His copy (Fig. 11-19a) is accurate and detailed, earning 33 of the possible 36 points (93 percent). However, when he was asked about 40 minutes later to draw the figure again from memory, he obtained the abnormally low recall score of 13.5 (38 percent) for the inaccurate and simplified drawing shown in Fig. 11-19b. In contrast, Figs. 11-19c and 11-19d on the right show the corresponding drawings of J. Du., a young girl who was tested two weeks after a right parietal cortical excision. At that time she still had considerable weakness and clumsiness of the left hand, which had been her preferred hand for writing and drawing. Both reproductions of the Taylor figure were therefore made with her unpracticed right hand, and no doubt the poor quality of the drawing is due in part to this fact. On other spatial tasks, such as maze learning, this patient showed evidence of spatial difficulty, such as is often seen in acute parietal-lobe injury, and her faulty reproduction of geometric shapes probably reflects the same underlying disorder. Nevertheless, she obtained 27 points (or 75 percent) for the copy, and on free recall later was still able to achieve a score of 22 (61 percent), since the main items of the original design had been preserved in their appropriate relationships, although the execution was extremely shaky.

This is only a pilot study and further data of this kind would be needed before a differential effect of right parietal and right temporal-lobe lesions on the performance of this particular task could be firmly established. The observations on individual cases are introduced here solely for purposes of illustration, to make the point that free recall can sometimes be used to highlight a dissociation between constructive and mnemonic defects.

B. RECOGNITION. In the various procedures involving recognition the study of human memory comes closest to the matching techniques used in work with subhuman forms and to Weiskrantz's conception (Chapter 8) of a memory task as one in which a present event has to be related in some way to an earlier event, the simplest relationships being identity and non-identity. Recognition methods also lend themselves better than free recall to assessing the retention of certain kinds of nonverbal material. Thus, memory for such complex and idiosyncratic patterns as human faces cannot be studied at all by an ordinary method of recall; yet such material has to be sampled if the effects of right-hemisphere lesions are to be appreciated. For these reasons, recognition tasks have been widely used in the study of memory after brain lesions in man.

Recognition is often assumed to be intrinsically easier than free recall. We have all experienced difficulty in recalling a name or a line of verse, only to recognize it immediately upon hearing it again; similarly, in most experiments involving both recall and recognition measures, more test items are correctly recognized than are recalled. Such comparisons are not, however, valid, since, as Judd and Sutherland (1959) have pointed out, there are normally a far greater number of possible competing responses in recall tasks than in recognition, where the number of items among which a choice has to be made is usually both finite and small. When this factor is controlled, Davis, Sutherland, and Judd (1961) find that at least as much information is transmitted in free recall as in recognition, so that recall is not necessarily the more demanding activity.

A major variable in recognition tasks is the similarity of the items among which a choice has to be made. As this similarity increases, a more and more precise memory of the original event is required in order

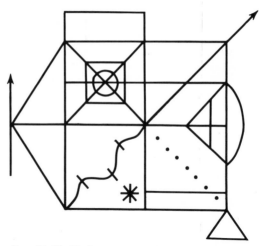

FIG. 11-18. Taylor version of the Rey figure.

for a correct choice to be achieved. Free recall offers a fairly direct estimate of the richness or poverty of the original impression, provided of course that the material is reproducible. On a recognition task, in contrast, if the inter-item similarity is low, successful performance may be achieved by remembering only the more salient features of the original material. Under such conditions, even verbal recognition tasks tend to be performed by memorization of only a fraction of the whole item (say, one or two distinctive letters), whereas free recall usually requires reproduction of the whole (McNulty, 1965, 1966). With material which is not primarily verbal, such as visual designs, there is a still greater likelihood that when the individual items are dissimilar recognition will be based only on the more striking cues. This is particularly undesirable if the task is intended to be language-free, since these cues may have been remembered by verbal recoding. On the other hand, if the inter-item similarity is high, then the distinction between the old and the new must be based upon slight variations of pattern which are not readily verbalized. In the application of recognition techniques to the elucidation of memory defect after brain lesions, it is such tasks which have proven most sensitive to right hemisphere lesions as opposed to left.

Many different procedures can be included under the broad heading of recognition tasks. Some of the more powerful are selected for discussion below.

1. *Delayed Matching from Sample.* The simplest form of a delayed matching task is one in which a single item is presented for scrutiny and then, after a short interval, the subject is required to pick out the identical item from an array of possible stimuli. This technique, which corresponds closely to the delayed matching tasks applied to lower primates, has been used by De Renzi and Spinnler (1966a, b) to compare the effects of left and right hemisphere lesions in man on the recognition of pictures of common objects and photographs of human faces. A variant of this method was also used earlier by Milner (1960, 1968) to study face recognition after different cortical excisions. In the latter version, an array of twelve different faces was first presented,

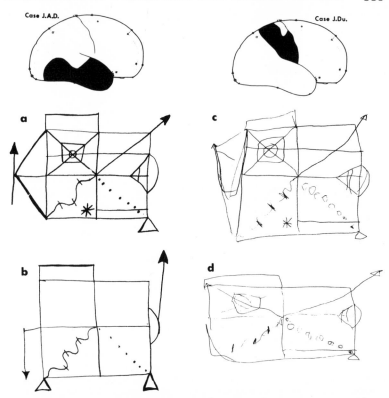

FIG. 11-19. Reproductions of the Taylor figure by two patients with different posterior cortical excisions for epilepsy. Case J. A. D., right temporal lobectomy. Case J. Du., right parietal lobectomy. Above: lateral extent of removal. Below: a and c, copy from model; b and d, delayed recall.

allowing ample time for inspection; recognition was then tested after a short delay, by requiring the subject to select the twelve matching faces from a group of 25 photographs (Munn, 1951). This particular set of material was chosen because it was difficult to use verbal coding to categorize the faces; patients with right temporal-lobe lesions would frequently complain that there were "so many faces to remember" and that "all the girls had long hair and necklaces." The simultaneous presentation of twelve faces does, however, introduce an additional and undesirable spatial element into the task, and hence there is the risk that patients with parietal-lobe lesions (or even patients with recently acquired hemianopias) may not scan the array completely during the inspection period. Despite this disadvantage, this quickly administered face-recognition task has proven extremely sensitive to lesions of the right temporal lobe, whereas patients with lesions of the left temporal lobe, or of the frontal or parietal cortex of either hemisphere, have obtained normal scores under all conditions of testing. The technique has also been of interest in uncovering the fact that normal subjects make more errors with zero delay than with a 90-second intra-trial interval. This unexpected finding suggests that some *nonverbal rehearsal* of the immediate trace of the visual material facilitates subsequent recognition, perhaps by making the trace more resistant to inter-ference, as the introspective reports of the subjects would suggest.

Delayed matching tasks share with free recall the advantage of being easily understood, even by confused or retarded subjects. Unlike free recall, they arouse little anxiety and can yield valid data not only under normal conditions but also under conditions of stress. For these reasons, we have come to depend upon such recognition tasks for the detection of memory loss in patients temporarily deprived of the functioning of the major part of one cerebral hemisphere by a technique which was mentioned earlier (pp. 324, 335): namely, injection of the barbiturate, Sodium Amytal, into the internal carotid artery of that side (Milner, Branch, and Rasmussen, 1962; Milner, 1966). The Amytal technique was developed in order to investigate speech lateralization in left-handed and ambidextrous subjects (Wada and Rasmussen, 1960). However, the risk to memory inherent in the operation of unilateral temporal lobectomy, whenever the patient harbors an additional and possibly unsuspected lesion of the mesial temporal region of the opposite hemi-sphere (Penfield and Milner, 1958), has led us to apply the method as a preoperative screening device in cases of temporal-lobe epilepsy. Here the assumption is that the unilateral carotid-Amytal injection will provoke transiently the effects of a temporal lobectomy.

In this procedure, 200 mg. of 10 percent Sodium Amytal solution are injected within three seconds into the common carotid artery of one side, with the patient counting aloud slowly, legs flexed, arms raised, and fingers moving. The immediate effects of this treatment typically include contralateral hemiplegia, hemianopia and partial hemianaesthesia, from which there is complete recovery in about six minutes. If the anaesthetized hemisphere is dominant for speech, dys-phasia will also be produced, sometimes lasting for ten to fifteen minutes. Most patients are able to cooperate with the examiner throughout this period (apart from an initial few seconds of con-fusion), so that it is possible to carry out simple memory testing (including delayed matching) shortly after the injection has been made.

To uncover a possible anterograde amnesia, two pictures of common objects are shown to the patient about three minutes after the injection and before the hemiparesis has cleared. He is then distracted from this memory task by being asked to repeat series of digits forwards and backwards, after which he is tested for recall of the pictures that he has just seen. If he is unable to recall one or both of them (as is often the case), we proceed to recognition testing, after a brief interruption for the assessment of motor function. The patient is shown a series of nine pictures, one after the other, and has to say, for each, whether he has seen it before or not. All this time he has been gradually recovering from the effects of the drug, so that, when recognition is tested, strength of grip has usually returned to normal. This does not matter, however; for this task to be considered a valid test of anterograde amnesia, we simply require that the patient be hemiparetic (but alert and responsive) at the time that the two pic-tures are first shown to him.

In this application of the delayed-matching procedure, the main purpose is to detect a global amnesia, and therefore the patient is allowed, in fact he is instructed, to name the pictures at the time of initial presentation and again during the testing of recognition, thus permitting the use of both verbal and nonverbal cues. It is noteworthy that a patient often recognizes as familiar a picture which he has been unable to name when it was first presented, because the Amytal injection had rendered him temporarily dysphasic. Conversely, an amnesic patient may fail to recognize pictures which he had named correctly, thus illustrating the dissociability of nominal dysphasia and generalized memory loss (Milner, 1966).

In the examples of delayed matching considered so far, the items among which a choice has had to be made have varied along many dimensions, and responses could only be scored as *right* or *wrong*. If, instead, the stimuli vary along a continuum, it is possible to establish a discrimination gradient and determine the intra-trial interval at which the sample stimulus loses control over the subject's response. Thus, Sidman and Stoddard (1966) have presented an ellipse as the sample and then required the subject (after a variable delay) to choose the matching ellipse from a group of eight which varied only in the length of the vertical axis. Scoville and Milner's patient, H. M., with a bilateral medial temporal-lobe resection and global amnesia, was unable to achieve a correct match with delays greater than 5 seconds, but his choices resembled the sample ellipse closely up to intervals of about 30 seconds, after which the sample ceased to influence the post-delay choice significantly (Sidman, Stoddard, and Mohr, in press). Normal children are said to bridge intervals of 40 seconds or more without error, and the authors attribute H. M.'s poor performance to a failure to develop a verbal code which would permit rehearsal during the delay. This argument is, however, not altogether compelling. Where verbal rehearsal is clearly appropriate, H. M. seems to make use of it. Thus, when trigrams were used instead of ellipses in the delayed matching procedure, he was observed to be overtly rehearsing this explicitly verbal (though not easily pronounceable) material through-out the intra-trial interval, and he was capable of normal and accurate matching over long delays. The question at issue is whether it is in fact obligatory to use verbal coding for success on the ellipse-matching task. This matter will be taken up again later, after related findings derived from other recognition tasks have been described.

Delayed matching can be administered somewhat differently from any of the ways outlined above, by having either the subject or the experimenter vary the post-delay stimulus continuously, or in very small steps, until it is judged identical to the sample. This is, of course, a standard psychophysical procedure, with an intra-trial delay added. Ghent, Mishkin, and Teuber (1962) adopted this technique to study memory for both verbal and nonverbal material in men with pene-trating brain wounds. It is of interest that on these tasks, as on the delayed matching of faces, frontal-lobe lesions produced no detectable impairment.

2. *Paired Comparison Following an Inspection Series: A Variant of Delayed Matching.* In a recent and rather unusual modification of delayed matching, Shepard (1967) first presented a very long inspec-tion series of 612 pictures, all quite different from one another and chosen to be visually interesting. In the next stage of the experiment, 68 of the original items were presented for a second time, each one being paired with a new picture. The subject's task was to identify in each pair the picture which had appeared before. This method led to nearly perfect performance for picture recognition, and also yielded

a high level of recognition for words and sentences when these were presented in the same way. The great advantage of this method over most recognition procedures is that it permits repeated testing at different delay intervals, because a fresh subset of stimuli can be used each time. Despite a single brief exposure to so much material, normal subjects show remarkably efficient recognition many hours afterwards. This method has not yet been adapted to the study of behavior after brain lesions or during temporary brain dysfunction, and in its present form the very long inspection series might make it unacceptable to some patients, and, if so, invalidate the results. Nevertheless, it is a potentially useful technique, which would allow one, for example, to compare recognition under the influence of a drug with recognition in the normal state.

3. *Delayed Paired Comparison.* It was pointed out earlier that the standard delayed-response procedure is inappropriate for use with man, since even long delays are readily bridged by verbal mediating cues. However, a somewhat different procedure for studying retention over short time intervals in experimental animals (Konorski, 1959) has been successfully adapted for use with human subjects (Stepien and Sierpinski, 1960; Prisko, 1963). This is the *compound-stimulus* method, in which two stimuli in the same sensory modality are presented in succession, separated by a short interval; the subject then has to say whether the second stimulus of the pair was, or was not, identical with the first. On half the trials, the two stimuli are the same; on half they are different. The task thus requires that the subject retain an impression of the first stimulus in order to compare the second one with it; at the same time he must be able to suppress the possible interfering effects of previous trials. Values are assigned to the stimuli such that the smallest difference within a given pair is well above threshold when one stimulus follows the other without delay, thereby ensuring that this is a memory rather than a discrimination task. A further requirement is that the comparison stimuli should not lend themselves to verbal categorization, otherwise this technique would be open to the same objections as delayed response.

Prisko used this delayed paired comparison method to study memory for both auditory and visual material in patients with different brain lesions. Five different tasks were constructed, each embodying a different kind of stimulus: clicks, light flashes, tones, colors, and irregular nonsense patterns. For clicks and flashes (both of which varied only with respect to rate), the frequencies were chosen so that they could not easily be counted, and, similarly, on the color task the stimuli were limited to different shades of red. To reduce further the risk of verbal labeling, at least five stimulus values were used on each task. Thus, verbal rehearsal was rendered difficult, but one cannot be sure that it was altogether excluded.

These tasks, even with a 60-second interval and an interpolated distraction, proved extremely easy for normal subjects, who averaged about one error in twelve trials under all conditions of testing. In addition, patients with unilateral temporal-lobe lesions obtained normal scores on all five tasks, except for an impairment on visual pattern recognition specific to the right temporal-lobe group. In contrast, unilateral frontal lobectomy was followed by marked impairment on three of the five tasks (clicks, flashes and colors), each of which involved only five stimuli recurring in different combinations throughout the test. On the nonsense figures task, where each stimulus pair was unique, the performance of patients with frontal-lobe lesions was indistinguishable from that of normal control subjects.

An analysis of those paired comparison tasks on which patients with frontal-lobe lesions do poorly and those on which they do well suggests that patients with these lesions have a heightened susceptibility to interference from preceding trials, rather than a disturbance of any basic mechanism concerned with information storage (Milner, 1964). If memory is narrowly conceived, then one can still maintain (as we have done) that the frontal-lobe patient does not have a memory impairment, but this conclusion may be overhasty. The results from the delayed comparison tests indicate that frontal lobectomy affects the ability to discriminate the most recent stimulus from ones appearing some time before; just as, in the traditional delayed-response task, monkeys with frontal-lobe lesions could be said to have difficulty in discriminating the most recently baited object from one baited on an earlier trial. If Yntema and Trask (1963) are right in supposing that items in memory normally carry time-tags which permit the discrimination of the more from the less recent, then it is possible that this time-marking process is disturbed after frontal lobectomy, and insofar as such temporal distinctions are blurred the frontal-lobe patient may be said to have a memory defect. Experiments bearing directly upon the discrimination of recency by patients with different brain lesions might shed further light on this question.

In the meantime, the main interest of Prisko's study is that it demonstrates impairment after frontal lobectomy in man on a task which embodies an intra-trial delay as an essential feature. There is thus a suggestion of convergence between the results of human and animal studies of frontal-lobe function. Against this is the fact that Weiskrantz and Mingay found that frontal lobectomy in the monkey had little effect on the performance of a paired comparison task modeled on the Konorski method (Weiskrantz, see Chapter 8). Such tasks are, however, difficult ones for monkeys to learn, and the lengthy training period may have attenuated any postoperative changes.

Prisko also tested the amnesic patient, H. M., and found him to be severely impaired on all five tasks with a 60-second intra-trial delay, regardless of whether or not a distraction was interpolated in the interval; performance at zero delay was normal. For the two auditory tasks (tones and clicks), responses remained accurate up to 30 seconds and were still above chance at 60 seconds. On the visual tasks, performance deteriorated more rapidly with increasing delay, showing marked impairment at 30 seconds and falling to a chance level by 60 seconds.

H. M.'s inability to recognize simple visual stimuli after delays of more than half a minute is consistent with the findings of Sidman, Stoddard, and Mohr for the same patient on the delayed matching of ellipses. The failure on these tasks was, however, unexpected and remains puzzling, since all our other data on this patient indicate that his short-term memory is essentially normal. Either this assumption is false (at least with respect to material of the kind used by Prisko), or these delayed comparison tasks require more than short-term memory for their successful performance. If the latter is the case, then the critical question is no longer "Why does H. M. fail?" but "How do normal subjects succeed?"

This question is still unresolved, but various possibilities come to mind. For example, the preliminary testing at zero delay may put the normal subject at an advantage compared with the amnesic patient, since it provides him with an opportunity to familiarize himself with the full range of possible stimuli and build up a reference scale. With only five stimulus values, all readily discriminable one from another, this would be easily accomplished (Miller, 1956). Then, on proceeding to delayed matching with a 60-second intra-trial interval, the normal subject would not have to retain an absolute impression of the first stimulus of a pair, but could merely remember its position on the five-point scale. Another possibility, and one which cannot be entirely ruled out, is that, in non-amnesic subjects, long-term representations of such simple visual and auditory percepts as a particular shade of red or the pitch of a pure tone may be rapidly established in the absence of interfering material of the same kind. King (1963a, b, 1965) has found that normal subjects can match simple visual and auditory stimuli with considerable accuracy and stability over intervals ranging from 15 seconds to 28 days, thus taking one well beyond the range of any hypothetical short-term memory process. Again, in a rather different task involving an interpolated continuous interfering stimulus, Wickelgren (in preparation) has found it necessary to invoke an intermediate-term memory component to account for pitch recognition in normal subjects over delays ranging from 1 to 180 seconds. Thus, on many counts, it seems quite probable that Prisko's tasks are not solely dependent upon short-term memory, in which case H. M.'s failure on them would not imply that he had a short-term memory defect.

By now it will be evident that one difficulty with the method of delayed paired comparison as applied to man is that we do not know how far it can be considered language-free. What might help here would be to apply Prisko's visual tasks to patients with section of the cerebral commissures, taking care to restrict the visual input to one hemisphere. If 60-second intervals could be bridged just as successfully when the information was channelled to the right, nondominant hemisphere, we would be more confident that we were dealing with a nonverbal task, although this hemisphere does appear to have some rudimentary verbal capacity (Sperry and Gazzaniga, 1967).

4. *Continuous Recognition.* In addition to posing problems of interpretation, delayed paired-comparison tasks have the serious drawback of being excessively time-consuming. We have seen that the normal subjects in Prisko's study made few errors with a 60-second intra-trial interval, and any attempt to work with still longer intervals would certainly prove tedious for both experimenter and subject. One way of getting round this problem is to use a continuous recognition procedure, in which a series of single stimulus-items is presented, one immediately after the other, and the subject has to decide for each whether it is old or new. If items of high similarity are used, this method allows one to study recognition over a short time-scale, since the procedure maximizes interference effects. It also permits the systematic investigation of recognition errors as a function of the number of other items intervening between the first and second presentations of a given stimulus (Shepard and Teghtsoonian, 1961). Continuous recognition also comes closer than paired comparison to the

conditions of everyday life, where one is constantly trying to retain recently acquired information in the face of changing environmental cues.

The continuous recognition method has been used extensively at the Montreal Neurological Institute to study the specific memory disorders produced by unilateral cortical excisions and also the global amnesias associated with bilateral mesial temporal-lobe destruction. In a "Recurring Nonsense Figures" task which was to become the prototype for tasks in other modalities, Kimura (1963) demonstrated convincingly that visual pattern recognition is impaired after right temporal lobectomy but not after similarly placed and equally extensive lesions on the left. In this task, the subject is shown a series of 160 cards (presented one at a time for 3 seconds), on each of which an unfamiliar figure is drawn; this may be either an irregular nonsense pattern (Fig. 11-20) or a regular geometric design. Eight of these figures are repeated in every block of 20 cards, interspersed at random with figures which occur only once. The first 20 cards constitute an inspection series, to which the subject is not required to respond verbally; thereafter, for each of the 140 test cards, he has to say "yes" if he thinks that the pattern has appeared before and "no" if he thinks that it has not. Normal subjects make many recognition errors within the first block of 20 test cards. They not only fail to identify the recurring figures immediately; they also show the very rapid build-up of false positive responses (mistaking new items for old) that seems to be a feature of the continuous recognition method (Melton, Sameroff, and Schubot, 1963; Shepard and Teghtsoonian, 1961). They show, however, considerable improvement from the first to the second block of test cards, with performance leveling off thereafter. In contrast, the patients with right temporal-lobe lesions in Kimura's study gave an abnormally high number of false positive responses throughout, and this fact contributed largely to their poor performance on the test as a whole.

FIG. 11-20. Sample item from Recurring Nonsense Figures task (Kimura, 1963). (By permission of Grune & Stratton.)

For convenience of analysis, Kimura used a net score, obtained by subtracting the total number of false positive responses from the total number of times a recurring figure was correctly identified as such. To facilitate comparison with her data, similarly derived single scores have been used in the analyses of data from continuous recognition tasks in other modalities. Nevertheless, it might be both more elegant and more informative to analyze separately the responses to recurring and non-recurring stimuli, thus permitting a more systematic study of response bias.

Kimura's findings were unambiguous in indicating a defect in visual pattern recognition after right temporal lobectomy; however, they raised fresh questions as to the nature and specificity of the defect. Thus, it could be that right temporal lobectomy simply resulted in a heightened tendency to perceive visual stimuli as familiar, when in fact they were new. Such a supposition is not too far-fetched when one considers the frequency with which experiences of *déjà vu* have been reported by epileptic patients after electrical stimulation in the periamygdaloid region of the right hemisphere (Mullan and Penfield, 1959). If this were the case, one would expect the right temporal-lobe group to show the same tendency with other kinds of visual material. If, instead, their defect is specific to the recognition of nonverbal visual patterns, they should have no difficulty with a continuous recognition task which uses only verbal material. To answer these questions, such a visual-verbal task was devised, using words, nonsense syllables, and three-digit numbers; the verbal and nonverbal recognition tasks were then administered on successive days to a further group of patients who had undergone unilateral temporal lobectomy.

The results were clearcut and emphasize anew the complementary role of the two temporal lobes in visual memory processes. On the Recurring Nonsense Figures task, Kimura's finding of impairment after right but not after left temporal lobectomy was confirmed, but on the verbal form of the test the converse was true: for the task as a whole and for each of the three kinds of verbal material treated separately, patients with left temporal-lobe lesions in the dominant hemisphere for speech were impaired, whereas patients with right non-dominant temporal-lobe lesions obtained normal scores (Milner and Kimura, 1964; Milner, 1967). Moreover, the left temporal-lobe group made more false positive responses on the verbal task than did the right temporal-lobe group, whose performance on this test differed in no way from that of normal control subjects; again the converse held for the nonverbal form of the task. In this study, unlike Kimura's, there was a high variance in the incidence of false positive responses in the impaired groups on either task. Such individual differences suggest that the false positive response is merely one way of dealing with a difficulty in recognition.

The differential sensitivity of these two formally similar visual recognition tasks to lesions of the left and right temporal lobes led us to adapt the *recurring stimuli* technique to the study of recognition in other sense modalities. In particular, it seemed desirable to construct a nonverbal auditory recognition task, using recurring sound patterns that would not call for a high degree of musical sophistication in the listener and yet would not readily permit of verbal labeling. It was expected that with such material, as with the Seashore Tonal Memory test, impairment would be found after right temporal lobectomy, but not after left. The material chosen consisted of 78 samples of birdsong (or other relatively unfamiliar animal sounds) which had been transcribed to tape from commercial recordings. Each sound lasted approximately 3 seconds, and the same procedure was followed as for the two visual tasks, with the possibly important difference that between successive stimuli there was a silent interval of 5 seconds, which could be prolonged by stopping the tape if the subject had not yet given his response. On the two visual tasks, there were no blank cards, so that the subject was still looking at the stimulus as he made his judgment of "old" or "new".

This "Recurring Birdsongs" task yields a clear learning curve over successive blocks of trials, but it is more difficult than either of the visual tasks for normal subjects. Contrary to our predictions of a lateralized defect, temporal lobectomy in *either* hemisphere was found to impair performance on this test, and although patients with right temporal-lobe lesions did tend to make more errors than patients with corresponding lesions on the left, this difference was slight and not statistically significant. Moreover, the impairment in both temporal-lobe groups was quite mild when contrasted with the marked defect shown by the right temporal-lobe group on the visual pattern recognition task. Nevertheless, the auditory defect was clearly related to the temporal locus of the cortical excision, because a group of patients with more extensive lesions of the left or right frontal lobe obtained normal scores.

If we ask why we failed to find either a clear-cut right-left difference or a severe defect on this difficult auditory recognition task, the answer may lie in the very complexity of the sound patterns used. The birdsongs, insect noises, and other animal sounds varied amongst themselves along many dimensions, including intensity, tone quality, and rhythm as well as pitch. With this multiplicity of auditory cues, recognition did not depend exclusively on differences in melodic pattern. This fact could account for the right temporal-lobe group showing only a mild impairment; it does not of course explain why the left temporal-lobe group was also significantly impaired on this nonverbal task, a finding which merits further investigation with other kinds of auditory material.

The normal performance of the frontal-lobe group on the Recurring Birdsongs task was surprising, because there are features of the continuous recognition procedure which make this kind of task difficult for patients after frontal lobectomy, and on Kimura's Recurring Nonsense Figures task patients with frontal-lobe lesions are as severely impaired as patients with right temporal-lobe lesions, although they may obtain normal scores when visual pattern recognition is tested in a different way (Milner, 1964). Moreover, as card succeeds card with monotonous regularity, the patient with a frontal-lobe lesion often appears to be saying "yes" or "no" either haphazardly or perseveratively, without due regard to the specific judgment he is being called upon to make, although he can verbalize the test instructions without difficulty. Frequently such patients change their responses in the nick of time (saying "Yes, . . . I mean no" significantly more often than other subjects); they are equally likely to tell you that when they said "yes," "a few cards back," it should have been "no;" and presumably still more likely to let the overhasty wrong response pass unnoticed. One patient with a right frontal lobectomy commented after completing the Nonsense Figures task that "half way through the test so many figures were going round and round in my head that I couldn't think anymore."

It is appropriate to say that such patients show a heightened susceptibility to proactive interference, but the label does not explain the disorder. Nor does it explain why the same patients perform normally on the more difficult auditory recognition task, unless the short pause between stimuli or the lively and more interesting character of the birdsong material could compensate for the confusion engendered by the continuous recognition procedure. Here the problem focuses clearly on the importance of the specific method of testing, the next step being to modify the visual task until it resembles the auditory one more closely, with the prediction that such changes will result in improved performance by patients with frontal-lobe lesions. In the meantime, the normal performance of patients after radical frontal lobectomy on a difficult auditory discrimination task provides indirect

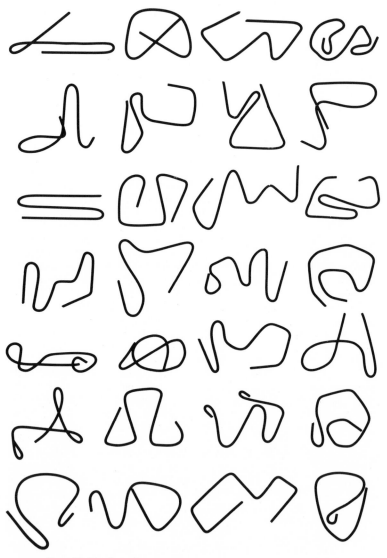

Fig. 11-21. Sample items from Tactual Recurring Figures task (Corkin, 1964). Recurring patterns shown in top row.

support for the view that the auditory-discrimination defects produced by frontal-lobe lesions in the monkey (Blum, 1952; Weiskrantz and Mishkin, 1958; Gross and Weiskrantz, 1964) have little to do with audition as such.

Finally, the method of recurring stimuli has been applied to the study of tactual pattern recognition (Corkin, 1964). In this case, by presenting blocks of stimuli alternately to the left and right hand, it has been possible to compare performance for the hand ipsilateral and the hand contralateral to a lateralized brain lesion, as well as comparing the effects of differently-placed lesions within a hemisphere upon performance on the test as a whole (Milner, Taylor, and Corkin, 1967). The original purpose of the study was to determine whether right temporal lobectomy would produce an impairment in tactual form recognition commensurate with the well-established defect in visual recognition. In fact, the most interesting finding concerned the frontal not the temporal lobes.

In order to facilitate comparison across modalities, the stimulus-items used in the Tactual Recurring Figures task were modeled on Kimura's visual nonsense patterns, although they were of necessity much simpler in design. They consist of 40 different irregular abstract patterns, each made from a 10-inch piece of wire coat-hanger, 0.1 inches in diameter (Fig. 11-21). The patient is first given eight of these patterns to feel, one at a time, for ten seconds, using the hand ipsilateral to his lesion. In each of eight subsequent test trials, four of the original patterns recur, intermingled randomly with new ones. The patient is instructed to feel each pattern carefully and then say "yes" if he thinks that he has felt it before and "no" if he thinks that he is feeling it for the first time. The hands are alternated on successive test trials.

All patients who have been tested in this way have also undergone extensive quantitative examination of sensory discrimination on the hand, by the methods described earlier in this chapter, because we were particularly interested in knowing whether defects on the Tactual Recurring Figures task could occur in subjects with normal sensory status. In the Montreal series of patients undergoing cortical excision for the relief of epilepsy, it is unusual to find lasting sensory defects unless the lesion invades the postcentral gyrus (Corkin, Milner, and Rasmussen, 1964). It was thus possible to compare the performance of groups of patients with frontal, temporal, and posterior parietal-lobe lesions on Tactual Recurring Figures, all the patients having normal sensory thresholds. The results were unexpected: patients with lesions invading the frontal lobe were significantly impaired on the contralateral hand, whereas the mean scores for patients with posterior lesions were normal and equal for the two hands. No impairment in tactual pattern recognition on the ipsilateral hand was seen in any patient group.

That patients with frontal-lobe lesions should be impaired on a tactual and proprioceptive task which embodies a continuous recognition procedure is not in itself surprising, if we bear in mind the difficulty such patients experience with the visual continuous recognition tasks. What is surprising is that the tactual defect, if it is of the same kind as the visual one, should be limited to the contralateral hand; this finding suggests a particularly close functional link between the central and frontal cortex of the same hemisphere.

Up to this point we have been considering the method of recurring stimuli either as a tool for analyzing the specific defects produced by unilateral temporal-lobe lesions or as a technique peculiarly sensitive to the changes produced by frontal lobectomy. However, the introduction of items which recur at irregular intervals throughout the test means that we are measuring learning over repeated trials, with the steady stream of interpolated items making rehearsal well-nigh impossible. It is reasonable to suppose that such tasks involve more than short-term memory, and hence one would predict that patients with continuous anterograde amnesia (such as Scoville and Milner's Case H. M.) would make very poor scores on all versions of the task, because they would fail to show the normal progress from one block of stimuli to the next. This is in fact what happens: low scores are obtained on both verbal and nonverbal continuous recognition tasks by patients with even attenuated forms of the amnesic syndrome. Indeed, the recurring stimuli tasks have proven to be more sensitive indicators of generalized memory disorder than have the delayed paired-comparison tasks of Prisko. In one important respect, however, the results obtained by these two methods are in striking agreement: amnesic subjects show more severe defects on the visual than on the auditory recognition tasks, although H. M. is certainly impaired on both. There is some indication in Prisko's study that the auditory paired comparison tasks were also a little easier than the visual ones for normal subjects, but this is not true for the continuous recognition tasks. Here, the most likely explanation of the better performance of amnesic subjects on the auditory task (Recurring Birdsongs) is that the pause between stimuli permits some silent rehearsal of the sound patterns, whereas the visual tasks are more truly continuous. An alternative interpretation of the findings, but one that seems less plausible, is that the visual memory defect had been enhanced by inadvertent damage to the inferior temporal neocortex. Against this is the fact that H. M. performs better than most of our normal control subjects on such complex perceptual tasks as the Mooney Faces Test and the McGill Picture Anomalies, tasks which are sensitive to lesions of the right temporal neocortex (Milner, 1958, 1968; Lansdell, 1968).

The method of *recurring stimuli* has been discussed in some detail because it provides one of the few instances in which comparable recognition tasks in different modalities (sampling both verbal and nonverbal material) have been applied to large groups of patients with brain lesions of known locus and extent. The results obtained thus far have contributed to the analysis of both material-specific and general memory disorders, and the method could clearly be extended to other kinds of stimuli, the sensitivity of the technique to mild defects making it a useful research tool. It does, however, have the practical limitation that performance falls off sharply with age, so that the tasks are best suited to young adult subjects and cannot be used at all with elderly or confused patients. It is, of course, a commonplace that older subjects do poorly on memory tests, but the continuous recognition procedure with its deliberate exploitation of retroactive and proactive interference appears to handicap them particularly.

The amount of data already gathered with the recurring-stimuli tasks enhances the value of the tasks in their present form. Nevertheless, there are ambiguities in the data which could perhaps be resolved if the techniques were modified slightly. These concern the subject's response bias, over which there is at present no control. Thus, whether a subject calls a particular item "old" will depend not only upon memory but also on how confident he has to feel before he will say that a particular item has appeared more than once. The criteria will be different for different patients and possibly for the same patient at different times during a given test. The discrepancy between recognition and response is sometimes apparent to the examiner, when the subject hesitates before calling a recurring item "new"; hence, it would probably be worthwhile to record response latencies and, also, if possible, obtain confidence ratings from the subject himself. Such supplementary data would permit a more careful analysis of the recognition process. An alternative solution would be to use the forced choice method described by Shepard and Chang (1963). In their modification of the continuous recognition procedure, all but the first few items are presented in pairs, one member of each pair being old and the other new. The subject then merely has to decide which of the two items has already appeared in an earlier pair. With such a symmetrical design, the results should be independent of any over-all bias in favor of calling items new or old. The forced-choice technique would also open up the possibility of manipulating the similarity between the old and new items of each pair.

C. LEARNING. Learning over repeated trials has entered indirectly into some of the procedures already mentioned, and most conspicuously into the continuous recognition tasks, in which a few stimuli recur several times during the test and the subject becomes gradually more proficient in discriminating the old from the new. In such tasks the subject is not, however, informed as to the correctness or incorrectness of his responses. In the methods that we are about to consider, an attempt is made to bring subjects to a criterion of mastery on a particular task, usually with knowledge of results as a guide.

Such methods (which involve repeated exposure to the test material, spread out over many minutes and sometimes over several days) are in some ways less elegant than one-trial learning tasks, which permit one to study the rate of forgetting of a particular event. Nor can they be used to assess the transient interfering effects of brain stimulation, carotid-Amytal injection and the like. Nevertheless, they have a place in the study of long-lasting memory disorder, and greatly increase the range and complexity of behavior which can be sampled.

Learning a task to a particular criterion has sometimes been used as a prelude to studying subsequent defects in recall of what has been learned. The assumption here is that all subjects are at the same level at the completion of training, so that any differences in performance at a later time would be attributable to differences in memory. Such an assumption is rarely justified; when a complex task is learned over many trials, parts of the task will inevitably have been overlearned by the time that criterion is reached for the task as a whole. Yet such criterion training can be informative in cases where the group which takes more trials to learn also proves to be the group which forgets more quickly, showing both a defect in learning and a defect in recall.

The second and less trivial application of learning tasks is to compare the effects of different lesions upon acquisition itself, and, in the special case of a global anterograde amnesia, to determine whether or not the patient can learn if given extended practice. In what follows, we shall be mainly concerned with this problem, viewed in the context of a few specific techniques which have been singled out either because they have already been used with amnesic patients, or because they have been of value in demonstrating the differential effects of left and right hemisphere lesions.

1. *Paired-associate Learning.* Probably the most widely used technique in both clinical and laboratory studies of human memory is that of paired-associate learning, the reason being that such tasks are easy to administer and can be objectively scored. Like most rote learning tasks, they are highly sensitive indicators of mild amnesic states (Zangwill, 1943), although performance may also be impaired in depressed or anxious subjects.

The paired-associate experiment in its most typical form involves the oral presentation of verbal material. Lists of arbitrarily paired words (e.g., apple-chair, inch-tree) are read aloud at a slow, regular rate; recall is then tested by presenting only the first word of each pair, in random sequence, the subject being requested to respond with the word which had been paired with it. If he fails to reply within ten seconds, or responds incorrectly, the examiner supplies the correct word. The whole series may be repeated until all responses are correct (in which case some of the pairs will have been over-practiced), or, as criterion is reached for a given pair, that pair may be omitted from succeeding trials (Inglis, 1959). Lists of word pairs can equally well be presented visually, at a regular pace, with the subject writing his response instead of saying it aloud (Milner, 1967).

In an interesting variant of verbal paired-associate learning, Nelson (1953) taught subjects the meanings of words with which they were previously unfamiliar. The task necessitates giving a vocabulary test until the subject fails to define five consecutive words. He is then told the meaning of each of these words, and testing is repeated until he has correctly defined each new word three times. Retention of the word meanings can be assessed again 24 hours later, as a measure of delayed recall. The procedure followed differs from that of the usual rote learning task in that the exact wording of the definition given to the subject is deliberately changed from trial to trial.

Patients with focal lesions of the left temporal lobe in the dominant hemisphere for speech are impaired on these various measures of verbal associative learning (Meyer and Yates, 1955; Milner, 1962a, 1967), whereas patients with lesions anywhere in the right hemisphere perform normally, as do patients with radical removals from the dominant frontal lobe anterior to Broca's area (Milner, 1967). These results are entirely consistent with those obtained for free recall of narrative prose, and indicate the specific contribution of the left anterior temporal region to verbal memory.

The findings for associative learning of nonverbal material are less clear-cut, but this is probably due to a shortcoming of the method itself. In principle there should be no objection to adapting the paired-associate technique to nonverbal items, although learning would usually have to be tested by recognition rather than recall (Meyer, 1957). In practice, however, we run into the problem that the subject often resorts to verbal coding to establish a link between the arbitrarily paired items, even when the material to be associated is not explicitly verbal. Not only will pictures of common objects evoke implicit naming responses; abstract designs of the kind used by Kimura in the Recurring Figures task will also, if presented in pairs, be analyzed verbally in an *effort after meaning* (Bartlett, 1932). It is probably for this reason that Meyer (1957) found no impairment after either right or left temporal lobectomy in the paired-associate learning of tactile patterns or visual geometric designs and that De Renzi (1968) found greater impairment after left-hemisphere lesions than after right in the paired-associate learning of visual patterns. In the latter case, the interpretation in terms of verbal coding is particularly convincing because the finding was reversed when the same subjects were tested with a continuous recognition procedure. One would therefore conclude that paired-associate learning is an inappropriate method for studying the nonverbal aspects of memory.

2. *Extended Span.* Tests of immediate memory span have already been described: they require the repetition in correct sequence of a number of disconnected items, usually single digits. Such immediate recall is frequently unimpaired in severe amnesic disorders but when the span is exceeded by even one digit there may be a sharp discontinuity of performance, because all the information can no longer be maintained in short-term memory. If a series longer than the span is presented repeatedly, normal subjects soon learn the sequence, whereas even moderately amnesic patients will require many more trials and may not learn within the limits of testing (Zangwill, 1943). This observation forms the basis of the method of *extended span*, in which the number of presentations required for one correct reproduction of a series provides an inverse measure of learning. Sets of digits of gradually increasing length are used, and at each step the number of trials required for learning is determined.

Drachman and Arbit (1966) have recently applied the extended-span technique to a group of amnesic patients which included H. M., the patient with bilateral mesial temporal-lobe lesions and profound anterograde amnesia. The normal control subjects in this study could be trained to reproduce up to 20-digit series in a few trials. In contrast, the amnesic subjects were markedly impaired as soon as the sequence exceeded their normal digit span, a finding which replicates Zangwill's earlier observations. H. M., who had the most severe memory loss on clinical examination, failed to extend his span by a single digit in the 25 trials allotted to this task. Drachman and Arbit obtained exactly similar results when, instead of strings of digits, the subjects were asked to remember sequences of paired lights. The amnesic patients showed a normal immediate-memory span for the light sequences, but had great difficulty in learning sequences which exceeded the span. These findings highlight the distinction between short-term and long-term memory processes.

3. *Maze Learning.* Maze tasks which can be solved in a single trial are designed to measure spatial orientation, but when, as in many tasks used with lower animals, the correct sequence of turns cannot be discovered by inspection but only by trial and error, successful performance depends upon remembering the experience of previous trials. Such tasks may be expected to be sensitive to memory disorder and not merely to disorders of space perception.

A stylus-maze task of this kind is illustrated in Fig. 11-22 (Barker, 1931). The subject is required to discover and remember the one correct path leading from the lower left-hand corner to the upper right-hand corner of a ten by ten array of boltheads, mounted on a

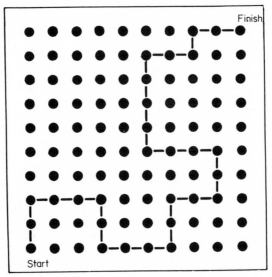

Fig. 11-22. Plan of stylus maze (Milner, 1965).
The black line indicates the correct path.

wooden board, and so wired at the back that every time the subject places his stylus on a bolthead that is not on the correct path, an error counter clicks loudly, informing him of the mistake. Training is carried out in blocks of 25 trials to a criterion of 3 successive error-less runs.

This task has been given to a large number of patients with focal brain lesions (Milner, 1965), and it has yielded not only quantitative but also qualitative differences in performance related to the locus of the lesion. For example, patients with frontal-lobe lesions are unique as a group in having difficulty in obeying the rather simple test in-structions. Such disorders are easily differentiated from the disorders of memory with which we are at present concerned.

The differential effects of right and left temporal lobectomy are also evident on maze learning tasks. The left temporal-lobe group learned this task as quickly as did normal control subjects, whereas after right temporal lobectomy there was a significant impairment which was, however, contingent upon whether or not the hippocampus had been included in the removal.

The stylus maze task has also been administered to the amnesic patients, including H. M., with bilateral mesial temporal-lobe lesions. H. M. failed to show any improvement in 215 trials spread over three days of training. This finding is consistent with the observations of Drachman and Arbit (1966) for the extended-span tasks and indicates the severity of the anterograde amnesia.

The possibility still remained that if the maze path were shortened considerably so that the sequence of correct turns could be encom-passed by the immediate memory span, then some cumulative learning from trial to trial might take place. Accordingly, the maze was covered with a board, leaving only the section of the path shown in Fig. 11-23 visible to the subject through an aperture.

With this simplified task, H. M. succeeded in learning the correct

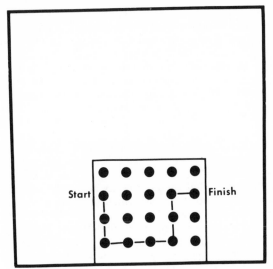

FIG. 11-23. Shortened form of stylus maze.

path, but only after 175 trials, and he was able to remember it for several days. Whether any residual effects of this prolonged training will be detectable after a longer interval remains to be determined.

Stylus maze learning can also be studied with vision excluded and Corkin (1965) has trained the same group of patients with focal brain lesions on a proprioceptively-guided alley maze. The results are strikingly consistent with those for the visual maze, showing that whatever functions are being tapped are not modality-specific. Moreover, the difficulties experienced by amnesic patients on both the visually and tactually guided mazes receive some external validation in the great difficulty H. M. experiences in finding his way home, to the house in which he has been living for the past six years.

It is sometimes argued that maze-learning tasks are of little value in the analysis of specific behavioral changes, since performance can be impaired for so many reasons, including spatial disorientation, impulsiveness, and memory impairment. We would maintain, however, that these different disorders manifest themselves in different and recognizable ways.

4. *Motor Learning*. It is noteworthy that so far the one exception to the generality of the learning disorder shown by amnesic patients has been the domain of motor skill. Such skills are notoriously resistant to decay in normal subjects and may not seem at first sight to be rewarding to the investigator of memory change. Yet, precisely because motor learning may be qualitatively different from other kinds of learning, we believe that it should be included in any representative sample of behavior. Moreover, motor skills are among the few kinds of learned behavior which are unequivocally nonverbal: no athlete can verbalize adequately the sequence of movements which make up his skill, and indeed the attempt to introspect upon such performance is likely to disrupt it.

The first motor learning task which was administered to patients with bilateral hippocampal lesions was a mirror-drawing test which embodies a standard laboratory procedure. The subject is required to trace a pencil line within the narrow outlines of a star-shaped pattern, but is never allowed to see his hand or the star in direct vision, only as reflected in a mirror. On this task, in marked contrast to the maze problems, H. M. showed a normal learning curve over a three-day period, beginning each new session at the level he had attained at the end of the previous day's training (Milner, 1962b). This was learning unaccompanied by any feeling of familiarity; even during the last training session he was completely unaware that he had performed the task on previous occasions.

Many other tasks would have served equally well as measures of motor learning. Recently, Corkin has trained H. M. over several days on a rotary pursuit task in which the subject has to keep a stylus on a small randomly moving target; Corkin also used various bimanual tracking and coordination tasks in which conflicting movements have to be performed simultaneously with the two hands. In all cases, H. M., despite the severity of his amnesia, showed consistent improvement over repeated trials. It seems fair to conclude that many motor habits are learned independently of the hippocampal system.

The dissociation in amnesic states between the acquisition of motor skill and other types of learning has an interesting parallel in experiments with normal subjects on short-term memory for kinesthetic distance, in which the subject is required to reproduce the extent of a movement made without visual feed-back (Bilodeau, Sulzer, and Levy, 1962; Posner, 1966; Posner and Konick, 1966). The retention of such kinesthetic information falls off with time, but the rate of decay is quite unrelated to what the subject does in the interval. In contrast, memory for visual location (the position of a circle on a line), like verbal memory, is dependent upon the amount and nature of the intervening activity. Much useful information might be gained by the application of such simple quantitative techniques to the analysis of memory change after brain lesions or other treatments.

Comment

B. Milner and H.-L. Teuber

In this survey of methods, we have with rare exceptions considered only the techniques that have already been used to investigate changes in perception and memory produced by brain lesions. Some of these techniques have been borrowed from the animal laboratory, thus permitting a comparison of the effects of similar treatments in monkey and man; other techniques have been modifications of traditional psychophysical procedures. Frequently the technique has been improvised to answer a clinical question, without due regard to the more exact methods already in use with normal subjects. Yet with our somewhat crude tools it has still been possible, by the strategy of multiple converging tasks, to demonstrate specific effects of differently placed brain lesions.

In analyses of perception and its disorders, the established procedures in all sensory spheres are those that attempt to define the adequate stimulus by varying its physical dimensions, such as intensity, duration, frequency or size. These classical measures of threshold can be supplemented, as we have seen, by introducing perceptual ambiguity. Reversible or embedded figures, reversible melodies, or syntactically ambiguous sentences have been employed to tap a level of input processing that goes beyond the level of sensation as traditionally conceived. Still more recently, perception has been studied by using empty or noisy fields or highly redundant patterns, and the relations between the perceiver and his environment have been systematically altered so that his own movements have unforeseen consequences (as in some of the rearrangement experiments). Much less exploited have been techniques that vary the probability structure of sequences of stimuli and techniques that apply probabilistic notions to the interpretation of responses. As our survey has indicated, a large proportion of current effort has been directed toward applying multiple simultaneous stimulation, in vision or touch, and to the analogous dichotic techniques for audition. Last, there have been at least some scattered attempts at defining tasks in which information has to be carried from one sensory modality to another.

Each of these techniques has some contribution to make to the analysis of altered perception. The traditional threshold tests may refine or possibly revise our views about the primary sensory projection systems. The hidden-figure tasks, in contrast, raise questions about the stages of perception where supramodal processes may have to be invoked, although it is still not clear how far performance on these tasks defines a unitary but not modality-specific form of disorder. Altered reactions to conditions of rearrangement between input and perceiver, as we have suggested, point to a heretofore unsuspected role of motor systems in perception and in the mechanisms for maintaining constancy. In spite of these limited successes, all these methods have so far failed to settle the issue of the agnosias.

In many instances, the question has been raised whether one is still dealing with perceptual or with mnemonic tasks, as soon as the perceiver has to relate some momentary sensory input to preceding or succeeding ones or has to withhold his report temporarily on some aspect of the stimulus while first making a report about some other aspect. Undoubtedly, comprehension of what one perceives involves (in addition to immediate input processing) some capacity for gaining access to more remote traces of previous input, so that our perceptions can be categorized. Yet none of these considerations can detract from the simple facts set forth in the immediately preceding part of this chapter: patients with profound and enduring anterograde amnesia can show normal perceptual capacities regardless of whether presentation of patterns is made abnormally brief or abnormally prolonged, and, in the case of multiple input, regardless of whether the inputs are simultaneous or successive. Moreover, the amnesic patient comprehends what he perceives, thus indicating that he finds access to those old-established trace-mechanisms that must be evoked for the interpretation of things seen, felt, or heard. It is this ready dissociation of syndromes involving perception from those involving memory that has induced us to treat these two in separate parts of this chapter.

In the assessment of memory change, we have focused on distinctions that seemed natural in view of the clinical findings. Appropriate use of verbal and nonverbal methods of testing disclosed complementary disturbances, depending upon whether a patient harbored a left or a right temporal-lobe lesion. Much remains to be done in the further characterization of these material-specific disorders. In the field of verbal learning, the precise quantitative methods that have in recent years added greatly to our understanding of normal memory function must be applied to patients with verbal memory impairment. At the same time, it is essential that some nonverbal techniques of equal precision be invented. It is here that the clinical findings have out-stripped research with normal subjects. As they stand, the designations of left and right temporal-lobe syndromes as verbal and non-verbal respectively, are clearly provisional, and a wider range of tasks is needed if we are to go beyond the purely negative description of right temporal-lobe symptoms as *nonverbal*.

A major question still to be resolved concerns the possible existence of modality-specific disorders of memory. The material-specific deficits just mentioned certainly transcend the distinction between vision and hearing: the patient with a left anterior temporal-lobe lesion shows forgetfulness for words and paragraphs regardless of whether they are heard or seen. Yet there are occasional claims that short-term retention in a single sensory modality might be selectively impaired, although the causative lesions remain in doubt. If such modality-specific losses can be demonstrated, they may indeed be difficult to separate from perceptual disorders as such. One promising way of searching for such specificity would be to use the technique of serial presentation of stimuli and to look for abnormal interaction between successive stimuli within a given sensory mode.

The nature of the global amnesia produced by bilateral mesial temporal-lobe ablation has been more fully delineated, at least as far as its main features are concerned. Memory for verbal as well as nonverbal material is affected, with the main difficulty occurring at the transition from some hypothetical short-term mechanism to long-term storage. Recent extensions of the range of tasks set for these patients have shown, however, that there are important aspects of learning that are spared: new motor skills can be acquired. Tests for perceptual learning are also needed, because preliminary observations indicate that it, too, may be spared. Moreover, we should stress that some new methods have to be devised for the rapid and reliable assessment of the transient changes in memory that can be induced by pharmacologic or other experimental means.

The ultimate goal to which all these methods for studying perception and memory are addressed is understanding the nature of altered behavior in terms of specific changes in normal mechanism. To reach this goal, normal physiology and pathophysiology will have to continue to converge. The gap between them may still seem wide, but the final test of any theory of brain function is its success in taking observations on breakdown of function into account.

REFERENCES: INTRODUCTION

AUBERT, H. 1861. Eine scheinbare bedeutende Drehung von Objekten bei Neigung des Kopfes nach rechts oder links. *Virchows Arch. pathol. Anat. u. Physiol.*, 20, 381–393.

BRICKNER, R. M. 1936. *The intellectual functions of the frontal lobes. A study based upon observations of a man after partial bilateral frontal lobectomy.* New York: Macmillan.

BRICKNER, R. M. 1952. Brain of patient "A" after bilateral frontal lobectomy;

status of frontal-lobe problem. *Arch. Neurol. Psychiat.* (Chicago), 68, 293–313.

CARR, H. A. 1913. Cited in Hunter, W. S., The delayed reaction in animals and children. *Behav. Monogr.*, 2, No. 1.

CHOROVER, S. L., & COLE, M. 1966. Delayed alternation performance in patients with cerebral lesions. *Neuropsychologia*, 4, 1–7.

GAZZANIGA, M. S., & SPERRY, R. W. 1967. Language after section of the cerebral commissures. *Brain*, 90, 131–148.

HUNTER, W. S. 1913–1915. The delayed reaction in animals and children. *Behav. Monogr.*, 2, No. 1, 1–86.

JACOBSEN, C. F. 1935. Functions of frontal association area in primates. *AMA Arch. Neurol. Psychiat.*, 33, 558–569.

LOEB, J. 1884. Die Sehstörungen nach Verletzung der Grosshirnrinde. *Pflügers Arch. ges. Physiol.*, 34, 67–172.

MILNER, B. 1958. Psychological defects produced by temporal lobe excision. *Res. Publ. Assoc. Res. Nerv. Ment. Dis.*, 36, 244–257.

MILNER, B. 1966. Amnesia following operation on the temporal lobes. In Whitty, C. W. M., & Zangwill, O. L. (Eds.), *Amnesia*. London: Butterworth. Pp. 109–133.

RYLANDER, G. 1939. *Personality changes after operations on the frontal lobes.* London: Oxford University Press.

RYLANDER, G. 1943. Mental changes after excisions of cerebral tissue. A clinical study of 16 cases of resections in the parietal, temporal and occipital lobes. *Acta psychiat. neurol.* (Copenhagen), suppl. 25.

SCOVILLE, W. B., & MILNER, B. 1957. Loss of recent memory after bilateral hippocampal lesions. *J. Neurol. Neurosurg. Psychiat.*, 20, 11–21.

SEMMES, J. 1965. A nontactual factor in astereognosis. *Neuropsychologia*, 3, 295–315.

SEMMES, J., WEINSTEIN, S., GHENT, L., & TEUBER, H.-L. 1955. Spatial orientation in man after cerebral injury: Analyses by locus of lesion. *J. Psychol.*, 39, 227–244.

SPERRY, R. W. 1961. Cerebral organization and behavior. *Science*, 133, 1749–1757.

SPERRY, R. W. 1964. Problems outstanding in the evolution of brain function. James Arthur Lecture on the evolution of the human brain. New York: *Amer. Mus. Nat. Hist.*

SPERRY, R. W. 1966. Hemispheric interaction and the mind-brain problem. In J. C. Eccles (Ed.), *Brain and Conscious Experience*. New York: Springer.

TEUBER, H.-L. 1950. Neuropsychology. Chapt. III (pp. 30–52) in *Recent advances in psychological testing: A critical summary.* Springfield, Ill.: Thomas (Am. Lect. Ser. no. 88).

TEUBER, H.-L. 1955. Physiological psychology. *Ann. Rev. Psychol.*, 6, 267–296.

TEUBER, H.-L. 1964. The riddle of frontal lobe function in man. In, *The frontal granular cortex and behavior*. Warren, J. M., & Akert, K. (Eds.), New York: McGraw-Hill. Chap. 20, pp. 410–444.

TEUBER, H.-L. 1966a. The frontal lobes and their function: Further observations on rodents, carnivores, subhuman primates and man. *Internat. J. Neurol.*, 5, 282–300.

TEUBER, H.-L. 1966b. Kurt Goldstein's role in the development of neuropsychology. *Neuropsychologia*, 4, 299–310.

TEUBER, H.-L., & MISHKIN, M. 1954. Judgment of visual and postural vertical after brain injury. *J. Psychol.*, 38, 161–175.

REFERENCES: PERCEPTION

AFTANAS, M., & ZUBEK, J. P. 1964. Interlimb transfer of changes in tactual acuity following occlusion of a circumscribed area of the skin. *Percept. Motor Skills*, 18, 437–442.

AHRENS, R. 1954. Beitrag zur Entwicklung des Physiognomie- und Mimiker-kennens. Z. exp. angew. Psychol., 2, 412–454, 599–633.

AUBERT, H. 1861. Eine scheinbare bedeutende Drehung von Objekten bei Neigung des Kopfes nach rechts oder links. Virchows Arch. pathol. Anat. u. Physiol., 20, 381–393.

AVERBACH, E., & SPERLING, G. 1961. Short-term storage of information in vision. In Cherry, C. (Ed.), Information theory. London: Butterworth. Pp. 196–211.

AXELROD, S. 1959. Effects of early blindness: Performance of blind and sighted children on tactile and auditory tasks. New York: American Foundation for the Blind, Research Series, No. 7.

AXELROD, S., & COHEN, L. D. 1961. Senescence and embedded-figure performance in vision and touch. Percept. Motor Skills, 12, 283–288.

BALINT, R. 1909. Seelenlähmung des Schauens, optische Ataxie, räumliche Störungen der Aufmerksamkeit. Mschr. Psychiat. Neurol., 25. 51–81.

BÁRÁNY, E. H., & HALLDÉN, U. 1948. Phasic inhibition of the light reflex of the pupil during retinal rivalry. J. Neurophysiol., 11, 25–30.

BARU, A. W., GERSUNI, G. V., & TONKONOGII, I. M. 1964. Korsakov Zh. Nevropat. Psikhiat., 64, 481.

BATTERSBY, W. S. 1951. The regional gradient of critical flicker frequency after frontal or occipital injury. J. exper. Psychol., 42, 59–68.

BATTERSBY, W. S., WAGMAN, I. H., KARP, E., & BENDER, M. B. 1960. Neural limitations of visual excitability: Alterations produced by cerebral lesions. Arch. Neurol., 3, 24–42.

BAY, E. 1950. Agnosie und Funktionswandel. Eine hirnpathologische Studie. Heidelberg: Springer.

BAY, E. 1953. Disturbances of visual perception and their examination. Brain, 76, 515–550.

BEECHER, H. K. 1959a. Generalization from pain of various types and diverse origins. Science, 130, 267–268.

BEECHER, H. K. 1959b. Measurement of subjective responses; Quantitative effects of drugs. New York: Oxford University Press.

BENDER, M. B. 1945. Extinction and precipitation of cutaneous sensations. Arch. Neurol. Psychiat., 54, 1–9.

BENDER, M. B., & TEUBER, H. L. 1946. Phenomena of fluctuation, extinction and completion in visual perception. Arch. Neurol. Psychiat. (Chicago), 55, 627–658.

BERINGER, K. 1927. Der Meskalinrausch, seine Geschichte und Erscheinungsweise. Berlin: Springer.

BEXTON, W. R., HERON, W., & SCOTT, R. H. 1954. Effects of decreased variation in the sensory environment. Canad. J. Psychol., 8, 70–76.

BIELSCHOWSKY, A. 1931. Der Sehakt bei Störungen im Bewegungsapparat der Augen. Handb. norm. pathol. Physiol. (ed. A. Bethe et al.), 12(2), 1095–1112. Berlin: Springer.

BIRCH, H. G., BELMONT, I., & KARP, E. 1967. Delayed information processing and extinction following cerebral damage. Brain, 90, 113–130.

BIRKMAYER, W. 1951. Hirnverletzungen. Vienna: Springer.

BOCCA, E. 1958. Clinical aspects of cortical deafness. Laryngoscope, 68, 301–309.

BOCCA, E., CALEARO, C., CASSINARI, V., & MIGLIAVACCA, F. 1955. Testing "cortical" hearing in temporal lobe tumors. Acta Otolaryng. (Stockholm), 45, 289–304.

BODAMER, J. 1947. Die Prosopagnosie. Arch. Psychiat., Z. Neurol., 179, 6–54.

BORING, E. G. 1957. A history of experimental psychology. 2d. ed. New York: Appleton-Century.

BOSSOM, J. 1965. The effect of brain lesions on prism adaptation in monkey. Psychonom. Sci. 2, 45–46.

BRAIN, R. 1941. Visual disorientation with special reference to the lesions of the right cerebral hemisphere. Brain, 64, 244–272.

BROADBENT, D. E. 1954. The role of auditory localization in attention and memory span. *J. exp. Psychol.*, 47, 191–196.

BROADBENT, D. E., & GREGORY, M. 1964. Accuracy of recognition for speech presented to the right and left ears. *Quart. J. exp. Psychol.* 16, 359–360.

BROWN, R., & BERKO, J. 1960. Word association and the acquisition of grammar. *Child Development*, 31, 1–14.

BRÜCKNER, A. 1917. Zur Frage der Lokalisation des Kontrastes und verwandter Erscheinungen in der Sehsubstanz. *Z. Augenheilk.*, 38, 1–14.

BRUNSWIK, E. 1934. *Wahrnehmung und Gegenstandswelt.* Leipzig: Deuticke.

BRUNSWIK, E., & REITER, L. 1937. Eindruckscharaktere schematisierter Gesichter. *Z. Psychol.*, 142, 67–134.

BRYDEN, M. P. 1960. Tachistoscopic recognition of non-alphabetical material. *Canad. J. Psychol.*, 14, 78–86.

BRYDEN, M. P. 1963. Ear preference in auditory perception. *J. exp. Psychol.*, 65, 103–105.

CARTERETTE, E. C. 1967. Review of D. M. Green & J. A. Swets. Signal detection and psychophysics. *Science*, 156, 632–633.

CHANEY, R. B., & WEBSTER, J. C. 1965. Information in certain multidimensional acoustic signals. *U. S. Navy Electronic Laboratory Reports*, San Diego, No. 1339.

CHASE, R. A. 1967. Discussion of Milner, B.: Studies of temporal lobes. In Darley, F. L. (Ed.), *Brain mechanisms underlying speech and language*, New York: Grune & Stratton. Pp. 135–145.

CHOMSKY, N. 1957. *Syntactic structures.* The Hague: Mouton.

CHOMSKY, N. 1965. *Aspects of the theory of syntax.* Cambridge, Mass.: MIT Press.

COBRINIK, L. 1959. The performance of brain-injured children on hidden figure tasks. *Amer. J. Psychol.*, 72, 566–571.

COHEN, L. 1959a. Perception of reversible figures by normal and brain-injured subjects. *AMA Arch. Neurol. Psychiat.*, 81, 765–775.

COHEN, L. 1959b. Rate of apparent change of a Necker-cube as a function of prior stimulation. *Amer. J. Psychol.*, 72, 327–344.

CORKIN, S., MILNER, B., & RASMUSSEN, T. 1964. Effects of different cortical excisions on senory thresholds in man. *Trans. Amer. Neurol. Assoc.*, 89, 112–116.

COWEY, A. 1963. The basis of a method of perimetry with monkeys. *Quart. J. exp. Psychol.*, 15, 81–90.

COWEY, A. 1967. Perimetric study of field defects in monkeys after cortical and retinal ablations. *Quart. J. exp. Psychol.*, XIX, 232–245.

COWEY, A., & WEISKRANTZ, L. 1963. A perimetric study of visual field defects in monkeys. *Quart. J. exp. Psychol.*, 15, 91–115.

CRITCHLEY, M. 1949. The phenomenon of tactile inattention with specific reference to parietal lesions. *Brain*, 72, 538–561.

CRITCHLEY, M. 1951. Types of visual perseveration: "Paliopsia" and "illusory visual spread." *Brain*, 74, 267–299.

CRITCHLEY, M. 1953. *The parietal lobes.* Baltimore: Williams & Wilkins.

CRITCHLEY, M. 1964. *Developmental dyslexia.* London: Heinemann.

DEJERINE, J. 1892. Contribution à l'étude anatomo-pathologique et clinique des différentes variétés de cécité verbale. *Mem. Soc. Biol.*, 4, 61–90.

DELAY, J. P. L. 1935. *Les astéréognosies* (Thèse). Paris: Masson.

DENNY-BROWN, D., MEYER, J. S., & HORENSTEIN, S. 1952. The significance of perceptual rivalry resulting from parietal lesions. *Brain*, 75, 433–471.

DE RENZI, E., & SPINNLER, H. 1966a. Facial recognition in brain-damaged patients. *Neurology*, 16, 145–152.

DE RENZI, E., & SPINNLER, H. 1966b. Visual recognition in patients with unilateral cerebral disease. *J. nerv. ment. Dis.*, 142, 515–525.

DE RENZI, E., & SPINNLER, H. 1967. Impaired performance on color tasks in patients with hemispheric damage. *Cortex*, 3, 194–216.

DIAMOND, I. T., & NEFF, W. D. 1957. Ablation of temporal cortex and discrimination of auditory patterns. *J. Neurophysiol.*, 20, 300–315.

DIDE, M. 1938. Les désorientations temporo-spatiales et la prépondérance de l'hémisphère droit dans les agnoso-akinésies proprioceptives. *Encéphale*, 33, 276–294.

DIRKS, D. 1964. Perception of dichotic and monaural verbal material and cerebral dominance for speech. *Acta Otolaryng.* (Stockholm), 58, 73–80.

DIX, M. R., HALLPIKE, C. S., & HOOD, J. D. 1948. Observations upon loudness recruitment phenomenon with especial reference to differential diagnosis of disorders of internal ear and eighth nerve. *Proc. Roy. Soc. Med.*, 41, 516–526.

DOANE, B. K., MAHATOO, W., HERON, W., & SCOTT, T. H. 1959. Changes in perceptual function after isolation. *Canad. J. Psychol.*, 13, 210–219.

DORGEUILLE, C. 1966. *Introduction à l'étude des amusies*. Thèse de Paris. (Polycopiée).

DRAKE, C. G., & STAVRAKI, G. W. 1948. An extension of the "law of denervation" to afferent neurons. *J. Neurophysiol.*, 11, 229–238.

DREVER, J. 1956. Early learning and the perception of space. *Amer. J. Psychol.*, 68, 605–614.

DUBOIS, J. HÉCAEN, H., ANGÉLERGUES, R., MAUFRAS DU CHATELIER, A., & MARCHE, P. 1964. Étude neurolinguistique de l'aphasie de conduction. *Neuropsychologia*, 2, 9–44.

DUDA, P. D., & ZUBEK, J. P. 1965. Auditory sensitivity after prolonged visual deprivation. *Psychon. Sci.*, 3, 359–360.

ETTLINGER, G. 1967. Analysis of cross-modal effects and their relationship to language. In Darley, F. J. (Ed.), *Brain mechanisms underlying speech and language*. New York: Grune & Stratton.

ETTLINGER, G., & WYKE, M. 1961. Defects in identifying objects visually in a patient with cerebrovascular disease. *J. Neurol. Neurosurg. Psychiat.*, 19, 254–259.

FEINBERG, I. 1956. Cortical flicker frequency in amblyopia ex anopsia. *Amer. J. Ophthal.*, 42, 473–481.

FEX, J. 1962. Auditory activity in centrifugal and centripetal cochlear fibres in cat, a study of a feedback system. *Acta, physiol.* (Scand.), 55, suppl. 189, 1–68.

FLYNN, J. T. 1967. Spatial summation in amblyopia. *Arch. Ophthal.*, in press.

FODOR, J. A., & BEVER, T. G. 1965. The psychological reality of linguistic segments. *J. verb. Learn. verb. Behav.*, 4, 414–420.

FOIX, C. 1922. Sur une variété de troubles bilatéraux de la sensibilité par lésion unilatérale du cerveau. *Rev. neurol.* (Paris), 29, 322–331.

FRANZ, S. I. 1933. Studies in cerebral function: VIII. Training in touch perception and cross-education. *Publ. Univ. Calif. Los Angeles Educ., Philos., Psychol.*, 1, 121–128.

FRISHKOPF, L. S., & GOLDSTEIN, M. H., Jr. 1963. Responses to acoustic stimuli from single units in the eighth nerve of the bullfrog. *J. acoust. Soc. Amer.*, 35, 1219–1228.

GARRETT, M., BEVER, T. G., & FODOR, J. A. 1966. The active use of grammar in speech perception. *J. Percept. Psychophys.*, 1, 30–32.

GELB, A., & GOLDSTEIN, K. 1920. *Psychologische Analysen hirnpathologischer Fälle*. Leipzig: Johann Ambrosius Barth.

GELB, A., & GOLDSTEIN, K. 1924. Über Farbenamnesie. *Psychol. Forsch.*, 6, 127–186.

GERSUNI, G. V. 1965. Organization of afferent flow and the process of external signal discrimination. *Neuropsychologia*, 3, 95–110.

GESCHWIND, N. 1962. The anatomy of acquired disorders of reading. In Money, J. (Ed.), *Reading disability*. Baltimore: Johns Hopkins Press. Pp. 115–129.

GESCHWIND, N. 1965. Disconnexion syndrome in animals and man. *Brain*, 88, 237–294, 585–644.

GESCHWIND, N. & FUSILLO, M. 1966. Color-naming defects in association with alexia. *Arch. Neurol.*, 15, 137–146.

GESCHWIND, N., & KAPLAN, E. 1962. A human cerebral deconnection syndrome. *Neurology*, 12, 675–685.

GHENT, L. 1956. Perception of overlapping and embedded figures by children of different ages. *Amer. J. Psychol.*, 69, 575–585.

GHENT, L., WEINSTEIN S., SEMMES, J., & TEUBER, H.-L. 1955. Effects of unilateral brain injury in man on learning of a tactile pattern discrimination. *J. comp. physiol. Psychol.*, 48, 478–481.

GIBSON, J. J., & GIBSON, E. 1955. Perceptual learning: Differentiation or enrichment. *Psychol. Rev.*, 62, 32–41.

GLONING, I., GLONING, K. HOFF, H., & TSCHABITSCHER, H. 1966. Zur Prosopagnosie. *Neuropsychologia*, 4, 113–132.

GLONING, K., & QUATEMBER, R. 1966. Methodischer Beitrag zur Untersuchung der Prosopagnosie. *Neuropsychologia*, 4, 133–142.

GOFF, W. R., ROSNER, B. S., & ALLISON, T. 1962. Distribution of cerebral somatosensory evoked responses in normal man. *EEG clin. Neurophysiol.*, 14, 697–713.

GOLDSTEIN, K. 1916. Über kortikale Sensibilitätsstörungen. *Z. ges. Neurol. Psychiat.*, 33, 494–517.

GOLDSTEIN, K., & REICHMANN, F. 1920. Über kortikale Sensibilitätsstörungen, besonders am Kopfe. *Z. ges. Neurol. Psychiat.*, 53, 49–70.

GOLDSTEIN, R. 1963. Electrophysiologic audiometry. In Jerger, J. (Ed.), *Modern developments in audiology.* New York: Academic Press. Chap. 5, pp. 167–192.

GOLLIN, E. S. 1960. Developmental studies of visual recognition of incomplete objects. *Percept. Motor Skills*, 11, 289–298.

GOTTSCHALDT, K. 1926. Über den Einfluss der Erfahrung auf die Wahrnehmung von Figuren. *Psychol. Forsch.*, 8, 261–317; 1929, 12, 1–87.

GREEN, B. F., WOLF, A. K., & WHITE, B. 1959. The detection of statistically defined patterns in a matrix of dots. *Amer. J. Psychol.*, 72, 503–520.

GREEN, D. M., & SWETS, J. A. 1966. *Signal detection theory and psychophysics.* New York: Wiley.

GREGORY, R. L., & WALLACE, J. G. 1958. A theory of nerve deafness. *Lancet* (January 11), 83–84.

HABER, W. B. 1955. Effects of loss of limb on sensory functions. *J. Psychol.*, 40, 115–123.

HARMS, H. 1937. Ort und Wesen der Bildhemmung bei Schielenden. *Graefes Arch. Ophthal.*, 138, 149–210.

HARMS, H. 1960. Die Bedeutung einer einheitlichen Prufweise aller Sehfunktionen. *Bericht über die 63. Zusammenkunft der deutschen ophthalmologischen Gesellschaft.* Heidelberg: Pp. 281–285.

HARMS, H. 1965. Visuelle und pupillomotorische Störungen bei Veränderungen des Okzipitallappens. *8th Intern. Congr. Neurol.*, Vienna.

HARROWER, M. R. 1939. Changes in figure-background perception in patients with cortical lesions. *Brit. J. Psychol.*, 30, 47–51.

HEAD, H. 1920. *Studies in neurology.* London: Oxford Medical Publications.

HEBB, D. O. 1939. Intelligence in man after large removals of cerebral tissue: Deficits following right temporal lobectomy. *J. gen. Psychol.*, 21, 437–446.

HÉCAEN, H., AJURIAGUERRA, J. DE, & DAVID, M. 1952. Les déficits fonctionels après lobectomie occipitale. *Mschr. Psychiat. Neurol.*, 123, 239–291.

HÉCAEN, H., ANGÉLERGUES, R. BERNHARDT, C., & CHIARELLI, J. 1957. Essai de distinction des modalités cliniques de l'agnosie des physionomies. *Rev. Neurol.* (Paris), 96, 125–144.

HÉCAEN, H., & GARCIA-BADARACCO, J. 1956. Séméiologie des hallucinations visuelles en clinique neurologique. *Acta neurol. Latino-Amer.*, 2, 23–58.

HÉCAEN, H., PENFIELD, W., BERTRAND, C., & MALMO, R. 1956. The syndrome of apractognosia due to lesions of the minor cerebral hemisphere. *Arch. Neurol. Psychiat.*, 75, 400–434.

HEILBRONNER, K. 1905. Zur klinisch-psychologischen Untersuchungstechnik. *Mschr. Psychiat. Neurol.*, 17, 115 132.

HELD, R. 1955. Shifts in binaural localization after prolonged exposures to atypical combinations of stimuli. *Amer. J. Psychol.*, 68, 526–548.

HELD, R., & FREEDMAN, S. J. 1963. Plasticity in human sensorimotor control. *Science*, 142, 455–462.

HELD, R., & HEIN, A. 1963. Movement-produced stimulation in the development of visually guided behavior. *J. comp. physiol. Psychol.*, 56, 872–876.

HINDE, R. A. 1966. *Animal behavior: A synthesis of ethology and comparative psychology.* New York: McGraw-Hill.

HIRSH, I. J. 1952. *The measurement of hearing.* New York: McGraw-Hill.

HOFF, H., & PÖTZL, O. 1937. Uber eine optisch-agnostiche Störung des "Physiognomiegedächtnisses," *Z. ges. Neurol. Psychiat.*, 159, 367–395.

HUBEL, D. H. 1958. Cortical unit responses to visual stimuli in nonanesthetized cats. *Amer. J. Ophthal.*, 46, 110–122.

HUBEL, D. H., & WIESEL, T. M. 1960. Receptive fields of single neurons in the cat's striate cortex. *J. Physiol.*, 150, 91–104.

HUBEL, D. H., & WIESEL, T. M. 1963. Receptive fields of cells in striate cortex of very young, visually inexperienced kittens. *J. Neurophysiol.*, 26, 994–1002.

HUBEL, D. H., & WIESEL, T. M. 1965. Receptive fields and functional architecture in two nonstriate visual areas (18 and 19) of the cat. *J. Neurophysiol.*, 28, 229–289.

IRIGARAY, L. 1967. Approche psycholinguistique du langage des déments. *Neuropsychologia*, 5, 25–52.

JAFFE, R. 1954. Kinesthetic after-effects following cerebral lesions. *Amer. J. Psychol.*, 67, 668–676.

JAKOBSON, R. 1942. Kindersprache, Aphasie und allgemeine Lautgesetze. *Sprakvetenskapliga Sällskapets i Uppsala Förhandlingar Universitets Arsskrift*, 9, 1–83.

JAKOBSON, R., & HALLE, M. 1956. *Fundamentals of language.* The Hague: Mouton.

KAILA, E. 1932. Die Reaktionen des Säuglings auf das menschliche Gesicht. *Ann. Univ. Aboensis, Ser. B. Humaniora*, 17, 9–114.

KATZ, J. J., & FODOR, J. A. 1963. The structure of a semantic theory. *Language*, 39, 170–210.

KENNARD, M. A., & ECTORS, L. 1938. Forced circling in monkeys following lesions of the frontal lobes. *J. Neurophysiol.*, 1, 45–54.

KIMURA, D. 1961a. Cerebral dominance and the perception of verbal stimuli. *Canad. J. Psychol.*, 15, 166–171.

KIMURA, D. 1961b. Some effects of temporal-lobe damage on auditory perception. *Canad. J. Psychol.*, 15, 156–165.

KIMURA, D. 1963. Speech lateralization in young children as determined by an auditory test. *J. comp. physiol. Psychol.*, 56, 899–902.

KIMURA, D. 1964. Left-right differences in the perception of melodies. *Quart. J. exp. Psychol.*, 16, 355–358.

KIMURA, D. 1966. Dual functional asymmetry of the brain in visual perception. *Neuropsychologia*, 4, 275–285.

KIMURA, D. 1967. Functional asymmetry of the brain in dichotic listening. *Cortex*, 3, 163–178.

KINSBOURNE, M., & WARRINGTON, E. K. 1962. A disorder of simultaneous form perception. *Brain*, 85, 461–486.

KINSBOURNE, M., & WARRINGTON, E. K. 1963. The localizing significance of limited simultaneous visual form perception. *Brain*, 86, 697–702.

KLEIN, G. S., & KRECH, D. 1952. Cortical conductivity in the brain-injured. *J. Personality*, 21, 118–148.

KLÜVER, H. 1928. Mescal: The "divine" plant and its psychological effects. London: K. Paul, Trench, Trubner.

KLÜVER, H. 1933. Behavior mechanisms in monkeys. Chicago: The University of Chicago Press

KLÜVER, H. 1942a. Functional significance of the geniculo-striate system. In Kluver, H. (Ed.), Biol. Symposia, 7, 253–299.

KLÜVER, H. 1942b. Mechanisms of hallucinations. Studies in personality. New York: McGraw-Hill. Pp. 175–207.

KÖHLER, W. 1923. Zur Theorie des Sukzessiv-Vergleichs und der Zeitfehler. Psychol. Forsch., 4, 115–175.

KÖHLER, W., & DINNERSTEIN, D. 1947 Figural after-effects in kinesthesis. Miscellanea psychologica (Albert Michotte), 196–220.

KÖHLER, W., & WALLACH, H. 1944. Figural after-effects: An investigation of visual processes. Proc. Amer. Philos. Soc., 88, 269–357.

KORIN, H. & FINK, M. 1957. Role of stimulus intensity in perception of simultaneous electrical cutaneous stimuli. J. Hillside Hosp., 6, 241–250.

KOZHEVNIKOV, V. A., & CHISTOVICH, L. A. 1965. Reih' Artikuliatsia i Vospriiatie. Moscow-Leningrad. (Tr. Speech: Articulation and Perception.) Joint Publications Research Service, Washington, D. C., JPRS: 30, 543.

KRAUTHAMER, G. 1959. Form perception across sensory modality. Am. Psychol. Assn. (Cincinnati). (Abstract).

KRUEGER, E. G., PRICE, P. A., & TEUBER, H.-L. 1954. Tactile extinction in parietal lobe neoplasm. J. Psychol., 38, 191–202.

LANSDELL, H. C. 1968. Effect of extent of temporal lobe ablations on two lateralized deficits. Physiol. & Behav., 3 (in press).

LANGE, J. 1936. Agnosien und Apraxien. In Bumke, O., & Foerster, O. (Eds.), Handbuch der Neurologie. Vol. VI. Berlin: Springer. Pp. 807–960.

LASHLEY, K. S. 1938. The mechanism of vision: XV. Preliminary studies of the rat's capacity for detail vision. J. gen. Psychol., 18, 123–193.

LASHLEY, K. S. 1941. Patterns of cerebral integration indicated by the scotomas of migraine. Arch. Neurol. Psychiat. (Chicago), 46, 331–339.

LECOURS, A.-R. 1966. Serial order in writing. A study of misspelled words in "developmental dyslexia." Neuropsychologia, 4, 221–241.

LELE, P. P. 1954. Relationship between cutaneous thermal thresholds, skin temperature and cross-sectional area of the stimulus. J. Physiol. (London), 126, 191–205.

LELE, P. P., & WEDELL, G. 1956. The relationship between neurohistology and corneal sensibility. Brain, 79, 119–154.

LENNEBERG, E. H. 1967. Biological foundations of language. New York: Wiley.

LIBERMAN, A. M., COOPER, F. S., STUDDERT-KENNEDY, M., HARRIS, K. S., & SHANKWEILER, D. P. 1966. Some observations on the efficiency of speech sounds. Proc. XVIII Intern. Congr. Psychol., Moscow.

LIEPMANN, H. 1900. Das Krankheitsbild der Apraxie ("motorischen Asymbolie") auf Grand eines Falles von einseitiger Appraxie. Mschr. Psychiat. Neurol., 8, 15–44, 102–132, 182–197.

LOEB, J. 1884. Die Sehstörungen nach Verletzung der Grosshirnrinde. Pflügers Arch. ges. Physiol., 34, 67–172.

LURIA, A. R. 1966. Higher cortical functions in man. New York: Basic Books.

LURIA, A. R., PRAVDINA-VINARSKAYA, E. N., & YARBUS, A. L. 1963. Disorders of ocular movement in a case of simultanagnosia. Brain, 86, 219–228.

MACKAY, D. G. 1966. To end ambiguous sentences. Percept. Psychophys., 1, 426–436.

MACKAY, D. G., & BEVER, T. G. 1967. In search of ambiguity. Percept. Psychophys., 2, 193–200.

MACKAY, D. M. 1957. Moving visual images produced by regular stationary patterns. Nature (London), 180, 849–850.

MacKay, D. M. 1966. Cerebral organization and the conscious control of action. In Eccles, J. C. (Ed.), Brain and conscious experience. New York: Springer. Chap. 17, pp. 422–445.

McMurray, G. A. 1950. Experimental study of a case of insensitivity to pain. Arch. Neurol. Psychiat. (Chicago), 64, 650–667.

Marshall, J. C. & Newcombe, F. 1966. Syntactic and semantic errors in paralexia. Neuropsychologia, 4, 169–176.

Matzker, J. 1958. Ein binauraler Hörsynthese-Test zum Nachweis zerebraler Hörstörungen. Stuttgart: Thieme.

Meier, M. S., & French, L. A. 1965. Lateralized deficits in complex visual discrimination and bilateral transfer of reminiscence following unilateral temporal lobectomy. Neuropsychologia, 3, 261–272.

Meyer, V., Gross, C. G., & Teuber, H.-L. 1963. Effect of knowledge of site of stimulation on the threshold for pressure sensitivity. Percept. Motor Skills, 16, 637–640.

Milner, B. 1954. Intellectual functions of the temporal lobes. Psychol. Bull., 51, 42–62.

Milner, B. 1958. Psychological defects produced by temporal lobe excision. Res. Publ. Assoc. Res. Nerv. Ment. Dis. 36, 244–257.

Milner, B. 1960. Impairment of visual recognition and recall after right temporal lobectomy in man. Paper read at Psychonomic Society Annual Meeting, Chicago.

Milner, B. 1962. Laterality effects in audition. In Mountcastle, V. B. (Ed.), Interhemispheric relations and cerebral dominance. Baltimore: Johns Hopkins Press. Pp. 177–195.

Milner, B. 1966. Amnesia following operation on the temporal lobes. In Whitty, C. W. M. & Zangwill, O. L. (Eds.), Amnesia. London: Butterworth. Pp. 109–133.

Milner, B. 1967. Brain mechanisms suggested by studies of temporal lobes. In Darley, F. L. (Ed.), Brain mechanisms underlying speech and language. New York: Grune & Stratton. Pp. 122–145.

Milner, B., Branch, C., & Rasmussen, T. 1964. Observations on cerebral dominance. In de Reuck, A. V. S., & O'Connor, M. (Eds.), Ciba Foundation symposium on disorders of language. London: J. & A. Churchill. Pp. 200–214.

Mohacsy, I., Krueger, E. G., & Teuber, H.-L. 1958. Relationship of disturbances of weight discrimination to other signs of parietal lobe disease. Am. Acad. Neurol. (Philadelphia). (Abstract)

Mooney, C. M. 1956. Closure with negative after-images under flickering light. Canad. J. Psychol., 10, 191–199.

Mooney, C. M. 1957. Closure as affected by configural clarity and contextual consistency. Canad. J. Psychol., 11, 80–88.

Mountcastle, V. B. 1961. Duality of function in the somatic efferent systen. In Brazier, M. A. B. (Ed.), Brain and behavior. Washington, D. C.: American Institute of Biological Science. Pp. 67–93.

Mullan, S., & Penfield, W. 1959. Illusions of comparative interpretation and emotion. Arch. Neurol. Psychiat, 81, 269–284.

Newcombe, F. 1968. Double dissociation after focal cerebral injury. In Kinsbourne, M. (Ed.), Hemispheric asymmetry of function. London: Tavistock (in press).

Newcombe, F., Oldfield, R. C., Wingfield, A. 1965. Object naming by dysphasic patients. Nature, 207, 1217–1218.

Oldfield, R. C. 1966. Things, words and the brain. (The Sir Frederic Bartlett Lectures: No. 1.) Cambridge, England: W. Heffer and Sons, Ltd. Pp. 1–16.

Oldfield, R. C., & Wingfield, A. 1965. Response latencies in naming objects. Quart. J. exp. Psychol., 17, 273–281.

Oldfield, R. C., & Zangwill, O. L. 1942a. Head's concept of the schema and its application in contemporary British psychology. Part I. Head's concept of the schema. *Brit. J. Psychol.*, 32, 267–286.

OLDFIELD, R. C., & ZANGWILL, O. L. 1942b. Head's concept of the schema and its application in contemporary British psychology. Part II. Critical analysis of Head's theory. *Brit. J. Psychol.*, 33, 58–64.

PATERSON, A., & ZANGWILL, O. L. 1944. Disorders of visual space perception associated with lesions of the right cerebral hemisphere. *Brain*, 67, 331–358.

POPPELREUTER, W. 1917. *Die psychischen Schädigungen durch Kopfschuss im Kriege 1914–16: Die Störungen der niederen und höheren Sehleistungen durch Verletzungen im Okzipitalhirn.* Vol. 1. Leipzig: Voss.

PÖTZL, O. 1928. *Die optisch-agnostischen Störungen.* Leipzig: F. Deuticke.

PROCTOR, F., RIKLAN, M., COOPER, I. S., & TEUBER, H.-L. 1963. Somatosensory status of Parkinsonian patients before and after chemothalamectomy. *Neurology*, 13, 960–912.

REED, C. F., & POLLACK, A. 1963. Statistically defined displays and pattern detection of cerebral palsied children. *Science*, 140, 1331–1332.

RICHARDS, W. 1966. Attenuation of the pupil response during binocular rivalry. *Vision Research*, 6, 239–240.

RICHARDS, W. 1967a. Apparent modifiability of receptive fields during accommodation and convergence and a model for size constancy. *Neuropsychologia*, 5, 63–72.

RICHARDS, W. 1967b. Size scaling and binocular rivalry. *J. opt. Soc. Amer.*, 57, 576.

ROSE, J. E., & MOUNTCASTLE, V. B. 1959. Touch and kinesthesis. In Field, J., Magoun, H., & Hall, V. E. (Eds.), *Handbook of physiology.* Section 1, Vol. 1. Washington, D. C.: American Physiological Society. Chap. 17, pp. 387–429.

RUBIN, E. 1915. *Synopslevede Figurer.* Copenhagen: Gyldendal. (German transl.: *Visuell wahrgenommene Figuren.* Copenhagen: Gyldendal, 1921.)

RUDEL, R. G. 1967. Intermodal and intramodal transfer of shape discrimination in normal and brain-injured children. *Eastern Psychol. Assn.* (Boston). (Abstract).

RUDEL, R. G., & TEUBER, H.-L. 1963. Discrimination of direction of line in children. *J. comp. physiol. Psychol.*, 56, 892–898.

RUDEL, R. G., & TEUBER, H.-L. 1964. Crossmodal transfer of shape discrimination by children. *Neuropsychologia*, 2, 1–8.

RUDEL, R. G., & TEUBER, H.-L. 1967. A study of spatial orientation in normal and brain-injured children. *Society for Research in Child Development.* (Abstract).

RUDEL, R. G., TEUBER, H.-L., & TWITCHELL, T. E. 1966. A note on hyperesthesia in children with early brain damage. *Neuropsychologia*, 4, 351–356.

RUSSO, M., & VIGNOLO, L. A. 1967. Visual figure-ground discrimination in patients with unilateral cerebral disease. *Cortex*, 3, 113–127.

SAETVEIT, J. G., LEWIS, D., & SEASHORE, C. E. 1940. Revision of the Seashore measures of musical talents. *Univ. Iowa Stud. Aims Progr. Res.*, No. 65. Iowa City: University of Iowa Press.

SANCHEZ-LONGO, L. P., & FORSTER, F. M. 1958. Clinical significance of impairment of sound localizations. *Neurology*, 8, 119–125.

SCHILLER, P. H. 1965. Metacontrast interference as determined by a method of comparisons. *Percept. Motor Skills*, 20, 279–285.

SCHILLER, P. H. 1966. Forward and backward masking as a function of relative overlap and intensity of test and masking stimuli. *J. Percept. Psychophys.*, 1, 161–164.

SEMMES, J. 1965. A nontactual factor in astereognosis. *Neuropsychologia*, 3, 295–315.

SEMMES, J., WEINSTEIN, S., GHENT, L., & TEUBER, H.-L. 1954. Performance on complex tactual tasks after brain injury in man: Analysis by locus of lesion. *Amer. J. Psychol.*, 67, 220–240.

SEMMES, J., WEINSTEIN, S., GHENT, L., & TEUBER, H.-L. 1955. Spatial orientation in man after cerebral injury: Analyses by locus of lesion, *J. Psychol.*, 39, 227–244.

SEMMES, J., WEINSTEIN, S., GHENT, L., & TEUBER, H.-L. 1960. *Somatosensory changes after penetrating brain wounds in man.* Cambridge, Mass.: Harvard University Press.

SEMMES, J., WEINSTEIN, S., GHENT, L., & TEUBER, H.-L. 1963. Correlates of impaired orientation in personal and extrapersonal space. *Brain*, 86, 747–772.

SHANKWEILER, D. P. 1961. Performance of brain-damaged patients on two tests of sound localization. *J. comp. physiol. Psychol.*, 54, 375–381.

SHANKWEILER, D. P. 1966. Effects of temporal-lobe damage on perception of dichotically presented melodies. *J. comp. physiol. Psychol.*, 62, 115–119.

SHANKWEILER, D. P., & STUDDERT-KENNEDY, M. 1967. Identification of consonants and vowels presented to left and right ears. *Quart. J. exp. Psychol.*, 19, 59–63.

SHERRINGTON, C. S. 1900. The muscular sense. In Schäfer, E. A. (Ed.), *Textbook of physiology.* Edinburgh and London: Young J. Pentland.

SILBERPFENNIG, J. 1941. Contributions to the problem of eye movements: III. Disturbances of ocular movements with pseudohemianopsia in frontal lobe tumors. *Confin. Neurol.*, 4, 1–13.

SOLOMON, R. L., & HOWES, D. H. 1951. Word frequency, personal values, and visual duration thresholds. *Psychol. Rev.*, 58, 256–270.

SPERRY, R. W. 1961. Cerebral organization and behavior. *Science*, 133, 1749–1757.

SPERRY, R. W. 1964. Problems outstanding in the evolution of brain function. James Arthur Lecture on the Evolution of the Human Brain. New York: American Museum of Natural History.

SPERRY, R. W. 1966. Hemispheric interaction and the mind-brain problem. In Eccles, J. C. (Ed.), *Brain and conscious experience.* New York: Springer.

SPERRY, R. W., & GAZZANIGA, M. S. 1967. Language following surgical disconnection of the hemispheres. In Darley, F. L. (Ed.), *Brain mechanisms underlying speech and language.* New York: Grune & Stratton. Pp. 108–121.

SPINNLER, H., & VIGNOLO, L. A. 1966. Impaired recognition of meaningful sounds in aphasia. *Cortex*, 2, 336–348.

SPITZ, R. A., & WOLF, K. M. 1946. The smiling response: A contribution to the ontogenesis of social relations. *Genet. Psychol. Monogr.*, 34, 57–125.

STEIN, H. 1923. Nachempfindungen bei Sensibilitätsstörungen als Folgen gestörter Umstimmung. (Adaptation) *Dtsch. Z. Nervenheilk.*, 80, 218–237.

STENGEL, E. 1948. The syndrome of visual alexia with color agnosia. *J. ment. Sci.*, 94, 46–58.

STEVENS, S. S. 1957. On the psychophysical law. *Psychol. Rev.*, 64, 153–181.

STREET, R. F. 1931. A Gestalt completion test. *Teach. Coll. Contrib. Educ.*, No. 481, pp. vii, 65.

SUTHERLAND, N. S. 1957. Visual discrimination of orientation and shape by the octopus. *Nature* (London), 179, 11–13.

SWISHER, L. P. 1967. Auditory intensity discrimination in patients with temporal-lobe damage. *Cortex*, 3, 179–194.

SYMMES, D., CHAPMAN, L. F., & HALSTEAD, W. C. 1955. The fusion of intermittent white noise. *J. acoust. Soc. Amer.*, 27, 470–473.

TAUSCH, R. 1954. Optische Täuschungen als artifizielle Effekte der Gestaltungsprozesse von Grössen- und Formkonstanz in der natürlichen Raumwahrnehmung. *Psychol. Forsch.*, 24, 299–348.

TEUBER, H.-L. 1950. Neuropsychology. In *Recent advances in psychological testing: A critical summary*. Springfield, Ill.: Thomas (Am. Lect. Ser. no. 88). Chap. 3, pp. 30–52.

TEUBER, H.-L. 1955. Physiological psychology. *Ann. Rev. Psychol.*, 6, 267–296.

TEUBER, H.-L. 1959. Some alterations in behavior after cerebral lesions in man. In *Evolution of nervous control*. Washington, D. C.: American Association for the Advancement of Science. Pp. 157–194.

TEUBER, H.-L. 1960. Perception. In Field, J., Magoun, H. W., & Hall, V. E. (Eds.), *Handbook of physiology*. Vol. 3. Washington, D. C.: American Physiological Society. Chap. 65, pp. 1595–1668.

TEUBER, H.-L. 1961. Sensory deprivation, sensory suppression and agnosia: Notes for a neurologic theory. *J. nerv. ment. Dis.*, 132, 32–40.

TEUBER, H.-L. 1962a. Effects of brain wounds implicating right or left hemisphere in man. In Mountcastle, V. B. (Ed.), *Interhemispheric relations and cerebral dominance*. Baltimore: Johns Hopkins Press. Pp. 131–157.

TEUBER, H.-L. 1962b. The search for physiologic bases of memory. In Schmitt, F. O. (Ed.), *Molecular specificity and biological memory*. Cambridge, Mass.: MIT Press.

TEUBER, H.-L. 1964. The riddle of frontal lobe function in man. In Warren, J. M., & Akert, K. (Eds.), *The frontal granular cortex and behavior*. New York: McGraw-Hill. Chap. 20, pp. 410–444.

TEUBER, H.-L. 1965a. Disorders of higher tactile and visual functions. *Neuropsychologia*, 3, 287–294.

TEUBER, H.-L. 1965b. Some needed revisions of the classical views of agnosia. *Neurosychologia*, 3, 371–378.

TEUBER, H.-L. 1966a. Alterations of perception after brain injury. In Eccles, J. C. (Ed.), *Brain and conscious experience*. New York: Springer.

TEUBER, H.-L. 1966b. Effects of occipital lobe lesion on pattern vision. *Suppl. 8th Internat. Congr. Neurol.*, 3, 79–102.

TEUBER, H.-L. 1966c. The frontal lobes and their function: Further observations on rodents, carnivores, subhuman primates and man. *Internat. J. Neurol.*, 5, 282–300.

TEUBER, H.-L. 1967. Lacunae and research approaches to them. In Darley, F. (Ed.), *Brain mechanisms underlying speech and language*. New York: Grune & Stratton. Pp. 204–216.

TEUBER, H.-L., BATTERSBY, W. S., & BENDER, M. B. 1960. *Visual field defects after penetrating missile wounds of the brain*. Cambridge, Mass.: Harvard University Press.

TEUBER, H.-L. & BENDER, M. B. 1948. Changes in visual perception of flicker, apparent motion and real motion after cerebral lesions. *Amer. Psychol.*, 3, 246.

TEUBER, H.-L., & BENDER, M. B. 1949. Alterations in pattern vision following trauma of occipital lobes in man. *J. gen. Psychol.*, 40, 37–57.

TEUBER, H.-L., & BENDER, M. B. 1950. Perception of apparent movement across scotomata in the visual field. *Amer. Psychol.*, 5, 271.

TEUBER, H.-L., & BENDER, M. B. 1951. Neuro-ophthalmology: The oculomotor system. *Progr. Neurol. Psychiat.*, 6, 148–178.

TEUBER, H.-L., & DIAMOND, S. 1956. Effects of brain injury in man on binaural localization of sounds. Paper read at the 27th Annual Meeting of the Eastern Psychological Association, Atlantic City.

TEUBER, H.-L., KRIEGER, H. P., & BENDER, M. B. 1949. Reorganization of sensory function in amputation stumps: Two-point discrimination. *Fed. Proc.*, 8, (pt. I), 156.

TEUBER, H.-L., & LIEBERT, K. S. 1958. Specific and general effects of brain injury in man: Evidence of both from a single task. *AMA Arch. Neurol. Psychiat.*, 80, 403–407.

TEUBER, H.-L., & PROCTOR, F. 1964. Some effects of basal ganglia lesions in subhuman primates and man. *Neuropsychologia*, 2, 85–93.

TEUBER, H.-L., & WEINSTEIN, S. 1956. Ability to discover hidden figures after cerebral lesions. *AMA Arch. Neurol. Psychiat.*, 76, 369–379.

THORNDIKE, E. L., & LORGE, I. 1944. *The teacher's word book of 30,000 words*. New York: Teachers College, Columbia University.

TINBERGEN, N. 1951. *The study of instinct*. Oxford: Clarendon Press.

TITCHENER, E. B. 1910. *Textbook of psychology*. Vol. 2. New York: Macmillan (see pp. 202 sqq.).

TREISMAN, M. 1965. Signal detection theory and Crozier's law: Derivation of a new sensory scaling procedure. *J. mathemat. Psychol.*, 2, 205–218.

VAUGHAN, H. G., Jr. 1966. The perceptual and physiologic significance of visual evoked responses recorded from the scalp in man. *Clin. Electroencephal.* (suppl. to *Vis. Res.*), pp. 203–223.

VAUGHAN, H. G., Jr., & HULL, R. C. 1965. Functional relation between stimulus intensity and photically evoked cerebral responses in man. *Nature*, 206, 720–722.

VERNON, J., & McGILL, T. E. 1961. Sensory deprivation and pain thresholds. *Science*, 133, 330–331.

VIGNOLO, L. A. 1967. Factors underlying impairment of visual figure-ground discrimination and sorting tasks in hemisphere-damaged patients. In Kinsbourne, M. (Ed.), *Hemispheric asymmetry of function*. London: Tavistock (in press).

VON BÉKÉSY, G. 1947. A new audiometer. *Acta otolaryngol.*, 35, 411–422.

VON BÉKÉSY, G. 1965. Loudness recruitment. *Trans. Amer. Otol. Soc.*, 53, 85–93.

VON FREY, M., & KIESOW, F. 1899. Über die Funktion der Tastköperchen. *Z. Psychol.*, 20, 126–163.

VON HOLST, E. 1957. Aktice Leistungen der menschlichen Gesichtswahrnehmung. *Stadium Generale*, 10, 231–243.

VON HOLST, E., & MITTELSTAEDT, H. 1950, Das Reafferenzprinzip (Wechselwirkungen zwischen Zentralnervensystem und Peripherie). *Naturwiss.*, 37, 464–476.

VON SKRAMLIK, E. 1937. Psychophysiologie der Tastsinne. *Arch. ges. Psychol.* (*Erg. Bd.*), 4, 1–510.

VON WEIZSÄCKER, V. 1923. Über den Funktionswandel, besonders des Drucksinnes, bei organisch Nervenkranken und über Beziehungen zur Ataxie. *Pflügers Arch. ges. Physiol.*, 201, 317–332.

WADA, J. 1949. A new method for the determination of the side of cerebral speech dominance. A preliminary report on the intracarotid injection of Sodium Amytal in man. *Igaku to Seibutsugaku* (Jap. Med. & Biol.), 14, 221–222.

WALD, G., & BURIAN, H. M. 1944. The dissociation of form vision and light perception in strabismic amblyopia. *Amer. J. Opthal.*, 27, 950–963.

WARRINGTON, E. K., & JAMES, M. 1967. Disorders of visual perception in patients with localized cerebral lesions. *Neuropsychologia*, 5, 253–266.

WEBER, E. H. 1846. Der Tastsinn und das Gemeingefuhl. In Wagner, R. (Ed.), *Handwörterbuch der Physiologie*. Braunschweig: Vieweg. Vol. 3, part 2, pp. 481–588.

WEINSTEIN, S. 1955. Time error in weight judgment after brain injury. *J. comp. physiol. Psychol.*, 48, 203–207.

WEINSTEIN, S. 1962. Differences in effects of brain wounds implicating right or left hemispheres: Differential effects on certain intellectual and complex perceptual functions. In Mountcastle, V. B. (Ed.), *Interhemispheric relations and cerebral dominance*. Baltimore: Johns Hopkins University Press. Pp. 159–176.

WEINSTEIN, S., SEMMES, J., GHENT, L., & TEUBER, H.-L. 1958. Roughness discrimination after penetrating brain injury in man: Analysis according to locus of lesion. *J. comp. physiol. Psychol.*, 51, 269–275.

WEISKRANTZ, L. 1961. Encephalization and the scotoma. In Thorpe, W. H., & Zangwill, O. L. (Eds.), *Current problems in animal behavior.* Cambridge, Mass.: Cambridge University Press. Pp. 30–58.

WEISKRANTZ, L. 1963. Contour discrimination in a young monkey with visual cortex ablation. *Neuropsychologia,* 1, 145–165.

WEISKRANTZ, L. & COWEY, A. 1967. Comparison of the effects of striate cortex and retinal lesions on visual acuity in the monkey. *Science,* 155, 104–106.

WELCH, K., & STUTEVILLE, P. 1958. Experimental production of unilateral neglect in monkeys. *Brain,* 81, 341–347.

WERTHEIMER, M. 1912. Experimentelle Studien über das Sehen von Bewegung. *Z. Psychol.,* 61, 161–265.

WHITFIELD, I. C. 1967. Coding in the auditory nervous system. *Nature,* 213, 756–760.

WHITFIELD, I. C., & EVANS, E. F. 1965. Responses of auditory cortical neurosis to stimuli of changing frequency. *J. Neurophysiol.,* 58, 655–672.

WICKELGREN, W. 1966. Distinctive features and errors in short-term memory for English consonants. *J. acoust. Soc. Amer.,* 39, 388–398.

WIESEL, T. N., & HUBEL, D. H. 1965. Extent of recovery from the effects of visual deprivation in kittens. *J. Neurophysiol.,* 28, 1060–1072.

WIESEL, T. N., & HUBEL, D. H. 1966. Spatial and chromatic interactions in the lateral geniculate body of the rhesus monkey. *J. Neurophysiol.,* 29, 1115–1156.

WITKIN, H. A. 1950. Individual differences in ease of perception of embedded figures. *J. Personality,* 19, 1–15.

WOLPERT, I. 1924. Die Simultanagnosie (Störung der Gesamtauffassung) *Z. ges. Neurol. Psychiat.,* 93, 397–415.

WUNDT, W. 1898. Zur Theorie der räumlichen Gesichtswahrnehmungen. *Philos. Stud.,* 14, 1–118.

YOUNG, J. Z. 1960. The visual system of the octopus: I. Regularities in the retina and optic lobes of the octopus in relation to form discrimination. *Nature* (London), 186, 836–844.

YOUNG, J. Z. 1961. Learning and discrimination in the octopus. *Biol. Rev.,* 36, 32–96.

ZUBEK, J. P., FLYE, J., & AFTANAS, M. 1964a. Changes in cutaneous sensitivity after prolonged exposure to unpatterned light. *Psychon. Sci.,* 1, 283–284.

ZUBEK, J. P., FLYE, J., & AFTANAS, M. 1964b. Cutaneous sensitivity after prolonged visual deprivation. *Science,* 144, 1591–1593.

REFERENCES: MEMORY

AARONSON, D. 1967. Temporal factors in perception and short-term memory. *Psychol. Bull.,* 67, 130–144.

AVERBACH, E., & SPERLING, G. 1961. Short-term storage of information in vision. In Cherry, C., (Ed.), *Information theory.* London: Butterworth. Pp. 196–211.

BARKER, R. G. 1931. The stepping-stone maze: a directly visible space-problem apparatus. *J. gen. Psychol.,* 5, 280–285.

BARTLETT, F. C. 1932. *Remembering: a study in experimental and social psychology.* Cambridge: Cambridge University Press.

BENTON, A. L. 1945. A visual retention test for clinical use. *Arch. Neurol. Psychiat.,* 54, 212–216.

BILODEAU, E. A., SULZER, J. L., & LEVY, C. M. 1962. Theory and data on the interrelationships of three factors of memory. *Psychol. Monogr.,* 76, No. 20.

BLUM, R. A. 1952. Effects of subtotal lesions of frontal granular cortex in delayed reaction in monkeys. *Arch. Neurol. Psychiat., Chicago,* 67, 375–386.

BROADBENT, D. E. 1954. The role of auditory localization in attention and memory span. *J. exp. Psychol.*, 47, 191–196.

BROWN, J. 1958. Some tests of the decay theory of immediate memory. *Quart. J. exp. Psychol.*, 10, 12–21.

CARMICHAEL, L., HOGAN, H. P., & WALTER, A. A. 1932. An experimental study of the effect of language on the reproduction of visually perceived forms, *J. exp. Psychol.*, 15, 73–86.

CORKIN, S. 1964. *Somesthetic function after focal cerebral damage in man.* Unpublished Ph.D. thesis, McGill University.

CORKIN, S. 1965. Tactually-guided maze learning in man: effects of unilateral cortical excisions and bilateral hippocampal lesions. *Neuropsychologia*, 3, 339–352.

CORKIN, S., MILNER, B., & RASMUSSEN, T. 1964. Effects of different cortical excisions on sensory thresholds in man. *Trans. Am. neurol. Ass.*, 89, 112–116.

DAVIS, R., SUTHERLAND, N. S., & JUDD, B. R. 1961. Information content in recognition and recall. *J. exp. Psychol.*, 61, 422–429.

DE RENZI, E. 1968. Nonverbal memory and hemispheric side of lesion. *Neuropsychologia*, 6 (in press).

DE RENZI, E., & SPINNLER, H. 1966a. Facial recognition in brain-damaged patients. *Neurology*, 16, 145–152.

DE RENZI, E., & SPINNLER, H. 1966b. The influence of verbal and nonverbal defects on visual memory tasks. *Cortex*, 2, 322–336.

DRACHMAN, D. A., & ARBIT, J. 1966. Memory and the hippocampal complex. *Arch. Neurol.*, 15, 52–61.

GHENT, L., MISHKIN, M., & TEUBER, H.-L. 1962. Short-term memory after frontal-lobe injury in man. *J. comp. physiol. Psychol.*, 55, 705–709.

GROSS, C. G., & WEISKRANTZ, L. 1964. Some changes in behavior produced by lateral frontal lesions in the macaque. In Warren, J. M., & Akert, K., (Eds.), *The frontal granular cortex and behavior.* New York: McGraw-Hill. Pp. 74–101.

HEBB, D. O. 1961. Distinctive features of learning in the higher animal. In Delafresnaye, J. F., (Ed.), *Brain mechanisms and learning.* London & New York: Oxford University Press. Pp. 37–51.

INGLIS, J. 1959. A paired associate learning test for use with elderly psychiatric patients. *J. ment. Sci.*, 105, 440–442.

JACOBS, J. 1887. Experiments in prehension. *Mind*, 12, 75–79.

JUDD, B. R., & SUTHERLAND, N. S. 1959. The information content of nonsequential messages. *Information & Control*, 2, 315–332.

KELLY, P. H. 1954. *A factor analysis of memory ability.* Unpublished Ph.D. dissertation, Princeton University.

KIMURA, D. 1961. Some effects of temporal-lobe damage on auditory perception. *Canad. J. Psychol.*, 15, 156–165.

KIMURA, D. 1962. Perceptual and memory functions of the left temporal lobe—a reply to Dr. Inglis. *Canad. J. Psychol.*, 16, 18–22.

KIMURA, D. 1963. Right temporal-lobe damage. *A. M. A. Arch. Neurol.*, 8, 264–271.

KING, H. E. 1963a. The retention of sensory experience. I. Intensity. *J. Psychol.*, 56, 283–290.

KING, H. E. 1963b. The retention of sensory experience. II. Frequency. *J. Psychol.*, 56, 291–298.

KING, H. E. 1965. The retention of sensory experience. IV. Short-delay versus long-delay intervals. *J. Psychol.*, 60, 103–115.

KONORSKI, J. 1959. A new method of physiological investigation of recent memory in animals. *Bull. Acad. Pol. Sci.*, 7, 115–117.

LANSDELL, H. 1968. Effect of extent of temporal lobe ablations on two lateralized deficits. *Physiol. & Behav.*, 3 (in press).

LURIA, A. R. 1966. *Higher cortical functions in man.* New York: Basic Books. Pp. 440–447.

LURIA, A. R., SOKOLOV, G. N., & KLIMKOWSKI, M. 1967. Towards a neuro-dynamic analysis of memory disturbances with lesions of the left temporal lobe. *Neuropsychologia*, 5, 1–11.

McNULTY, J. A. 1965. An analysis of recall and recognition processes in verbal learning. *J. verb. Learn. verb. Behav.*, 4, 430–436.

McNULTY, J. A. 1966. A partial learning model of recognition memory. *Canad. J. Psychol.*, 20, 302–315.

MELTON, A. W. 1963. Implications of short-term memory for a general theory of memory. *J. verb. Learn. verb. Behav.*, 2, 1–21.

MELTON, A. W., SAMEROFF, A., & SCHUBOT, E. D. 1963. Short-term recognition memory. Paper read at 4th Ann. Meeting, Psychonomic Soc.

MEYER, V. 1957. *Cognitive changes following temporal lobectomy for the relief of focal temporal lobe epilepsy.* Unpublished Ph.D. dissertation, University of London.

MEYER, V., & YATES, A. J. 1955. Intellectual changes following temporal lobectomy for psychomotor epilepsy. *J. Neurol. Neurosurg. Psychiat.*, 18, 44–52.

MILLER, G. A. 1956. The magical number seven, plus or minus two: some limits on our capacity for processing information. *Psychol. Rev.*, 63, 81–97.

MILNER, B. 1958. Psychological defects produced by temporal-lobe excision. *Res. Publ. Assoc. Res. nerv. ment. Dis.*, 36, 244–257.

MILNER, B. 1960. Impairment of visual recognition and recall after right temporal lobectomy in man. Paper read at 1st Ann. Meeting, Psychonomic Society, Chicago.

MILNER, B. 1962a. Laterality effects in audition. In Mountcastle, V. B., (Ed.), *Interhemispheric relations and cerebral dominance.* Baltimore: The Johns Hopkins Press. Pp. 177–195.

MILNER, B. 1962b. Les troubles de la mémoire accompagnant des lésions hippocampiques bilatérales. In *Physiologie de l'hippocampe*, Colloques Internationaux No. 107. Paris: C. N. R. S. Pp. 257–272.

MILNER, B. 1964. Some effects of frontal lobectomy in man. In Warren, J. M., & Akert, K., (Eds.), *The frontal granular cortex and behavior.* New York: McGraw-Hill. Pp. 313–334.

MILNER, B. 1965. Visually-guided maze learning in man: effects of bilateral hippocampal, bilateral frontal, and unilateral cerebral lesions. *Neuropsychologia*, 3, 317–338.

MILNER, B. 1966. Amnesia following operation on the temporal lobes. In Whitty, C. W. M., & Zangwill, O. L., (Eds.), *Amnesia.* London: Butterworth. Pp. 109–133.

MILNER, B. 1967. Brain mechanisms suggested by studies of temporal lobes. In Darley, F. L., (Ed.), *Brain mechanisms underlying speech and language.* New York: Grune and Stratton. Pp. 122–145.

MILNER, B. 1968. Functional asymmetry of the temporal lobes of man. In Kinsbourne, M., (Ed.), *Hemispheric asymmetry of function.* London: Tavistock (in press).

MILNER, B., BRANCH, C., & RASMUSSEN, T. 1962. Study of short-term memory after intracarotid injection of Sodium Amytal. *Trans. Am. Neurol. Assoc.*, 87, 224–226.

MILNER, B. & KIMURA, D. 1964. Dissociable visual learning defects after unilateral temporal lobectomy in man. Paper read at 35th Ann. Meeting, Eastern Psychol. Assoc., Philadelphia.

MILNER, B., TAYLOR, L. B., & CORKIN, S. 1967. Tactual pattern recognition after different unilateral cortical excisions. Paper read at 38th Ann. Meeting, Eastern Psychol. Assoc., Boston.

MIRSKY, A. F., & ROSVOLD, H. E. 1960. The use of psychoactive drugs as a neuropsychological tool in studies of attention in man. In Uhr, L. M., & Miller, J. G. (Eds.), *Drugs and behavior.* New York: Wiley. Pp. 375–390.

MULLAN, S. & PENFIELD, W. 1959. Illusions of comparative interpretation and emotion. *A. M. A. Arch. Neurol. Psychiat.*, 81, 269–284.

MÜLLER, G. E., & PILZECKER, A. 1900. Experimentelle Beiträge zur Lehre vom Gedächtnis. *Z. Psychol.*, 1, 1–288.

MUNN, N. L. 1951. *Psychology*, 2nd Edn. Boston: Houghton Mifflin. P. 212.

NELSON, E. H. 1953. *An experimental investigation of intellectual speed and power in mental disorders*. Unpublished Ph.D. thesis, University of London.

OSTERRIETH, P. 1944. Le test de copie d'une figure complexe. *Arch. Psychol.*, 30, 206–356.

PENFIELD, W., & MILNER, B. 1958. Memory deficits produced by bilateral lesions in the hippocampal zone. *A. M. A. Arch. Neurol. Psychiat.*, 79, 475–497.

POSNER, M. I. 1966. Components of skilled performance. *Science*, 152, 1712–1718.

POSNER, M. I., & KONICK, A. F. 1966. Short-term retention of visual and kinesthetic information. *Organizational behavior & human performance*, 1, 71–86.

PRISKO, L. 1963. *Short-term memory in focal cerebral damage*. Unpublished Ph.D. thesis, McGill University.

REY, A. 1942. L'examen psychologique dans les cas d'encéphalopathie traumatique. *Arch. Psychol.*, 28, No. 112.

ROBSON, J. G., BURNS, B. D., & WELT, P. J. L. 1960. The effect of inhaling dilute nitrous oxide upon recent memory and time estimation. *Can. Anaes. Soc. J.*, 7, 399–410.

SAETVEIT, J. G., LEWIS, D., & SEASHORE, C. E. 1940. Revision of the Seashore measures of musical talents. *Univer. Iowa Stud. Aims. Prog. Res.* No. 65. Iowa City: University of Iowa Press.

SCOVILLE, W. B., & MILNER, B. 1957. Loss of recent memory after bilateral hippocampal lesions. *J. Neurol. Neurosurg. Psychiat.*, 20, 11–21.

SHEPARD, R. N. 1967. Recognition memory for words, sentences and pictures. *J. verb. Learn. verb. Behav.*, 6, 156–163.

SHEPARD, R. N., & CHANG, J.-J. 1963. Forced-choice tests of recognition memory under steady-state conditions. *J. verb. Learn. verb. Behav.*, 2, 93–101.

SHEPARD, R. N., & TEGHTSOONIAN, M. 1961. Retention of information under conditions approaching a steady state. *J. exp. Psychol.*, 62, 302–309.

SIDMAN, M., & STODDARD, L. T. 1966. Programming perception and learning for retarded children. In Ellis, N. R., (Ed.), *International review of research in mental retardation, Vol. II.* New York: Academic Press. Pp. 151–208.

SIDMAN, M., STODDARD, L. T. & MOHR, J. P. 1968. Some additional quantitative observations of immediate memory in a patient with bilateral hippocampal lesions. *Neuropsychologia*, 6, (in press).

SPERLING, G. 1960. The information available in brief visual presentations. *Psychol. Monogr.*, 74, No. 11 (Whole No. 498).

SPERRY, R. W., & GAZZANIGA, M. S. 1967. Language following surgical disconnection of the hemispheres. In Darley, F. L., (Ed.), *Brain mechanisms underlying speech and language.* New York: Grune and Stratton. Pp. 108–121.

STEINBERG, H., & SUMMERFIELD, A. 1957. Influence of a depressant drug on acquisition in rote learning. *Quart. J. exp. Psychol.*, 9, 138–145.

STEPIEN, L., & SIERPINSKI, S. 1960. The effect of focal lesions of the brain upon auditory and visual recent memory in man. *J. Neurol. Neurosurg. Psychiat.*, 23, 334–340.

SUMMERFIELD, A. 1964. Drugs and human behaviour. *Brit. med. Bull.*, 20, 70–74.

TEUBER, H.-L., BATTERSBY, W. S., & BENDER, M. B. 1951. Performance of complex visual tasks after cerebral lesions. *J. nerv. ment. Dis.*, 114, 413–429.

TONKONOGII, I. M., & TSUKKERMAN, I. I. 1965. An information-theoretical approach to the study of perceptual disturbances. *Voprosy psikhologii*, 1, 26–33.

TONKONOGII, I. M., & TSUKKERMAN, I. I. 1966. Functional structure of operative memory. In Symposium 21, *Short-term and long-term memory*. XVIIIth International Congr. Psychol., Moscow. Pp. 83–86.

WADA, J., & RASMUSSEN, T. 1960. Intracarotid injection of Sodium Amytal for the lateralization of cerebral speech dominance. Experimental and clinical observations. *J. Neurosurg.*, 17, 266–282.

WARRINGTON, E. K., KINSBOURNE, M., & JAMES, M. 1966. Uncertainty and transitional probability in the span of apprehension. *Brit. J. Psychol.*, 57, 7–16.

WAUGH, N., & NORMAN, D. A. 1965. Primary memory. *Psychol. Rev.*, 72, 89–104.

WECHSLER, D. 1945. A standardized memory scale for clinical use. *J. Psychol.*, 19, 87–95.

WEISKRANTZ, L., & MISHKIN, M. 1958. Effects of temporal and frontal cortical lesions on auditory discrimination in monkeys. *Brain*, 81, 406–414.

WICKELGREN, W. A. 1968. Strength theory and decay in short-term memory for H. M. *Neuropsychologia*, 6 (in press).

WICKELGREN, W. A. Associative strength theory of recognition memory for pitch. (In preparation).

WICKELGREN, W. A., & NORMAN, D. A. 1966. Strength models and serial position in short-term recognition memory. *J. math. Psychol.*, 3, 316–347.

YNTEMA, D. B., & TRASK, F. P. 1963. Recall as a search process. *J. verb. Learn. verb. Behav.*, 2, 65–74.

ZANGWILL, O. L. 1943 Clinical tests of memory impairment. *Proc. Roy. Soc. Med.*, 36, 576–580.

CHAPTER 12

The Neurological Examination of Animals

G. ETTLINGER

OVER THE centuries various specialized methods have been developed
for the localization of brain lesions or other disease of the central
nervous system in man. Taken together, such methods comprise the
neurological examination of clinical medicine. The examination is
both complex and lengthy (even when the patient is able to cooperate
optimally), because such diverse items of behavior as "mental capacity"
and the plantar response represent just two of the varied and numerous
manifestations of activity of the nervous system that can be affected
in disease. It will have taken the neurologist many years of training
to acquire his skills. However, as a result of his examination, the neurologist is in a position to make certain statements of fact, for example,
that no abnormality has been found in the visual system whereas
the motor system is abnormal in a specified manner. Drawing upon his
compilation of objective evidence, that is, upon his findings in the
neurological examination, and taking the case history and the patient's complaints into account, the neurologist attempts to deduce the
nature and site of the disease process or injury. This is the purpose of
the neurological examination in clinical medicine.

In the course of his research, the neuropsychologist generally does
not seek to know the nature and the site of a neurological lesion in the
experimental animal because he himself has produced the lesion and
can, if he so desires, ultimately obtain histological verification. (There
are a few occasions, admittedly, when unexpected postoperative manifestations occur and when the experimenter may desire to find out,
while the animal is still alive, what structures have been unintentionally
damaged.) The chief immediate objective of neuropsychological research that involves neurosurgical procedures on animals is to determine and to understand the behavioral consequences of restricted
brain removals or destruction. In a broad view, all behavioral tests
undertaken with such animals represent part of a neurological examination, for they yield objective evidence about the functioning of the
nervous system. However, in most neuropsychological experiments,
only a restricted class of the behavioral repertoire is sampled with any
one group of animals (generally the class of behavior concerned
with learning, discrimination, or emotion). It is rare for the experimenter to evaluate a wide range of activities of the nervous system.

Ideally, when studying the effects of experimental brain lesions, drug treatments, or other procedures likely to alter the animal's behavior, as rigorous an examination should be made of the state of the sensory and motor systems as is made of the animal's capacity to perform complex behavior. In practice, this is not possible. Therefore, resort may be made to clinical methods of evaluating neurological status. At the least this procedure yields clues as to the presence of unforeseen deficits that can subsequently be isolated and analyzed with further experimental studies.

It is the purpose of this chapter to show that essential information may be lost by the omission to undertake neurological examinations with certain groups of experimental animals, to discuss some methods of examination, and to advocate a close liaison between the neuropsychologist and the clinical neurologist.

The Need for Neurological Examination in Certain Animal Experiments

In one sense, as already mentioned, all behavior tests undertaken with animals may be regarded as forming part of a neurological examination. To show that this claim is not absurd, we need only be reminded of certain clinical tests, for example, the Babcock sentence, when the patient is required to learn to repeat perfectly over a series of trials a sentence longer than the immediate memory span; or the Name, Address, and Flower test, when the patient is asked to recall (after an interval of time) certain items of information previously supplied; or, to move from learning and memory to discrimination, tests of the ability to recognize objects by vision and touch. These and similar tests form part of every systematic neurological examination in the clinic. In this sense, then, every neuropsychological experiment with animals contains one or more items of a neurological examination.

However, we can make a useful distinction between the classes of behavior that are evaluated. This distinction is not arbitrary, as it is based upon the reasoning of the experimental design. In most instances, the experimenter will wish to determine the effects that a given neurosurgical procedure or other treatment has on the animal's performance under certain experimental conditions or on one or more tasks. We may designate the animal's behavior under these conditions or on such tasks as the chief dependent variable of the experiment; and the animal's behavior under all control conditions or on all control tasks (not excluding its performance during neurological examination) as the subsidiary dependent variables of the investigation. Then, advocacy for a more extensive use of the neurological examination reduces to a plea for more control procedures, whether these be formal tests conducted with standard testing apparatus and yielding quantitative results, or whether these be systematic observations of behavior under controlled conditions in the home cage or in a special chair.

It is possible to be more specific yet. Control procedures as such are not obviously deficient in neuropsychological research. For example, if the chief dependent variable of the experiment is to be tactile discrimination performance following removals of parietal cortex, then care is usually taken to demonstrate the selective nature of any tactile defect by excluding associated defects on, say, visual discrimination tasks or on delayed response tasks (the subsidiary dependent variables of the experiment). In other words, control procedures are commonly used to show that of a particular class of behavior (e.g., the class of discrimination learning) only one element (e.g., the tactile element) is defective; but little is done to show whether elements of behavior belonging to an entirely different class (e.g., the class of emotional behavior) are changed as a result of the parietal removal.

But why should one trouble to assess in a single experiment such diverse classes of behavior as tactile discrimination performance, on the one hand, and emotional reactivity, on the other? There is a simple answer: an emotional change toward the more fearful could interact with the conditions of tactile testing (for example, darkness, which is used in most, but not all, investigations of tactile performance) to give rise to defective performance on tactile tasks. Such defective performance, having its origin in an emotional change, could not be termed a genuine defect of tactile discrimination but would merely amount to an apparent tactile discrimination defect. In the same way a change in motor behavior toward lesser activity could also interact with the conditions of tactile testing (for example, the extra movements necessary for palpation in the dark but not necessary for visual discriminations) to give rise to an apparent tactile discrimination defect. Or a decrease in somatosensory sensitivity (i.e., a simple sensory loss or tactile hypaesthesia) could, of course, readily give rise to an apparent tactile discrimination defect on standard two-choice discrimination tasks (it being assumed, although without compelling evidence to support the assumption, that a genuine discrimination defect, irrespective of modality, does not result from simple sensory loss; i.e., blindness and visual discrimination defects are here not synonymous). This does not exhaust the classes of behavior that do not belong to the class of discrimination learning but nonetheless could in some way be concerned with performance on tactile discrimination tasks. Moreover, emotional changes, decreased motor activity, and somatosensory defect all represent components of animal behavior that can be assessed under standardized conditions of testing, or, if necessary, under conditions of systematic observation. All these components are touched upon even in the most cursory neurological examination in the clinic. Whether a quantitative or a less formal assessment of these or similar elements of behavior is made with animals, it constitutes at least a partial neurological examination. The value of such control procedures in distinguishing between a genuine or a merely apparent tactile discrimination defect should now be clear. And a similar case could be made for the value of neurological examinations in investigations of many other kinds of behavior. Put differently, the neurological examination should and can provide us with essential information about the neurological background against which the behavior that is of especial interest to the experiment can be isolated.

Methods of Neurological Testing with Animals

As has already been mentioned, there are many aspects of behavior that are likely to be important subsidiary dependent variables in neuropsychological experiments, and these can either be measured quantitatively under standard test conditions or can be evaluated by systematic observation. The experimenter will choose between these alternative examination procedures by taking into account both the degree of confidence he wishes to place upon his results and the amount of time that he has available for an assessment to be made of this particular item of behavior. To take a concrete example, the visual fields of the monkey can be plotted to an accuracy of 2.5° to 5° of arc by applying a technique devised by Cowey and Weiskrantz (1963). However, it would take many months of training to obtain reliable results with this method. Alternatively, the clinical method of field testing to confrontation can be adapted for use with the monkey. With a cooperative monkey, the visual fields can be examined in this way within 15 minutes or so. However, a lesser degree of confidence would inevitably be attached to such observations.

In this section, both quantitative and observational tests will be described in relation to the item of behavior they are designed to assess. No further reference will be made to the different advantages of the more-or-less formal methods of testing. Nor will reference be made to tests of so-called intellectual functions in animals, and for two reasons. (1) If there is little agreement as to the ways of testing intellectual functions in man, there is even less in the case of animals. This is partly because of difficulties of test validation in different species (there being no analogue, for animals, to such a standard as level of scholastic achievement). (2) Such tests as there are (learning sets or oddity problems for monkeys, maze tests for rats) are likely to form the chief dependent variables of many neuropsychological experiments and are only seldom likely to be needed as control procedures. Certain key references only will be given in relation to the assessment of each kind of behavior to be discussed. The references are not intended to be exhaustive or even representative of the work done in any field. It is merely intended that the reader be able to find at least one publication where a particular method is fully described or elegantly applied.

As will be seen in the following sections, certain aspects of the neurological examination as practiced in the clinic can be directly applied to tests with animals. For example, pupillary responses can be elicited in animals under the same conditions as in man. Details of the examination procedure are then not given, as the reader can refer to standard textbooks of neurology such as those written by Brain (1962), De Jong (1958), and Wechsler (1963).

Assessment of Emotional Changes

Emotional behavior is as yet poorly understood (cf. Chapter 4). Therefore, recourse is had to a variety of empirical procedures for evaluating possible changes in emotional behavior. The one most often used is systematic observation of the animal in an individual cage. For example, Rosvold, Mirsky, and Pribram (1954) and Mirsky, Rosvold, and Pribram (1957) were concerned with the effect of removing respectively the amygdaloid complex and the cingular cortex in monkeys. They devised a rating scale for measuring the aggressiveness (and/or fearlessness) of each animal during acceptance of food from the observer. Different categories of behavior were separately scored (for example, vocalization, position of the animal at the start of feeding, and threatening behavior). Using this rating procedure, observations were taken independently by two experimenters both before and after surgery with a high degree of reliability.

A similar scale was developed by Mirsky, Rosvold, and Pribram (1957) for measuring the relative dominance of individual monkeys within a group forming a stable social hierarchy. The scores on this scale also reflect the animals' aggressiveness and/or fearlessness, but in relation to other animals rather than toward the examiner.

The method of systematic observation can, of course, also be used without allocating scores on a rating scale. If the examiner has been in daily contact with an animal for a period of months, he becomes familiar with its individual emotional characteristics. Following surgery or other experimental manipulation, he is in a position to assess the nature of any emotional change. With monkeys, such observations have been made by many investigators, for example by Klüver and Bucy (1938) and by Denny-Brown and Chambers (1958).

In applying these or any other methods of assessing emotional behavior, it is well to bear in mind that all methods are at present necessarily empirical in the sense that we do not yet know how to meaningfully classify different kinds of emotional behavior. The tests can be defined operationally (that is, a test for aggressiveness is one on which animals that attack obtain a high score), but, even if we assume our methods of classification to be valid, we do not know whether we measure aggressiveness, fearlessness, or some other emotional trait present in animals that attack. It should also be noted that relatively few points along the immense spectrum of emotional response recognized in man can as yet be adequately assessed in animals.

Assessment of Visual Function

In the neurological clinic, perimetry is a time-honored method of determining the responsiveness of different regions of the visual field. There are short perimetric test procedures (a single size and color of the target moved along only a few meridians) and also detailed examination procedures (various sizes, intensities, and colors of targets, various levels of background illumination, both moving and stationary targets or continuous and intermittent target lights over many meridians). However, it is not yet known which physiological mechanisms (such as spatial and/or temporal summation, contour discrimination dependent upon contrast processes, and/or sense of movement, etc.) are affected in patients having a lesion at a given level of the visual system that gives rise to an amblyopic or anopic region of the field. In other words, perimetry is a test of the ability to see, and failure in a given region of the field may reflect many different kinds of disordered visual process.

Because of technical difficulties, perimetry has not often been applied in work with animals. A sophisticated technique has recently been developed by Cowey (1963) and by Cowey and Weiskrantz (1963) for use with monkeys. However, the training procedures are time consuming and require complex apparatus; and, insofar as the test situation as used differs from clinical perimetry (for example, by the use of stationary targets against a heterogeneous level of background illumination), it is not possible to compare directly the results obtained in monkeys with those obtained in man. Cowey and Weiskrantz (1963) have themselves discussed in detail the extent to which any such comparisons are validly made, irrespective of technical differences in the methods of examination.

Less sophisticated, but nonetheless quantitative, methods of detecting gross field defects had earlier been described by Harlow and Settlage (1934) and since then by others (e.g., Ettlinger, 1959).

A rapid form of perimetric examination with the monkey is derived from the clinical confrontation test. The animal is restrained in a special chair that permits it full freedom of movement of the upper limbs. One observer faces the monkey with an article of food to attract and hold the monkey's fixation. A second observer stands behind the monkey and noiselessly brings another food item into the animal's field of vision from the periphery. If this second food object is closer to the animal than the first, the monkey will shift its fixation and reach for the food as soon as this has been moved into an intact portion of the peripheral field. This procedure plainly allows the first observer to make only an estimation (and not a measurement) of the extent of the animal's peripheral field of vision.

Tests of visual acuity are designed to reflect the subject's ability to resolve small spatial separations or extents (that is, to detect the position of a small gap in a regular shape, the direction of slope of fine parallel lines, or the position of a single fine line). The subject's fixation is not controlled, as it is in perimetry, because acuity determinations are expected to represent only foveal functioning, that is, the performance of the region of the retina that can best resolve small separations (whereas, in perimetry, an attempt is made to determine the level of function of representative positions throughout the whole visual field). Again, a sophisticated test method (based upon the resolution of parallel lines) is available. This will yield a measure of acuity in terms of the angular size subtended at the eye of the components of a visual display that can just be resolved. Using a device originally designed by Ives (1910), this method can be adapted for determining the visual acuity of most vertebrates. Weiskrantz and Cowey (1963) have reported their results with monkeys. It is clear that small changes in the training procedure and also the duration of overtraining (that is, training continued after the basic discrimination has been learned) can affect the ultimate value of the acuity measure obtained. Many months of training were found necessary by Weiskrantz and Cowey to secure truly stable values.

Again simple alternative methods are available. Small pieces of food can be scattered on a surface offering good visual contrast, and observations can be taken of the food's retrieval by the animal. Or food items can be placed beyond the reach of, say, a moneky. Threads of varying diameter are attached to the food and placed, one at a time, within the animal's reach. If the monkey is able to resolve the thread against the ground (and has some preliminary experience with this task), it will pull on the thread to gain the food (method of Klüver, 1933). Acuity can also be determined by using methods of visual stimulation that elicit optokinetic nystagmus, although such a reflex method of measuring acuity gives results that have possibly a different meaning from those obtained with the other methods described.

It should be added that a variety of other tests of visual function have been devised for use with animals, for example, tests of the ability to discriminate hues, size, brightness, the total light flux and rate of intermittance and to perceive visual test objects at short durations of exposure. However, formal training procedures are required for all these tasks, often over periods of many months. Therefore, none of these methods of examination are suitable as control procedures, and they will not be further described.

Tests of Pupillary and Oculomotor Function

Many of the pupillary and oculomotor function tests are readily carried out with animals in the same way as with man. This is true of the direct and consensual pupillary light reflexes. With some animals, it is possible to restrain the head and then to observe the extent of the ocular responses made by the subject in following a food object moved by the examiner in various directions. Again by use of a food object the eye movements and the pupillary changes associated with convergence can be observed. Eyelid position and reflex blink to startle can be noted. Much work has been done on optokinetic nystagmus in animals. Here it is necessary to ensure that a large proportion, or preferably the whole, of the visual field consists of rotating stripes. This can be achieved by placing the animal in the center of a rotating cylinder or drum having vertical stripes painted on the inner wall. Lastly, the effects of rotational acceleration and caloric stimulation upon nystagmus can be tested under special conditions with certain animal species.

Assessment of Auditory Function

We owe the most sophisticated procedures for testing auditory function to Neff and to Diamond and their colleagues (see, for example, Diamond, Goldberg, and Neff, 1962). These workers have devised sensitive tests of the ability to discriminate pitch, intensity, temporal patterns, and spatial location of sound; but in every instance the animal used has been the cat. Attempts to train monkeys to perform these same auditory discrimination tasks have generally not been successful (see Wegener, 1964, for further discussion), although monkeys can be trained to perform gross auditory discriminations.

It is common knowledge that monkeys will come to react by vocalization to certain complex sounds, for example to the sound of a particular door opening, when this door is regularly opened just prior to feeding, or will react to the sound of a particular bunch of keys. In practice, the response to such sounds cannot easily be used for testing the auditory sensitivity of an individual monkey (because vocalization in a particular monkey may be a response to the vocalization of the other monkeys or because, if it is removed from the colony and fails to vocalize, it might be too frightened by the strange surroundings). However, it is simple to isolate a monkey and to observe its response to the noise made in cracking the outer shell of a peanut or in shaking the food container (provided that these objects cannot be seen by the monkey). It is also easy to test for localization of loud sounds by observing the animal's orienting response, that is, a turning of the head and eyes. Such tests are crude (even when compared to tests of the visual fields by confrontation), and there exists a real need to devise more refined tests of auditory function for the monkey that, nonetheless, do not require too many training sessions. A simple test situation that has not as yet been tried to this author's knowledge would consist of using a repetitive sound (on a variable-interval schedule) to inform the animal that an access door to food has been unlocked. The sound could be varied in frequency, intensity, and duration, and the animal should quickly learn to respond to the door only when it can hear the sound. (This proposed method is analogous to certain avoidance situations used, for example, with cats.)

Assessment of the Other Cranial Nerves

The function of the remaining cranial nerves can generally be assessed in animals in the same way as in man. Smell might be tested informally if normal monkeys, restrained in a chair, were found to avert their heads from strong-smelling substances. A formal test has been described by Brown, Rosvold, and Mishkin (1963). Taste can be assessed informally by giving the animal bread treated with various solutions (for example, quinine). Schwartzbaum and Wilson (1961) have devised a formal method for evaluating the sense of taste. An asymmetry of facial movement in the monkey is most readily observed by provoking the animal to show its teeth in response to threat. Sensation on the face and head should be tested separately with an artist's brush, a jet of air, and a pin (see the section on somatosensory function for further details). The corneal reflex can be tested in animals that are not too fearful.

Assessment of Motor Function

In many animals the examination of motor function can be carried out as in man. Observations are made of movements and of the standing position in the home cage or in some other enclosure. Then the animal is restrained in a special chair, and each limb is separately assessed for its posture, tone, power, coordination, and the bulk of its muscles. In practice, agreement is not always reached between different observers; for instance, when evaluating the tone of a limb.

A quantitative method of assessing motor power has been described by Cole (1952), and various formal tests of motor dexterity are also available (e.g., Blum, 1951).

Assessment of Reflexes

Monosynaptic reflexes (e.g., the knee-jerk) are readily and reliably elicited in many animals once they are accustomed to the special restraining chair. However, even a normal monkey will show a great variability in its response when the superficial reflexes (for example, the plantar response) are tested. The variability of response seems to be independent of both the exact method of plantar stimulation and of the position in which the limb to be tested is held. Moreover, the variability persists despite an apparently constant level of relaxation on the part of the animal. Therefore, it has been found necessary (e.g., by Ettlinger and Kalsbeck, 1962) to test the plantar response 10 times in each limb in order to secure a measure of the reliability of the response. Repetitive testing has also proved necessary in the case of the palmar response. The precise nature of the stimulation (whether stationary or not) of the palmar surface accounts only in part for the variability of the response. Denny-Brown and Chambers (1958) have discussed in detail the methods to be used in testing certain reflexes in the monkey.

Assessment of Somatosensory Function

As with vision and audition, a variety of formal tests of somatosensory function are available. For example, Klüver (1933) described methods of testing monkeys for the ability to discriminate weights of known mass. He also showed that a monkey could be trained to feel for and to grasp fine threads by touch alone. Numerous investigators have studied the ability of the monkey (and, occasionally, the cat) to discriminate by touch between specified grades of roughness (e.g., Ruch, Fulton, and German, 1938) or between test objects differing only in size (e.g., Blum, Chow, and Pribram, 1950). Nevertheless, all such tests are relatively time consuming.

In the more rapid clinical assessment of somatosensory function, it is the experience of various observers that some normal (that is, untreated) monkeys will fail to respond to pinprick or to light touch. The reason for this variability in response to painful or tactile stimulation is not known. However, some of the animals do respond (by withdrawal) to a jet of air (which can be silently delivered from a hypodermic syringe). A useful procedure in assessing somatosensory function in monkeys is to compare one body half or limb with that on the other side. Sensory abnormality may be inferred to exist if reponse is present to stimulation on one side but not on the other. If response is absent on both sides, then abnormality can be claimed with confidence only after extensive and repeated testing with a variety of methods.

Somatic sensitivity should be assessed to stimulation by touch (an artist's brush or cotton wool), air jet, and pinprick. Although the animal is restrained in a special chair, its limbs should be free to move and withdraw. The animal should not be allowed to see or hear the somatosensory stimulus. Double simultaneous stimulation to homologous left- and right-sided regions of the skin can be given to elicit tactile extinction (or inattention). A clip may be lightly attached to various regions of the body surface, and the animal's ability to remove (and, therefore, localize) this constant-pressure stimulus with either hand and without vision can be observed. Position sense can be tested by blindfolding the animal and by placing a food object into one hand, which is then held by the examiner in various positions relative to the body. Many monkeys will quickly find and remove the food object with the other (free) hand.

There are both formal and informal tests of the ability to recognize form or shape by tactile palpation. The formal tests (e.g., Blum, 1951) require at least some weeks of training. The informal tests are somewhat crude, the monkey being blindfolded and various small objects, edible and inedible, being placed in the hands. Certain animals will actively palpate these objects and bring only the edible objects to the mouth. However, other animals will tend to allow all objects to fall or will hold onto all of the objects without palpation.

Assessment of the Accuracy of Reaching

The accuracy of reaching for a small target can be decreased in association with a variety of disorders (motor, sensory, visual, cerebellar, etc.). Various quantitative tests of the accuracy of reaching with vision have been devised (e.g., Myers, Sperry, and McCurdy, 1962), and these require very little time to administer. If the animal is to be tested in a special chair, then care must be taken to allow full freedom of movement to the hands. Each hand should be separately tested with targets first in the left, then in the right half-field of vision. Again, one of the animal's hands can be held by the examiner in various positions, and a food object can be placed in it. The animal is then allowed to reach (with or without vision) for the food with the other hand. These tests are fully described by Ettlinger and Kalsbeck (1962). It should be noted that in many animals showing a severe defect of reaching, with or without vision, the hand can nevertheless be accurately brought to the mouth. Therefore, reliance cannot be placed upon this movement as an indication of the ability to reach accurately for targets other than parts of the body.

Assessment of the Placing, Righting, and Hopping Reactions

Many animals will raise and then extend the relevant limbs for support if they are held by the trunk, and either a horizontal surface is seen to come within reach, or the edge of the surface is touched against the dorsum of the hand, foot, or paw. This supporting reaction is termed *visual placing* or *tactile placing*. Visual placing can be assessed separately for each limb with vision of the surface allowed to both half-fields or predominantly to only one particular half-field. Tactile placing is assessed in the blindfolded animal. Only a light touch against the dorsal surface of the extremity is permissible, because any stimulus strong enough to flex the phalanges or wrist may elicit proprioceptive placing (which may be preserved when tactile placing is absent and which can be separately assessed). Light tactile stimulation of one limb should give rise to the placing of that limb and also of the contralateral limb (crossed placing). Each limb should be tested for placing at least three times (separately for vision and touch) to obtain a measure of the reliability of the response. The neural systems concerned with the placing reaction have been described by Bard (1938), by Denny-Brown and Chambers (1958), and, more recently, by Meyer, Horel, and Meyer (1963).

Denny-Brown and Chambers (1958) have described the method of testing for the ability of the animal to right itself during free fall and, therefore, to land with the feet toward the ground. Bard (1938) and Peele (1944) have described the hopping reaction and have defined the neural systems involved.

Some General Principles To Be Adopted
with Informal Neurological Assessment

In the foregoing it has been made clear that there is a considerable range of variability in the response of different animals to the same test procedure (e.g., presence or absence of response to pinprick; response or not with the free hand to food-objects placed in the restrained hand; etc.). It is therefore of considerable importance to perform the neurological examination both before and after the experimental treatment (by surgery or drugs). If then one or two of a group of animals have been shown to be unresponsive to a particular test situation before the experimental treatment, this same unresponsiveness observed after treatment will not be attributed to the experimental procedure as such. However, variability between animals is not the only source of possible error. The variability of the responses given by an individual animal in certain of the test situations (e.g., superficial reflexes, placing reaction, etc.) has also been stressed. A simple way to assess this latter variability is to make a number of observations under constant test conditions during the one neurological examination. However, a better procedure is to give each animal repeated neurological examinations both before and after the experimental treatment. In the study of Curzon et al. (1963), each animal was given 10 neurological examinations before the experimental treatment took place and 4 examinations after the treatment had begun. The examiner then became familiar with the reaction of each individual animal to the test situation before the experimental treatment had begun, and he also obtained a large sample of each animal's performance (thus controlling to some extent both for interindividual and intraindividual variability). The animals, in their turn, slowly became familiar with the conditions of neurological assessment and showed progressively less variability of response.

The Need for a Close Liaison
Between Neurologist and Psychologist

It can be argued that the psychologist can and should perform the neurological examination of animals without further reference to the clinical neurologist. When such an examination consists solely of various formal control procedures, each requiring training of the animal under standard conditions, this line of argument has both logical and practical force. When the examination consists only of certain informal procedures that are not routinely applied in the clinic (such as tests of reaching, placing, and righting), there appears to be no good reason why the psychologist should not become as competent in conducting the examination as a neurologist would. However, if a variety of informal test procedures based upon clinical practice are to be used, the psychologist has two alternatives: either to learn from the neurologist how to apply these methods of assessment properly or to enlist the active cooperation of a neurologist. In practice, many psychologists will prefer the latter alternative, being reluctant to invest the time necessary to learn adequately the methods of neurological examination and the range of normal variability in the clinic.

Independently of the identity of the examiner, an interpretation will have to be made of any findings in the informal examination that either clearly indicate or else raise doubts concerning the presence of abnormality. The experimenter will wish to know: the degree of certainty with which the abnormality has been established; what structures in the central nervous system are likely to have been affected by the treatment so as to produce the demonstrated abnormality; and also how the abnormality that has been identified can be expected to influence other kinds of behavior.

The degree of confidence with which a doubtful abnormality can be established as reflecting genuine but mild defect depends ultimately upon the experience of the observer with this kind of examination; the ability to infer the correct localization of the responsible lesion again depends upon the neurological knowledge and experience of the observer; and the assessment of the effects of the identified abnormality upon other kinds of behavior must be based either upon past experience of such abnormalities or else upon lengthy control experiments when the consequences of such an abnormality are formally investigated. In each instance, the psychologist is likely in practice to call upon a clinical neurologist for help (although this is not inevitably so). Such cooperation between neurologist and psychologist in selected areas of research is likely to be of personal profit to each; and ultimately, what is of greater importance, this cooperation will lead to investigations that are more comprehensive and therefore more informative than those undertaken by either neurologist or psychologist alone.

REFERENCES

BARD, P. 1938. 7 Harvey Lectures, 1937–1938, 33, 143–169.

BLUM, J. S. 1951. Cortical organization in somesthesis: Effects of lesions in posterior associative cortex on somatosensory function in macaca mulatta. Comp. Psychol. Monogr., 20, No. 105, 219–249.

BLUM, J. S., CHOW, K. L., & PRIBRAM, K. H. 1950. A behavioral analysis of the organization of the parieto-temporo-preoccipital cortex. J. comp. Neurol., 93, 53–100.

BRAIN, R. 1962. Diseases of the nervous system. (6th ed.). London: Oxford University Press.

BROWN, T. S., ROSVOLD, H. E., & MISHKIN, M. 1963. Olfactory discrimination after temporal lobe lesions in monkeys. J. comp. physiol. Psychol., 56, 190–195.

COLE, J. 1952. Three tests for the study of motor and sensory abilities in monkeys. J. comp. physiol. Psychol., 45, 226–230.

COWEY, A. 1963. The basis of a method of perimetry with monkeys. Quart. J. exp. Psychol., 15, 81–90.

COWEY, A., & WEISKRANTZ, L. 1963. A perimetric study of visual field defects in monkeys. Quart. J. exp. Psychol., 15, 91–115.

CURZON, G., ETTLINGER, G., COLE, M., & WALSH, J. 1963. The biochemical behavioral and neurologic effects of high L-tryptophan intake in the rhesus monkey. Neurology, 13, 431–438.

DEJONG, R. N., 1958. The neurological examination. (2nd ed.). London: Pitman.

DENNY-BROWN, D., & CHAMBERS, R. A. 1958. The parietal lobe and behavior. P.A.R.N.M.D., 36, 35–117.

DIAMOND, I. T., GOLDBERG, J. M., & NEFF, W. D. 1962. Total discrimination after ablation of auditory cortex. J. Neurophysiol., 25, 223–235.

ETTLINGER, G. 1959. Visual discrimination following successive temporal ablations in monkeys. Brain, 82, 232–250.

ETTLINGER, G., & KALSBECK, J. E. 1962. Changes in tactile discrimination and in visual reaching after successive and simultaneous bilateral posterior parietal ablations in the monkey. J. Neurol. Neuros. Psychiat., 25, 256–268.

HARLOW, H. F., & SETTLAGE, P. H. 1934. Comparative behavior of primates. VII. Capacity of monkeys to solve patterned string tests. J. comp. Psychol., 18, 423–435.

IVES, H. E. 1910. A visual test object. Elect. World, 55, 939–940.

KLÜVER, H. 1933. Behavior mechanisms in monkeys. Chicago: University of Chicago Press.

KLÜVER, H., & BUCY, P. C. 1938. An analysis of certain effects of bilateral temporal lobectomy in the rhesus monkey, with special reference to "psychic blindness." J. Psychol., 5, 33–54.

MEYER, P. M., HOREL, J. A., & MEYER, D. R. 1963. Effects of DL-amphetamine upon placing responses in neodecorticate cats. *J. comp. physiol. Psychol.,* 56, 402–404.

MIRSKY, A. F., ROSVOLD, H. E., & PRIBRAM, K. H. 1957. Effects of cingulectomy on social behavior in monkeys. *J. Neurophysiol.,* 20, 588–601.

MYERS, R. E., SPERRY, R. W., & McCURDY, N. M. 1962. Neural mechanisms in visual guidance of limb movement. *Arch. Neurol.* (Chicago), 7, 195–202.

PEELE, T. L. 1944. Acute and chronic parietal lobe ablations in monkeys. *J. Neurophysiol.,* 7, 269–286.

ROSVOLD, H. E., MIRSKY, A. F., & PRIBRAM, K. H. 1954. Influence of amygdalectomy on social behavior in monkeys. *J. comp. physiol. Psychol.,* 47, 173–178.

RUCH, T. C., FULTON, J. F., & GERMAN, W. J. 1938. Sensory discrimination in monkey, chimpanzee and man after lesions of the parietal lobe. *Arch. Neurol. Psychiat.* (Chicago), 39, 919–937.

SCHWARTZBAUM, J. S., & WILSON, W. A. 1961. Taste-discrimination in the monkey. *Amer. J. Psychol.,* 74, 403–409.

WECHSLER, I. S. 1963. *Clinical neurology.* (9th ed.). London: Saunders.

WEGENER, J. G. 1964. Auditory discrimination behavior of normal monkeys. *J. aud. Res.,* 4, 81–106.

WEISKRANTZ, L., & COWEY, A. 1963. Striate cortex lesions and visual acuity of the rhesus monkey. *J. comp. physiol. Psychol.,* 56, 225–231.

CHAPTER 13

Ethological Methods of Observing Behavior*

P. P. G. BATESON

THE DIFFERENCES in interest which once separated ethologists from the main stream of experimental psychology have largely disappeared. With the growth of interest in developmental processes on the part of the ethologists the classification of behavior into learning and instinct has been abandoned; as a result it has become less easy to dichotomize those who work on behavior. Furthermore, the theories which characterized ethological thinking have acquired much the same status as the old learning theories. Worship of the old gods and the intellectual baggage that went with it still survives quaintly in remote corners. But for the most part proponents of a Grand Theory have either been forced to close their eyes to awkward evidence or modify their ideas to the point of unfalsifiability. Explanations have thus become much more limited in scope and in the process have converged with those offered by psychologists. For all this, behavioral scientists with a zoological background do still differ in their approach to the study of animal behavior from those not originally trained as zoologists. The old classification of the subject into ethology and comparative psychology is still used, though the distinction is in many ways undesirable and often meaningless.

The zoologist is trained to compare and contrast diverse species. Impregnated as his thinking is with the Darwinian theory of evolution, he will constantly speculate on the adaptive significance of differences between species. To a considerable extent this way of thinking has carried over into the study of behavior. Many ethologists are primarily interested in the biological function of behavior and others are wary of proceeding far in causal analysis without first relating their findings to the context in which the behavior naturally occurs. If an animal is to be studied in an unrestricted environment and the measures of its behavior are to be quantitative, special techniques of observation and recording are needed. The development of such methods, as much as anything else, characterizes the work of ethologists, but an interest in function is not a necessary condition for either using or refining these methods. Many ethologists with no particular interest in function have extended them for use in the causal analysis of behavior. In this chapter

* I am grateful to R. A. Hinde and Joan G. Stevenson for their comments on the manuscript.

I shall try to show that such methods are more reliable and powerful than is commonly supposed by the psychologist, and that they are of direct relevance to many of his problems. Before reviewing the methods of direct observation I shall consider in more detail the biological approach to behavior.

When an ethologist asks what is the function of behavior, he is concerned with two separate issues: why did the behavior evolve; and what is its survival value at the present time? At first glance neither of these questions seems easily answered. The approach to the historical question must necessarily be indirect, since a behavioral fossil record obviously does not exist. Nevertheless, some progress has been made by comparing the behavior of species which on other grounds are regarded as being closely related (e.g., Tinbergen, 1959). Thus, the derivation of a courtship display may become apparent when a closely related species is observed to perform in the same situation a recognizable movement, such as preening a particular feather. Employing this approach and relating an animal's behavior to its natural habitat it is often possible to suggest why the behavior evolved in the way it did, but such hypotheses must involve a number of assumptions about the nature of the environment in the history of the species.

At one time the uncertainties of the evolutionary argument surrounded hypotheses about survival value. In recent years an increasing number of studies, notably by Tinbergen and his co-workers, have shown that the problem is susceptible to experimental analysis. For example, Tinbergen et al. (1962) analyzed the survival value of the black-headed gull's tendency to remove egg shell from its nest a few hours after a chick has hatched. There were a number of possibilities. The sharp edges of the shell might injure the chicks; the shell might tend to slip over an unhatched egg thus trapping the chick in a double shell; it might interfere in some way with brooding; it might provide a breeding ground for bacteria or moulds; finally, it might attract the attention of predators and thus endanger the brood. Because species such as the kittiwake, which nest on steep cliffs and are safe from predation, do not carry away their egg shells from the nest, it was concluded that the last possibility was most likely. Therefore Tinbergen and his co-workers examined the effects on predation of leaving egg shells alongside intact eggs and found that the level of predation was much higher than when no shells were left with the eggs. They concluded that the adults' tendency to remove these shells functions to decrease predation and thus increases the chances of the brood surviving.

Those who are unaccustomed to think in functional terms sometimes belittle such studies on the grounds that everyone knows behavior has survival value. This misses the point of the analysis, which is, of course, to determine a particular consequence of the behavior pattern which increases the chances of an individual leaving offspring (see Tinbergen, 1963). There is thus an exact analogy with causal analysis by which the experimenter determines particular antecedents which are necessary for the occurrence of a given event. It must be emphasized that the demonstration of ways in which a given behavior pattern increases the chances of survival does not necessarily furnish the explanation for the evolution of this behavior pattern. If we suppose that it does, we assume that the habitat and the predation pressure have remained unchanged. The assumption may often seem reasonable but it should always be explicit.

Before considering how functional studies affect the ethologists' approach to the study of mechanism, it is necessary to digress slightly because for many psychologists there are offensive teleological implications in functional accounts of behavior. Admittedly evolutionary arguments are frequently couched in teleological terms. But this is a short-hand which is so well accepted that many ethologists regard statements about the goal towards which an animal's behavior is directed as a loose way of saying that the behavioral outcome increases the chances of survival. However, the way in which the behavior pattern has evolved has no bearing on any statement, teleological or otherwise, about the way the system operates in the present. The way in which the behavior pattern increases the chance of survival may reflect a quite different consequence from the one which brings the behavior pattern to an end. It is important therefore to distinguish between teleological and functional explanations of behavior.

Twenty or thirty years ago the concept of goal-directed behavior was tainted with vitalism. With the building of increasingly elaborate servomechanisms and the rise of cybernetics it has become clear that the statement that an animal is goal-directed can be public and testable; it suggests that the system will operate in such a way as to increase the probability of an event (the goal) occurring and is likely to continue operating until that event does occur. As Wiener (1948) pointed out, this is not an exclusive property of living organisms and to characterize the system in this way is certainly not the prerogative of biologists (e.g., Hamilton's [1940] principle applied to problems in dynamics).

The advantages of characterizing behavior in terms of the event which brings it to an end are in many instances so obvious that the reluctance of research workers to do this seems astonishing. Where a variety of antecedents lead to a common end the first step in analyzing the mechanism would seem, sensibly, to be the determination of that end, for by doing so, one is provided with a means of classifying those antecedents and thus establishing some relationship between them and the outcome to which they lead. Clearly it is possible to arrive at mechanistic laws without employing teleological explanations. Their usefulness is only apparent when dealing with complex systems, for they draw attention to the ways in which the systems are controlled and thus furnish hypotheses which can be tested experimentally.

While teleological explanations have their place in the causal analysis of behavior, functional explanations have not. Many different mechanisms may serve the same function and conversely many different functions may be served by the same mechanism. So it may be reasonably argued that however successful the ethologist is in determining ways in which a particular behavior pattern increases the chances of survival, and however plausible is his speculation about the way in which it evolved, his studies are totally irrelevant to an investigation of the mechanisms that underlie the behavior. Even so, information obtained about an animal under natural conditions is often useful to the experimenter in the laboratory. While looking at animals in an unrestricted environment, the observer becomes aware of the context in which each behavioral component occurs and at least some of the conditions necessary for its occurrence. To take a limited but instructive example provided by Bindra (1961), the observation that rats become immobile when there is a sudden change in their environment has been helpful in explaining their poor performance in a shuttle box.

Another point is that a comparative study of different species can emphasize their differences. For anyone who has generalized about the behavior of animals after studying a single species, this can be salutary. It may also draw his attention to aspects of behavior he had previously ignored in the familiar species, in much the same way that a lesioned animal can highlight facets of the normal animal's behavior that had previously seemed unimportant.

The advantages of the ethologist's approach to causal analysis do not stem from any direct relations between function and causation but from the additional information which he picks up while looking at behavior in a broad context. Such observation can generate hypotheses about the factors which affect the onset of behavior and the events which bring it to an end. This in turn leads him back to the laboratory.

Observing behavior in situations in which no particular outcome has been predicted obviously raises difficulties. How is one to measure if one does not know what measurements to make? While it is a truism that no man is free from preconceptions or observes without initially selecting certain features from the stream of events and rejecting others, the extent to which he selects information is very largely dependent on the precision with which he seeks to measure it. There are obvious limits on the number of things which he can take down at any one time, or the number of recording devices that can be practicably operated. The more he focuses his attention, the more he is likely to disregard—the greater the magnification the smaller the field of view. The older ethologists did not always hamper themselves with precise measurements and their behavioral categories arose from their observations rather than being imposed on them. Some made a virtue of necessity and anecdotes about animals kept in natural or semi-natural conditions provided not only the initial basis but the primary evidence for subsequent analysis. However, the danger and limitations of this approach soon became apparent: greater weight is more easily given to the first observation than to subsequent ones; differences are exaggerated or minimized; temporal correlations may be missed altogether; and so on.

The need for quantitative evidence in observational studies raises two main problems. The first is to decide on those features of behavior that need recording. The second is to record them reliably when they occur. It has been in resolving these difficulties that the ways of the ethologist and the psychologist have unnecessarily parted.

Properly anxious to avoid errors in judgment and in recording, the psychologist will usually look for unequivocal consequences of behavior that can be readily measured and require little or no training to detect. Such an approach leads naturally into automatic recording with its attendant advantages of objectivity and convenience, and has been spurred in this direction both by Skinner's (1959) views and by the application of control theory to behavior. In principle, automatic recording frees the experimenter so that he can make additional notes on the behavior of the subject; in practice, it frequently allows him to go off and do something else. This can be rationalized on the grounds that the experimenter is not interested in what else the animal is doing in the apparatus, that the control of the behavior operates through those parts of the environment which he monitors, and that, anyway, his research life is much more productive if he can run five experiments at the same time. While this approach to certain problems has obvious attractions, it has its dangers when used as the only method of research. By measuring a consequence of the animal's behavior on its environment the way in which it is brought about is deliberately (and often usefully) ignored. In certain instances possession of such information might lead to a very different interpretation of the animal's behavior. Take an extreme case: approaching a certain part of the apparatus, as measured by the depression of a microswitch, could be because the animal was crawling, jumping, running, etc. towards that point; or because it was backing away from some other part of the apparatus. An actual example is provided by the work on *maze bright* and *maze dull* rats. Searle (1949) observed that the dull rats were more timid than the bright ones, which at once suggested that the single measure of performance in the maze was misleading.

To clarify the differences in the way behavior is measured, Hinde (1959, 1966) has drawn a distinction between description of behavior by its consequences and *physical* description of the motor patterns. Physical descriptions, which have all too rarely been used by experimental psychologists, are obviously needed when control of behavior does not operate through the environment (see Hinde and Stevenson, 1967). And even when control does operate through the environment, they can yield information about the state of the animal which suggests further observations and experiments. For example, I found that in the course of learning visual discriminations rhesus monkeys prick up their ears in anticipation of the next trial (Bateson, in preparation). The amount of time for which their ears are raised declines as the number of correct operant responses increases. Since the monkeys tend to raise the ears when they are selectively responsive to particular changes in their environment, this observation suggests that as they master the problem they attend less, and that physiological measures of *orientation* would be worth employing in a discrimination learning situation.

Machines which replace the need for physical description by the observer can sometimes be devised. However, there are many difficulties. First, the animal's behavior may be totally disrupted when it is festooned with recording devices. Second, machines which can detect patterns are still very limited in scope; the difficulties of building in size and distance constancies and establishing equivalence (say, between a grin as seen in full-face and in profile), are immense. While the human senses may need tutoring and disciplining they are still very often the best pattern detectors we have.

The early stages of a study in which physical descriptions are to be employed are probably the most difficult. An excellent discussion of the problems involved is given in the final chapter of Marler and Hamilton's (1966) book. The observer has to classify the behavior into categories on a largely inductive basis. His preconceptions and the terms he applies to his categories will influence the classification, but there is more to it than that. He will perform a sort of unconscious statistical analysis on his observations; probably he will take account of common causal factors, common consequences and temporal correlations in establishing equivalence between events; all the while his ability to detect differences will improve and tentative classifications will be improved or abandoned. The end result should be a set of categories that are characterized so clearly that he can communicate the classification to somebody else who will be in a position to test its reliability. It is always worthwhile testing how explicit and public are the criteria for each behavioral category by getting two observers to record the same events at the same time. The closeness of the correlation between the two sets of data can then be determined (see Denenberg and Banks, 1962). This procedure is particularly useful if the classification arbitrarily cuts across some continuum. For example, if the position of a monkey's ears is to be classified into *raised* or *lowered*, intermediate cases could be troublesome if the categories were not carefully defined.

In addition to specifying the criteria for each category the observer must define what he means by a *bout*—the period for which an activity lasts. Among other things, he must specify the minimum interval between actual occurrences of the activity which will be recognized as a bout interval.

For certain types of statistical analysis the categories must be mutually exclusive and cover all the activities which the animal is likely to perform. The latter difficulty is commonly overcome by having a *miscellaneous category* which is defined by exclusion.

An important part of the art of establishing behavioral categories is the use of neutral labels: terms which imply knowledge of the motivational state of the animal or of the function of the behavior may mislead the observer and anyone else who tries to use his classification. Thus, if he had a category for vocalizations called *distress calls* rather than, say *peeps*, he might be tempted to include in the category vocalizations which descriptively did not meet the established criteria but which he felt were given by an animal in a distressed state.

In the process of establishing his categories the observer must also decide what measuring scale he is going to use for each of them. The all-or-nothing nominal scale is probably the most widely used and poses the fewest problems from the point of view of recording and from that of interpretation. Interval scales are very rarely used, but attempts are sometimes made to use an ordinal scale with the behavioral category being rated in terms of intensity or according to some index. Such scales often involve assumptions about the underlying organization of the behavior which may not be justified at the descriptive stage. To begin with, it is probably better to treat every point in the scale as a separate event; underlying relations between these separate events can be postulated and looked for later. The observer must always be alert to the possibility that what he has treated as separate events are parts of a continuum.

Even when the observer has decided what to look for his problems are by no means over. He must decide on a method which will provide him with a permanent record of what he has observed. There are advantages to recording visual events on cine film or video tape, particularly when observations are not easily repeated; when the behavior has auditory components a tape recorder is very often essential. A cine film can be run frame by frame so that the events occurring on each frame or on sample frames can be carefully noted. The speed at which video tape is played back can be varied, with the advantage that visual patterns which might have been missed at the normal running speed are detected. Such techniques are already widely used and it would be foolish to belittle their importance. While the relatively static field of view of the camera lens does mean that the techniques are more selective than is sometimes supposed, the records obtained with them can be analyzed at a later stage using a fresh set of behavioral categories.

It is by no means always sensible to use these techniques. Quite apart from the expense, the time involved in examining the film or tape after the event may outweigh any additional information obtained. The equipment may upset the animals in a way that is not easily overcome. The difficulties of observing without disturbing should never be under-estimated—and closed-circuit television is not always the answer. Finally, the problem may be at a stage at which elaborate, expensive, and time-consuming recording is unjustified. A simpler and less expensive alternative to the direct techniques of recording is to dictate into a tape recorder as events occur. The noise of dictation may disrupt the animal's behavior and the record has to be transcribed later; this method can be both troublesome and time-consuming.

The opposite extreme then from recording via a machine is a pencil, paper, and some form of timer. Indeed, sometimes the recording of time adds very little information. In studying the sequences such as those involved in courtship it is enough simply to record the temporal order of events. Subsequently, the observed frequency with which one event follows another is compared statistically with the estimated frequency if the components were given in a random order (e.g., Andrew, 1957).

If events occur slowly enough it may be possible to write down the time and the event; for example, the time of feeding or drinking could easily be recorded this way. If events are occurring more rapidly, a more elaborate technique has to be used. R. A. Hinde devised a simple way of recording a number of events using pencil, stop-watch, and graph paper. Each vertical division on the graph paper corresponds to, say, five seconds; and each horizontal division to successive minutes of an observation period. The observer trains himself to move his hand horizontally so that the pencil point moves from one division to the next in five seconds. When a minute is up, the pencil point is moved down a line and moved across at the same rate as before. The position of the pencil point is, of course, checked periodically against a stop-watch. Every time an event occurs the observer marks the graph paper with a symbol representing that event. Although some experience is needed before this technique can be used fluently, it is surprisingly effective and eliminates the need to mark time of occurrence as well as the event. Difficulties begin to arise when the observer wishes to record a number of different events occurring at the same time, or overlapping in time. At this stage mechanical aids become necessary.

The simplest mechanical device is one in which paper from a roll feeds continuously past the observer's hand. If a stop-watch is placed so that the observer does not have to look down, he can quickly record an event and time of occurrence. A logical development of this is a similar device with a time-marker, a pen which is deflected at regular intervals. And once time is recorded automatically with a pen, an event can be recorded by the deflection of a pen. The observer is now liberated from pencil and stop-watch and operates keys instead; when he presses a key it deflects a pen which stays deflected as long as the key is depressed. Commercially made polygraphs, equipped with up to twenty pens and with gears so that paper can be moved past the pens at a number of different speeds, are readily available. An extension of such techniques is to record events in a form that can easily be fed into a digital computer. A great deal of time can be saved with a machine which records digitally on computer tape either the events which occurred in a unit period of time, or the time when an event began and ended (e.g., Tobach *et al.*, 1962).

Frequently, the observer has decided on the way in which he wishes to express his data before collecting it. To save time he may be able to roll the processes of recording and analysis into one. With a cumulative timer he can directly record the total time spent in an activity over a given period of time. Alternatively, the number of bouts of an activity per unit time can be recorded with a counter. These methods lose information and ideally the observer should initially record both when and for how long an event occurred. Direct measures of the total time spent in an activity and the frequency of its occurrence are often used from the outset since they require little in the way of equipment and are less exacting on the observer.

There are other ways, of course, of making recording less difficult without losing so much information. One way is to record whether or not an event has occurred in a given period of time ignoring the frequency and the duration of its occurrence. Thus, if a period of fifteen seconds is chosen, the maximum number of times an event can be recorded in any minute is four. The observer can facilitate recording by drawing up beforehand a check sheet with rows for each time period and columns for each behavioral category. This Period technique requires continuous observation of the subject.

An alternative is to observe and record at regular intervals; in other words, to sample from the stream of events. This Sampling technique has the advantage that the observer can look elsewhere in the intervening periods of time. The relaxation obtained from such rests should not be under-estimated since prolonged continuous observation can be extraordinarily tiring. The rests not only give the observer time to complete his notes, but allow him to look at other animals in the same overall period of observation. An observer may have four cages in front of him: using the Sampling technique he can record what is happening in the first cage on, say, every quarter-minute; the second cage on every half-minute; the third cage on every three-quarter-minute; and the last cage on a full minute. An advantage of the Sampling technique is that different aspects of the same animal's behavior can be regarded on alternate samples. Thus, at the half-minute its activity can be recorded and at the full minute its position relative to some part of its environment. Sampling can also be done with time-lapse photography (e.g., Delgado, 1964) and each frame analyzed subsequently. Alternatively, as with the Period technique, check sheets with columns for each event and rows for each Sample period can be prepared, and filled in at the time of observation. Various aids to recording at regular intervals can be used. If the interval is short enough a metronome can be used; timers which close a circuit operating a click or flash are readily available. If there is a danger that the animal will be disturbed, the click can be supplied through headphones, and the flash at a point where the animal is unable to see it.

If Period or Sampling techniques are used, the observer must usually reconcile himself to losing information about the order of events and about absolute measures of their frequency and duration. He will be able to measure the relative frequency of each event provided the overall period of observation is long enough. The time over which it is necessary to record in order to obtain a reliable picture of frequency is best determined empirically by recording for a long period of time and comparing parts of the record with the whole. It is worth pointing out that there will be an optimal sample interval for a given period of observation. If the interval is too short an unnecessarily large number of observations will be made; if it is too long the number of samples taken in the period of observation will be inadequate.

Some of the practical advantages of the Sampling technique have already been mentioned. Its drawback is that activities which occur infrequently or in brief bursts may be missed altogether (or if they are recorded, their relative frequency may be exaggerated). The longer the interval between samples the more likely this is to happen. The Period technique consistently exaggerates the frequency of rare events and, again, the longer the period the more pronounced the effect. Thus, if the observer is interested in rare or briefly occurring events the Period method is to be preferred.

Information is usually lost with the Period and Sampling techniques. If the time periods or intervals between samples are shorter than the shortest bout of activity or the shortest interval between bouts, nothing will be lost, and the Sampling technique is to be preferred because it does not require continuous observation. The longest interval between samples that can be used without significant loss of information has to be determined empirically from a continuous record. If this is done the observer has the best of both worlds for he is able to rest between observations without losing anything. However, he must be on his guard lest the bout lengths of the activities he is measuring diminish in length at a later stage.

If the observer settles for a technique which deliberately discards information it does not follow that he has a hypothesis about the outcome. It does mean that he will become much more selective, and if possible he should check the assumptions which the recording technique imposes on him against a continuous record of the events which he is observing. The purist might argue that a continuous record is always desirable, but apart from the difficulties involved in obtaining such a record, the process of analysis can be extraordinarily tedious. Half an hour's recording with a polygraph may yield 15 feet of paper; to total the time for which an event occurred during that half-hour by measuring deflections with a ruler or map measurer can be time-consuming, and obtaining temporal correlations between events can involve many hours of work. There is a strong case here for computer-analysis of data, and moves have already been made in this direction (e.g., Tobach et al., 1962). Recording equipment and adequate programing and computer facilities may not be available to many laboratories, in which case a balance has to be struck between saving information and saving time—the point of balance being decided by how easily the observations can be repeated. The use of cumulative stop-watches or counters that are read at regular intervals obviously saves time spent on analyzing records, and the entries on check sheets used in Period or Sampling techniques are quickly totaled.

The ways in which results are analyzed will obviously depend on the measures used and the interests of the research worker. At the simplest level, one could ask whether or not an event occurred during a period of observation: did the animal approach the object; did copulation occur; and so on. The occurrence is usually expressed as a function of time, in which case three different types of analysis are commonly used. These provide measures of intervals between events (latencies), frequencies, or durations. Sometimes the observer is merely interested in knowing how many times an event occurred or for how long it occurred over the whole period of observation; the mean bout length can be obtained by dividing the first of these measures into the second. If frequencies or durations are calculated for shorter units of time, measures of rates of change can easily be obtained.

Some of the most interesting results that can come from a study in which a number of different measures are used are the correlations between those measures. There are certain pitfalls, of course, in looking for temporal correlations between events (see Cane, 1961). Thus, if an activity occurs very often during the period of observation, all the other activities which it excludes will, of necessity, occur infrequently. It is worth noting, though, that mutually exclusive activities that occupy a relatively small proportion of the total observation period can be positively correlated with respect to time. For example, the various components of a courtship chain are often temporally related even though they cannot occur together. The information that can come from a careful analysis of a record in which a large number of measures of behavior are used will very often surprise the observer and can play a very important role in setting up hypotheses which can be tested experimentally at a later stage.

While the techniques I have described here are in many ways crude and imperfect, the difficulties and dangers of using them are nothing like as great as they are sometimes made out to be. Admittedly the approach that underlies their use to a certain extent runs counter to the current mood in experimental psychology. It can be argued that elaborate methods of observing behavior are not required by someone who is interested in a specific problem and who is armed with special techniques for solving it, but his research life may not always be as clear-cut as that. If, for example, he removes a bit of an animal's brain, injects a drug into it, or restricts its early experience, the use of only a few dependent variables will probably damage his chances of understanding the effects of the manipulation. If the background information is not available, and it by no means always is, he must examine as many facets of the animal's behavior as possible.

It is, to say the least, arguable whether ill-defined behavioral problems will be brought into sharper focus by prematurely applying biochemical or physiological techniques; in such cases, clarity must surely be sought at the behavioral level. In working towards this end, the broad inclusive techniques of the ethologist complement those of the psychologist and should be regarded as preliminary to precise experimental analysis.

REFERENCES

ANDREW, R. J. 1957. The aggressive and courtship behaviour of certain emberizines. *Behaviour*, 10, 255–308.
BINDRA, D. 1961. Components of general activity and the analysis of behavior. *Psychol. Rev.*, 68, 205–215.

CANE, V. 1961. Some ways of describing behaviour. In Thorpe, W. H., & Zangwill, O. L. (Eds.). *Current problems in animal behaviour.* Cambridge: Cambridge University Press. Pp. 361–388.

DELGADO, J. M. R. 1964. Free behavior and brain stimulation. *Int. Rev. Neurobiol.,* 6, 349–449.

DENENBERG, V. H., & BANKS, E. M. 1962. Techniques of measurement and evaluation. In Hafez, E. S. E. (Ed.). *The behaviour of domestic animals.* London: Baillière, Tindall & Cox. Pp. 201–243.

HAMILTON, W. R. 1940. *Collected papers,* 2. Cambridge: Cambridge University Press.

HINDE, R. A. 1959. Some recent trends in ethology. In Koch, S. (Ed.). *Psychology: a study of a science.* Study 1, Vol. 2. New York: McGraw-Hill. Pp. 561–610.

HINDE, R. A. 1966. *Animal behaviour: a synthesis of ethology and comparative psychology.* New York: McGraw-Hill.

HINDE, R. A., & STEVENSON, J. G. 1967. Goals and response control. In Lehrman, D. S., Rosenblatt, J. S., & Tobach, E. (Eds.). *Development and evolution of behavior.* 1. San Francisco: Freeman. (In press.)

MARLER, P. R., & HAMILTON, W. J., III. 1966. *Mechanisms of animal behavior.* New York: Wiley.

SEARLE, L. V. 1949. The organization of hereditary maze-brightness and maze-dullness. *Genet. Psychol. Monogr.,* 39, 279–325.

SKINNER, B. F. 1959. A case history in scientific method. In Koch, S. (Ed.). *Psychology: a study of a science.* Study 1, Vol. 2. New York: McGraw-Hill. Pp. 359–379.

TINBERGEN, N. 1959. Comparative studies of the behaviour of gulls (*Laridae*): a progress report. *Behaviour,* 15, 1–70.

TINBERGEN, N. 1963. On aims and methods of ethology, *Z. Tierpsychol.,* 20, 410–433.

TINBERGEN, N., BROEKHUYEN, G. J., FEEKES, F., HOUGHTON, J. C. W., KRUUK, H., & SZULC, E. 1962. Egg shell removal by the black-headed gull, *Larus ridibundus* L.; a behaviour component of camouflage. *Behaviour,* 19, 74–117.

TOBACH, E., SCHNEIRLA, T. C., ARONSON, L. R., & LAUPHEIMER, R. 1962. The ATSL: An observer-to-computer system for a multivariate approach to behavioural study. *Nature, Lond.,* 194, 257–258.

WIENER, N. 1948. *Cybernetics.* Cambridge, Mass.: M.I.T. Press.

CHAPTER 14

Treatments, Inferences, and Brain Function

L. WEISKRANTZ

THE SET of techniques analyzed and reviewed in the earlier chapters of this book enable us to draw conclusions, in particular instances, about the effects of various treatments on behavior. These conclusions will be simply descriptive, although it is a moot point whether description can ever be simple: because there can be no description without classification, description already implies some sort of prejudgment as to what one considers to be the important variables in the control of behavior, and this prejudgment may reflect, therefore, assumptions of a theoretical sort, perhaps ill-formed, as to how the organism actually works. But there is another question: How far can certain treatments *reveal* anything about how the organism works? So long as our interest is purely practical (e.g., Is drug X a treatment for headache or is it not?), the theoretical question need not concern us. But students of behavior sometimes cannot refrain from philosophical indulgence and are apt to issue dire warnings to their colleagues about the futility of particular approaches and to offer their own approach as the only road to salvation. In particular, it is often said that an understanding of the brain, derived from the most common treatments—ablation and stimulation—will be difficult if not impossible, because these treatments are disruptive; properties of mechanisms cannot be deduced from properties of abnormal behavior, except under severely limited conditions. This attitude warrants serious consideration. It is one that we consider to be far too narrow, but its longevity is astonishing. To the extent that it unjustly discourages research on the actual biological organ known as the brain (in contrast to various hypothetical bits of hardware in a black box), it does a great disservice. Obviously, we ought to try to determine what is possible and what is not.

When we ask *How far can treatments reveal anything about how the organism works?* we need not consider the obvious instances where the treatment effects are being used to test theoretical predictions. We are concerned here not merely with the testing of theories but with their possible genesis. But, as we shall see later, there is certain danger in being overly obsessed with theory (or "structure") as such in our analysis—often, when we understand (or think we do) how an organism, or some part of it, works, "the structure" simply withers away into empty and useless casting.

The first question to which we direct our attention is whether we can classify treatments in advance in terms of how they will affect the inner workings of the organism rather than arbitrarily in terms of the physical units by which they are defined. A treatment may affect the organism through its usual receptor mechanisms, or it may by-pass these altogether, as in the case of brain stimulation. Usually we study treatment effects not directly on the output of the organism, but on the change which is introduced between input and output, and, in this sense, we may talk of treatments changing the *state* of the organism. In commonsense terms we might want to say that some treatments induce states that are simply attenuations or augmentations of states that may normally occur, as when stimulation of the lateral hypothalamus is said to make an animal "hungry," or they induce states that are unusual. Of the unusual states, some might be considered to be unusual only in the statistical sense that they otherwise rarely occur, as when a vitamin-deficient diet produces "night-blindness." But other unusual states are said to be bizarre and disorderly and appear to reflect a malfunctioning of the organism, as in the case of the effects of various hallucinogenic drugs or of extreme sensory isolation.

On reflection, it will be seen that often we make these judgments not on any profound knowledge of the internal mechanisms of the organism and how these are affected by a specific treatment, but on the basis of external criteria. Stimulation of the hypothalamus is said to increase hunger because the effects show the same properties as those produced by other variables also said to increase hunger, i.e., food deprivation and not because we know from any physiological evidence why or how stimulation has such an effect. But there are instances when our knowledge of internal mechanisms is invoked to help us decide whether treatment effects are bizarre. The example of night-blindness caused by vitamin deficiency can be shown to follow quite nicely from what is known of the metabolism of photosensitive pigments in the retina (Wald, 1959). Perhaps in time the peculiar effects of hallucinogenic drugs will also find a similar resolution. But the point must be conceded that we can make judgments about how some treatments affect the inner workings of the organism only if we already know something about the way they already work. Does it follow, however, that treatments can *never* tell us anything about mechanisms? Because the effects of certain brain ablations, say, are difficult to interpret and produce bizarre results, does it follow that all brain ablations are useless to one who wishes to discover something new about brain mechanisms? Is it the case that "to deduce the function of a part from the effect upon the output of removing or stimulating this part we *must* know at least in general terms how the machine works" (Gregory, 1961, p. 322)?

We will spell out our answer very shortly. Regardless of what answer the reader eventually accepts for himself, it must be the case—returning to our original question—that there are no logical grounds for determining in advance whether some specific treatments are going to affect the inner workings of the organism differently from others. Some treatments of an environmental type, such as sensory deprivation, will produce "bizarre" results, whereas some direct manipulations of the brain, such as hypothalamic stimulation, will produce commonplace results. Whether we affect the brain indirectly through its receptor system or directly through surgical techniques is irrelevant to the question, and, if we wish to maintain that we cannot deduce anything about brain manipulations without prior knowledge as to how the brain works, then, similarly, we must say this of any treatment, and thus logically commit ourselves to a nihilism to which few could subscribe in practice.

It must be pointed out immediately that the steps involved in making inferences about mechanism from the results of treatments are often very complex. In fact, there is usually not an orderly sequence of deductions, but there is a series of guesses and hunches that, in turn, generate further tests, reformulations, and refinements. The ultimate value of these does not stem from their particular genesis, but is entirely pragmatic. Casting the discussion in the form of the logic of the procedure rather than in terms of the behavior of the scientist, about which we know very little indeed, is to misplace the emphasis and to draw distinctions, such as that between structure and embodiment, which may be of interest to the logician but not necessarily to the practicing scientist. We will return to this question of what we think actually goes on, rather than what engineers or philosophers think ought to go on, at a later point, and we will consider as well some of the weaknesses that would result if we were to follow their wishes. But let us try to formulate rather abstractly how inferences about the inner workings of the organism can be derived from the study of treatment effects. There are five points to be made.

1. Inferences About Sequences

In studying the relationship between input and output, questions are bound to arise about how many intervening sequential operations occur within the organism and about what sort of time course they possess. Sometimes the input-output relationship itself can be studied in such a way as to point up a clear temporal discontinuity, as in the case of the "psychological refractory period" (Vince, 1948; Welford, 1960). But there are instances of a perfectly smooth relationship between input and output that can be shown, by treatment effects, to be a complex resultant of separate sequential processes. The clearest instance, perhaps, is in the case of memory. The results of experiments with ECS drugs spreading depression and of other treatments indicate quite convincingly that there is a consolidation period for inputs to the storage mechanism of mammals (see Chapter 8). Research in this area is currently very active, and conclusions as to the precise temporal limits of this period are risky, but many experiments seem to point to a period of approximately 30 minutes. Retrograde amnesia caused by many forms of brain pathology, in a general way lends support to such a view. It is fair to say that no one understands why or how ECS or any other treatment affects memory processes precisely, yet the type of dysfunction caused by them is, nevertheless, highly informative as to the inner workings of the organism.

Different types of memory disorders can be produced experimentally by different brain ablations. For example, it can be argued that temporal-lobe lesions in monkeys produce a "long-term" retention impairment, whereas frontal lesions produce a "short-term" impairment. The nature of the impairment in both instances is under active examination and is currently the source of some lively argument, but the point is that the fact that these different types of disorders can be clearly dissociated from each other lends support to a hypothesis that there are different types of memory processes. It should be made clear that this conclusion does not follow logically, but, nevertheless, the hypothesis has been a very fruitful one.

2. Inferences About Independence of Known Categories

Input-output relationships lend themselves to a variety of classifications. Often, in principle at least, we can make statements about the independence of certain of the classes from external manipulations. If perceptual capacity is unaffected by food deprivation, for example, then we have support for a claim that drive and perception are independent. Many electronic instruments, such as wireless sets, have their independent categories externalized in the form of knobs and meters, which enable one reasonably quickly to determine useful input-output categories and to assess their independence. Biological creatures, particularly mammals, although they are built in this manner to a limited extent, bear no very close analogy to such gadgets, and, indeed, much of the argument by engineers based on electronic analogies may be as misplaced as the argument based on hydraulics of earlier writers, e.g., Descartes. True, we can quickly make inferences about the independence of the sense modalities, for example, but it is of some significance that lively debate still continues about the degree of intersensory interaction and even about the possibility of sensory channels being under mutual influence at peripheral stages. When we consider that we must also often feel compelled to analyze biological behavior in terms of storage, motivation, selective attention, and cognition, then the task becomes more formidable. It is true that the more complex computers also might be said to raise similar difficulties, but here the designer often literally places his independent categories in separate boxes. At any rate, the problem is entirely different because, with a computer, we know its design prior to its construction, whereas, with biological organisms, we wish to determine the design. The determination of independent categories of input-output relationships is one of the first steps towards achieving this.

The study of treatment effects lies at the very core of any such analysis. If we wish to know whether perceptual thresholds are influenced by drive, then we study the effects of food deprivation on perception. If we wish to know whether animal intelligence is independent of environmental influences, then we rear litter-mates in different environments, e.g., "enriched" or "impoverished," and so on. Again, the question arises whether there are some treatments that are better than others: Are there "U" and "non-U" treatments? Are brain ablations, stimulation, interventricular injections, etc., to be excluded as trouble-makers?

Aside from the difficulty of formulating any consistent principle on which to determine club membership, such manipulations have already told us a lot about classification of behavior (and a good deal else in addition). As examples, we may cite the research on ablation and stimulation of the hypothalamus, showing that separate drives are differentially affected by distinct anatomical sites of lesions or stimulation; or the dissociation found between learning deficits involving different sensory modalities following ablations in the monkey's posterior association cortex; or the differential effects of damage to left and right hemispheres in man on linguistic and perceptual skills. There are many other examples. But there are two qualifications that must be made. First, it is not the case that all effects of separate treatments that are found to be dissociable carry any information for purposes of categorization of input-output relations. Any complex machine can be altered in such a way as to produce results that are complex and often incomprehensible, not only by tampering with its inside but also by subjecting it to certain external treatments, e.g., extreme temperature changes. There would be no virtue in simply making a catalogue of all dissociable treatment effects. So there is, then, a priority among treatments, but this priority stems not from the treatment itself but from the effects of the treatment. Some effects are more interesting for classification than others, and the most interesting are the ones that already correspond to input-output relations that have already received prior classification, albeit just a tentative one. The proper distinction to draw for "club membership," then, is not among treatments of different origin but among different effects, regardless of the origin of the treatment.

Second, it does not follow that because certain effects are found to be independently manipulable by physiological treatments such as ablation and stimulation that these input-output relations will always remain independent in the normal functioning of the organism. For example, it might be shown by hypothalamic manipulation that hunger and thirst can be independently manipulated, but this does not mean that in normal functioning these would always remain independent, and, indeed, there is evidence that they do not. But this is precisely the value of such an investigation: it enables us to say that up to a certain stage such functions are independently controlled within the organism, and, as more physiological evidence becomes available, the investigation enables us to make guesses as to the stage at which interaction takes place—in other words, the investigation enables us to sort out just how the physiological mechanisms are organized in broad outline.

Aside from the question of independence, there is a point that is so obvious as scarcely to require reiteration but that seems, nevertheless, to have been overlooked by certain critics. If a category of known interest, such as, say, hunger can be affected selectively by a particular treatment, so that stimulation only to hypothalamus has the effect of turning eating behavior on (or off) and such that the stimulation has only this effect, then we have gone a way in knowing where to look for the control mechanism and in trying to understand how it relates to the events that are involved in eating behavior. This, in turn, will lead to further experiments, and so on. We will return to the general question of progress in brain research presently, but we introduce this point here simply to remind the reader of the obvious. A point that is perhaps less obvious and bears repeating is that not all effects of treatments are of interest—the neurological literature is full of bizarre effects that may be of clinical and diagnostic interest but that remain entirely incomprehensible. With such a complex organ as the brain, this is almost bound to be the case. But this does not mean that certain nonbizarre effects are not of the greatest interest and importance. What will be classified as bizarre will not remain static but will depend on the general background of knowledge, and, for example, certain disturbances of vision associated with faulty control of eye movements might have been thought bizarre a few years ago but are now of great interest because of the increase in our understanding of the relationship between eye movements and the stability of the perceptual world.

3. Inferences About Fractionation

We have already considered instances of how treatments can help to generate inferences about sequential processes. The present point is similar in that it deals with the use of treatments to generate inferences about components, not necessarily sequential, of an input-output relationship. There are many examples taken, again, from the field of brain stimulation and ablation. Consider the fact, for example, that lesions in the inferior temporal lobe of a monkey, a region of the brain that is clearly outside the classical visual projection system, produce a marked deficit in the animal's ability to learn visual discrimination tasks. Two points that are important about the results are (1) that the deficit is limited to the visual modality (although lesions elsewhere in posterior association cortex produce other modality-specific defects) and (2) that the deficit can occur without any known impairment in sensory capacity. Indeed, lesions within the projection pathways, as in the striate cortex, produce clear sensory changes with much less-marked alterations in learning capacity. Considerable work has been undertaken to produce a more precise specification of the inferotemporal impairment, but that is not really relevant here, interesting as it might be. The point is that it is a reasonable inference to assume that visual discrimination involves more than a single process. Anatomists and physiologists would have been unable to predict any involvement of this region in vision let alone would have said what the nature of any deficit ought to be. Indeed, the ablation has led directly to a successful search for the detailed anatomical interconnections between the critical area in question and the visual pathways. The present author has no doubt that before long we will have detailed flow diagrams of the visual system, including those portions beyond the striate cortex, which will stem directly from studies founded on treatment effects. It is a fair guess that they will continue to be quite different from what generations of theorists have told us they ought to be.

Another example lies in the comparison of effects of lesions in the amygdala (a structure lying medially in the temporal lobe) and lesions in the ventral medial nucleus of the hypothalamus. Both these lesions affect eating behavior drastically, but in differing and somewhat complementary ways. The hypothalamic animal overeats and becomes markedly obese. It has been shown, however, that the animal is very fussy about what food substances it will accept. The amygdala animal, on the contrary, usually does not become obese but is remarkably unfussy about what food it will accept—in fact, many animals will ingest just about anything that is ingestible. In one case, then, we have an example of heightened control by sensory features of the food and of decreased control by calorific features; in the other case, just the opposite. It is reasonable to infer, therefore, that eating behavior is under the control of two separate factors. Moreover, the anatomical relation of these two parts of the brain with each other and with sensory inflow becomes easier to interpret in the light of the inference.

It should be emphatically stressed that such inferences as these do not follow inescapably from such data. It is always possible that the balance of a highly complex organ has been upset in such a way as to bear no relation to its normal functioning. But just as emphatically it should be stressed that one is at liberty to draw inferences from such material as one wishes and that the final judgment is entirely pragmatic rather than logical. Where anatomy, physiology, and behavior appear to fit together in the manner just described and where further predictions can be derived from such inferences, this kind of use of treatments will no doubt continue to be of powerful assistance in unravelling the "gray box" within us.

4. Inferences About Normal Function from Exaggerated Dysfunction

Here we have one of the classical arguments in support of the value of the study of pathology. The stress, once again, lies not on the origin of the causative factor—although, naturally, this is of great interest— but on the nature of the change. Often, in pathology, in fact, one is at a loss to identify the causative factor. Similarly, with treatment effects, we may be at a loss to understand how the treatment caused the effect, but the effect may, nevertheless, be of considerable interest. Just how interesting it will be depends in part upon the general background of knowledge of the particular field and, in part, upon the ingenuity of the interpreter. It may require a Freud to exploit certain psychopathological symptoms for theoretical purposes.

But there are some effects of treatments that invite certain forms of inferences with great ease; in fact, this very ease sometimes leads to a type of carelessness that justifiably has been severely criticized. One inference is of the following form: if the effect is the appearance of X, then X could be seen normally (or could be seen more readily) were it not for the fact that it is being suppressed or inhibited by whatever organ or system is affected by the treatment. Another inference is: if the effect is disappearance of Y, Y being normally seen without the treatment, then Y is being sustained by whatever organ or system is affected by the treatment. The first form leads to an inference about inhibition, the latter to an inference about facilitation by structures within the organism. Terms like *inhibition* and *facilitation* are bandied about with great ease, as is demonstrated by the fact that, depending on how one imagines one's treatment affects the structure in question, one can convert inhibition into facilitation by postulating inhibition of inhibition and can convert facilitation into inhibition by postulating facilitation of inhibition.

It is easy to show that one can make notorious errors by formulating such inferences. Gregory (1961) has given a nice example: if one removes a component from a wireless set, the result might be a peculiar squeak. It would be misleading to assume that the particular component suppresses or inhibits squeaks. The statement would obviously lead one seriously astray in trying to determine how a wireless set works. This kind of hazard is one that we must always bear in mind in interpreting the effects of treatments on anything as complex as a biological organism.

On the other hand, this is not an inevitable difficulty, and it is fair to say that exactly this type of inference has been one of the most fruitful in advancing our understanding of physiological mechanisms controlling behavior. There are countless examples: Sherrington's early researches on decerebrate rigidity led him to postulate a "release" of inhibition from extensor muscles and led eventually to the postulation of a system important for supporting ("antigravity") reactions of the body. Fulton rightly describes Sherrington's analysis as "one of the principal milestones of modern physiology" (1949, p. 157). Again, we have already cited the work on hypothalamic lesions that has led to the postulation of facilitatory and inhibitory regions controlling eating behavior. There is no doubt that this simple interpretation (which is consistent with other treatment effects, e.g., electrical stimulation has the opposite effect of ablation or local anesthetization) has led to a most fruitful hypothesis, many details of which are now undergoing examination (Deutsch, 1960; Teitelbaum, 1961). A final example is that of the ascending reticular formation, widely agreed to be an important general facilitatory or "arousing" system. The gradual emergence of this notion over the past fifteen years has been one of the significant developments in recent neuropsychology. It stemmed very largely from the effects of traditional treatments such as stimulation and ablation and from the drawing of the very simplest forms of inference—that the structure was normally sustaining that feature of behavior that was severely attenuated when the structure was damaged. No doubt, the reticular formation has tended to be overplayed as an explanatory device, but no one could deny that not only has our understanding of the brain been deepened but also many psychological problems, such as selective attention, dreams, and habituation, have received fresh reexamination as a result.

Because this type of inference is only rarely fruitful with electronic devices, it is just worth considering whether gadgets such as the wireless set may not be misleading types of analogy to biological organisms, although they always serve as useful reminders of possible dangers. Biological organisms differ from electronic ones in a variety of ways, two of which deserve brief mention. First, from the level of the neurone upwards, processes of inhibition and facilitation are fundamental in the interaction of neural events of living animals. This, in fact, stems from the digital nature of neural events. Complexes of switching devices, such as relays, would be much more suitable but still far from adequate as an analogy than wireless sets. Not only individual units but also large collections of units within the nervous system appear to exert effects that are most easily characterized as inhibitory or facilitatory—as, for example, when stimulation of the brain stem can be demonstrated either to increase or decrease spinal reflexes. Given this fundamental feature, inferences of the type just considered are not unreasonable, whereas they usually are quite inappropriate with the wireless set, where the interaction of components tends to be a dynamic one.

Second, biological organisms have evolved, and the mammalian brain in some ways preserves a kind of stratified record of that evolution. Not only does this help to provide a convenient anatomical classification of subparts of the brain but also it is a reasonable assumption that the organization is hierarchical—that the newer parts tend, in part, to modulate the older parts. Many biologists have explicitly made such an assumption, and, although it is a personal opinion that a hierarchical view is far too simple, there is no doubt that pragmatically it has been most useful. At any rate, modern wireless sets do not so carefully preserve their ancestral organization, whereas it would be extraordinary if this feature of living brains were not of great significance for purposes of interpretation.

This point becomes particularly important when one considers for what sort of devices it obviously *would* be natural to make inferences about function from the results of "ablation" or other treatments. In general, one would feel optimistic about such a procedure wherever the physical structure itself of the machine lent itself to assumptions about division of function. If a complex computer is arranged in a collection of boxes, one is tempted to remove one of them and to study the result. One might easily conclude from such an operation that a particular box, say, had to do with the memory store of the computer. Exactly similar temptations exist for anatomical tissues that are conveniently segregated, one obvious case being the endocrine glands. Endocrinology could never have gotten off the ground if someone had not allowed himself to see what happened when a gland was removed—because he was afraid of obtaining the analogue of squeaks from a wireless set. The fact that the brain has retained an evolutionary record, together, of course, with our general knowledge of its anatomical construction, helps one to make the sort of assumptions for it that one makes more naturally in the case of other devices with a more convenient physical layout. Of course, this does mean knowing something about the phylogeny and anatomy of the brain, and, in the absence of this, some of our engineering critics are right to be apprehensive. This is not to belittle either the complexity or the difficulties but is simply to counter any exaggeration of them.

5. Inferences About Capacity of Subparts

As a final example of the types of inferences possible from the study of treatment effects, we again turn to the brain. It is to be hoped that if we could understand what isolated but major subdivisions of the brain were capable of, the information might help us to understand the brain as a whole. Of course, it is not often possible to study the properties of an isolated system, but some examples of successful attempts involving the study of treatment effects ought to make the point.

First, we can consider the mammalian visual system. It has long been known that there are two outputs from the retina to the brain—one going to the lateral geniculate body, and, after a synapse, to the striate cortex; the other going to the midbrain in the region of the superior colliculus. One can study the capacity of one of these routes by a suitable lesion that abolishes the other route. Thus, with total removal of striate cortex (which produces retrograde degeneration in the lateral geniculate), one can study the properties of the superior colliculus pathway. Generally it has been thought that a mammal without striate cortex can discriminate only differences in total energy level of light. More recent evidence suggests that the animal can discriminate two inputs that give rise to different total levels of retinal ganglionic activity, so two patterns differing in total amount of "edginess" can be discriminated, even though their luminous fluxes are equal (Weiskrantz, 1963). Such findings tell us not only something of the capacity of a channel but also something qualitative about the type of coding that must take place in it. It would be impossible, moreover, to make such a specification without going inside the organism.

Another example is the study of transmission between the two cerebral hemisphere when the corpus callosum has been cut and when the sensory inputs are suitably directed to only a single hemisphere—the so-called split-brain preparation. From such studies (Sperry, 1961) the capacity of the corpus callosum and of other interhemispheric commissures is being established, and, as often is the case, a number of ancillary problems are illuminated that are often of far greater interest than the original problem. For example, Meyers (1961) has shown that, if a cat is trained on a discrimination task with visual input directed only to one hemisphere (by cutting the optic chiasma and by blindfolding one eye) and if the corpus callosum is then severed after training, the originally "untrained" hemisphere nevertheless continues to benefit; i.e., the animal shows savings when the visual input is directed to it. This finding, in conjunction with earlier results (e.g., that no such savings occur when the callosum is cut prior to training) makes it clear that training can result in storage of information in more than one location in the brain and that the corpus callosum mediates the multiple storage. Many more details remain to be worked out with this technique and with related techniques such as "spreading depression," but there is no question that they have produced fundamental advances in our understanding of brain function.

If the previous arguments are accepted it will be conceded that useful inferences about the inner workings of the organism can be drawn from the study of treatment effects. A number of points arose, two of which ran through several of the arguments as a common thread: the first was that there is no inescapable logic whereby an inference follows from such a study; it emerges only as a suggestion, as a hypothesis that can then be put to further test. The second was that the nature of the effect is of greater interest than the type of treatment itself. Nevertheless, most of our examples came from the study of treatments like ablation and stimulation on various categories of behavior and, therefore, constitute instances of what is often called "neuropsychology." Having gone through the foregoing exercise, there is one point that must now be made, which is that in practice, fortunately, neuropsychology "ain't like that." In its more productive forms, at least, neuropsychology is not simply the squeezing of inferences from the effects of ablations and stimulation. Such a characterization would be both highly artificial and distorting. Critics of these techniques often tend to assume that ablation and stimulation are ends in themselves, that it is the techniques that define the subject rather than the problems. But what has been neglected in our discussion is the fact that one calls on a wide variety of information about the nervous system into the context of which one attempts to fit one's results. One way of putting this, somewhat pedantically, is to say that the nervous system serves not only as locus of the action of independent variables, such as ablations, but also as the source of dependent variables from studies of evoked potentials, gross and experimental anatomy, cytoarchitecture, neuroembryology, and neurophylogeny. Critics of neuropsychology some-

times talk as if the aim of the whole endeavor is "localization of function." No doubt, localization of function, in the strict empirical sense
of what defect goes with what lesion, is of great importance to the
clinician, and we may perhaps forgive him if he sometimes talks as
if "speech is localized in the left temporal lobe," because that is a
convenient shorthand when the scalpel is about to be lowered. But the
experimental study of neuropsychology is best represented as a convergence of a multitude of sources of information, including the study
of input-output relations themselves. Any one source of information
may be meager and perplexing, but, in conjunction, they may fit together. The pursuit of neuropsychology is like the waging of a major
campaign in modern warfare; it involves the joint action of diverse
forces, together with the careful use of "intelligence" about the layout
of enemy territory. Occasionally a particular development allows a
breakthrough at one point along the front, but a broad advance depends
on no single weapon or stratagem. There are those who grow impatient
and advocate "mystery" weapons or flanking operations. These can
never be ignored without first receiving a fair hearing, but too often
they involve a course of action that simply ensures that the enemy will
never be engaged.

    In recent years there has been a certain amount of disillusionment
with the studies of treatments involving direct manipulation of the
nervous system. One of the objections has already been considered—
that such treatments are disruptive and that function cannot be inferred from dysfunction—and its weakness exposed. Another type of
objection does not deny that such treatment effects can be informative
but argues that information may not have the importance often attached to it. Deutsch (1960) has argued cogently that

> there has been no clear distinction between that part of an explanation of
> behavior which can be expressed as an abstract system and the identifica-
> tion of the elements of this system in terms of actual physical counterparts.
> . . .Once the distinction is clear it becomes fairly obvious that a psychologist
> need only speculate about the system and not its embodiment. (p. 14).

Elsewhere he argues that

> the relevant and enlightening information is about this abstract system and
> not about its particular embodiment. Further, given the system or abstract
> structure alone of the machine, we can deduce its properties and predict
> its behaviour. On the other hand, the knowledge that the machine operates
> mechanically, electromechanically or electronically does not help us very
> much at all. (p. 13).

    Now, it should be said that Deutsch himself does not take the posi-
tion that direct manipulation of the nervous system gives us information
only about embodiment, although he is, on the other grounds, less than
enthusiastic about ablation work. (Deutsch is also less than consistent
in his strictures about ablation work, because he also says, "Another direct approach [to finding out about internal mechanism] is to observe
or *manipulate* changes within the internal structure to see how they
correspond with changes in behaviour. Such a neurophysiological approach is the most direct one logically" [p. 167, italics added].) But it
could be argued, and sometimes is, that, insofar as ablation and stimulation are concerned merely with "localization," they are simply giving
information about anatomical disposition and nothing about how the
system works. From the point of view of explanation, it might be said
that it matters not one bit whether Broca's Area lies in the third

frontal convolution or in some other convolution. This bald argument, however, need not trouble us, because we have seen that the value of treatments lies in a variety of inferences that they permit us to formulate. Conclusions about "localization," aside from their importance to the clinician, are mainly of use in telling us where to concentrate our efforts for more refined analysis.

Although treatment effects, therefore, are not simply to be degraded into giving "embodiment information," it is worth considering whether the distinction between structure and embodiment is a very useful one. There is no question that logically the distinction is a valid one, and failure to maintain it sometimes gives rise to confusion; a theory is rejected merely because its author has made a rash guess about its embodiment. But, if we assume that the brain is a complex machine and if we consider how we tackle other complex mechanisms whose operation we do not understand, our strategy is not necessarily schizophrenic—we do not say we must first understand the abstract principles underlying its operation and only then can we be concerned with its embodiment. We painstakingly look at its physical layout; observe what happens inside when various inputs are delivered to it or when various outputs are delivered by it; tinker with it; and manipulate parts of it to try to understand the relations which obtain between components. Once we understand it, we could no doubt build another one using entirely different parts—but this comes at a final stage, and is not, in any case, the goal. In the case of the brain, our techniques are severely limited, and we are driven to formulating theories, but this is not in itself a desirable state of affairs. The assertion *a psychologist need only speculate about the system and not its embodiment* is apt to concentrate attention on theory construction when much more would be gained by developing new techniques or, indeed, by exploiting existing techniques much more fully.

Not only is it the case that for any theory there is a large set of possible embodiments but also, in practice in psychology, we have for any limited set of facts a large number of theories. It will be said in reply that, insofar as they make different predictions, they cannot all be correct. But the usual state of affairs in psychology is that we have a large number of theories all of which are wrong in certain details. It is no comfort to say that some are more wrong than others or to witness patches placed upon patches and a proliferation of *post hoc* modifications. This situation may exist merely because a good theory has not yet been produced, and, if we wait, one will eventually be produced. But it may also exist because the input-output relations in psychology are so complex and so easily influenced by background parameters that the possibility of reliable predictions being confirmed across situations and across experimenters is only slight. Alternatively, the set of relations may be so restricted that a theory can fit them and yet be fundamentally wrong.

Consider a few instances for which there would be general agreement that we have come to understand something about how internal mechanisms work. Visual perception offers a good example of where an ounce of proper observation is worth a ton of theory. Hubel and Wiesel (1962) and others have recorded responses in the visual system to various types of visual inputs to the eye and have thereby elucidated the nature of coding of patterns. They have already found examples of limited "receptor generalization"—where a response to an input remains invariant regardless of which receptor at the periphery is stimulated—about which psychological theorists have for decades had a field day, from the Gestaltists to Hebb, and even Deutsch. Deutsch has published (1955) a theory of receptor generalization, for example, that fits the facts, but Hubel and Wiesel render it superfluous. Its superfluity has nothing to do with any distinction between structure and embodiment. Its abstract properties are such that it leads to the correct predictions, but it is, nevertheless, wrong—coding just does not work that way. Indeed, once one has observations of the proper kind, the whole distinction between structure and embodiment can evaporate so far as its pragmatic value is concerned. Similar examples can be cited for the nature of differential absorption by pigments in the eye as a basis for the facts of adaptation and color vision. Arguments among color theorists as to the nature and number of color receptors, which are practically impossible to arbitrate, will no doubt be settled by methods of direct observations, such as those of Rushton (1962), and already techniques of electrophysiological recording indicate that combinations of mechanisms may be used in arrangements not necessarily envisaged by theorists (Svaetichen and MacNichol, 1958). From this point of view we must take strong exception to Deutsch's assertion that "psychologists need only speculate about the system and not its embodiment" or to the claim that "knowledge that the machine operates mechanically, electromagnetically, or electronically does not help us very much at all." It is true that equivalent devices can often be built from quite different types of components, but it does not follow that different components do not suggest somewhat different types of machines. If we opened a black box and found only sets of levers and gears, we would not imagine the device to be a wireless set. But the real point is that our very investigation of the machine itself never can be described as pure examination of embodiment. By examining the components of a machine, particularly in relation to each other, we at once hope to determine what the parts are and how they work.

Everyone will agree that methods of direct observation are superior to speculation. Speculation is superior to nothing at all, and we do not wish to argue that theories about mechanism do not have fundamental importance. It will be a long time before changes in the nervous system associated with, say, memory can be subjected to direct observation. But, to repeat, stressing the distinction between mechanism and embodiment no matter how valid logically, may have consequences that are pragmatically harmful, if it tends to favor the construction of theories at the expense of development of techniques or of theories that draw on physiological facts highly selectively simply to muster support for a particular assumption.

Another bit of advice to psychologists is somewhat similar to that of Deutsch's. Gregory distinguishes blueprints, circuit diagrams, and block diagrams and argues that block diagrams are what we seek because "only the last describe how a system works" (1961, p. 319). He goes on to conclude that "ablation and stimulation data can only be interpreted given a model, or a "block diagram," showing the functional organization of the brain in causal, or engineering, terms" (p. 325). It is obvious that the block diagram bears certain formal similarities to Deutsch's "structure," because both are independent of specific embodiments and because both refer simply to formal relationships.

Gregory, however, is at once more stringent and more vague than Deutsch. He is more stringent in that he claims that manipulations of the nervous system can be interpreted only if we have a block diagram.

The critical word is *interpreted*. Gregory is correct when he says that "to deduce the function of a part from the effect upon the output of removing or stimulating this part we must know at least in general terms how the machine works." (p. 322). But deduction is only one form of interpretation. We are at liberty to draw whatever inferences we wish from the results of our manipulation, and then put the inferences to test. That much Deutsch allows. Gregory is more vague, however, in that he says very little about the genesis of these marvelous creatures, "block diagrams." With man-made systems they are simple enough, but, with biological systems, they are a goal, not a starting point. It is of no help to tell one not to tinker with a mysterious mechanism until he understands "in general terms how it works"—that is precisely why he wants to tinker. We would agree with Deutsch that the contribution of experimental psychology "consists in discovering the properties of the organism by subjecting it to various tests. From the results of these tests we attempt to infer the system operating inside" (p. 167). The block diagram is itself an inference. As is the case with all inferences, there are no clear-cut rules—anything is fair game; the only validation depends on the utility of the inference itself and on the consequences that can be derived from it.

But is the block diagram our ultimate goal? Psychology abounds with block diagrams, and too often these are no more than what Skinner terms "logical fictions," that is, they are simply equivalent to a set of input-output relations. Boxes with words like *filter* often are defined merely by the empirical laws relevant to stimulus selection, e.g., novelty, recency, and reinforcement.

Block diagrams in such cases are just a labeling device but possess even less utility than most labels, because they have not even the virtue of providing us with the opportunity to learn what the labeled entity looks like (although, strangely enough, they do seem useful for the development of brand loyalty). A block diagram can be said to provide information of an important variety when it specifies one order of events out of a larger set of possible orders; e.g., does the "filter" come before or after the "short-term" store? But some of these events must be hypothetical in this case, otherwise we would again be dealing simply with input-output relations. That being the case, we are back to making inferences about the hypothetical events, and the sources of the inferences are varied and difficult to specify. However, even granting that block diagrams are useful goals in those instances where the ordering of events is a problem, it is presumptuous to assert that it is our desired goal in all cases. There are many examples that we have considered (e.g., Hubel and Wiesel and visual coding), where the properties of a mechanism are uncovered and where block diagrams are simply inappropriate. No doubt one could always go through the ritual of drawing the diagram, but it would merely be an empty gesture.

It is, in fact, unnecessary to specify in advance a particular form in which one's inferences will fall once they are made. There is usually agreement among scientists when a significant advance in understanding comes about, even though it is often difficult to specify just what its properties are: disparate events "hang together", predictions can be made more precisely, there is an increase in generality, etc. When there is disagreement, it is generally not because of something as trivial as whether the specification involved block diagrams or not, but on issues of economy, consistency, etc.

What one would like, of course, is advice on how to arrive at useful inferences, and here one's advice amounts to telling one how to be a creative scientist, which is at the moment quite impossible. It certainly has little to do with advice about specific techniques. In the case of psychology, where we are concerned with trying to understand how organisms work, it seems obvious that observations of the interior of the animal are desirable, but it seems equally obvious that techniques are severely limited and that some are difficult to use and interpret. Even if we could monitor all neurons simultaneously, it might be that the task of understanding their combined action would be impossible and that we would require models akin to those in statistical mechanics. The job of unravelling the brain will require, for some time to come at least, physiological and anatomical knowledge, sophisticated theory, proper studies of input-output relationships, plenty of speculation, and individuals who are willing and able to combine all of these. Above all, it should be remembered that the color of the box we wish to understand is gray, not black or white. Eclecticism is never a flag that attracts many followers, but scientific chauvinism is likely to win the wrong battles.

REFERENCES

DEUTSCH, J. A. 1955. A theory of shape recognition. *Brit. J. Psychol.*, 46, 30–37.

DEUTSCH, J. A. 1960. *The structural basis of behavior.* Chicago: University of Chicago Press.

FULTON, J. F. 1949. *Physiology of the nervous system.* New York: Oxford University Press.

GREGORY, R. L. 1961. The brain as an engineering problem. In Thorpe, W. H., & Zangwill, O. L. (Eds.), *Current problems in animal behaviour.* Cambridge: Cambridge University Press, Pp. 307–330.

HUBEL, D. H., & WIESEL, T. N. 1962. Receptive fields, binocular interaction and functional architecture in the cat's visual cortex. *J. Physiol.*, 160, 106–154.

MYERS, R. E. 1961. Corpus callosum and visual gnosis. In Fessard, A., Gerard, R. W., & Konorski, J. (Eds.), *Brain mechanisms and learning.* Oxford: Blackwell.

RUSHTON, W. A. H. 1962. Visual pigments in man. *Scient. Amer.*, 207, No. 5, 120–132.

SPERRY, R. W. 1961. Cerebral organization and behavior. *Science*, 133, 1749–1757.

SVAETICHEN, G., & MACNICHOL, E. F., Jr., 1958. Retinal mechanisms for chromatic and achromatic vision. *Ann. N.Y. Acad. Sci.*, 74, 388–404.

TEITELBAUM, P. 1961. Disturbances in feeding and drinking behavior after hypothalamic lesions. In Jones, M. R. (Ed.), *Nebraska symposium on motivation.* Lincoln, Nebr.: University of Nebraska Press.

VINCE, M. A. 1948. The intermittency of control movements and the psychological refractory period. *Brit. J. Psychol.*, 38, 149–157.

WALD, G. 1959. The photoreceptor process in vision. In Field, J., Magoun, H. W., & Hall, V. E. (Eds.), *Handbook of physiology*, Vol. 1. Washington, D.C.: American Physiological Society. Pp. 671–692.

WEISKRANTZ, L. 1963. Contour discrimination in a young monkey with striate cortex ablation. *Neuropsychologia*, 1, 145–164.

WELFORD, A. T. 1960. The measurement of sensory-motor performance: Survey and reappraisal of twelve years' progress. *Ergonomics*, 3, 189–230.

CHAPTER 15

Some Traps and Pontifications

L. WEISKRANTZ

Although it is always, to a degree, presumptuous to tell anyone what to do or not to do in conducting research, there is no doubt that the study of treatment effects involves certain traps that it would be well to expose. In all research, of course, there are the traditional problems of appropriate controls, statistical variations, and so forth, with which the reader is probably already familiar. But in this chapter we want to analyze certain unique aspects of treatment-effect studies that are likely to cause one to make incorrect inferences from one's results. In general, there are sources of difficulty that arise from the behavioral tasks themselves, namely, their multideterminancy, and from the treatment effects themselves, namely that they are unlikely to be all-or-none.

Multideterminancy of Behavioral Tasks

This point has arisen in every chapter of this book that describes techniques for measuring changes in particular categories of behavior. There is no such creature as a "pure" behavioral test. In order to determine whether an animal can, say, discriminate, it must generally be able to attend, to contract muscles, and to be motivated, i.e., to have a host of capabilities beyond the mere possession of receptors. It follows that a change in performance on a discrimination produced by a treatment may be due to a change in any one of these capacities. A simple statement that Task X is affected by Treatment A is inadequate except insofar as a confession that one has a research program. Yet it is surprising how often just such a statement continues to appear in research journals.

The impurity of behavioral tasks also contributes to errors of omission in that it is possible for a treatment to affect more than one aspect of performance in such a way that the aspects cancel out to yield a null result. (For example, an animal that normally prefers the visual to the auditory modality may change his preference after a treatment that impairs visual function and may be perfectly normal in performing in a maze situation containing both visual and auditory stimuli. Noisy environments may increase both arousal and distraction in such a way that detection of signals in a vigilance task is unchanged.) So, again, a statement that Task X is unaffected by Treatment A is not conclusive, because it does not rule out the possibility that aspects of behavior were being powerfully affected in that task. Similarly, two treatments may affect different aspects of a task and yet yield similar net changes—Treatment A may decrease motivation, Treatment B may impair acuity, and each may, therefore, impair visual performance.

Single tasks, then, because of their impurity, are never sufficient for the study of treatment effects. At the very least, further analysis or paring down will be necessary. Even after that has taken place, however, it is still possible that the treatment is capable of having effects on quite different types of behavioral processes not revealed by the paring down. So, ideally, we want a spectrum of tasks, but when we wish to compare the effects of a treatment on more than one task we are likely to encounter further traps set by a formidable devil who renders some tasks more sensitive than others.

Test Sensitivity

If one wished to show that a specific treatment, such as a so-called psychotropic drug, affects emotional behavior exclusively, one might naturally compare the effects of the drug on a task like avoidance conditioning and on some other task like discriminative performance, in the hope of showing that only the first is altered by the drug. But by accidental or intentional selection of parameters one can obtain from a drug that potentially has general and widespread effects on behavior almost any profile that one wishes. For example, any student of animal behavior worth his salt can manipulate the avoidance performance of his animal over a considerable range by altering such independent variables as shock strength, the schedule of delivery of shock, the type of response required by the animal, and so forth. With a bit of juggling the avoidance situation might be made insensitive and the discrimination task made sensitive. A statement that a treatment affects one type of behavior tested under a single set of parameters and does not affect another type of behavior, similarly under a single set of parameters, is virtually meaningless.

Why should tasks vary in sensitivity to treatments? There appear to be three principal reasons. First, treatment effects are commonly not all-or-none. A drug may change the threshold for aversive stimuli but not eliminate the response to them altogether. Therefore, if the task employs a shock that is well above threshold it may be insensitive to drug effects. A lesion may affect rate of acquisition for difficult mazes, but simple mazes may be unaffected. A second reason is that the pretreatment performance may be at a level from which little deviation is possible in a given direction. If an animal performs at 95 percent correct in a discrimination task prior to treatment, it will be difficult to study possible beneficial effects of a treatment on his performance. Conversely, if the performance is low, decrements will be difficult to measure. This would appear to be so obvious that it scarcely warrants discussion, but we will see later that the matter is frequently overlooked in the matching of control and experimental groups. The third reason stems from what we have already said about multideterminancy of behavioral tasks—the treatment might affect only one component that is itself only partially determining the behavior in the task. Thus, an animal may be blinded by a treatment, but his performance in a maze will depend on the extent to which other sources of stimulation are available. Or two components may be affected in such a manner as to cancel out each other.

The factor of difficulty of task is without doubt one of the important variables affecting task sensitivity in many studies of brain function. Lashley (1929) showed, for example, that impairments on maze learning by rats following cortical ablation varied directly with the difficulty of the maze. The inferotemporal visual discrimination learning deficit in monkeys shows a similar relationship—the more difficult the task for the normal animal, the more likely a deficit is to be found in temporal monkeys. So often has such a relationship appeared that it is surprising that it is overlooked in studies purporting to demonstrate an effect on one task but not another. For example, it has been claimed that cortical lesions in cats impair auditory "pattern discrimination" but not frequency or intensity discriminations (See Chapter 9). The first question that ought to be asked is whether pattern discriminations are more difficult to learn. Exactly the same issue arises when it is claimed that cortical ablations or manipulations affect "instrumental" but not "classical" conditioning. Any assertion in experimental neurology that Treatment A affects Task X but not Task Y ought to be treated with suspicion if Task Y is much simpler than Task X. Conversely, those instances where the same assertion can be made even though Task Y is more difficult than Task X, offer strong support to claims of specific effects.

What can we do about this dilemma of test sensitivity? One obvious answer is to subject the test situations to large variations in many parameters. Logically this is sound enough, but practically it may amount to advice to embrace the infinite. Unfortunately there may be no logically tight alternative, but there are two bits of advice, both pragmatic, that may be helpful. The first concerns the construction of the tasks themselves, the second concerns pattern of results to be sought.

Taking up the first point, it is obvious that a range of tasks varying in difficulty or complexity possesses considerable advantages over a single task arbitrarily placed within the range. It is often difficult, of course, to specify such a dimension very precisely in advance and preliminary empirical work is required. For example, one knows empirically that certain visual patterns are easier than others for monkeys to learn to discriminate, as defined by number of trials required for learning. Alternatively one often can select a dimension on a priori considerations, as when the difficulty of a discrimination is varied by changing the physical properties of the stimuli along some single dimension such as size or intensity. At any rate, no matter how the dimension of difficulty has been defined, there are very considerable advantages in constructing the task so that its difficulty is constantly varied in accordance with performance, a technique sometimes called titration. The general principle is that the difficulty is varied inversely with the success of performance, so that when the animal is performing well the task is made more difficult, and when it is performing poorly the task is made easier. Békésy (1947) used the technique for the determination of auditory thresholds in man, and Blough (1958) adapted it for threshold determinations in pigeons. Provided a dimension of difficulty exists, the same principle can be applied to a variety of tasks. Weiskrantz and Cowey (1963) used the device in studying visual acuity, Schekel (1965) and Buffery (1964) have used it in delayed matching from sample. Adjusting ratios have been used to measure reinforcement strength by Verhave (see Chapter 2). The titration technique offers two very strong advantages. First, it guarantees that all tasks and all animals will yield the same mean level of performance (e.g., percent success), so that differences in treatment effects cannot be attributed to any such differences in difficulty. Second, the threshold value at which the animal can merely perform adequately is itself a powerful statistic with which to measure treatment effects. Thus, in conventional delayed matching from sample testing one may find that frontal baboons can solve a delayed response of five seconds (a value of delay very commonly selected by experimenters), whereas in Buffery's situation the titration technique very clearly demonstrates that the frontal baboon has a delay threshold of only between five and ten seconds, the normal and inferotemporal control threshold being of the order of 60 to 90 seconds. Where the titration technique can be applied there is no question as to its great utility.

But variations in task difficulty, important as they are, will not be sufficient to guarantee that tasks of equal difficulty will be equally sensitive to treatment effects, because as noted above, the particular values of large numbers of parameters may affect sensitivity, whereas typically one varies only a single parameter to alter the difficulty. The soundest advice, if followed, will produce much perspiration—to subject the task situations to large variations in many parameters. But there is a paradigm that has found increasing application in the analysis of effects of brain lesions in recent years, which brings us to our second point.

The paradigm has been called double dissociation (Teuber, 1955). To return to our example of the effects of a drug on avoidance conditioning and discrimination performance: suppose it has been found that the drug affects the avoidance but not the discrimination task. The skeptic will ask, after the preceding discussion, whether a sensitive discrimination task was used. The argument will be considerably strengthened if it can be shown that another drug does affect the discrimination task, but does not affect the avoidance task. The paradigm is—Treatment I affects Task A but not Task B; Treatment II affects Task B but not A.

It should be noted that it does not follow that double dissociation, once found for a particular set of parameters, will continue to hold over-all values of the parameters appropriate to the two tests; that is, it might be the case that the two treatments will affect both tasks equally under certain conditions. Hence, it is not logically permissible to conclude that Treatment I will affect only Task A under all conditions, but it is highly likely that the two treatments will show different clusters of effects.

Although we have discussed the double dissociation paradigm in the context of test sensitivity, its principal relevance is to the drawing of inferences about qualitatively different effects of different treatments. For example, if we have only single dissociation (Treatment I affects Task A but not Task B, Treatment II affects neither Task A nor B), then it is possible to argue that the two treatments are qualitatively similar but they differ in strength. It is also obvious that the value of the particular treatments and tasks being dissociated will vary with the particular experimental context. In general it may be said that the maximum information is conveyed when the two treatments are alike in all but one critical aspect (e.g., for brain lesions—same mass, same damage to meninges, but difference in locus) and that the two tasks similarly are alike in all but one critical aspect (e.g., same training procedures, same cue-response contingencies, but difference in sensory modality). This is simply to restate the essence of analytical control procedures, and the double dissociation paradigm is simply a way of combining two control procedures into a single pattern.

But even when double dissociation has been demonstrated, it is unfortunately not sufficient for the demonstration of qualitative differences in the treatment effects. A simple example will make the point. Suppose our two treatments both affect arousal or motivation or activity, which we might postulate is related to performance by an inverted U-function, an example of which would be the Yerkes-Dodsen law. Suppose Treatment I causes an increase in activity, and Treatment II a decrease. Two tasks could be selected that produce different initial values of activity. Then, as shown in Fig. 15–1, Treatment I will affect Task B and not A, Treatment II will affect Task A and not B. Depending on the initial levels of A and B, it would be possible for the two treatments to produce a complex constellation of changes of performance on the two tasks. The results might not be unravelled in practice until normal control animals had been run on the two tasks under varying conditions of arousal, as set by some independent variable such as deprivation—assuming such a variable were available. This example is deliberately contrived; nevertheless it demonstrates the logical insufficiency of double dissociation for drawing an inference that different treatments are having qualitatively different effects.

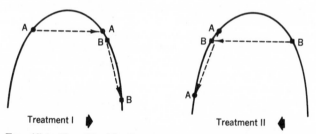

Fig. 15-1. How "double dissociation" might be obtained without qualitative differences between tests and treatments.

Finally, a much more obvious trap is one of generalizing from a particular instance of dissociation between two tests to all classes of tests bearing similar labels. There is, of course, strong temptation to classify tests on the basis of some observed or hypothetical common factor and there is no doubt that to do so helps in making predictions. But there are also great risks of reifying a dissociation between tests into a dissociation between functions and arguing that the affected function has been isolated by a single instance of dissociation. To take a concrete example: under certain conditions inferotemporal monkeys show normal performance on a perceptual learning task but impaired retention for the task a few hours later; frontal monkeys on the same tasks show impairment on perceptual learning tasks but normal retention—hence, double dissociation. Hence—here is the trap—the frontal "deficit" is one of perceptual learning, the inferotemporal "deficit" one of memory. But it does not follow that inferotemporals will never be impaired on other perceptual tests, including those that do not involve obvious retention of specific material. Studies of right temporal lesions in man suggest that such impairments do occur, e.g., on tests of identifying anomalous features of drawings. And more recently Humphrey (unpublished) has demonstrated that inferotemporal monkeys have a stable impairment in a size constancy task for which no explanation in terms of a memory deficit is readily invoked. Obviously tasks are much more easily dissociated than all-embracing "deficits"!

Despite these points, there is no doubt that the double dissociation paradigm has been a most useful one. It has been used as the basis for many hypotheses in brain ablation studies. One of the most instructive examples is by Wilson and Mishkin (1959) who applied it to the effects of inferotemporal and striate cortex lesions and showed that the former affects tasks principally concerned with perceptual learning, the latter, tasks principally concerned with perceptual capacity. But this study also illustrates quite a different problem that arises in treatment studies: the dissociation was not complete—the inferotemporals were impaired most severely on perceptual learning tasks but were nevertheless impaired on perceptual capacity tasks compared with controls; and the same was true of the striate animals on perceptual learning tasks. This type of result might be taken as another example of the multideterminancy of tasks: an animal that cannot see efficiently will have certain difficulties in learning tasks, and an animal that cannot learn efficiently will have difficulty in capacity tasks because these generally involve learning. But as treatments become more extensively studied they are likely to become associated with effects on a whole spectrum of tasks that may be superficially quite dissimilar. Failure to consider the interdependence of the tasks may seriously distort inferences drawn from the treatment effects, but the analysis of such interdependence is itself fraught with danger. We turn to a discussion of some of the problems.

Spectra of Effects from Single Treatments

When a number of tasks are affected by a single treatment, one naturally attempts to search for common factors in the tasks. Sometimes one is fortunate and the search is easy—it might be, for example, that all the tasks affected use visual stimuli, all those unaffected do not. Sometimes the tasks can be ranked according to some dimension (the degree to which learning is a factor in discrimination, in the case of Wilson and Mishkin's study) and the impairment shown to vary correspondingly. Such profiles provide extremely useful material for the generation of hypotheses. But there is one property of biological organisms that makes a static ordering of results into profiles somewhat misleading, and that is their adaptivity. Even when only a single capacity is affected by a treatment, as in, say, deafness caused by surgical intervention, the organism we study is one that adjusts to that condition in a variety of ways, e.g., by exploiting other skills more efficiently, by being emotionally sensitive (deaf persons are often said to be likely to be paranoid), and so forth. One way of putting the case formally is to say that various input-output relations are not independent—a change in one produces changes in others. Moreover, an organism is behaviorally altered not only by the treatment, but also by the alteration caused by the treatment. When we have good reason to know how the treatment changes the capacity of an organism, we are not in difficulty about separating primary from secondary changes. For example, monkeys with total visual cortex ablations sometimes become tame soon after the operation, possibly because their severe visual handicap makes them more dependent on human support. No doubt other types of handicap could also produce similar emotional changes. When we find that a new drug produces tameness, is the emotional alteration a response to the treatment or to some other change produced by the treatment? This is the heart of the problem of the analysis of treatment effects. Here we merely wish to point out that profiles of treatment effects by themselves in no way illuminate the difference between primary and secondary or derived effects of treatments. Further analysis is always necessary; without it one is always in danger of characterizing the treatment simply in terms of its most dramatic results, and designating what may be the primary effect as a mere side effect.

From another point of view, failure to distinguish between primary and secondary effects can be seen to be the result of a particular type of inadequacy of control procedure, and this type of inadequacy has scarcely been recognized in most studies of treatment effects. Typical control groups are of the type that might be called passive. For example, suppose it is found that a brain lesion produces a defect on two tasks. Our typical control group has another type of brain lesion, and let us suppose it has a defect on neither task. If we wish to know whether the experimental group is affected on one of the tasks as a result of a deficiency on the other, then the appropriate control group is one that ought to be matched with the experimental group on one of the tasks. Occasionally by chance we will find a control treatment that affects only one of the two tasks, and then it is clear that a deficiency in one task is not sufficient to produce a deficiency in the other. But usually such a group will have to be experimentally generated, and might therefore be termed an active control group. Perhaps a concrete example will make the issue clear.

It is well known that frontal lobe lesions in monkeys produce a delayed response impairment. It has also been reported that such animals tend to perseverate their responses in delayed response and other situations. But it is known that normal animals who perform badly in a discrimination task are apt to adopt position preferences, i.e., to perseverate their responses to position. Do frontal animals perseverate in delayed response tasks because they cannot succeed at the task, or do they fail delayed response because they perseverate? To answer this question we could wait until we happened upon frontal animals that failed delayed response but did not perseverate. In fact, such instances have been found (Weiskrantz, Mihailović, and Gross, 1962; Gross and Weiskrantz, 1964). But in the absence of such instances, we could provide evidence on the question by arranging that normal animals fail on delayed response by increasing the delay and determining whether they perseverate as a consequence. With the titration procedure (cf. previous) such an operation would be relatively simple, but so far as we are aware no one has carried out the appropriate experiment. Indeed, the titration procedure itself should provide relevant data even without pushing the delay intervals beyond threshold values because it guarantees that all animals will tend to make a relatively high number of errors. At any rate, the point is clear that to answer questions on the interdependence of one of two behavioral alterations it is necessary to have control groups matched not only in treatment variables (e.g., size of lesion or route of injection) but also on performance level itself on one of the tasks. We can either wait for this to occur by chance or we can take active steps to ensure that the condition is fulfilled.

We can consider more formally the relationships that exist between two tasks, B and C, both of which are affected by the same treatment. There are three relationships: (1) C is affected merely because B is affected. (2) B is affected merely because C is affected. (3) B and C are independently affected. Relationships 1 and 2 are sometimes called "hierarchical" relationships. The third relationship precludes 1 and 2, but it is possible for both 1 and 2 to hold simultaneously. Therefore, there are four possibilities: (1) 1 but not 2 or 3. (2) 2 but not 1 or 3. (3) 1 and 2 but not 3. (4) 3 but not 1 or 2. By the displaying of the configuration of results for each of these four possibilities, it will be seen that a minimum of two control procedures will always be necessary to classify the relationship correctly.

TABLE 15-1

1

Task	Treatment	Control for B			Task	Treatment	Control for C
B	X – – – – X		and		B	X	0
C	X	X			C	X – – – – X	

2

Task	Treatment	Control for B			Task	Treatment	Control for C
B	X – – – – X		. and		B	X	X
C	X	0			C	X – – – – X	

3

Task	Treatment	Control for B			Task	Treatment	Control for C
B	X – – – – X		and		B	X	X
C	X	X			C	X – – – – X	

4

Task	Treatment	Control for B			Task	Treatment	Control for C
B	X – – – – X		and		B	X	0
C	X	0			C	X – – – – X	

By simply substituting different treatments for the two control procedures in Table 15–1, it will be seen that precisely the same argument applies to comparison of treatment affects on more than a single task. Because one treatment affects both tasks and the other treatment just one of the tasks, it cannot be concluded that a hierarchical arrangement is the correct one. It is easy to find an example of such a conclusion being false. Suppose tasks B and C are both dependent on A (i.e., there is a hierarchical relationship between A and B, C). Suppose A is affected by Treatment I, B by Treatment II, and C by Treatment III. Then either of the following two results might lead one falsely to assume that a hierarchical relationship exists between B and C.

		Treatment				Treatment	
		I	II			I	III
Task	B	X	X	or	B	X	0
	C	X	0		C	X	X

If, however, we have both results, it can be correctly concluded that B and C are independent.

		Treatment	
		II	III
Task	B	X	0
	C	0	X

In short, it does not follow that given the absence of double dissociation between two tasks with two treatments, I and II, dissociation will not be found with other treatments. This is tantamount to saying that demonstrating a hierarchical relationship is demonstrating the universal negative. Arguments, therefore, such as whether epicritic and protopathic sensitivity are hierarchically arranged or are dissociable (Teuber, 1961) may have to wait some time for their resolution.

Interaction of Multiple Treatments on a Single Task - Synergism and Antagonism

We have just considered the effects of treatments on a spectrum of tasks, the consideration being essential to deciding how specific the behavioral effects of a treatment are. One of the complications was that tasks are not necessarily independent. Interesting issues arise when we attempt to consider cases where deliberate efforts are made to find treatment effects that are not independent. Consequences of great practical and theoretical importance can follow from a demonstration of interaction among treatments, particularly when the two treatments are shown to be antagonistic. The study of antagonistic relationships has proved of fundamental importance in pharmacology and biochemistry, and generally the very idea of a "cure" implies the isolation of a specific antagonism. The strong interest in "psychotropic" drugs will guarantee that behavioral situations will be used to study the interaction of treatment effects, and indeed, on a simple level this has already proved of great importance. For example, Bein (1964, p. 405) states that

psychopharmacological drugs which are claimed to be active in the clinic, whether antidepressent like imipramine, or antipsychotic or neuroleptic like reserpine or chlorpromazine, have very marked anti-mescaline activity in the mouse. . . . The barbiturates, however, have practically no anti-mescaline activity, but enhance the mescaline-induced motor activity.

The "anti-mescaline" effect is most conveniently measured by using activity cages, mescaline producing a marked increase in activity in the mouse.

The fact that behavior in a given situation usually can be altered by a variety of manipulations makes definite conclusions about antagonisms difficult to achieve. Let us take an example where we know exactly what is wrong with someone and see what we infer from the effects of various treatments. Let us suppose that someone limps— he has a pulled tendon. Let us suppose, however, that our experimenter does not know this; in fact, let us assume that all he has discovered is that this person does not run a distance of 100 yards in anything like the time a normal person does. Being enterprising, the experimenter will see if there is anything he can do to make the person run the distance in the normal time. He may electrify the 100-yard track and find that the man runs faster—even, perhaps, within normal limits. At this point the experimenter might conclude that the man suffered from lack of motivation or uncommonly heavy torpor. He may even conduct further experiments and show that rewarding him with a large sum of money on each occasion when he runs fast also increases the mean running speed, thereby confirming the hypothesis.

That the issue is far from academic can be seen from an examination of various treatments that have been claimed to antagonize the delayed-response deficit produced by frontal-lobe lesions in the monkey. These include keeping the animal in the dark during the delay period (Malmo, 1942), allowing it a predelay reward (Finan, 1942), changing the baiting situation from a spatial to a nonspatial one (Mishkin and Pribram, 1956), and administering barbiturates (Wade, 1947; Pribram, 1950; Mishkin, Rosvold, and Pribram, 1953). Each treatment is associated with a different but definite hypothesis as to what it is that ails the frontal monkey. It seems unlikely that all the hypotheses are true. A strong possibility is that all the allegedly antagonistic treatments affect the delayed-response performance in the same way as electric shock might affect the running speed of the lame man—by increasing motivation or by making the task easier. The formal nature of the trap is as follows: whenever a performance is subject to control by several variables, it may be falsely assumed that two treatments are antagonistic when one affects the action of one variable and the other affects the action of another variable, which in combination leads to what appears to be a cancellation of the effects of one by the other.

It is evident that not only can we reach quite erroneous conclusions from such experiments but also it is difficult to know in any particular instance that we are not in error. From a practical point of view, perhaps, the issue is not critical—one may be interested in counteracting a maladaptive state by any means available without engaging in worrisome reflection about the reasons why some treatments are successful. But one's practical control is often greatly enhanced by asking the questions. The issue is similar to the distinction between "cure" and "relief of symptoms" in medicine and to the pharmacologist's question of whether two drugs are genuine antagonists in the sense that they compete for "the same receptors" (Gaddum, 1964).

Is there any protection against the trap? There is one criterion that, if met, appears to serve admirably, but, unfortunately, it is often difficult to apply it practically to behavioral situations. The criterion, which we can call the "specificity criterion," is this: if a behavioral task is affected by treatment A, then treatment B is said to antagonize treatment A specifically if treatment A plus treatment B produces no effect and if, further, any other treatment C that alone produces an effect comparable to treatment A is just as effective in combination with treatment B. We can represent the problem schematically as follows. Let us assume that performance on a task is under the control of three variables *a*, *b* and *c*, as shown in Fig. 15–2. Suppose treatment A reduces the effectiveness of variable *a*, whereas treatment B enhances the effectiveness of variable *b* (Figs. 15–3 and 15–4). In combination, treatment A plus treatment B cancel out and are equivalent to no treatment (Fig. 15–5). If treatment B will also counteract the effects of treatment C, then the effects of treatment B are shown not to be restricted to the same variable as is affected by treatment A, and, therefore, the criterion is not satisfied (Fig. 15–6). The criterion set forth is equivalent to Gaddum's (1964) pharmacological criterion of antagonism specificity.

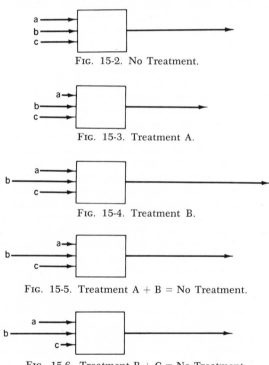

FIG. 15-2. No Treatment.

FIG. 15-3. Treatment A.

FIG. 15-4. Treatment B.

FIG. 15-5. Treatment A + B = No Treatment.

FIG. 15-6. Treatment B + C = No Treatment.

The difficulty lies with treatment C. One problem is entirely practical —it is often difficult to find an alternative way of altering the performance precisely to the level to which it is altered by the original treatment A. For example, in considering the effects on delayed response of frontal-lobe lesions, and a possible antagonism by drugs, we can ask: What other treatment, C, will produce a comparable deficit in delayed response? Well, possibly it could be achieved by decreasing the hunger of the animal, but it is doubtful that this would mimic the frontal-lobe deficit. Let us assume, for the sake of argument, that it does, and let us also assume that the same drug that counteracts the frontal-lobe delayed-response deficit also counteracts the delayed-response deficit produced by decreased hunger.

We are now faced logically with two alternatives. We could conclude, according to the argument just set forth, that the drug is not a genuine antagonist of frontal-lobe lesions. Or, we could assume that the lesion makes the animal less hungry, i.e., that the lesion is strictly equivalent in its action to treatment C. In order to choose between these alternatives, we must press on and find yet another treatment, D, which will produce a change in the delayed response of the same order of magnitude as that produced by the lesion or by treatment C. Again, it is not going to be easy to find one, but let us assume, for the sake of argument, that putting displacement prisms over the animal's eye has the desired effect. Then if treatment B cancels out the effect of frontal lesions (treatment A), decreased hunger (C), and displacement prisms (D), we would be confident in concluding that treatment B is not a specific antagonist of frontal lesions. Alternatively, if it cancelled the effects of C but not D, we could entertain the hypothesis, for example (among others), that C is equivalent to A and that B is a specific antagonist of A.

But it is important to stress that the crux of the analysis depends upon knowing in advance that treatments A and C work on different mechanisms or, failing that, that C and D work on different mechanisms—in other words, one cannot draw conclusions about the specificity of antagonistic effects unless one already has reached prior conclusions about the mode of action or classification of different treatments themselves. If one had reason to suspect in our hypothetical example that decreased hunger and displacement prisms were, in any sense, equivalent, we would have to keep pressing on until we found another treatment that, on some basis, we could assume to be different from either. It is interesting that Gaddum also admits that advance information is necessary before it is "reasonable to conclude" that two drugs are "competing for the same receptors", because one of the conditions he says ought to be fulfilled is that "the drugs have a common pharmacodynamic group, which would make it likely that they would combine with pharmacological receptors in the same way" (1964, p. 387).

Given sufficient numbers of treatments all producing comparable alterations in performance and given sufficient advance knowledge about how some, at least, of these treatments produce the change in performance, the procedure just outlined would undoubtedly prove to be a powerful generator of hypotheses. But it is obvious that the difficulties are formidable and it is not surprising that the literature seems entirely barren of examples carried through to the extent indicated in our hypothetical analysis.

Well, then, if the criterion for specificity is going to be difficult to fulfill, perhaps there are much simpler criteria that will apply to subclasses of antagonistic relationships. There is at least one criterion, which is derived from a consideration of the effects of the suspected antagonistic treatment when it is working alone. Heretofore we have ignored this information. For example, we have asked whether drugs counteract the effects of frontal-lobe lesions, but we have not explored the effects of the drugs themselves on the unoperated animals.

When we speculated that drugs may counteract the effects of frontal-lobe lesions not directly, but only by making the task simpler or by increasing the animal's motivation, the implication was that the drugs ought to improve the performance of normal unoperated animals. As a matter of fact, normal animals generally perform the delayed-response task, as it is normally administered, so efficiently that probably there would not be much scope for improvement. That is, they generally perform at 90 percent correct or better. However, as we have discussed previously, this is easily overcome in principle by using a titration method. If, in fact, we find that drugs affect the performance of normal animals in the same direction as they affect frontal animals, then we have grounds for suspicion that the drugs may be producing their effect on frontals only indirectly. In fact, it is surprising how rarely the question has been asked in connection with supposed frontal-lobe antagonists (cf. Weiskrantz, 1964). More formally, we can say that if treatment B counteracts the effects of treatment A and if treatment B by itself has an effect that goes in the same direction as would be required to counteract treatment A, then we cannot rule out the possibility—without further evidence—that treatment B's effect in counteracting treatment A is completely nonspecific.

On the other hand, if treatment B is genuinely without effect by itself but does counteract the effects of treatment A, we can take it as strong evidence that it is acting specifically on the same mechanism as treatment A itself.

It should be clear that we cannot insist upon fulfilment of this criterion. It is sufficient but not necessary. Given that treatment A has an effect in one direction, it is logically possible for treatment B by itself to have an effect in the opposite direction, in the same direction, or to have no effect whatever and yet to be a genuine antagonist of treatment A. The first case, where treatments A and B given singly work in opposite directions is a very familiar one, perhaps the best examples being stimulants and depressants. The second case is less familiar, perhaps, but easily found—radiation treatment and tumors, or in fact stimulants and depressants if either happen to be applied to the performance when it is at the peak of an inverted U shaped curve relating performance and "arousal." The third case, the one for which we should thank our good fortunes if we hit upon it, is also the ideal treatment B in medical practice—because it has no effects except when its effects are desired. Reverting to our earlier example of the lame man, we might increase his running speed not only by electric shock but also by putting his leg in a plaster cast for a few weeks. The latter treatment has great benefit not only for the poor man in question, whose patience with this discussion is probably now somewhat depleted, but also for answering the question of whether the treatment helped him directly or only fortuitously. The running speed of nonlame persons is helped not one bit by plaster casts. In other words, plaster casts help only certain lame persons.

Because the question of frontal-lobe drug antagonism has been referred to frequently, it is worth mentioning that a treatment B has, in fact, been found that is without effect on normal monkeys' performance of delayed response but that significantly alleviates the deficit on that task produced by frontal-lobe lesions (Weiskrantz, Gross, and Baltzer, 1965; Weiskrantz, 1964). In this instance an examination of the effects of the particular treatment, an injection of meprobamate, on the performance of normal monkeys on tasks other than delayed response is particularly helpful because it suggests a possible explanation of its effects on frontal animals. The fact that the drug significantly impairs perceptual discrimination performance of unoperated animals (Gross and Weiskrantz, 1961; Weiskrantz and Baltzer, 1965) supports the idea that the frontal monkeys suffer from "sensory disinhibition" (Buffery, 1964; Rosvold and Mishkin, 1961). And, now, we hope our lame friend can take a well-deserved, extended rest.

We cannot resist the temptation to indulge in one final pontification in the general area of interactions of treatments on behavioral tasks. The idea of an isolated treatment is a fiction. We always have a treatment among certain background conditions on a particular species with a particular history. In this sense we can no more have a treatment in isolation than we can have an animal with a heredity but no environment or an animal with an environment but no heredity. This kind of sophisticated nihilism is popular among psychologists, who long ago discovered that nihilism and pontification are by no means incompatible. But the aim here is more humble: it is to offer a practical warning. The background conditions against which a treatment is administered and assessed often themselves interact powerfully with the treatment. One must house the animal after the treatment, and, in so doing, a specific environment is provided; the animal has a particular social (perhaps nil) relationship with other animals, it is kept hungry, or satiated, and so forth. The effects of treatments can not only be shifted quantitatively by altering the size of the social groups within which the treated animals are kept (Wilson and Mapes, 1964) but also the qualitative results of a treatment such as amygdalectomy may depend upon the type of custodial care offered animals after the brain operation (Weiskrantz, 1956). The concept of a "treatment effect" is a convenient reification as long as we are not blinded to the possibility that the reification may be highly specific to a given set of conditions and procedures.

REFERENCES

BEIN, H. J. 1964. Discussion in Steinberg, H. (Ed.), *Animal behaviour and drug action.* London: Churchill. P. 405.

BÉKÉSY, G. VON 1947. A new audiometer. *Acta otolaryngol.,* 35, 411–422.

BLOUGH, D. S. 1958. A method for obtaining psychophysical thresholds from the pigeon. *J. exp. anal. Behav.,* 1, 31–43.

BUFFERY, A. W. H. 1964. *The effects of frontal and temporal lobe lesions upon the behaviour of baboons.* Unpublished doctoral dissertation, University of Cambridge.

FINAN, J. L. 1942. Delayed response with pre-delay reinforcement in monkeys after removal of the frontal lobes. *Amer. J. Psychol.,* 55, 202–214.

GADDUM, J. H. 1964. Discussion in Steinberg, H. (Ed.), *Animal behaviour and drug action.* London: Churchill. Pp. 386–389.

GROSS, C. G., & WEISKRANTZ, L. 1961. The effect of two "tranquillizers" on auditory discrimination and delayed response performance of monkeys. *Quart. J. exp. Psychol.,* 13, 34–39.

GROSS, C. G., & WEISKRANTZ, L. 1964. Some changes in behavior produced by lateral frontal lesions in the macaque. In Warren, J. M., & Akert, K. (Eds.), *The frontal granular cortex and behavior.* New York: McGraw-Hill. Pp. 74–102.

LASHLEY, K. S. 1929. *Brain mechanisms and intelligence.* Chicago: University of Chicago Press.

MALMO, R.B. 1942. Interference factors in delayed response in monkeys after removal of frontal lobes. *J. Neurophysiol.*, 5, 295–308.

MISHKIN, M., & PRIBRAM, K. H. 1956. Analysis of the effects of frontal lesions in monkey: II. Variations of delayed response. *J. comp. physiol. Psychol.*, 49, 36–45.

MISHKIN, M., ROSVOLD, H. E., & PRIBRAM, K. H. 1953. Effects of Nembutal in baboons with frontal lesions. *J. Neurophysiol.*, 16, 155–159.

PRIBRAM, K. H. 1950. Some physical and pharmacological factors affecting delayed response performance of baboons following frontal lobotomy. *J. Neurophysiol.*, 13, 373–382.

ROSVOLD, H. E., & MISHKIN, M. 1961. Non-sensory effects of frontal lesions on discrimination learning and performance. In Fessard, A., Gerard, R. W., & Konorski, J. (Eds.), *Brain mechanisms and learning.* Oxford: Blackwell. Pp. 555–567.

SCHEKEL, C. L. 1965. Self-adjustment of the interval in delayed matching: Limit of delay for the rhesus monkey. *J. comp. physiol. Psychol.*, 59, 415–418.

TEUBER, H.-L. 1955. Physiological psychology. *Ann. Rev. Psychol.*, 6, 267–296.

TEUBER, H.-L. 1961. Brain behavior: Summation. In Brazier, M.A.B. (Ed.), *Brain and behavior, Vol. I.* Washington, D.C.: Amer. Inst. Biol. Sci. Pp. 393–420.

WADE, M. 1947. The effect of sedatives upon delayed response in monkeys following removal of the frontal lobes. *J. Neurophysiol.*, 10, 57–61.

WEISKRANTZ, L. 1956. Behavioral changes associated with ablation of the amygdaloid complex in monkeys. *J. comp. physiol. Psychol.*, 49, 381–391.

WEISKRANTZ, L. 1964. Discrimination and the frontal lobes of monkeys. In Steinberg, H. (Ed.), *Animal behaviour and drug action.* London: Churchill. Pp. 83–90.

WEISKRANTZ, L., & BALTZER, V. 1965. A note on further experiments on the effects of meprobamate on discrimination performance in the monkey. *Quart. J. exp. Psychol.*, 17, 169–172.

WEISKRANTZ, L., & COWEY, A. 1963. Striate cortex lesions and visual acuity of the rhesus monkey. *J. comp. physiol. Psychol.*, 56, 225–231.

WEISKRANTZ, L., GROSS, C. G., & BALTZER, V. 1965. The beneficial effects of meprobamate on delayed response performance in the frontal monkey. *Quart. J. exp. Psychol.*, 17, 118–124.

WEISKRANTZ, L., MIHAILOVIĆ, Lj., & GROSS, C. G. 1962. Effects of stimulation of frontal cortex and hippocampus on behaviour in the monkey. *Brain*, 85, 487–504.

WILSON, C. W. M., & MAPES, R. E. A. 1964. The effects of group composition on drug action. In Steinberg, H. (Ed.), *Animal behaviour and drug action.* London: Churchill. Pp. 238–247.

WILSON, W. A., Jr., & MISHKIN, M. 1959. Comparison of the effects of inferotemporal and lateral occipital lesions on visually guided behavior in monkeys. *J. comp. physiol. Psychol.*, 52, 10–17.

Index of Authors

Montgomery, K. C., 108, 109, 110, 112, 114, 116, 117, 118, 122
Montpellier, G. de, 130
Mooney, C. M., 294, 299
Moore, R. Y., 37, 95
Moreno, O. M., 15
Morgan, C. T., 36
Morgan, L., 136
Morgan, M. J., 19–44
Morse, P., 21
Morse, W. H., 75
Morton, A., 142
Mote, F. A., Jr., 99
Mountcastle, V. B., 305, 317
Mowrer, O. H., 20, 21, 24, 31, 32, 40, 51, 53, 134
Moyer, I. K. E., 28
Mrosovsky, N., 163
Muenzinger, K. F., 57
Mulder, D. W., 178, 180
Mullan, S., 284, 346
Munn, N. L., 91, 99, 128, 130, 131, 132, 339
Murphy, J. V., 205, 207, 208, 209, 211, 212
Muntz, W. R. A., 221
Myers, A. K., 27, 111
Myers, J. L., 4
Myers, J. S., 28
Myers, R. E., 384

Nagy, Z. M., 61, 69
Nakao, H., 36
Nakkash, S., 39
Nauta, W. J. H., 97, 98
Neet, C. C., 78
Neff, W. D., 224, 225, 226, 227, 254, 255, 256, 321, 382
Nelson, E. H., 352
Newcombe, F., 292, 294, 299, 323
Nielsen, I. M., 99
Nissen, H. W., 112, 115, 136, 165, 167, 170, 172, 215, 218
Norman, D. A., 332
Norton, S., 61
Nott, K., 77
Notterman, J. M., 30, 62, 63
Nowlis, V., 165, 172
Nyswander, D. B., 129

Ochs, S., 183
Oldfield, R. C., 294, 299
Oldfield-Box, H., 148
Olds, J., 14, 15, 75
Orbach, J., 162, 163, 244
Ordy, J. M., 199, 201, 259
Orr, A., 99
Oscar, M., 167
Osterrieth, P., 336
Oswald, I., 159, 196
Otis, L. S., 69
Overmier, J. B., 35
Overton, D. A., 180
Oxbury, J. M., 151, 152, 175, 177

Palmer, M. E., 28

Papanek, M. L., 260
Paquette, R., 99
Pasik, P., 194
Pasik, T., 194
Paterson, A., 284
Pavlov, I. P., 79, 80, 250
Peacock, L. J., 99
Pearl, J., 54, 55
Pearlman, C. A., Jr., 163, 178
Pechtel, C., 56, 61, 79, 80, 81
Peele, T. L., 385
Penfield, W., 181, 184, 284, 299, 340, 346
Perin, C. T., 130
Peterson, M. E., 218
Peterson, N. J., 197, 218, 222
Pfaffmann, C., 193
Pickersgill, M. J., 159
Pinto-Hamuy, T., 63, 64
Pittendrigh, C. S., 95, 96
Pliskoff, S. S., 15
Polidora, V. J., 133–134, 206, 207, 211, 212, 214, 230
Pollack, A., 298
Polt, J. M., 67
Polyak, S. L., 191
Poppelreuter, W., 294, 298
Porter, R. W., 78, 79
Posner, M. I., 356
Potegal, M., 290
Pötzl, O., 285, 299
Premack, D., 101, 112, 121
Pribram, K. H., 7, 61, 70, 95, 163, 167, 172, 174, 175, 194, 379, 384, 424
Price, P. A., 311
Prisko, L., 329, 331, 342, 343, 344, 350
Prockop, E. S., 152, 262
Proctor, F., 289, 307

Quatember, R., 299

Rabinovich, N. S., 132, 133
Rajalakshmi, R., 143
Ranson, S. W., 97
Raskin, D. C., 24, 26
Rasmussen, T., 175, 181, 183, 184, 304, 306, 324, 340, 349
Razran, G. H. S., 136
Reed, C. F., 298
Reed, J. D., 91, 99
Reese, H. W., 142
Reeves, C. D., 198, 200
Reichardt, W., 196
Reichmann, F., 302
Reid, L. S., 92, 99, 100, 134
Reid, R. L., 143
Reighard, J. E., 197
Reiter, L., 300
Rescorla, R. A., 21, 167, 168, 170
Rey, A., 336
Reynierse, J. H., 27, 28
Ribbands, C. R., 163
Rich, I., 36
Richards, W., 278, 287
Richter, C. P., 91, 92, 93, 96, 98, 192
Riddle, W. C., 24

Index of Subjects